D1162701

A Harvest of World Folk Tales

A Harvest of
World Folk Tales

EDITED BY MILTON RUGOFF

WITHDRAWN
FROM
UNIVERSITY OF PENNSYLVANIA
LIBRARIES

WITH ILLUSTRATIONS & DECORATIONS BY JOSEPH LOW

NEW YORK · *The Viking Press* · MCMXLIX

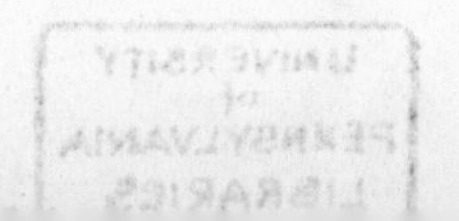
UNIVERSITY
of
PENNSYLVANIA
LIBRARIES

COPYRIGHT 1949 BY THE VIKING PRESS, INC.

PUBLISHED IN OCTOBER 1949

PUBLISHED ON THE SAME DAY IN THE DOMINION OF CANADA
BY THE MACMILLAN COMPANY OF CANADA LIMITED

SECOND PRINTING BEFORE PUBLICATION

GR
25
R8
1949

398.2
B845

Many of the stories in this book are included by special arrangement with the holders of copyright and publication rights and may not be reproduced without their consent. The editor's thanks are due to those listed below and on the two pages following, for permissions granted:

Harper & Brothers: "The Khevsouri and the Eshmahkie" from *Yes and No Stories* by George and Helen Papashvily, copyright 1946 by George and Helen Papashvily.

Alfred A. Knopf, Inc.: "The Rabbit Huntress" and "The Hermit Mítsina" from *Zuñi Folk Tales* by Frank Hamilton Cushing, copyright 1901 by Emily T. Cushing, 1931 by Alfred A. Knopf, Inc.; "The Adventures of Renard" from *Three and the Moon* by Jacques Dorey, copyright 1929 by Alfred A. Knopf, Inc.; "The Yara" by Affonso Arinhos de Melo Franco, "The Incubus" by Ricardo Rojas, "Brer Rabbit, Businessman" by Carmen Lyra, from *The Golden Land*, translated by Harriet de Onis, copyright 1948 by Harriet de Onis.

Little, Brown & Co.: "Lesson for Lesson," from *Tongues of the Monte* by J. Frank Dobie, copyright 1935, 1947 by J. Frank Dobie.

PRINTED IN U.S.A. BY AMERICAN BOOK–STRATFORD PRESS

ACKNOWLEDGMENTS

The editor wishes to thank the following publishers and persons for their kind permission to reprint in this volume excerpts from the books listed below:

George Allen & Unwin Ltd., London, *Lion and Jackal* by Frank Brownlee.

American Folklore Society, Inc., Philadelphia, selections from *Journal of American Folklore.*

Behrman House, Inc., New York, *The Wise Men of Helm* by Solomon Simon; and *The Memoirs of Glückel of Hameln,* translated by Marvin Lowenthal.

Francesco M. Bianco, New York, *The African Saga,* translated by Margery Bianco.

The Bodley Head Ltd., London, *The Pentamerone of Giambattista Basile,* translated by Benedetto Croce, edited by N. M. Penzer.

Cambridge University Press, London, *Jataka Tales,* selected by H. T. Francis and E. J. Thomas from the edition of E. B. Cowell.

The Clarendon Press, Oxford, *Folk-Tales of Iraq,* translated by E. S. Stevens.

Coward-McCann, Inc., New York, *Tall Tale America, A Legendary History of Our Humorous Heroes,* by Walter Blair, copyright 1944 by Walter Blair.

Crown Publishers, New York, *Gargantua and Pantagruel* by Rabelais, translated by Samuel Putnam, copyright 1929 by Covici Friede, Inc.; *A Treasury of Jewish Folklore,* edited by Nathan Ausubel, copyright 1948 by Crown Publishers; and *A Treasury of Mexican Folkways,* edited by Frances Toor, copyright 1947 by Crown Publishers.

J. M. Dent & Sons Ltd., London, *Caucasian Folk-Tales,* translated by Lucy Menzies.

Duell, Sloan & Pearce, Inc., New York, *Palmetto Country* by Stetson Kennedy, copyright 1942 by Stetson Kennedy.

E. P. Dutton & Co., Inc., New York, *The Pentamerone of Giambattista Basile,* translated by Benedetto Croce, edited by N. M. Penzer.

Aurelio M. Espinosa, Berkeley, California, for the story "Pedro the Trickster," translated by Samuel Putnam.

Harcourt, Brace and Company, Inc., New York, *Paul Bunyan* by Esther Shephard, copyright 1924 by Esther Shephard; and *Davy Crockett* by Constance Rourke, copyright 1934 by Harcourt, Brace and Company, Inc.

Lucien Harris, Atlanta, *Uncle Remus and His Friends* by Joel Chandler Harris.

Henry Holt and Company, Inc., New York, *The Cow-Tail Switch and Other West African Stories* by Harold Courlander and George Herzog, copyright 1947 by Henry Holt and Company, Inc.

Houghton Mifflin Company, Boston, *Jack Tales* by Richard Chase.

Dr. Douglas Hyde for his translation from the Gaelic of "Teig O'Kane and the Corpse."

Jewish Publication Society of America, Philadelphia, *Ma'aseh Book*, translated by Moses Gaster; and *The Legends of the Jews* by Louis Ginzberg, translated by Henrietta Szold.

J. B. Lippincott Company, New York, *The Chinese Fairy Book*, edited by Dr. R. Wilhelm and translated by Frederick H. Martens, copyright 1921 by J. B. Lippincott Company.

J. B. Lippincott Company, Philadelphia, *Mules and Men* by Zora Neale Hurston, copyright 1935 by Zora Neale Hurston; and *Heroic Tales from Greek Mythology* by Katharine Pyle, copyright 1928, 1934 by J. B. Lippincott Company.

Longmans, Green & Co., Inc., New York, *The Book of Romance* by Andrew Lang, copyright 1902, 1930 by Longmans, Green & Co., Inc.; *Three Golden Oranges* by Ralph Steele Boggs and Mary Gould Davis, copyright 1936 by Longmans, Green & Co., Inc.; and *Once the Hodja* by Alice Geer Kelsey, copyright 1943 by Alice Geer Kelsey.

Julian Messner, Inc., New York, *Heroes of the Kalevala* by Babette Deutsch, copyright 1940 by Babette Deutsch.

Methuen & Co., Ltd., London, *Egyptian Tales*, edited by W. Flinders Petrie.

Pantheon Books, Inc., New York, *Russian Fairy Tales*, translated by Norbert Guterman.

G. P. Putnam's Sons, New York, *More English Fairy Tales*, *English Fairy Tales*, and *Celtic Fairy Tales*, all edited by Joseph Jacobs.

Rinehart and Company, Inc., New York, *Broad and Alien Is the World* by Ciro Alegria, translated from the Spanish by Harriet de Onis, copyright 1941 by Rinehart and Company, Inc.; and *Skazki: Tales and Legends of Old Russia* by Ida Zeitlin, copyright 1926 by Rinehart and Company, Inc.

Routledge and Kegan Paul, Ltd., London, *Wide-Awake Stories*, collected by F. A. Steel and R. C. Temple; and *Chinese Fairy Tales* by Wolfram Eberhard.

Stackpole and Heck, Inc., New York, *African Genesis* by Leo Frobenius and Douglas C. Fox.

Talbot Press, Limited, Dublin, *Standish O'Grady: Selected Essays and Passages.*

Texas Folk-Lore Society, Austin, Texas, Texas Folk-Lore Society Publications, Vols. XII and XIV.

The University of Chicago Press, Chicago, *The Panchatantra*, translated by Arthur W. Ryder.

Vanguard Press, Inc., New York, *Tyll Ulenspiegel's Merry Pranks* by M. A. Jagendorf, copyright 1938 by Vanguard Press, Inc.

Albert Whitman & Co., Chicago, *Tales from a Finnish Tupa* by James Cloyd Bowman and Margery Bianco.

CONTENTS

RUSSIAN

SCANDINAVIAN

SPANISH

FOREWORD

Here for your beguilement is a harvest of the tales men have told since men first told tales. Most of them were originally passed by word of mouth, but all of them have made their way into books, and I like to think that those collected here make as good reading as once they made good listening. Readability was in fact the major criterion governing my choice. Of course other factors—authenticity, national characteristics, antiquity, popularity (in both senses), and so on—played a part, but it was readability that proved most persuasive.

If you, who are perhaps descended from Scottish or Hungarian or Australian or Afghan ancestors, fail to find here tales you have heard and have liked, remember only that I had to stop somewhere and that I did not stop until I had assembled a book that is about as large as a book for reading, not reference, dare be. Indeed, my only regret is that that confirmed cheater of anthologists, "considerations of space," prevented me from including tales from other countries that were likely for inclusion. But a choice had to be made between representing a score of peoples fully and several score meagerly, between a fairly representative selection and an encyclopedic sampler. I chose the former way. In the end I found so much overlapping that I was satisfied that the tales told among the major groups were in essence all the tales told anywhere.

As for standards, the household tale, or *Märchen*, was accepted as the fundamental type, but drolls, legends, and *novelle* were also included when they were clearly traditional narratives based on stories told by the people. In a few instances a tale from an epic—for example, the story of Odysseus and Polyphemus—was included when it seemed to fit this description. I drew the line at medieval chivalric romances, finding few satisfactory translations, and even fewer that lent themselves to excerpting. But what seemed more important in terms of form was that the narrative be complete and coherent—as compared with the fragment that might interest an anthropologist. And what was most important of all was, as I have said, that it be beguiling.

An attempt was made to present these stories in such a way that they might be representative of nations or peoples. But folk tales are international characters, and for the most part all that is local about them is their names, their outer garments, and the language they speak. Thus there is hardly a story in this volume for which a parallel could not be found in the folklore of another people, or, in some instances, of a score of other peoples. Of course the Russian version would seem quite Russian, and the Irish peculiarly Irish, and only the specialist would know that the twain had met and perhaps been one in the dim backwards of time.

And now to my debts. One of the greatest of these is to those collectors and editors who over the years and around the earth have recorded the tales from which I made my choice; I have done my best to acknowledge them in the footnotes throughout and in the Bibliographical Note.

For comments and suggestions I thank Benjamin Crocker Clough and B. A. Botkin. I also profited from the general editorial advice of Malcolm Cowley and from helpful letters from May Lamberton Becker, Marvin Lowenthal, Leo J. Henkin, and Aurelio M. Espinosa. For a special translation from the Spanish I am indebted to Samuel Putnam, and for assistance in checking the manuscript I am grateful to Sylvia Harris. Finally, for aid and advice at every step and stage of the work I owe to my wife Helen more than words can express.

MILTON RUGOFF

A NOTE ON FOLK TALES

HOW DATELESS and how broad in appeal a folk tale may be was vividly illustrated when a group of American critics recently selected a film called *Treasure of Sierra Madre* as the best picture of the year. The makers of the picture indicated that it was based on a modern novel. But what they did not add was that almost six hundred years ago Geoffrey Chaucer had told fundamentally the same story, set in medieval Flanders, in his *Canterbury Tales*. And in the Jatakas, Buddhist birth stories of ancient India, there is a version that was well known two thousand and three hundred years ago.

It is for such tales, told since the dawn of man's imagination, that we should reserve the words timeless and universal. It would be difficult indeed to find other narratives that have been repeated since the early morning of recorded history and circulated in one form or another from Siberia to South Africa, from India to Mexico. Where is there a literary tradition that has developed characters as popular as the heroes and gods, the wise men and fools, the inspired beasts and birds, the demons and bony-legged witches, the princes and beggars, the faithless wives and cunning tricksters, of folk story —names as familiar as Sindbad, Polyphemus, Hansel, Reynard, Cinderella, Deirdre, and Thor? A literary masterpiece becomes famous only among the few who are sufficiently literate; the audience for a folk tale is all mankind.

One can only wonder who created these tales—and when. Indeed, how old they are and how they originated are questions that no one has answered satisfactorily. And their very nature, the fact that they belong to groups rather than individuals and were handed down by word of mouth, seems almost a guarantee that they will always come trailing mystery. They, or traces of them, appear in Egyptian records one thousand and six hundred years before Christ, and in Indian, Greek, Persian, and Hebrew writings and inscriptions well over two thousand years old. But who can say how old they were when they became popular enough to be put into writing or to be referred to in inscriptions?

As for their origin, some have suggested that every folk tale was a nature myth, a primitive attempt to explain natural phenomena. William Tell was, they say, only a last reflection of the Sun-god, who always hit the apple or any other target with his mighty bow. For them, all the stories of a snow-white maiden held in a dark tower and delivered by a young, bright hero go back to myths in which Spring is released from the bonds of Winter or the Sun is rescued from the grip of Night. According to them, the loves and feuds of the powers of nature were first told as stories of gods, then of heroes, and, finally, when Christianity destroyed the old gods, of anybody and nobody. Others suggested that the tales were survivals of savage practices, that crude *Märchen* came first and civilized myths later. Still others argued that all folk tales were invented by literate storytellers and then debased in the course of being retold among uncivilized peoples. And when psychoanalysis was feeling its oats a few years ago, several scholars suggested that the tales originated in dreams.

The debate on the origin of folk tales has long since died down. It ended without being settled, but it was not fruitless, for almost every one of the theories it evoked will here and there seem to cast light on a puzzling character or an otherwise obscure passage.

Although it did not involve going back quite so far into the cloudy past, the question of how similar tales turned up among peoples long remote from each other seemed to be wrapped in almost as much mystery. The brothers Grimm believed the stories came from an Indo-Germanic parent culture, even as had the languages of Europe. For a time Andrew Lang thought they had sprung up independently in different places. A third school saw India as the womb of all story; and since this theory was suggested when it was the fashion to consider India the Aryan cradle of civilization, it was popular for a time. Again there was much speculation coupled with some evidence, but again there was no generally accepted conclusion.

Such conscious literary interest in folk tales had not, however, really begun until the early eighteenth century. Charles Perrault collected his first "Mother Goose" tales in 1697, and a few years later, a fellow Frenchman, Antoine Galland, published the first translation of *The Arabian Nights' Entertainment*. The polite tone and oriental richness that they introduced became the fashion, and a spate of similar collections followed, reaching its peak in the forty-one volumes of *Le Cabinet des Fées*. But it was not until the next century that compilations seeking to reproduce tales as actually told by the people began to appear. The first of these, in 1812, was the *Kinder- und Hausmärchen* of Wilhelm and Jacob Grimm. Later came a host of other collections and translations. Before long, folk tales became a focus of controversy among students. Collecting variants and parallels, tracing familiar tales back into antiquity, or speculating about their origin became a scholarly passion.

Meanwhile, only simple folk and children continued to consider the tales wonderful stories conceived when the world was somewhat younger. And when, with the coming of the twentieth century, more and more of the simple folk turned away from them, the tales were left, by default as it were, almost entirely to the children. The spread of literacy and the circulation of books may help account for this. And possibly the fact that many stories were first written down in the middle of the nineteenth century, when it was fashionable to bowdlerize fiction, has contributed to the change in their reputation. Shorn of their vigor and candor—and sometimes that very vulgarity that marked them as folk stories—dressed up as fairy tales (although fairies are not common in the tales as a whole and seem to have been popularized by the prettified versions of eighteenth-century French editors), it is hardly surprising that they lost much of the appeal they had had for mature audiences.

But if we are bound to answer questions, let us deal with those that ask what kind of world these tales create. To answer that we must consider at least two types: one is the tale of wonder, set in a world of magic and peopled by magicians, gods, and leprechauns. The other is set in the everyday world and generally depends for its effect on cleverness—either that unfortunate cleverness we call cunning or that great lack of it from which fools and numskulls suffer.

Any question about the first of these, the world of wonder, invites talk of the forests of enchantment, the landscape of Nowhere. It is a realm in which all the truly deserving live happily ever after and justice is more "poetic" than in most poetry, a realm in which the wish is truly father to the deed, and the deed lives up perfectly to the wish. Here at last is that "just society" in which the poor and humble, the innocent, the brave and fair, triumph, while the wicked and the cruel are worsted.

But even such tales begin with the world of reality, where the poor suffer, the humble are downtrodden, and the brave and the fair are often born into squalor. No realistic novelist ever invented more painful and lowly circumstances from which to extricate a heroine than the folk who created Cinderella. To get from such beginnings to happy endings requires the aid of agencies unheard of on land or sea, undreamed of in cold philosophy. It requires that obstacles give way in a trice, that reason abdicate without a murmur, that logic leave off. It requires magic. Carpets must fly, birds prophesy, caps grant invisibility, tablecloths produce food, bags contain the winds, mirrors tell the truth, apples and combs have magic powers, geese lay golden eggs, dead men come to life, words thrice repeated work miracles, lanterns summon jinn, and jinn summon whatever the heart desires. Here wishful thinking is the only wisdom. Here miracles are daily bread.

As for the wishes made here, or granted even before they are made, they are most often for great wealth, a fair mate, or a table staggering under its burden of food. Away with him who whispers that all we are saying is that the land of folk tales' desire is a Cockaigne in which the object is all a man can want, and more than he can use, of money, sex, and food! Make whatever you will of it, rare is the wish for health or peace or wisdom or happiness for others. If any generalization is possible, it is that folk tales are success stories—success achieved not through merit or hard work, but through magic, luck, or cunning. Perhaps that explains their appeal for the mass of mankind, for hard-pressed, earthbound, luckless Everyman.

But no matter how the story ends, drama requires that there be trials and tribulations, darkness before the light. Of these there is the devil's plenty in these pages. Such threats as confront folk heroes are surpassed only in nightmares—child-devouring witches, bloodthirsty giants, foul demons, murderous brothers, jealous gods, crowds of assassins, trials by fire and flood, poison and sword, dragon and siren. One cannot help seeing in these, as in the raw horrors that Shakespeare occasionally fed the groundlings, something profoundly to the taste of the common folk. With what amoral relish little Grethel shovels the poor old witch into the oven! The cruelty in such tales is exceeded only in those latest penny dreadfuls—children's comic books—and radio horror stories. The latter are designed for the young; it is a question whether any of the oldest folk tales were meant for children.

But there are other types of tales besides these of wonder and sorcery, supernatural heroes and unearthly heroines. There is in particular the kind that deals with ordinary folk and their very worldly matching of wits. These include tales not only of cunning people, but also of fools and sillies—both those with too much wit and those with less than enough.

That wit and witlessness should play such a part in folk fiction has perhaps no great significance beyond the fact that stories of both extremes flatter the listener—or reader—and are often amusing. How satisfying to follow Donald O'Neary as he gets the best of Hudden and Dudden, or Finn MacCoul's wife as she outwits the great Cuchullin, or the Russian soldier as he teaches the demon a lesson. Is there any need to explain why folk have always relished the tale of the blithe innocent who tricks giants into doing his bidding, or of the scorned youth who answers the riddle and wins the princess? And what could be more flattering to an audience than tales of whole communities peopled exclusively by utter fools. Every nation has had them: the stories the English tell of the "wise men of Gotham" are told by the Jews of the *Helden* of Helm, by the Germans of the Schildbürger, by the Persians of their Hums, by the Greeks of the Boeotians, by the Finns of their Holmolaiset, and so on, back to Adam's time. Read one set and you have read them all; read them all and you will be convinced that most folks think any old tale is good enough for beating a fool.

The reader will surely note how many of the stories of deceit deal with the duplicity of women. Perhaps such an attitude is traceable to the relations between the sexes in primitive societies, or to the East, where the bondage in which women once lived might well have given rise to doubts concerning their fidelity. But whatever the source, such stories seem to have become almost as popular in medieval Europe as they had been in the East. Here and there a woman is portrayed, as Griselda was, as a model of chastity, patience, or devotion, but more often she seems to inherit all the taints of Delilah, Circe, and Eve.

Hardly less common in folk tales are animals. All early peoples seem to have felt a deep kinship for them, and even fairly advanced civilizations—from the Egyptians with their jackal-headed god

Anubis to the Hindus with their sacred cows—have considered some of them magical or divine. In the most common type of animal tale, the fable, the poor beasts are made to seem all too human. They live in field or wood, but they think, talk, and act like so many men and women. Sometimes, as in the tale of the loyal mongoose, a beast performs a deed that can be accepted as natural to its kind; but more often it abandons its animal nature, like the wolf in "Little Red Ridinghood," merely by donning a shawl. Occasionally it is little more than the embodiment of a single trait—not so much an animal as a symbol. Reynard, Bruin, Chanticleer, Pertelot, Isengrim, are brothers under the skin to such characters of medieval literature as Covetousness, Sir Glutton, Aunt Abstinence, and Pernel Proud-heart. But the fabulists plainly knew wonderfully well what they were doing, for animals were popular in the first folk stories and, witness Brer Rabbit, are popular in the latest.

Folk tales fade and die out even as do the tales conceived and written by professional literary men, but the best folk tales, or at least the best known, have powers of accommodation that are rarely found among works of literary art. And that may well be why such tales have been able to serve in the nurseries of royalty, in the huts of peasants, in the imagination of artists, in the warp and woof of many cultures.

There are those who feel that, as literacy spreads, folk tales will be abandoned or forgotten—perhaps supplanted by the stories created by professional writers. But many an old tale has already outlasted a dozen civilizations together with countless stories fashioned by men who were considered masters of the art. Not only do Odysseus and Deirdre live on with undiminished vitality in man's fictions and fantasies, but new folk figures—Raven and Johnny Appleseed and Bunyan—spring up with every new culture. And they will surely continue to do so as long as men have dreams and need no license to tell what they have dreamed.

African

The Old Woman

THE STORIES that African tribesmen tell outside the kraal after nightfall—for that, traditionally, is the only propitious time for tale-telling—are usually of more interest to the anthropologist than to the general reader. But Africa is vast and has so many stories to tell that the exceptions to such a generalization afford us a handful of tales of impressive quality by any standards. "The Old Woman," for example, is so remarkable a narrative that it must be said to fall into the folk tale category only because those who created it preferred oral to written composition and no one man called it his own. Those who tell this story, the Hausas, are hardly a primitive jungle tribe. They are farmsteading people who live in Upper Nigeria, but, as traders, have ranged far and wide across the Sudan. Some of them were long ago converted to Mohammedanism, and this may account not only for the pious Moslem allusions in "The Old Woman," but also for the fact that its subject, the mischief-making of an old vixen, is fairly common in the lore of the Mediterranean world. But no matter where the theme comes from, the Hausa story-tellers have used dramatic scenes, suspense, and a mounting intensity to build it into a narrative that approaches classic tragedy.

It is possible to find other European influences or parallels in these stories: particularly in the fantastic transformation in "Takise," the cumulative pattern in "Talk," and the last ruse in "Marandenboni" which resembles the Donald O'Neary prank described on page 494. As for "Talk," it is plainly a "talking dog" story, and one clever enough, despite its origin on the Dark Continent, to compete with similar jests that are still, and will always be, current in smart cosmopolitan periodicals. Many of Africa's animal tales are virtually international, cousin to stories told of Reynard in Europe and Coyote in the American Southwest. But such family ties scarcely prevent a folk tale from establishing its independent identity. These stories are distinctly African, abounding in settings, characters, and moods peculiar to the people who tell them.

THE OLD WOMAN

A HAUSA LEGEND

INTO the land of Matasu there came a man who could not see, a Makapho, a blind man. The Makapho passed through the gate into the city, and there he met an old woman who had her house near the city wall. The Makapho was going along the street when the old woman saw him, and when the old woman saw that he was blind she said to herself, "That is good."

The old woman went to the Makapho and said, "You are blind. Everyone helps the blind, and Allah will be good to me if I take care of you. Come to my house and live with me." The Makapho said, "Very well, I'll live with you. The only thing I possess is this basket." And the old one answered, "Come along, now, I'll show you your room." The old woman brought him home.

The blind man then said to the old woman, "I'll go out immediately and see if I can earn something. Meanwhile, I've brought a hen with me in that basket there. Will you take it out of the basket, look after it, and see if it lays any eggs?" The old woman answered, "I'll do that very thing. Allah will be good to me if I take care of you and your hen." The old woman took the hen. As soon as the blind man had gone she slaughtered it, cooked it, and prepared a good meal which she devoured.

When the blind man, who had spent all day in the market, came home that night to the old woman, he asked, "How is my hen?" "The hen! The hen!" the old woman said. "That miserable hen. A jackal caught your hen, my Makapho, and ate it up." The blind man said, "Allah will help me with my hen."

The next day the blind man rose early and said to the old woman, "I'll go out at once and see if I can earn something." And the old woman answered, "Do that, my Makapho. Everyone gives gladly to the blind! Go then, and people will give you plenty." The blind man went. He went through the town. He met a rich man. The rich man had just told his servant to bring him his goat to look at. The rich man looked at his goat. The rich man saw the blind man and gave him the goat, saying, "Take the goat. Allah will be good to me for my kindness." Makapho took the goat and went home.

When he came into the house with the goat he said to the old woman, "Can you take my goat and look after it for me?" And the old woman answered, "I'll do that very thing. Allah will be good to me if I look after you and your goat." The old woman took the goat, and as soon as the blind man had gone out again she took it to the butcher. The butcher slaughtered it and sold the meat.

At night when the Makapho returned to the old woman he asked, "How is my goat?" The old woman answered, "The goat! The goat! The wretched goat! Kurra, the hyena, caught it and tore it to pieces." The blind man said, "Allah will help me with my goat."

The next day the blind man rose early and told the old woman, "I'll go out at once and see what I can earn." The old woman answered, "Do that, my Makapho. Everyone gives gladly to the blind. Go then. The people will give you richly." The blind man went. He went through the city and encountered a Madugu, a leader of a caravan. The Madugu had come to the city with many heavily laden donkeys, had sold everything, and was now rich. The Madugu counted up what he had earned. Then he saw the blind man. The Madugu took a donkey, gave it to the blind man and said, "Take this donkey. Allah will reward me for it." Makapho took the donkey and went home with it.

Makapho came home with the donkey and asked the old woman, "Can you take my donkey and look after it for me?" And the old woman answered, "I'll do that very thing. Allah will reward me if I take care of you and your donkey." The old woman took the donkey. The blind man went out again. As soon as he was gone the old woman took the donkey and brought it to the Ssongo, where the dealers are. At the Ssongo she asked, "Is there no one here who will buy a good donkey?" The people came and looked at the donkey. A man bought the donkey; the old woman took the money and went home.

When the Makapho returned that evening he asked the old woman, "How is my donkey?" The old woman said, "Oh, the donkey! The unfortunate donkey! I gave him something to eat. I must have given him too much for he became very strong, broke the rope that held him, and ran away." Makapho said, "Then I'll go and look for him." The old woman said, "My poor Makapho, remember that you are blind. I have run around and looked for him. And I can see. But I did not find the donkey. So how do you expect to find him?" The blind man said, "You are right. But Allah will help me to get my donkey back."

The next morning the blind man rose early. Makapho the blind man said to the old woman, "I'll go out at once and see if I can earn something." The old woman said, "Do that, my Makapho. Everyone gives gladly to the blind. Go then, the people will give you plenty." The blind man went. He went across the market. He went farther. And so he met riders and soldiers. He met the Jerima, the crown prince, in the midst of the Lafidi, the armored knights. The Jerima was returning from the war. The Jerima had laid waste a city and had captured camels and horses. The Jerima saw the blind man. He waved to his followers and said, "Bring me that large camel that we captured." The camel was brought before him. The Jerima gave the camel to Makapho and said, "Take the camel. Allah will reward me for it." Makapho took the camel home.

Makapho came home with the camel and said to the old woman, "I've just received a very fine camel as a present from the Jerima. Can you take good care of the camel so that it cannot run away or cannot be stolen?" The old woman said, "I can do that very thing. You'll find your camel here when you come home again. Allah is witness to what I say." Makapho gave the old woman the camel. The old woman tied it up by the side of the house. Makapho went away again.

When the blind man had gone the old woman unbound the camel and took it to the stream to drink. The old woman gave the camel poison so that it might die. But the camel did not die. The old woman gave the camel still more poison. But the camel did not want to die. The old woman took a lot of poison and shoved it down the camel's throat. The camel did not die, but it lay down and began to bellow. Then the old woman called to some men who were passing and said, "Come, come, the blind man's camel is dying. Come here and kill it so that it may die quickly." The men came close. They saw that the camel was very sick. The men killed the camel with their lances. Then they tied the legs of the camel with ropes and dragged it into the town. They came to the old woman's house. The old woman said, "Leave the camel here in front of the door. Allah will reward you for the service which you have rendered the blind man."

In the evening Makapho came home to the old woman. The blind man stumbled against the legs of the dead camel. The blind man said, "*Kai!* [Hey, there] old woman. Do you put firewood across your threshold when a blind man lives in your house? Shall the blind man fall and break his legs?" The old woman said, "Have you ever seen firewood with legs and a head?" The blind man asked, "How is that?" The old woman answered, "Feel it, take hold of it, and you'll find out. The firewood is your camel. The camel is dead. They gave you a wounded camel with a lance wound in its side." The blind man touched the camel, nodded his head, and said, "Allah will help me with my camel."

The next morning the blind man rose early. He said to the old woman, "I'll go out at once and see if I can earn something." The old woman said, "Do that, my Makapho. Everyone gives gladly to the blind. Go then, the people will give you plenty." The blind man went. The blind man went through the city. The blind man came to the house of the king.

It was the day of the great Salla, the New Year celebration. The noble and the wealthy went in to see the king and greeted him. The king gave food to each. To one he gave a horse, to another a garment. Makapho sat at the entrance to the hall. The king saw Makapho and said to his people, "Call me the blind one here." His servants brought the blind man. The king said, "Today is the great Salla. I will give the blind man a great present. Bring me a maiden. Bring me one of my most beautiful maidens." The maiden was brought. The king looked at her and said, "Yes, that's what I want. I'll give this lovely maiden to the blind man. My blind man, take this maiden and marry her. I give her to you. Allah will reward me for it." Makapho took the maiden. He took her home with him.

Makapho brought the maiden into the house and said to the old woman, "Look at the maiden, a lovely maiden. Today is the great Salla. The king gave her to me to marry. Will you take care of her?" The old woman said, "I'll take care of the maiden, and in a way you won't easily imagine. You'll see when you return. Allah is witness to what I say." The blind man said, "You mean to say that no wild beast will take her, that no man will steal her, and that she will not get lost?" And the old woman answered, "No beast shall take her, if you do not regard me as a beast. No man shall take her away if I do not give her away myself. And I must be worse than the devil if she gets lost!"

The blind man said, "No one will believe that you are worse and stronger than the devil. Here, take the maiden." And the blind man went out again.

When the blind man had gone the old woman said to the maiden, "You are a very lovely maiden. I have promised Makapho to take care of you. I will take care of you. Do you want to marry today?" The maiden said, "The king said I should marry today. I want to marry today." The old woman said, "Then wait here for a little while." The old woman locked up the maiden in her house. The old woman ran to a young man who had a great deal of money and always wore beautiful clothes and slept at night with beautiful maidens. The young man's house was scented because so much *muardi*, a perfumed water, had been sprinkled there, and noisy because other young people came together there. The old woman ran to this young man.

The old woman said to the young man, "Have you still something left of that which you inherited from your father?" The young man said, "What girl do you want to bring me? I know all the Karua [whores] in the town. I do not want any more Karua." The old woman said, "I have another maiden: she is no Karua. She is a maiden lovelier than any in the town." The young man asked, "Which maiden is she?" The old woman said, "This maiden has never lived with a man." The young man said, "I still have a good part of that which my father left me." The old woman said, "The king himself gave the maiden away because she was the loveliest of all and because today is the great Salla. But the man to whom he gave her shall not have her." The young man said, "I'll give you five hundred thousand cowrie shells." The old woman said, "This maiden will be the greatest delicacy for him who has her. He will be able to enjoy her again and again, day after day. He will never be satiated with her." The young man said, "I'll go to my friends and borrow the money. I can give you two hundred thousand cowrie now." The old woman asked, "Will you bring the money later?" The young man said, "I'll send people to you with the money." The old woman said, "That will be fine."

The old woman went home. The old woman went into her house

and seated herself on the lovely maiden's bed. The old woman said to the maiden, "Have you seen the man you are to marry?" And the maiden answered, "I've seen the Makapho." The old woman said, "I know a young man who is strong and handsome, his hands are white and his face is like an Arab lady's. The young man is rich. His house perfumes a whole quarter of the town, so much *muardi* has he sprinkled there. His people eat good meat every day and he gives women to his slaves. All the women of the city have run after this young man, and the Karua wanted to give him vast sums if he would let them sleep with him. But the young man has had enough of that. The young man asked me if I did not know of a beautiful young maiden for him."

The maiden asked, "Does the young man live in this town?" The old woman answered, "Yes, the young man lives in this town. But tell me, my beauty, do you know that your Makapho has nothing and goes out daily to beg his bread?" The maiden answered, "Yes, I know that." The old woman said, "Then you know that you must lead him. You know that you must wear old clothes because he is poor." The young maiden said, "Yes, I know." The old woman said, "You have seen the Makapho. You know that his clothes are old and torn. You have seen that he has scars on his legs and feet and shoulders because a blind man in the street falls over stones and bumps into trees and walls." The young maiden said, "Yes, I know." The old woman said, "If you ever have a lovely dress, if you decorate your hair, he will not see it. If you give yourself the trouble to paint your toes he will not see them. If you paint your eyes with *kolli* he won't see it. If you paint your brow with *katambiri* he won't see it. If you laugh he will not see it, nor will he hear it either, for he will be worrying about whether people will give him food. If you cry he will beat you and say, 'How dare you cry when you can see? I am poor and blind and I do not cry.' And when you bear children he will go off and say, 'How will I be able to beg more food for them?' And he'll put your children on the street to beg for themselves. Do you know that?"

The young maiden threw herself on the ground and wept and cried, "My old mother, I beg you, I beg you! Bring me quickly to the young man." The old woman said, "Wait a while." The old woman went out. She brought *katambiri* and with it she adorned the lovely maiden's brow. She brought *kolli* with which she circled the lovely maiden's eyes. She brought a dress which she put on the lovely maiden's body and she brought a shawl with which she decorated the lovely maiden's head.

The young man ran around the town. He begged his friends, "Lend me a few thousand cowrie, I am getting a new girl for us." Some lent him two thousand cowrie, others lent him five thousand cowrie, and still others lent him ten thousand cowrie. The young man put all the money in a pile. And to it he added the rest of the money which he had inherited from his father. But there was still not enough money there. The young man called a few slaves. He sold a slave. Then he sent all the money to the old woman. He also sent the old woman four dresses and two chains of pearls. The old woman took the money. The old woman hid the money. The old woman took a dress and a string of pearls and gave them to the young maiden. The old woman said, "These are presents for you from the young man. Put them on. Now you look lovely. Come now, we'll hurry to the young man before Makapho comes." The old woman brought the lovely young maiden to the handsome young man. The handsome young man took the lovely young maiden. The handsome young man said to his slaves, "Throw the old woman out!" The old woman said, "One of these days you'll call me back again." The old woman went home.

That evening Makapho came home to the old woman. Makapho had been given a dress and he brought food with him. Makapho went into his room. Makapho said, "Maiden, where are you?" Makapho said, "My maiden, you are ashamed. But I do not demand that you speak. I will find you even though I am blind." Makapho went to the bed. Makapho explored the bed with his hands. Makapho said, "My maiden, you are not on the bed. My maiden, you are ashamed. You are still a maiden. But I will find you, even though I am blind." Makapho seated himself on the bed and said, "My maiden, I am blind. My maiden, I am poor. But Allah blesses the blind if they are not evil. I am blind but I have never done an evil thing. I am blind but I have never deceived. I am blind but I have never been a Monafiki, a malicious gossip with a friendly front. I have never been bad. And for that reason Allah has always taken care of me. You will marry me but you will never have to go on the street for the whores to see and make friends with. You are becoming my wife on the day of the great Salla and therefore Allah will take care of us both. Maiden mine, be not ashamed. Maiden mine, come to me!"

Makapho said, "Maiden mine, where are you? Maiden mine, I am blind; it is not as it is when other people marry. Maiden mine, come to me."

Makapho said, "Maiden mine, you will that I find you. Maiden, I come." The blind man rose. The blind man went along the wall. He felt the wall and went to the other side of the room and felt the wall there. He felt along all the walls and did not find the maiden. Makapho sat down on the bed and said, "My maiden has gone out." Makapho rose and went out to the court where other people lived. Makapho questioned them, saying, "I came here this morning with a maiden whom the king had given me. I brought the maiden here and went away to find a wedding dress for her. I returned with the wedding dress, but now I cannot find my maiden. Can you tell me where my maiden is?" Some of the people said, "I do not know." Others said, "The maiden must have gone away." Still others said, "Someone must have taken her away." Some said, "Someone must have spoken with the maiden." And others said, "It must be a deal." An old man said, "They arrayed the maiden beautifully. It was a very lovely maiden." Makapho said, "Can one of you give me a very stout stick?" The old man gave him a stick and said, "Here, take this, but see to it that you do not get into trouble with the Alkali, the judge. Perhaps the wood of the stick will be harder than the bones of an old woman." The blind man said, "It is well."

The blind man took the stick and said, "Now comes the fight." The old man said, "My Makapho, remember the judge." Makapho said, "This is no concern of the Alkali." Makapho went to the old woman. He entered the old woman's house. The old woman said, "You have been away for a long time, my Makapho." The blind man said, "Where is my lovely maiden?" The old woman said, "That maiden! That maiden! That was no maiden. That was a whore." The blind man closed the door behind him and said, "Where is my maiden? Where is my lovely maiden?" The old woman shrieked, "The wicked maiden, the maiden was evil. She has a Facka, a paramour. The Facka came here and the maiden wanted to sleep with him in your room." The blind man went across to the old woman and said, "Where is my maiden? Where is my lovely maiden?" The old woman yelled, "That evil maiden! How could I hold such a wicked creature? Her Facka came. Her Facka beat me. Then they both went away." The blind man raised his stick and said, "My maiden, where is my lovely maiden?" The old woman threw herself on the ground and cried, "That evil maiden! She cursed me! She stole the last bit of money I had. I wasn't able to hold her." The blind man made as if to strike the old woman, and she, in her fear, befouled the floor.

But the blind man did not strike. The blind man said, "It is better that I do not touch you now. You said, 'No animal shall take that maiden, if you do not look on me as a beast!' You said, 'No man shall take that maiden away if I do not give her to him!' You said, 'I must be worse than the devil if that maiden gets lost.' You are worse than the devil. But Allah will see if you can accomplish more than the devil can. With the theft of a chicken the evil of old age begins and with the death of many men it ends so long as Allah takes no steps to block its progress. Woe to you. And now I must see if Allah has chosen me to block your path." The blind man went out.

Makapho locked the door behind him. The old woman in the house began to scream. The blind man went away. The blind man went to the king. The blind man said to the king, "My king, lend me ten strong men." The king said, "What do you want the ten strong men for? Do you want to put a new roof on your house?" The blind man said, "No, I wish to put no new roof upon my house. It is not my affair. It is an affair of Allah's. Allah has delivered an old woman into my hands, an old woman worse than the devil." The king said, "Then take the ten strong men." The blind man left with the ten strong men. The blind man went to the chief of the slaughterers' guild, Serki Faua. The blind man said, "Give me ten *kiri*, ten leather thongs with which the bulls are bound so that they cannot defend themselves against the slaughterer." The chief of the slaughterers said, "What do you need ten *kiri* for? Do you want to build a trap for lions?" The blind man said, "No, I wish to build no trap for lions. It is not my affair. It is an affair of Allah's. Allah has delivered an old woman into my hands, an old woman worse than the devil. The king has lent me ten strong men." The chief of the slaughterers said, "Then take the ten *kiri*."

The blind man went with the ten strong men and the ten leather thongs to the house of the old woman. The blind man unlocked the door. The blind man said to the ten strong men, "Tie these thongs around the old woman's body, around her head, around her arms, and around her legs. Beat her and kick her. Pull her back and forth. Strangle her and stick her. Punch her and squeeze her." The ten strong men bound the thongs around the old woman's limbs and her head, around her neck and her body, and beat the old woman and kicked her. They pulled the old woman here and there. They throttled and poked her. They squeezed and punched her. The old woman screamed and the old woman yelled. The old woman spat blood. The blind man said,"Now we will see whether with all this stench the evil has come out of her too. It is Allah's will that she be paid in her own coin."

The ten strong men let the old woman go. The ten strong men went away with the leather thongs. But the blind man lighted a fire in the old woman's house. He threw pepper on it. Then he went out and locked the door. The fire smoked. Thick smoke filled the room. In her fear the old woman ran from one side of the room to the other. The smoke filled the whole house. At first the old woman screamed, but then the smoke filled her throat. The old woman fell to the floor. Thereupon the blind man opened the door. He said, "It is not Allah's will that you die." The smoke went out of the house. The old woman stood up again.

The blind man called a barber and had him shave off the old woman's hair. The blind man did not let the barber use any water for it. Then the blind man took a heavy iron ring, laid it on the old woman's head, and said, "That is your *useka*. And now I will give you a load." The blind man gave the old woman a heavy stone which she had to carry on her head with the iron ring as a cushion. The blind man said, "Now go into the country round about and trade." The old woman had to go. The blind man drove her before him. For seven months the old woman had to carry the stone on her head. Then the blind man said to her, "Now throw the stone and the iron ring away. You followed the path of theft from the stolen chicken to the stolen girl. Then Allah threw this stone in your path. My quarrel with you is at an end. I will not do anything more to you. I am going my way. And go you yours."

Makapho went. The old woman threw the stone and the iron ring away. The old woman said, "This blind man is very stupid. But I'll go home quickly and see if my money is still there." The old woman went back to the town. The old woman went to the market and sold spice. She had spice for sale at the market. Iblis the devil appeared in the market. The devil came to the old woman and said, "That was a bad affair you had with Makapho." The old woman said, "*Kai!* Don't laugh at me! You may be strong but I can outdo you." The devil said, "How is that? Don't you, the old woman from Matusu, recognize me?" The old woman said, "Why shouldn't I know you? You are the devil. But even if you are the devil, were your head, your limbs, and your body ever tied with ten leather thongs? Have ten strong men ever punched and kicked and squeezed and pinched and beaten you? Were you ever shut in a room with fire and pepper smoke for so long that the smoke filled your throat and you fell unconscious? Have you ever had your skull dry shaved and an iron ring laid on it, and have you ever had to carry a heavy stone for seven months on that iron ring? *Kai!* Devil, could you stand that?"

The devil said, "What are your other big achievements?" The old woman said, "What are my other big achievements? I do not recall them. But this much I remember. I have estranged more than eleven thousand people who were married and have made them hate each other. I have so antagonized two thousand people, who were courting each other, that they never met again, never married and had children." The devil said, "That's a pretty good record, my old woman. That's really fine. But that is no reason for you to say that you outdo me. I'll give you an example here on the market of something you won't be able to copy. For I am Iblis the devil." The old woman said, "You are the devil and competent enough, that I know. And you will probably do a pretty big thing, that I know. Whether I can imitate it or outdo it, I cannot say—for you were never tied with ten leather thongs and never sat in pepper smoke. You never had to carry a rocky weight on an iron ring on a shorn head for months at a time. So I'll wait before I say anything till you've done what you are going to do." The old woman packed up her market basket and went home.

The devil wandered around the market. He sat down and listened to what the girls who sold kola nuts were saying. He sat down and listened to what the clothesmakers were saying. Iblis went to where the linen dealers sat, crouched near by, and listened to what was said. Iblis listened to what the people of the town said, and he heard what the heathen Magussaua, who had come with their women to the market to sell sheep and wood and *dauwa*, related. Iblis listened to all of them. Some quarreled maliciously. Some spoke well of each other and some related evil of each other. But Iblis was on the watch only for the evil words they spoke. Iblis went to a group of people. Iblis said, "You bought that from that man over there. I heard him say how he had cheated you." Iblis went to another group and said, "This man cheated that man and you ought to do something about it." Iblis went to others and said, "Those people say that one of you cheated them. But they say it only because one of them misused one of your women when she brought him food the other evening." Iblis went to others and said, "You must help these people against those, for those are evil and say evil for they have done evil things." Iblis went to a well-respected man whose caravans plied here and there all over the country. He said to this man, "People say that you are a malicious gossip who starts quarrels between people because you don't get enough money from them." The man was really a Monafiki, a mischief, and outside of that he was used to taking the last bit of money that people had so that they had to bond themselves and were never able to earn their freedom again.

But when the Monafiki heard the devil say what had been said, he drew his sword. The Monafiki ran to the people who had gossiped about him and cried, "Who called me a Monafiki?" There was a man there who had long been in bondage to the Monafiki and who now had no more to lose. This man cried, "You are a Monafiki! It is true! You are a Monafiki! I'll repeat it before everyone. Everyone shall hear it!" The Monafiki struck at the man with his sword. The rich Monafiki struck the poor man. Whereupon some of the people cried, "First this man took our money. Now he takes our lives!"

A few people struck at the rich Monafiki. The Monafiki's slaves ran to help him. The rich Monafiki fell to the earth. A few shouted with pleasure. Others shouted in protest. Some cried, "This man cheated that one." Others shouted, "And that one misused this one's woman!" All began to strike out. Each one grabbed whatever weapon lay to hand. Finally twelve hundred people were killed. Then the Dogari, the king's bodyguard, came and drove all the people away from the market.

The devil went to the old woman and said, "Come with me and I will show you what I can do in a single day." The old woman went with the devil. The devil led the old woman to the market. On the ground there lay baskets and clothes, kola nuts and bean cakes, shoes and meal cakes, roast meat and thread. The dead lay here and there. And everywhere the Dogari were patrolling back and forth among the chaos of goods and bodies on the bloodstained ground. The devil said to the old woman, "See now, I did all that in a single day."

The old woman looked around the market place. The old woman said, "That is no more than twelve hundred dead and a wrecked market." The devil said, "Yes, it is twelve hundred dead and a wrecked market." The devil said, "And I did all of it in a single day." The old woman turned away in contempt and said, "Is that all? Do you think you can do more than I can with that? Devil, go home. Come again tomorrow evening and then I'll show you what the old woman can do."

The next morning the old woman went out and bought a hundred first-rate kola nuts; she bought a jar full of perfumed water; she bought a handful of *truare-djubuda* [civet excretion]. Of all of this the old woman took fifty of the kola nuts and the *truare-djubuda* and set out for the house of the king. The Serki, as the king was called, had married a young wife not long before. The young maiden whom he had married was particularly lovely, so lovely that all the people of the town spoke of her, and the king liked her so well that he preferred her to his other wives and set her beside his first wife.

The old woman came to the king's young wife. The old woman looked at the young wife of the king. The old woman said, "Now that I have seen you I understand his words, the words of Susso, words which at first seemed crazy to me." The young woman said, "What is the matter with me?" The old woman said, "You are very lovely. You are lovelier than all other women. And now that I have seen you I understand the words which at first seemed crazy to me." The young wife of the king said, "*Kai*, old woman! You cannot say such things here. You are in the court of the king. Come, I'll give you a shawl. Now tell me quickly a bit of gossip from the town and then go." The old woman looked at the lovely wife of the king. The old woman said, "Yes, he said too, 'You will go into the house of an old man, the king.' He said, 'There you will see the young wife of the king, lovelier than all other women.' Now that I have seen you I understand the words that seemed crazy to me before." The king's young wife said, "Quickly now, tell me something new."

The old woman put down the fifty kola nuts and the *truare-djubuda* and said, "What else can he send you but a trifle! You have everything. And should he give you a golden ring, the king would see it." The young wife asked, "Who sends that here? How dare anyone send anything here in my house?" The old woman said, "Only one man can do that. No other young man in the town would dare to send a kola nut to this house of the king, into the house where the old king has shut you up!" The young wife of the king said, "Who sends you?" The old woman answered, "It can be only he who rides at the front in war. It can be only he whose coming the enemy fears more than that of a thousand other riders." The young wife of the king said, "Who sends you here?" The old woman said, "He who sends me is the son of the Jerima."

The young wife of the king said, "Does not the son of the Jerima fear to send this to the favorite wife of the king?" The old woman said, "If a hundred lions charge him, the son of the Jerima will have no fear. If a hundred elephants charge him, the son of the Jerima will have no fear. Why should he then be afraid of an old man?" The young wife of the king said, "What thinks the son of the Jerima?" The old woman said, "The son of the Jerima thinks no more of prayer. The son of the Jerima thinks no more of his father and mother. The son of the Jerima thinks only of you!"

The young wife of the king took the kola nuts. The young wife of the king took the *truare-djubuda*. The young wife of the king said, "Whenever my white teeth bite into these kola nuts, then I will think of the son of the Jerima. When the perfume of the *truare-djubuda* permeates my garments, I will think of the son of the Jerima." The old woman said, "Think of him when you hear that he is going to the wars again. Think of him when you hear that he has been killed in battle." The young wife of the king said, "Is the son of the Jerima going to the wars again soon?" The old woman said, "The son of the Jerima does not wish to live any longer. He thinks only of you. He is going to the wars again tomorrow. And he will not return." The young wife of the king said, "He will not return?" The old woman said, "No, the son of the Jerima will not return to this city, the city in which you live shut up within the walls of the king's house. The son of the Jerima wishes to die."

The young wife of the king said, "He will let himself be slain in battle!" The young wife of the king wept. The young wife of the king said, "Tell me, old woman, how will it be possible for me to see the son of the Jerima today?" The old woman said, "That is a difficult thing. The son of the Jerima told me, 'How is it possible for me to see the young wife of the king again before I go to the wars?' That is a difficult thing." The young wife of the king said, "You, old woman! The son of the Jerima dare not let himself be killed in battle! You, old woman, I must see the son of the Jerima today, today! Listen, old woman, when I want the king to do something, he does it. Tell me now how it will be possible for me to see the son of the Jerima today."

The old woman said, "O young and beautiful wife of the king, go you to the king and say, 'I hear that my mother is ill. Permit me to go to her. Before evening falls I will return.' And when the king has given you permission, then come quickly to me in the small house by the city wall." The young wife of the king said, "Yes, that is what I will do. I'll go to the king at once. And then I will come to you in the small house by the city wall." The old woman said, "Come to me. And then I will go to the son of the Jerima and tell him that you are in my house."

The young wife of the king gave the old woman a head shawl and a dress. The old woman went. The young wife of the king took the kola nuts. She took a shawl and laid four of the nuts in the shawl. The young wife of the king said, "The son of the Jerima is young and handsome." The young woman took four more nuts, laid them in the shawl, and said, "The king is old." The young woman took four other nuts, laid them in the shawl, and said, "The son of the Jerima said that I was the most beautiful woman in all the city." The young wife took four more nuts, laid them in the shawl, and said, "The son of the Jerima shall not go to war." The young wife took four more kola nuts, laid them in the shawl, and said, "I will beg the young son of the Jerima not to go to war." The young wife of the king took the remaining nuts, threw them into the shawl, and said, "Now I am going to the son of the Jerima. Now I'll throw myself to the ground before the son of the Jerima. Now I'll beg him and beg him and beg him. Now I'll go and make myself beautiful, and now I know at last for whom I am doing it!"

The young wife of the king threw off her clothes. The young wife of the king put on lovely garments and then put on old clothes over them. With her lovely garments hidden by the old clothes she left the house. She went into the house of the king. She told a slave, "Go tell the king that I must see him!" The slave said, "This is not the time for that. The king is giving audience." The young woman said, "*Kai*, slave, go—or I'll go myself and ask the king to have you thrashed. Go to the king and tell him, 'Your young wife will speak with you. Your young wife fears a death.' Go!" The slave went to the king's audience chamber. All the influential people sat there around him. The slave threw himself to the ground before the king. The king said, "What is the matter?" The slave said, "Your young wife will speak with you. Your young wife fears a death." The king stood up. The king went out. The Tschiroma, a princely chamberlain, said to the Galadima of the city, "The king is getting old. Any woman can do what she wants with him." The Galadima said, "Yes, the king is getting old."

The king entered the house in which the young woman was waiting for him. The young woman threw herself to the ground before the king. The young wife wept and said, "Serki! Serki! Serki! King! King! King!" The king said, "You weep and wear old clothes! Haven't I given you enough new and beautiful garments?" The young wife wept and cried, "King! King! King!" The king bent over her and raised her to her feet. The king said, "What is the matter?" The young wife cried, "I fear a death! I fear a death! I fear a death!" The king said, "Why shall you die?" The young wife wept and said, "I won't be the first to die. But a person dies and then another person must die too." The king asked, "Who, then?" The young wife wept and said, "Allow me to go to my mother. Let me go at once. I have just had news. I'll be back again this evening." The king said, "Has your mother been ill for long?" The young wife wept and said, "No, but may I go?" The king said, "Go." The young woman hurried away.

The young wife ran through the court. The young wife ran through the city. The young wife ran to the end of the city. The young wife ran to the small house by the city wall. The young woman entered the old woman's house. The old woman said, "You! But why do you come in poor old clothes?" The young wife said, "Never mind! Go quickly and call the son of the Jerima!" The old woman went. The old woman went through the city and said to herself, "The hunter in the bush has fired a stalk of grass on the steppe. Soon comes the wind. The wind will drive the fire through the bush, and the fire will destroy the homesteads and the granaries of the people."

The old woman ran through the city. The old woman ran into the Jerima's court. The Jerima had but one son. And the son of the Jerima was in his house. The slaves of the Jerima sat before him and sharpened his swords and daggers and lances. The old woman threw herself to the ground before the son of the Jerima. The old woman lay there. The son of the Jerima said, "What is wrong?" The old woman said, "The son of the Jerima fears not and robs the lion of its cub." The son of the Jerima said, "What is the matter?" The old woman said, "What two ears would like to hear need not necessarily be shared by eight." The son of the Jerima said to the slaves, "Get out!" The slaves got out.

The Jerima's slaves went out. The son of the Jerima said, "What is it?" The old woman took the fifty kola nuts out of her head shawl. The old woman set the jar of perfumed water before him. The old woman said, "That is sent by a young woman." The son of the Jerima said, "What are you trying to say?" The old woman said, "You shall not go to war. You shall not die. For if one person dies then another must die too, for the one cannot live if the other does not return." The son of the Jerima stood up. The son of the Jerima said, "Who is the young woman? Isn't her man good enough for her?" The old woman said, "The young woman always looks over the wall when you go forth to war. The young woman cannot sleep when you are in battle. She suffers in the night when you are at the wars. The young woman looks over the wall when you return. Then she can live again by day. When you are at the wars the young woman gives presents to beggars and the blind, so that Allah may help you. And when you return from the wars the young woman gives presents to beggars and the blind, so that Allah may keep you in the city."

The son of the Jerima said, "Old woman, tell me who the young woman is!" The old woman said, "She is the most beautiful woman in the city. But she lies between the lion's paws. Only a brave one may see her and greet her." The son of the Jerima took his sword and raised it. The son of the Jerima said, "Old woman, tell me quickly who the young woman is." The old woman said, "It is the young wife of the king." The son of the Jerima said, "The young wife of the king!" The son of the Jerima threw his sword away. The son of the Jerima said, "Where is the lovely young wife of the king?" The old woman said, "The lovely young wife of the king is in my house. The beautiful young woman is sitting on the edge of the bed." The son of the Jerima said, "Lead on! Show me the way!"

The old woman went. The son of the Jerima took a man of his

father's with him. The son of the Jerima and the man followed the old woman. The old woman and the man and the son of the Jerima went through the city. They came to the city wall. The man withdrew. The old woman opened the door of her house. The young wife rose from the side of the bed. The son of the Jerima went in the door. The young woman let the old clothes fall to the ground. The young woman stood before the son of the Jerima. She was very beautiful. And she wore lovely garments. The old woman shut the door. The son of the Jerima stayed there, in the house, with the lovely young wife of the king.

The Jerima's man stood outside. The door of the old woman's house was on the latch. The old woman ran away. The old woman ran through the city. The old woman ran to the royal quarters. The influential people had greeted the king, and the king had reached them the morning dish. The king had retired to an inner chamber. The prominent people were gone. The king was alone. The old woman ran through the corridor. The old woman ran into the chamber in which the king sat. The old woman threw herself to the ground and cried, "O King! King! King!" The old woman wailed and cried, "Now you'll kill me for it!" The king said, "Why should I kill you?" The old woman cried, "You will kill me because others deceive you." The king said, "What is the matter?" The old woman wept and said, "How can I help it that the son of the Jerima does not respect you?" The king said, "In what way does he not respect me?" The old woman wept and said, "If only the son of the Jerima would make free with other people's wives! Could not the son of the Jerima leave at least this one lovely young wife alone? Must the son of the Jerima devote himself to just this one particular beautiful young wife whom you love above all others and have placed at the side of your first wife?" The king said, "Old woman, tell me the truth. Tell me if you have seen the son of the Jerima with my wife." The king said, "Old woman, tell me the truth!" The old woman said, "They are in my house!" The king shouted, "You lie!" The old woman said, "Look at my white hair. I cannot lie. At this very moment they are sitting on my bed in my house." The king said, "I'll send a messenger to see." The king called one of his men. The king said, "Go with the old woman and see whether it is true that the son of the Jerima is courting my wife in the old woman's house." The messenger took a dagger. The messenger went with the old woman.

The old woman led the king's messenger to her small house by the city wall. At some distance from the house stood the Jerima's man. The king's messenger went to the door of the old woman's house. He opened it. The king's messenger saw the son of the Jerima. The king's messenger saw the lovely young wife of the king. But the lovely young wife of the king and the son of the Jerima did not see the king's messenger. For they had eyes only for each other. The king's messenger drew his dagger. The king's messenger stabbed the son of the Jerima in the back. The blood spurted out and poured over the lovely young wife of the king. The lovely young wife screamed. The son of the Jerima said, "That's an evil way to die!" The son of the Jerima was dead.

The old woman stood outside with the Jerima's man. The son of the Jerima said, "That's an evil way to die." The Jerima's man heard it. The Jerima's man rushed into the house and struck down the king's messenger. Then the Jerima's man tripped over the clothes of the young wife of the king which were lying on the floor and fell to the ground. The old woman ran away. The old woman ran through the city. The old woman ran as fast as she could. The old woman said to herself, "Now the wind is driving the flames over the homesteads and granaries of the people. Nothing of this city shall remain." The old woman ran as fast as she could.

The old woman ran into the house of the Jerima. The old woman cried, "Jerima, why haven't you saddled your horse?" The Jerima replied, "Why should I saddle my horse, old woman?" The old woman said, "Will you then go to war on foot, like a common soldier?" The Jerima said, "Who is making war?" The old woman said, "When the king wanted to sack a foreign city you rode ahead and were the first. But now, now when the king has had your son killed, you stay there lying on your mat." The Jerima leaped to his feet. The old woman said, "Was not this son your only son?" The Jerima cried, "Saddle my horse! Saddle my horse!"

The old woman ran out. The old woman ran through the streets. The old woman ran as fast as she could. The old woman said to herself, "Now the wind is driving the flames over the granaries and homesteads of the people. Nothing shall remain of this city." The old woman ran as fast as she could.

The old woman ran into the house of the king. The old woman yelled down the royal corridor, "O King! King! King! Saddle your horse!" The king said, "What is wrong, then?" The old woman said,

"King you were! King you are no longer! The Jerima has slain your messenger. The Jerima is to horse. The Jerima is riding through the city with his knights." The king called, "Dig a grave for a king!" The old woman ran away. The old woman said to herself, "Now I'll heap wood and dry grass on the flames." The old woman ran as fast as she could.

The old woman ran to where the beggars and thieves lived. The old woman called the beggars and thieves together. The old woman said, "When the great beasts have killed each other the worms feast on their bodies." The beggars and thieves said, "What's up?" The old woman said, "Hear the drums beat. Hear the noise of the horsemen. The king and the Jerima have started a war. Everyone is in the streets." The beggars and thieves said, "Well, we aren't here to fight. Let the others fight. What are we to do?" The old woman said, "All the men are in the streets. No one is watching the houses. Go here and there. Fire the houses. Steal clothes and pearls, steal silver and gold." The beggars and thieves said, "The old woman is right. We'll do that." The old woman said, "What sort of women can you afford? Think of the women you can have today. All the men are in the streets. Throw their wives and daughters to the ground. You'll find them better than the Karua!" The beggars and the thieves ran off.

The beggars and the thieves ran off. All the menfolk ran with weapons through the streets. Drums thundered. Knights put the spurs on their horses. The Jerima collected his followers and rode with them to the royal quarters. The king collected his followers and rode with them against the house of the Jerima. The hostile parties met. The Jerima cried, "You have slain my only son." The king cried, "Your son made love to my young and beautiful wife!" The king and the Jerima raised their swords and charged. The king and the Jerima struck home. The king and the Jerima fell from their horses. The king and the Jerima died.

The king's followers yelled. The Jerima's followers yelled. Some charged here; some charged there. Some struck here; some fought there. Some lunged with lances; others struck with clubs. Some shot arrows; others threw stones. The women fled into their houses and hid their children. The maidens fled into the granaries and storerooms and crouched there together. But the beggars and thieves ran through the city. The beggars and thieves fired here a granary, there a house. The women shrieked; the children screamed. The beggars and thieves went into the houses. Some stole. Others threw maidens to the floor. The men in the streets ran away to save their possessions. The flames were everywhere. Children were killed by arrows. Women were crushed by the horses. Many people were burned alive.

Houses and granaries burned and were destroyed. Men and women and children died. The mat walls roared in the flames. The women screamed in the street. Whoever could grab something ran out of the city. Dead men lay in the streets. Pillars of fire twisted over the courtyards. The beggars and thieves carried away what

they found. Whoever could run fled through the gate in the city wall out into the bush.

The old woman stood on the city wall above the gate. The old woman danced. The old woman sang. The old woman sang, "I haven't danced once since I was young. Since I was young I haven't once danced. But today I'll be king of the city, and Kurra, the hyena, and Angulu, the buzzard, will prostrate themselves before me and cry, 'King! King! King!' They'll thank me for the feast that I brought them with this fire. They'll thank me for the bones which I will throw to them. *Kai!* Makapho! You had ten men bind me with ten leather thongs around my limbs, my head, my neck, and my body. The ten strong men beat me and kicked me, squeezed me and punched me, pinched me and choked me. *Kai!* Makapho! You shut me in a room with pepper smoke and fire till my throat was filled with smoke and I fell down. *Kai!* Makapho! On my dry-shaved skull you laid an iron ring as a cushion for a heavy stone that I had to carry for seven months long. *Kai!* Makapho! Look at the city in which you lost your chicken, your goat and donkey and horse and camel! *Kai!* Makapho! You taught me all that!"

The old woman danced on the city wall above the city gate. The town was burned. The people either lay around as corpses or had run away. The old woman danced and sang, "*Kai!* Iblis! Now come and see what an old woman can do! *Kai!* Iblis! Haven't I outdone you?" The devil came.

The devil climbed to the top of the city wall. The devil looked down on the city. The devil saw the corpses and the burned houses. In the center of the city lay the dead king and the dead Jerima side by side. Not a person lived within the city. The hyenas crept up through the bush. The buzzards circled over the smoke in the still air.

The devil saw it all.

The devil said, "What, you, a single old woman, have done all that in a single day? If you've just done that, what will you do then tomorrow?" The devil began to be afraid of the old woman. The devil sprang down. The devil disappeared into the earth. The old woman did not see him again.

The sun set.

From *African Genesis*, by Leo Frobenius and Douglas C. Fox (New York: Stackpole Sons, 1937).

TAKISE

A HAUSA TALE

ONE OF the cows belonging to a Peuhl herder wandered off when just about to calve and was brought down in an old lougan. After she returned to her master's herd, the bulls, seeing that she had dropped her calf, at once began to search for it, but though they hunted all through the brush they could find nothing, and they returned sadly to the pasture, saying that the calf must have been devoured by wild beasts.

An old woman who went to the abandoned lougan to get sorrel leaves to make sauce for her couscous, saw the calf crouched under a bush. She took it home with her and fed it on bran, salted millet, and grass.

The calf grew up into a fine big bull.

One day a butcher came by and asked the old woman to sell him her bull, but she refused. "Takise," she said, for that was the name she had given to her adopted pet, "Takise is not for sale." The butcher, annoyed at her refusal, went to the king and said to him, "Old Zeynebou has a big bull which only you should eat, he is so fine."

The Sartyi sent the butcher, together with six other men, commanded by one of his messengers, to fetch the old woman's bull. When the little troupe arrived at Zeynebou's house the chief's messenger said to her, "The Sartyi has sent us to fetch your bull, which will be killed tomorrow." She replied, "It is not for me to oppose the king's wishes. I only ask you one favor, which is not to take Takise away until tomorrow morning."

The next morning at daybreak the Dansama and the seven butchers came to the old woman's house and approached the picket to which Takise was tethered. The bull came toward them with his horns lowered, snorting loudly. The eight men, very uneasy at this, drew back, and the Dansama, calling the old woman, said to her, "Old woman, tell your bull to let us put the cord around his neck."

The old woman went up to the bull. "Takise, my Takise," she said, "let them put the rope round your neck." The bull obeyed, and they put a halter on him and tied a rope to one of his hind legs, to lead him to the Sartyi. When they were in the king's presence the butchers threw the bull on his side and tied his four legs; then one of them drew near with a knife to cut his throat. But the knife could not cut so much as a hair, for Takise had the power to prevent iron from grazing his skin.

The head butcher begged the Sartyi to send for the old woman. He declared that without her it would be impossible to kill Takise, who must have some charm against iron. The Sartyi sent for the old woman and said to her, "Unless they are able to kill your bull without any more delay, I will have your head cut off."

The old woman went up to Takise, who still lay bound and upon his side, and said to him, "Takise, my Takise, let yourself be killed. Everything now is for the chief!"

The head butcher then killed Takise without any trouble. The butchers flayed the body, cut it up, and took the meat to the Sartyi, who told them to give the old woman back the fat and the guts for her share.

The old woman took everything in an old basket and carried it home. There she put the guts and fat in a big jar, for she had not the heart to eat the animal which she had brought up and of which she had been so fond.

The old woman had neither child nor slave, so she had to do the housework herself. But it so happened that after she put Takise's remains into the jar she found her hut swept every morning and her water jars filled to the brim. And this happened every time she went away for a moment. For the guts and fat changed themselves every morning into two young girls, who did her work for her.

One morning the good woman said to herself, "Today I will find out who sweeps my floor and fills my water jars." She went out of the hut and closed the entrance with a mat; then, hiding behind the mat, she sat down and spied through the holes to see what went on inside.

She had scarcely sat down when she heard a noise in the hut. She listened without stirring. It was the strokes of a broom on the floor that made this noise. All at once she threw down the mat and saw two young girls who ran to hide themselves, as quickly as they could, in the big jar. "Don't go away," she cried to them. "I have no child, as you know. We will all three live here together."

The young girls stopped in their flight, then drew near the old woman. She gave to the prettiest of the two the name Takise; the other she called Aisa.

For a long time they lived with the old woman without anyone knowing that they were there, for they never went outside. One day a Gambari came to the hut and asked for a drink of water. It was Takise who brought the water, and the stranger was so overcome by her beauty that he forgot to drink.

When he visited the king the Gambari told him how, in the house of an old woman in the village, he had seen a young girl of unrivaled beauty. "This girl," he added, "should be married only to a Sartyi."

The Sartyi at once ordered his Griot to go, together with the Dioula, to fetch this young girl. She came, followed by the old woman. "Your daughter is wonderfully beautiful," said the Sartyi to the old woman. "I shall take her for my wife." "Sartyi," the old woman replied, "I will gladly give her to you in marriage, but on condition that she never goes out in the sun, or goes near a fire, for she would melt at once, like a bit of fat."

The Sartyi promised the old woman that Takise should never go out while the sun shone, and never do any cooking. Thus there would be no fear of her ever being exposed to heat, which was fatal to her.

So Takise married the king, who put her in the place of his favorite wife. The latter, deposed from her position, became no better than an ordinary wife, such as may never, without express permission, enter the presence of her husband.

After seven months the Sartyi went on a journey. The day he set forth the women gathered together and said to Takise, "You are the chief's favorite, and you never work. Unless you roast us these grains of sesame at once, we will kill you and throw your body into the sump."

Takise, frightened by this threat, drew near the fire to roast the sesame seed in a pot, and as she bent over their roasting her body began to melt like butter in the sun, turning into a greasy fluid which gave rise to a great stream.

The other wives watched this transformation unmoved. When all was over the former favorite said, "Now we are ruined, mark my words! When the Sartyi comes back he will have our heads cut off. He will never forgive us for making his favorite work at the fire until she melted. And the very first to have her head cut off will be me!"

Until the husband's return the king's women lived in fear and trembling. The Sartyi came back from his journey several days later. Before he even drank the water offered him, he called for his favorite. "Takise! Takise!"

The former favorite then came to him and said, "Sartyi and husband, I can hide nothing from you. While you were away the little ones" (she meant the other wives) "made Takise work by the fire. She melted like butter, and that new stream you see there in the distance is the stream to which she gave rise in melting."

"I must have my Takise! I must have my Takise!" the Sartyi cried. He ran at once to the watercourse, followed by the former favorite.

When they reached the edge of the delta the king turned into a hippopotamus and plunged after Takise. The ex-favorite, who loved

her husband deeply, took the shape of a cayman and plunged into the water also, so as not to leave the Sartyi.

Ever since that time, hippopotamus and cayman have always lived in the deltas.

From *The African Saga*, translated by Margery Bianco from the *Anthologie Nègre* of Blaise Cendrars (New York: Payson & Clark, 1927).

MARANDENBONI

A SONINKE TALE

THERE was a witch who had seven beautiful daughters. It was said that whoever passed a night with one of them would be eaten by the witch, for it is the habit of witches to live on human flesh.

In the country where this witch lived there were eight brothers, of whom the youngest, who was only a few months old, was named Marandenboni, child of evil.

One day Marandenboni advised his brothers to go and sleep with the witch's daughters. They said, "But don't you know that not one of their lovers has ever been seen again?"

"Do what I tell you," said Maran, "and don't be afraid."

The eight brothers went to the witch's house. She made them very welcome and gave them a fine meal, after which she said, "Go and sleep, each of you in one of those seven huts. You will find pleasant companions for the night."

They went.

Maran, who had not been offered anything, said, "How about me, grandmother? Shall I sleep with you?"

"Yes," said the old woman.

When the young men had gone into the huts, as they were told, the old woman and Maran went into another hut and lay down side by side.

Toward the middle of the night the old woman coughed a little. to find out if Maran were asleep. The boy said nothing and did not move. The old woman got up, and Maran said, "Hi, mama, where are you going?"

"What, are you awake, little one?"

"Oh, I never sleep until my mother has poured a basket of water over my head."

She took a basket and went to fill it at the well, but in bringing it back to the house the water all ran out. The old woman started out again, and in the end she spent all night trying to carry water in the basket.

The next day nothing happened. When night came the young men went to sleep with the girls again, and Maran with the old woman.

Overcome with sleepiness, because she had been awake all the night before, the old woman slept soundly. A little before midnight Maran got up very quietly and went from hut to hut, saying to each of his brothers, "Put the witch's daughter on the outside, in your place, and cover her with your blanket." This done, Maran went back and lay down. At midnight the old woman woke up. She coughed, moved about, then rose, but Maran did not stir. She went from hut to hut, cutting the throat of each one that lay on the outside of the bed. Then she came back and began to make a sauce with the blood of her victims. When she was about to begin eating, Maran cried, "I want some too, mother!"

"What, Maran, you want to eat human blood?"

"Why, yes," said Maran, not seeming at all shocked. "It is so good!"

The meal over, they lay down again. The old woman slept, and Maran took this moment to go and say to his brothers, "Run away quickly, for when the old woman learns what she has done she will kill you." Then Maran went back again to his place.

In the morning the old woman said to him, "Go and see if your brothers are awake." Maran came back and said, "No, they are still sleeping."

A little later the old woman said to him, "What are your brothers doing now?"

He replied, "Oh, they went away a long time ago, but your daughters are sleeping forever!" And he ran away.

The old woman, suspecting some evil, went to her daughters' huts and saw the trick that had been played on her. She swore to revenge herself on this wily Maran.

Like all witches, she was able to change herself into any shape she chose. She went to Maran's village. This village had only one baobab, so the people who lived there had to go a long way to get leaves for sauce. The old woman transformed herself into a fine baobab, which all the village urchins at once began to climb.

But Maran, who was playing with them, said, "What? Does a great tall baobab like that grow out of the earth in one night, like a mushroom?"

"Surely," said the baobab, "and if you want to gather my leaves you are very welcome!" And one of the branches bent down so as to help Maran up.

"Oh! Oh!" said the child. "A baobab that talks and bends its branches about! That isn't at all as it should be. Climb up and gather the leaves if you like. I, for my part, shall stay here."

The baobab shook with rage, and, seeing that Maran kept away, it disappeared, taking with it all the rash children who were gathering leaves.

The witch thought that the village people would send Maran to fetch the children, and she gloated beforehand over her vengeance. But Maran never came.

One day, behind Maran's village, the boys saw a donkey running loose, and, having nothing better to do, they caught it, and all tried to get on its back at once. When Maran caught up with them there was no more room on the donkey's back, but the donkey very kindly began to lengthen out his backbone.

"Oho!" said Maran. "This donkey must belong to the same family as the baobab!" And he ran away.

The donkey disappeared with the children on its back, and the unhappy mothers said to Maran, "You are so clever about not falling into the witch's snares, use your wisdom now to get our children back for us!"

Maran promised. He set out, taking with him some dried meat in a goatskin.

The witch had a little daughter the same age as Maran.

She also had a cow that was due to calve, and as she always went in fear of Maran she said, at the moment when her cow was about to calve, "If my cow has a little red calf, it will mean that Maran is in the calf's belly; if she has a little white calf, then it won't be Maran."

The little calf was white, so after that the old woman had no suspicion; but Maran, who was more cunning than she, was really in the little calf's belly all the same.

Like all young calves, this one jumped and ran about very fast. One day, while passing near the little boys, it said to them, "When the old woman lets me free among you, you must catch hold of me by the ears or the tail or wherever you can, and I will take you back to your homes."

This he did, and the old woman was in despair. However, whether because she was quicker than he, or because Maran really meant her to, she somehow got hold of him.

She put her prisoner in a goatskin, which she carefully tied up and put in another goatskin, which she closed the same way. This she put once more in a third goatskin and tied it very strongly.

The witch posted her little daughter near the prisoner to watch him, while she herself dug, in the yard of her house, a pit into which she threw wood and dried grass, and set it on fire.

Meanwhile the little girl could hear Maran nibbling something, so she asked, "Have you got some food there, Maran?"

"Oh, I have something much better than food. I have some real goodies!"

"Oh, Maran, do give me some!"

"How can I give you any, tied up as I am? Undo me a little, and then we'll see."

The foolish little girl opened the goatskins. Maran jumped out, undressed her, and put her in his place, together with his own things, tied up the goatskins and went away, wearing the little girl's waistcloth.

When the old woman picked up the goatskin a tiny voice said to her, "Take care, mother! Maran has put me in his place, and it is your little daughter you are going to kill!"

"Yes, yes!" said the old woman. "I have heard that story before, Maran. I know you! You can imitate my daughter's voice all right, but that won't change your fate." And without more ado she threw the bundle on the flames. A little while after the child's body burst with a loud noise, and Maran sprang up before the old woman, crying, "How now, old witch! You have killed your last daughter!" And he ran away.

The old woman sat down, in despair, to think of the best means to avenge herself upon Maran. They say that she is thinking yet.

From *The African Saga.*

THE LEGEND OF THE ELEPHANT

A FAN TALE

In those days, and that was very long ago, further back than one can think, mankind lived all together in one big village, and the animals did the same, each in his village, each according to his race; the antelopes with the antelopes, the boars with the boars, the leopards with the leopards, the monkeys with the monkeys.

But in each village, as chief, there lived an elephant, and the elephants were thus scattered, each family of elephants commanding a different village. The chief of them all, the father elephant, lived alone in the forest, but when there was a palaver everyone appeared before him, and he judged with wisdom. When the father elephant thought that his time had come, he passed on his spirit to his successor and disappeared. Never, never was he seen again, but his spirit remained alive.

The men lived apart, far, far in the forest, and no animal lived with them, not one, not even a dog. I know nothing at all about the chickens, but I think the chickens must have lived with the other birds.

The men were apart; they ate the fruits of the forest, but often, too, they killed animals and ate their flesh, and then there were palavers without end. The animals came and complained to the elephant. The elephant ordered the men to appear, but they never came, and they continued to kill the animals.

There were so many complaints against the men that the elephant said at last, "Since they will not come here, I must go to their village."

He made preparations for his journey and set off for the men's village. But first he had to find this village, and that was quite difficult, for the men had hidden it very well. The elephant set out. On his way he came first of all to the leopard village.

"Where are you going, Father Elephant?"

"I am going to the men's village, to judge their palaver with you."

"That's a good idea. We'll go with you."

"No, they would be too frightened. I would rather go alone."

And the elephant said that because he knew very well that Nzame had created the men, and that the chief of the men was the son of Nzame, like himself.

"Very well, go alone, Father Elephant, but first rest a day in our village."

The elephant agreed, because they treated him very well, and he stayed two whole days in the leopard village. He would have stayed three days, and even longer, but there was nothing left to eat. So he continued his journey, and came to the antelope village.

"And where are you going, Father Elephant?"

"I am going to the men's village to judge their palavers, for I am getting tired of them."

"That's a very good idea. We'll go with you."

"No, I would rather go alone, for perhaps they might kill you in the night."

And the antelopes answered, "Very well, but at least stay two days with us."

And the father elephant willingly agreed, for the antelopes treated him very well, and he stayed two whole days in their village. He would have stayed three days, and even longer, but there was nothing left to eat and he was very hungry.

Father Elephant then went to the boars' village. And so, from village to village, the elephant continued on his way.

For some time past, however, the chief of the men, who often consulted his fetich (an antelope with a mirror imbedded in it), had known of the elephant's journey. That he did not want at all. And so in all the paths which led to his village from far, far away, he, together with the other men and with women who carried the earth, dug deep pits, with pointed stakes at the bottom; three, four, five traps one after another, at one hour's, two hours', three hours' march distant. And when the farthest pit was finished he said to his men, "Go and cut me some manioc stems."

And the men went and cut some manioc.

"Throw the stems down so that they cover the pit."

And the men laid the stems carefully, and some days after they began to sprout, so one no longer saw the bare wood. And at an hour's march from there, on the same path, the chief of the men had another pit dug. And he said to his men, "Go and fetch some potato stalks."

And they went, and came back with a lot of potato stalks. And their chief said, "Lay these stalks over the pit."

And they laid them well, so that the pit could not be seen.

And so he had five different pits dug along the path, each with a different plant. And on each path leading to the village he had five pits dug like this. The chief of the men was very cunning! He thought to himself, "If the elephant sees a heap of manioc in his path he will suspect something, for he is very clever." And so on the path, a long, long way off, at four or five different places, he had manioc thrown down; but underneath this there was no pit; and farther on still, after the first pit, he put more manioc again, and then potatoes, and then other plants. He put them all along the road!

Father Elephant was then well on his way to the men's village. And there on the road he came upon a heap of manioc. He turned it over and over with his trunk, for he was very wily, but he found nothing at all suspicious. "It is a present from my children," he said. "They wanted to leave food for me along the road; they are very good." But as he was still a little suspicious he ate only a tiny piece of the manioc.

It was good; he ate a second piece, and then the whole heap of it; there was not very much, and Father Elephant was very big, much bigger than the elephants nowadays. A little farther on there was a fresh heap of manioc. Father Elephant drew near cautiously, then he bit a little piece–nothing suspicious. "Ah," he said. "What good children!" And he ate the whole heap, for Father Elephant was big and the heap was very little. And Father Elephant had walked a long, long way! And when evening came, there in the path he saw a fresh heap of manioc, and as he was very hungry again he rushed toward it.

Plop! This time it was the pit! And as Father Elephant ran very fast he fell head first onto the pointed stakes. And that was lucky for him! For otherwise the stake would have pierced his belly and he would have been killed. But his head broke the stake. And all night Father Elephant stayed in the bottom of the pit, crying and groaning, "I am dead!" But in the morning the chief of the men, who was near by with all his warriors, came to the edge of the pit.

"Why, what is this!" he exclaimed. "What? It is Father Elephant! Oh, how could he have fallen down there!" And at once he began to throw earth and branches into the hole, but as soon as he saw that the pit was nearly filled and the elephant just about to climb out, he scuttled away with all his men as fast as he could.

Father Elephant, however, climbed out of the pit, and, all bruised and smarting, very angry, went on his way. But his head ached very much, his eyes were all full of earth, and he could hardly manage to walk. At last, after many adventures, and many appeals both to his great fetiches and to all the other elephants, Father Elephant overcame all the obstacles and reached the men's village.

But when he arrived there was no one there! At his command, all the other animals gathered together and went in pursuit of the men, to bring them back. The monkeys pursued them in the trees, the boars and leopards in the forests, the birds called out when they found their hiding places, the snakes bit them from the grass, and at last they were brought back to judgment.

The men were then brought before Father Elephant, and the chief of the men was very much afraid in his heart, for he saw death before him. He went cold all over, for who has seen what lies beyond death? Death is like the moon; no one has seen the other side of it.

The chief of the men was cold. He shivered. But Father Elephant said, "Do you confess your sin?" And the chief of the men said, "I confess it."

"Then you now look upon death."

"Oh, Father Elephant, I am so small and you are so strong! Oh, pardon, pardon!"

And Father Elephant replied, "It is true; I am strong and you are weak, but Nzame has made you chief. Therefore I pardon you."

And the chief of the men cried, "Thank you! Thank you!" And his heart was content.

But the chief of the leopards came forth, furious. "Father Elephant, you have not spoken well! These men have killed my brother. I want vengeance!"

And so the man paid gifts to the leopard. And then Father Elephant said, "Now you shall 'make brothers' and the quarrel will be over."

The chief of the men called his brother and said to him, "Make the blood exchange with the leopard." And the leopard chief said to his brother, "Make the blood exchange with the men." The man made the blood exchange and the leopard made the blood exchange, and they dwelt as brothers in the same village.

Then the eagle chief came forward in his turn and made the same palaver, and the boar chief, and the gorilla chief, and many others, but they exchanged blood, and the palaver was ended.

And when the palavers were all decided, the elephant chief said in his turn, "I want to make brother with the man chief." So they killed a kid, for these had not made brother; he was the slave of man. They killed a big male kid, and Father Elephant and Father Man made brothers. Father Elephant recognized the fetiches of Father Man, and Father Man recognized the fetiches of Father Elephant. And ever since that time Father Elephant has become the *ototore* of men, and that is why they honor him very much. Those who do not honor him are savages.

Amanda. That is the end.

From *The African Saga.*

THE ISINYANDENDE

A BOY and a girl one day decided to go and rob the nest of the Isinyandende. "We must be careful when we approach the nest," said the boy, "for if the Isinyandende, a very fierce bird, sees us, he will surely catch and kill us, for though he is unable to fly he is very fleet of foot."

The two set out, taking with them three hen's eggs with which to replace those that might be in the nest. While they were on their way, the boy, looking back, saw the Isinyandende close behind. The children ran as fast as they could, but the bird gained on them. As it was about to pounce, the girl, who was carrying the eggs, threw one down and broke it. Immediately a very long wide chasm formed between the children and the bird. While the bird was filling up the chasm the children ran on.

When the chasm was filled the Isinyandende resumed its chase and soon began to gain on the children. When it was quite close to them the girl threw down a second egg. Again a wide chasm formed, and once more the bird was delayed. As they ran on the boy said to the girl, "If the Isinyandende catches up with us again, throw the last egg at its head. That will put an end to it." They ran on, but the bird, being very fleet of foot, was overtaking them when the girl threw the third egg at it. The egg struck it on the forehead, and it fell down dead.

The girl and the boy went on until they reached a stream, on the far side of which there was a kraal. The girl said, "I'll stay here while you go on to the kraal." The girl remained at the stream and climbed into a tree which overhung the water. The boy went on to the kraal.

The next morning an old woman who lived at the kraal went down to the stream with a clay pot to fetch water. She came to a spot under the tree into which the girl had climbed. She put down her pot and looked down to see if the water was clear. To her amazement and joy she saw the face of a beautiful young girl looking up at her from the water. Concluding that this was the reflection of her own face, she left her water pot beside the stream and hurried back to the kraal. When she got there she was asked why she had not brought water. Her old face beamed with satisfaction as she replied with the question, "Why did you people who have come to regard me as an old woman not tell me that I was still young and beautiful?" The people, laughing, asked, "Who has deceived you, you withered and bent old thing?" When she heard this she returned to the stream to fill her water pot. She took with her a friend who was as old and wrinkled as herself. At the stream they found the empty water pot, and the second old woman, looking down into the water, saw the reflection of a beautiful young face looking up at her.

The two old women hurried back to the kraal, dancing with tottering steps as they went. "Look at us," they said, "we are young and beautiful. We have seen the reflection of our own faces in the water." They did not know that the reflection they had seen was that of the young girl who had climbed up the tree after having been chased by the Isinyandende.

From *Lion and Jackal, with Other Native Folk Tales of South Africa,* by Frank Brownlee (London: George Allen & Unwin, Ltd., 1938).

TALK

AN ASHANTI TALE

ONCE, not far from the city of Accra on the Gulf of Guinea, a country man went out to his garden to dig up some yams to take to market. While he was digging, one of the yams said to him, "Well, at last you're here. You never weeded me, but now you come around with your digging stick. Go away and leave me alone!"

The farmer turned around and looked at his cow in amazement. The cow was chewing her cud and looking at him.

"Did you say something?" he asked.

The cow kept on chewing and said nothing, but the man's dog

spoke up. "It wasn't the cow who spoke to you," the dog said. "It was the yam. The yam says leave him alone."

The man became angry, because his dog had never talked before, and he didn't like his tone besides. So he took his knife and cut a branch from a palm tree to whip his dog. Just then the palm tree said, "Put that branch down!"

The man was getting very upset about the way things were going, and he started to throw the palm branch away, but the palm branch said, "Man, put me down softly!"

He put the branch down gently on a stone, and the stone said, "Hey, take that thing off me!"

This was enough, and the frightened farmer started to run for his village. On the way he met a fisherman going the other way with a fish trap on his head.

"What's the hurry?" the fisherman asked.

"My yam said, 'Leave me alone!' Then the dog said, 'Listen to what the yam says!' When I went to whip the dog with a palm branch the tree said, 'Put that branch down!' Then the palm branch said, 'Do it softly!' Then the stone said, 'Take that thing off me!' "

"Is that all?" the man with the fish trap asked. "Is that so frightening?"

"Well," the man's fish trap said, "did he take it off the stone?"

"Wah!" the fisherman shouted. He threw the fish trap on the ground and began to run with the farmer, and on the trail they met a weaver with a bundle of cloth on his head.

"Where are you going in such a rush?" he asked them.

"My yam said, 'Leave me alone!' " the farmer said. "The dog said, 'Listen to what the yam says!' The tree said, 'Put that branch down!' The branch said, 'Do it softly!' And the stone said, 'Take that thing off me!' "

"And then," the fisherman continued, "the fish trap said, 'Did he take it off?' "

"That's nothing to get excited about," the weaver said. "No reason at all."

"Oh, yes it is," his bundle of cloth said. "If it happened to you you'd run too!"

"Wah!" the weaver shouted. He threw his bundle on the trail and started running with the other men.

They came panting to the ford in the river and found a man bathing. "Are you chasing a gazelle?" he asked them.

The first man said breathlessly, "My yam talked at me, and it said, 'Leave me alone!' And my dog said, 'Listen to your yam!' And when I cut myself a branch the tree said, 'Put that branch down!' And the branch said, 'Do it softly!' And the stone said, 'Take that thing off me!' "

The fisherman panted, "And my trap said, 'Did he?' "

The weaver wheezed, "And my bundle of cloth said, 'You'd run too!' "

"Is that why you're running?" the man in the river asked.

"Well, wouldn't you run if you were in their position?" the river said.

The man jumped out of the water and began to run with the others. They ran down the main street of the village to the house of the chief. The chief's servant brought his stool out, and he came and sat on it to listen to their complaints. The men began to recite their troubles.

"I went out to my garden to dig yams," the farmer said, waving his arms. "Then everything began to talk! My yam said, 'Leave me alone!' My dog said, 'Pay attention to your yam!' The tree said, 'Put that branch down!' The branch said, 'Do it softly!' And the stone said, 'Take it off me!' "

"And my fish trap said, 'Well, did he take it off?' " the fisherman said.

"And my cloth said, 'You'd run too!' " the weaver said.

"And the river said the same," the bather said hoarsely, his eyes bulging.

The chief listened to them patiently, but he couldn't refrain from scowling. "Now this is really a wild story," he said at last. "You'd better all go back to your work before I punish you for disturbing the peace."

So the men went away, and the chief shook his head and mumbled to himself, "Nonsense like that upsets the community."

"Fantastic, isn't it?" his stool said. "Imagine, a talking yam!"

From *The Cow-Tail Switch and Other West African Stories*, by Harold Courlander and George Herzog (New York: Henry Holt & Co., 1947).

American

Davy Crockett: Sunrise in His Pocket

Compared with the well-developed oral literature of an Old World culture, the folk tales of the United States may seem to be a whimsical mixture of traditional themes borrowed at random and new themes raw or unshaped. In a relatively short time Americans have sown a vast area with folk story new and old, but the fact is that much of the nation's growth has taken place in the era after written literature and other story media had already begun to influence and, in some instances, displace oral forms. Even the most popular of original American tales, that of Paul Bunyan, the giant lumberjack, is a twentieth-century creation fostered almost from its very beginning by professional writers. Much the same may be said of many of America's major legendary heroes from Davy Crockett to Johnny Appleseed: the best tales about them are being written by poets and short-story writers. The Sandburgs, Benéts, and Lindsays have wrought remarkably with the rude metal of American legend, but such a story as Stephen Vincent Benét's "The Devil and Daniel Webster" is not so much a New England folk tale as Benét's contribution to New England literature.

Of what, then, does American folk story consist? First, there are traditional themes more or less naturalized in America. Rip Van Winkle is one of the earliest of these; but since Irving's source was evidently not local Catskill storytellers but a legend of the Kyffhäusen mountain (page 371) related by Otmar, a German writer of the late eighteenth century, Rip seems to belong more to Washington Irving and to American literature than to folk story. "The Tar Baby," which appears in many forms among Indian, Negro, and white groups in the Western Hemisphere, has been traced to a Jataka probably two thousand years old; and "Old Gally Mander" is a traditional tale that was recorded in North Carolina but might have been found in much the same form in England.

Much more completely Americanized are the "Jack tales" of the South. "Jack and the Varmints" is a variant of the Valiant Little

Tailor theme, and "Jack's Hunting Trips," is an offshoot of Munchausen lies, Britain's Cockaigne, and Germany's Schlaraffenland, but their tone is unmistakably that of robust, exuberant, early nineteenth-century rural America. The main character in all of them is cousin to the hero of European folk tale but brother to Crockett, Boone, and Bunyan. Sometimes, in fact, the welding of old theme to new matter is incomplete, and the effect is something like that of those pictures of Buffalo Bill visiting the King of England or of Ben Franklin at the court of Louis.

If America's Negroes have proved somewhat richer in folk tales and ballads than their white neighbors, the reason may well be that they have been compelled to rely far more on their own resources for entertainment. But they, too, have drawn heavily on the well of European themes: thus the story of Big John the Conqueror, recorded in Florida a few years ago, no less than the Uncle Remus tales from Georgia of the 1870's, are in theme among the Old World's oldest. The most common of folk-tale themes, the triumph of the little man over the giant, or of craft over might, seems to have suited Negro storytellers perfectly. In the guise of Brer Rabbit or a Negro named John, the underdog is forever outwitting his master, whether called Brer Wolf or "the Massa."

But the New World also found new forms of expression, forms that developed in ways appropriate to a land where men struggled with raw wilderness. It was natural that the mythology of frontiersmen, Indian fighters, hunters and trappers, steamboatmen, railroad builders, and lumberjacks should make much of extraordinary physical prowess or natural phenomena, that their storytelling manner should be boisterous and boastful, and their favorite form the tall tale. If this had been the twentieth century B.C. instead of A.D., the heroes of such tales might in time have developed into epic heroes and even gods; as it is they tend to be giants rather than superhumans, master workmen rather than master wizards. They are figures of farce and comedy, almost never of tragedy. The first of these was Davy Crockett, who in the 1830's practically fathered the tradition of the brag outrageous, the boast American. The stories he told of himself or that others were soon inspired to tell of him have since been told of Paul Bunyan (with echoes of Hercules, Gargantua, and Cuchullin), of Negro hammer-drivin' John Henry (Thor in a brown skin), of Mississippi keelboatman Mike Fink, cowboy Pecos Bill, Febold Feboldson, and an ever-growing host of others.

JACK AND THE VARMINTS

JACK was a-goin' about over the country one time, happened he passed by a place where a man had been rivin' boards, saw a little thin piece and picked it up, started in to whittlin' on it. Jack was so lazy he never noticed much what he was doin' till he'd done made him a little paddle. He didn't know what he'd do with it, just carried it along. Directly he came to a muddy place in the road where a lot of little blue butterflies had lit down to drink. So Jack slipped up right close to 'em and came down with that paddle right in the middle of 'em—splap! Then he counted to see how many he'd killed.

Went on down the road, came to a blacksmith shop. He got the blacksmith to take some brads and make him a sign in big letters on his belt; buckled that around him and went on.

Pretty soon here came the king on his horse, says, "Hello, Jack."

"Howdy do, King."

"What's all that writin' you got around ye, Jack? Turn around so's I can read it."

The old king read it off:

"STRONG-MAN-JACK—
KILLED-SEVEN-AT-A-WHACK."

"You mean you've done killed seven at one lick, Jack? You must be gettin' to be an awful stout feller. I reckon you could do pretty nigh anything, couldn't ye?"

"Well," says Jack, "I don't know. I've pulled a few tricks."

King says, "Well, now, Jack, if you're up to that adver-tize-ment you got on your belt there, you're the very man I'm a-lookin' for. There's a big wild hog been tearin' around in my settle-ment, killin' lots of sheep. If you help us get shet of that hog, I'll pay ye a thousand dollars. All my men are scared of it."

"Well," says Jack, "I'll try."

So the king took Jack over on the mountain where that wild hog was a-usin'. Time he got up in the holler a ways, he turned his horse around, says, "You go on up in the mountain and find it, Jack. I got im-portant business, back home."

And the king gave his horse a lick and made it go back in a hurry.

Jack he knowed that if the king was so scared of that hog, it must be awful dangerous. Decided he'd just not get mixed up with such a varmint. Said he'd wait a little while and then he'd slip out and get away 'fore that old hog smelled him. Well, directly Jack got to plunderin' around in there trying to get out, heard that hog a-breakin' bresh up the mountain, and then he saw it comin'. So Jack lit out through the woods–him and the hog . . .

Whippety cut!
Whippety cut!
Whippety cut!

and the wild hog right in behind him.

Jack looked behind and saw it was gettin' closer; they say Jack com-menced jumpin' fifteen feet ever' step, but the old hog kept right on a-gainin'. Jack came out in a field, looked down it a ways and saw a old waste-house standin' there with no roof on it. Jack made for that house, ran in the door, and scrambled up the wall. That old hog was so close it grabbed hold on Jack's coattail, but

Jack was a-goin' so fast it jerked his coattail plumb off. Jack got up on top of the wall, looked down at the hog standin' there with his forefeet up on the logs a-lookin' up after him. Then Jack jumped down and ran around outside, pushed the door to, and propped it right quick with some timbers. Saw the hog couldn't get out, so then he pulled back to the king's house.

"Hello, Jack. Did ye do any good?"

"Why, no, King. I couldn't find no wild hog up there. Hunted all over that mountain, didn't see nothin'."

"Why, Jack, that old hog just *makes* for ever'body goes up there. You must 'a seen it."

"Well, there wasn't nothing but a little old boar shoat, came bristlin' up to me, kept follerin' me around. I ran it off a time or two, but it kept on taggin' after me. The blame thing got playful after a while, jumped up, and jerked a piece out of my coattail. That made me a little mad, so I took it by the tail and ear and throwed it in a old waste-house up there, barred it in. I don't reckon that was what you wanted. You can go up and see if ye want to."

When the king rode up there and saw it was that wild hog, he like to beat his horse to death gettin' back. Blowed his horn and fifty or sixty men came runnin' up. They took a lot of Winchester rifles and went on up to that old house; but they were so scared they wouldn't go close enough to get a shoot at it. So fin'ly Jack he went on down there, poked around with a rifle, and shot two or three times. That old hog went to tearin' around, and when it fell it had tore that house plumb down.

So the king's men skinned it out. Hit made two wagonloads of meat.

The king paid Jack the thousand dollars, and Jack started to pull out for home.

The king called him, says, "I got another job for ye, Jack. They say there's a unicorn usin' back here on another mountain, doin' a sight of damage to people's livestock. Hit's a lot more dangerous than that hog, but a brave feller like you oughtn't to have no trouble killin' it. I'll pay ye another thousand dollars too."

Well, Jack tried to back out of it, but he saw he couldn't, so the king took him up there where they said the unicorn was, turned his horse around and just burned the wind.

Jack watched the king out of sight, says, "Thousand dollars'll do me a right long while. I don't want to get mixed up with no unicorn. I'll get out of here and go back another way. I'm not a-goin' to fool around here and get killed."

But Jack hadn't gone very far 'fore he heard that varmint breakin' bresh and a-comin' straight down the mountain. So Jack started runnin' around in amongst the trees as hard as he could tear. Looked around directly and saw that old unicorn so close to him it was just about to make a lunge and stick that horn right through the middle of his back. Jack reached out and grabbed hold on a white oak tree, swung around behind it. The unicorn swerved at him, hit that oak tree and stove its horn plumb through it. Horn came out the other side, and like to stuck Jack. Time he saw that, he snatched some nails out'n his overhall pocket, grabbed him up a rock right quick, and wedged the horn in tight. Then he got him a switch and swarped the unicorn a few times to see could it break loose; saw it couldn't, so he pulled on back down to the king's house.

"What luck did ye have this time, Jack?"

"Why, King, I didn't see no unicorn."

"Now, that's a curious thing to me, Jack. Nobody else ever went in there but what that old unicorn came right for 'em. What did ye see, Jack?"

"Nothin' much, just some kind of a little old yearlin' bull, didn't have but one horn. Came down there actin' big, a-bawlin' and pawin' the ground. Got to follerin' me around pretty close and sort of gougin' at me with that horn, till fin'ly hit kind of aggravated me. So I took it by the tail and neck, stove its horn through a tree. I reckon it's still fastened up there where I left it at. We can all go on up and see it if ye want to."

So Jack took the king and his men with all them rifles up where the unicorn was. They wouldn't none of 'em get close enough to get a good aim, so Jack went on up to it, cut him a little branch, and switched it two or three times, says, "See, men? There's not a bit of harm in him."

The men fin'ly shot it, and when it fell, they say it tore that oak tree plumb up by the roots.

Then they skinned it and brought back the hide.

The king paid Jack another thousand dollars, says, "Now, Jack, they've just brought in word here that a lion has come over the mountains from somewhere in Tennessee, been makin' raids on a settle-ment over the other end of this country, killin' ever'thing it comes across: cattle, and horses, and they say it's done killed several men tried to go after it. I told 'em about you, Jack, and they made me promise to send ye."

"Well, King, that sounds like the dangerest thing of all."

"I'll pay ye another thousand dollars, Jack."

"I don't know as I favor workin' any more right now, King. They'll be worried about me if I don't get back in home 'fore dark. Besides, my daddy's cuttin' tobacco and he needs me bad."

"Come on now, Jack. I'll pay ye two thousand dollars."

"Well, I don't know. I'll have to study on it awhile."

"Here's a thousand dollars down, right now, Jack, and I'll pay ye the other thousand when ye get it killed. I'd sure like to get shet of that lion."

"I reckon I'll do it then," says Jack—"try to."

So the king took Jack up behind him on his horse, and they rode over to where they said the lion was last seen.

The king says, "Now, Jack, that lion's right up in yonder somewhere. I'll not venture any further."

Jack slipped off the horse.

The king turned him around, says, "When hit smells ye, Jack, you'll sure hear from it!" And then the king left there a-gallopin'.

Well, Jack felt of that three thousand dollars he had down in his overhall pocket, said he'd try to get out of there for good and go on back home. But 'fore he'd hardly took a step or two, that old lion smelled him and com-menced roarin' up there in the woods, roared so hard it jarred the mountain. Then Jack saw it comin'—tearin' down trees, breakin' logs in two, bustin' rocks wide open—and Jack didn't waste no time tryin' to run. He made for the tree nearest to him and skinned up it like a squirrel. He didn't stop neither, till he was clean to the top.

The old lion growled around down there, smelled up the tree a time or two, and then it went right in to gnawin' on the tree trunk. Jack looked, and it was a sight in the world how the bark and the splinters flew. It nearly shook Jack out the tree.

But it seemed like the lion got tired when he had the tree about half gnawed through; he quit, laid up against the foot of the tree, and went sound asleep.

Jack waited awhile till his heart quit beatin' so fast, and then he 'lowed he might have a chance to slip down and get away from there 'fore the old lion woke up. So he started slidin' down the tree. He was keepin' such close watch on that lion's eyes to see would he wake up or not, Jack never noticed when he set his foot on a brickly snag. Put all his weight on that rotten limb, and hit broke, and Jack went scootin' down, landed right straddle the old lion's back.

Well, that lion started in roarin' and jumpin' around, but Jack he just held on. Then the old lion got to runnin', and he was so scared he didn't know he was headed right for town. Got on the public highway and kept right on till next thing Jack knowed they were sailin' all around the courthouse. All the people were runnin' in the stores and climbin' trees gettin' out the way, and ever'body shoutin' and hollerin', and the king's men came and started in tryin' to shoot the lion without hittin' Jack, till fin'ly one of 'em drawed a bead on the old lion's head and tumbled him up.

Jack picked himself up out the dirt, com-menced breshin' it off. Ever'body came over directly to see that lion, when they saw it was sure 'nough dead.

The king came along right soon and Jack says to him, says, "Look-a-here, King. I'm mad."

"Why, how come, Jack?"

"These men have done killed your lion."

"My lion? What ye mean, Jack?"

"Why, I'd 'a not had it killed for three thousand dollars, King. After I'd caught it and 'gun to get it gentled up, now, bedads, your men have done shot it. I was just a-ridin' it down here to get it broke in for you a ridey-horse."

So the old king went over to where his men were and raised a rumpus with 'em, says, "Why, I'd 'a felt big ridin' that lion around.

Now you men will just have to raise Jack three thousand dollars for killin' our lion."

So Jack went on home after that; had a whole pile of money down in his old ragged overhall pocket.

And the last time I went down there Jack was still rich, and I don't think he's worked any yet.

From *The Jack Tales*, set down and edited by Richard Chase, with notes and contributions by Herbert Halpert (Boston: Houghton Mifflin Company, 1943).

JACK'S HUNTING TRIPS

THEN there was that time I went huntin' with Jack. I had stayed all night down there, and Jack and I made it up to go out together the next mornin'. I didn't have my gun with me, but that didn't differ. We aimed to take turns with the long rifle Jack had. We went down the river a pretty far piece, and then we struck out through the woods where the timber hadn't been cut off. We didn't have much luck, and about twelve we stopped to eat the rations Jack's mother had fixed up for us. Jack sat down on a stump and I got up on a big black log. I took out my bread and started eatin'. Then I opened my knife, cut me off a chunk of meat, and jobbed my knife down in that log. Then I noticed Jack wasn't where I thought he was.

"Where you goin', Jack?"

"I ain't goin' nowhere," says Jack. "What are you slippin' down that log for?"

"I ain't slippin' down no log," I told him. "Why are you a-riding' that stump off like that?"

"This stump's right here. You're the one that's a-movin'."

Then I saw a bush came between me and Jack, so I looked around me, and I'll be confounded if I wasn't ridin' right along through the bresh. I jumped off that log in a hurry and it crawled on off. Hit was the biggest blamed blacksnake you ever saw.

Well, we finished our snack and went on. We fooled around shootin' squirrels and pheasants and one thing and another. Came out in a big pasture on top of the mountain directly and went along the rail fence lookin' for bobwhites and turkeys and rabbits.

All at once Jack stopped, says, "Look yonder!"

There set about twelve big wild turkeys stretched out along the top of that fence.

"I wish they was all settin' on one rail," says Jack. "I might get several with one shot."

"That's a fact," I told him. "You ain't goin' to get but one this-a-way. Take the big gobbler on this end."

Jack didn't hear what I said. He had slipped his rifle barrel between two little saplin's growin' side by side, and was pullin' against the stock.

"What in the world ye doin', Jack?"

"I'll show ye in a minute," he says.

Jack kept lookin' first at that fence where the turkeys were settin', then he'd bend his gun again. Well, sir, Jack put a crook in his gun for every crook in the fence and when he shot the ball went zigzaggin' down that row of turkeys and killed ever' last one. So I went and got 'em while Jack straightened out his gun.

We had a pretty good load of wild meat by that time, so we started on back. Got on down the mountain and came out in a wide swag toward the river, and a big deer jumped, ran off a little ways, and stopped. Jack hadn't loaded his gun and he poured some powder in right quick and reached in his pocket for a ball. Then he jerked his hand out and reached in another pocket.

"Blame it!" he says. "I'm plumb out of lead, sure's the world!"

I didn't think I had any shot with me, but I com-menced searchin' through all my pockets too. I couldn't find a thing but some peach seed where I had been eatin' peaches and saved the pits to take home and plant.

Jack saw me take out a handful of 'em, says, "Hand here one of them peach rock."

He grabbed one and rammed it down in his rifle; raised up and shot. Hit that deer somewhere on the shoulder, 'cause we saw the blood fly, but the deer ran off. Then directly we jumped two more deer. It looked like a whole flock of 'em was in that swag. So Jack loaded up with another peach rock, and the next deer that jumped he tried again. Blam! He didn't bring it down, but we saw blood on the leaves and rocks when we went on a piece, so we knowed it had been hit all right. Well, sir, Jack kept loadin' up with peach seed and the deer kept jumpin' and Jack kept on tryin' to get one till I didn't have any peach rocks left.

Well, we were gettin' down closer to the river when all at once a big black bear came out of a laurel thicket, and 'fore we saw it hardly the blame thing r'ared up and growled and came right straight at us with its mouth wide open. Me and Jack we dropped ever'thing right there and up two trees we went, and Jack went up his little hickory saplin' so fast he cloomb six feet out the top. But he caught on a branch when he fell back in the tree and we both just waited till the old bear went on off.

Then we headed up the river, came to a little creek, and we was lookin' for a place to jump when we both noticed the water in the creek bed was movin' awful slow.

Jack got down and stuck his finger in it, tasted of it. "Honey," he says.

"No," I told him.

"Taste it," he says.

So I tasted of it, and sure as I'm a-livin' it was honey runnin' down the creek bed in the place of water. Then we noticed considerable buzzin' up the holler, and we went on up that honey creek. Well, sir, ever' tree in that holler was a bee tree. The bees were so thick you couldn't hardly see the trees and bresh. And the honey was a-drippin' and oozin' out ever'where. It ran down in little branches into that creek.

"Now, ain't that a sight in the world!" says Jack, and he leaned back on a little tree to watch the bees fly and the honey run, and when he jarred that tree something started floppin' down on the ground around us.

I picked one up and looked at it, then I smelled of it, and then I tasted of it, then I says to Jack, "Fritter!"

"Surely not," says Jack.

"Pick one up and taste it," I told him.

So Jack tried one, and don't you know, there we stood in a little grove of fritter trees. They were the best fritters you ever tasted. We shook down a mess of 'em and dipped 'em in that honey creek and eat fritters and honey till we was nearly floundered.

And just about that time we heard a racket up above us, and here came a little roast pig runnin' out the bresh with a knife and fork stuck in its back, a-squealin' to be eat. But we wasn't hungry by then, so we ran it on back.

Well, boys, Jack and me we got back in about dark, and next mornin' we divided up the squirrels and pheasants and rabbits, and Jack gave me half of his wild turkeys, and I went on home.

About four years after that, Jack came to my house one day and told me, says, "You remember that swag where I shot at all them deer with them peach rock you had?"

I told him I did.

"I came through there yesterday," Jack says, "and I saw a little tree full of ripe peaches, so I got to lookin' at it and a-wonderin' about peaches a-growin' out in the woods like that when I looked further up the holler and there was a lot of other little peach trees just like it. So I went on over to the first tree I saw. It was growin' up on the other side of a log, and I got up on that log to pull me off a peach when all at once that tree jumped up from the ground and ran off. Then blamed if that whole peach orchard didn't rise up and run off through the woods! Them peach rock had took root in ever' deer we shot. Some of 'em had the trees a-growin' out their shoulders and some out their backs, and you remember that 'un I hit between the eyes? Well, it had a six-foot peach tree growing up right between its horns. Hit sure was a sight in the world."

Now, boys, don't ask me too much about where it was Jack and me went huntin' that day. It was pretty far back when I was a young feller, and I can't remember exactly which way we went nor which part of which mountain that swag was in. I'd like to get some of them peaches myself.

From *The Jack Tales*. This is Part II of the story as it is set down by Richard Chase.

OLD GALLY MANDER

ONCE they was an old woman and she was so stingy she wouldn't spend a penny and she lived on ash cakes and water. She had a big long leather sack hanging up in the chimney with her money in hit. She didn't have any money 'cept gold and silver. So her hired girls got so they pilfered around and tried to find her money. So she sent her son over the ocean to git a girl who wouldn't know anything about her money. So he went and got her a girl that evenin'. And the girl fixed 'em the supper. So after supper the old woman wanted to go out a-visitin'. So the old woman says, "Don't you look up the chimney." So of course as soon as the old woman was out of the house, the girl went and looked up the chimney and got to gougin' 'round with her stick, and directly the big long leather purse fell down, and she looked in hit and seed the silver and gold and she just tuk hit and started out.

Directly she passed old cow. Old cow says, "Oh, come, pretty lady, milk my old sore bag." "I've got no time to fool with your old sore bag. I'm goin' over the ocean." Went on a little way and met an old horse. "Oh come, pretty lady, wash my old sore back." "I've got no time to wash your old sore back. I'm goin' over the ocean." Went on a little way, met a peach tree all loaded down to the ground with peaches. "Oh, come, pretty lady, and pick off some of my peaches and rest my poor tired limbs." "I've got no time to pick your old peaches. I'm goin' over the ocean."

Old woman come home, seed the girl was gone, looked up the chimney and seed her purse was gone, and just tuk out down the road a-hollerin'. "Gally Mander, Gally Mander, all my gold and silver's gone, and my great long leather purse." So she started off down the road at a loop-loopy-te-loop. Met the old cow. "Old cow,

have you saw anything of a girl with a long leather purse?"—"Yes, run, old woman, and you'll soon overtake her." "Gally Mander, Gally Mander, all my gold and silver's gone, and my great long leather purse." Pretty soon met the old horse. "Old horse, have you saw a girl with a long leather purse?" "Yes, old woman, and you'll soon overtake her." "Gally Mander, Gally Mander, all my gold and silver's gone and my great long leather purse." Met the peach tree. "Peach tree, have you saw a girl with a long leather purse?" "Yes, old woman, she's right down there at the side of the ocean." "Gally Mander, Gally Mander, all my gold and silver's gone, and my great long leather purse." And got to the ocean, caught her, flogged her up, and pitched her into the ocean.

Old woman tuk her purse, went back home, lives long time by herself. Then sent her son out to hunt her another girl away out where nobody didn't know 'em. So the girl come, and the old woman liked 'er very well. After while old woman says, "Now, I'm goin' out to visit, don't you look up the chimney while I'm gone." So when she got out of sight the girl wanted to look up the chimney for curiosity. Got her stick, got to gougin' into hit, and directly the leather purse fell down. Looked inside, and it was full of gold and silver, and she tuk out down the road. Directly she met old cow. "Oh, come, pretty lady, and milk my old sore bag." "I've got no time to milk your old sore bag. I'm goin' across the water." Went on, met the horse. "Oh come, pretty lady, and wash my old sore back." "I've got no time to wash your old sore back. I'm goin' across the water." Went on, met the peach tree. "Oh, come, pretty lady, pick off some peaches and rest my poor tired limbs." "I've got no time to pick off your peaches. I'm goin' over the water." So the old woman come in, looked up the chimney. "Gally Mander, Gally Mander, all my gold and silver's gone, and my great long leather purse." So she tuk out down the road. Directly she come to old cow and said, "Have you saw a girl with a long leather purse?" "Yes, old woman, and you'll soon overtake her." "Gally Mander, Gally Mander, all my gold and silver's gone, and my great long leather purse." Directly she met old horse. "Old horse, have you saw a girl with a long leather purse?" "Yes, old woman, and you'll soon overtake her." "Gally Mander, Gally Mander, all my gold and silver's gone, and my great long leather purse." Come to peach tree. "Pretty peach tree, have you saw a girl with a long leather purse?" "She's right down by the side of the water." So the old woman shuck her and flogged on her and pitched her into the water. Then she tuk her long leather purse and went back home. "I'll stay by myself and eat ash cakes all the days of my life 'fore I'll bother with ary other girl."

But atter a while her son went away off where nobody didn't know 'em and brought her back another girl. Old woman, she jest stayed there and wouldn't go out un visit, but atter a while she went out to visit. Says, "Don't you look up that chimney." So the girl tuk her stick and went to the chimney un gouged, un gouged, un directly the purse fell down. She opened it, and it was full of gold and silver, so she grabbed hit up and started. She passed old cow. "Pretty fair maid, come milk my old sore bag." She says, "Yes, I'll milk your old sore bag," and she milked it and bathed it and bathed it. She passed the old sore horse. "Pretty lady, won't you bathe my old sore back?" "Yes, I'll bathe your old sore back." So she bathed it and bathed it. So she come to the pretty peach tree. "Pretty fair lady, won't you pick off some of my peaches and rest my poor tired limbs?" "Yes, I'll pick off some of your peaches." So she picked un picked un picked. Peach tree says, "You climb up here in my limbs. The old woman ul be here in a minute."

Old woman come home, looked up chimney, seed her long leather purse was gone, "Gally Mander, Gally Mander, all my gold and silver's gone, and my great long leather purse." She tuk out down the road. "Old cow, have you saw a girl with a long leather purse?" "Yes, she passed here long, long ago and forgot about hit." "Gally Mander, Gally Mander, all my gold and silver's gone, and my great long leather purse." Met old horse. "Old horse, have you saw a girl with a long leather purse?" "Yes, she passed here long, long ago and forgot about hit." "Gally Mander, Gally Mander, all my gold and silver's gone, and my great long leather purse." Come to peach tree. "Pretty peach tree, have you saw a girl with a long leather purse?" "Yes, but she's over the ocean long ago." Old woman, "What'll I do, what'll I do?" "Go home and eat ash cakes all the days of your life."

And that's what she got fer bein' so stingy.

Contributed by Isabel Gordon Carter to the *Journal of American Folklore*, Vol. 38 (1925).

THE TAR BABY

ONCE upon a time there was a water famine, and the runs went dry and the creeks went dry and the river went dry, and there wasn't any water to be found anywhere, so all the animals in the forest met together to see what could be done about it. The lion and the bear and the wolf and the fox and the giraffe and the monkey and the elephant and even the rabbit—everybody who lived in the forest was there, and they all tried to think of some plan by which they could get water. At last they decided to dig a well, and everybody said he would help—all except the rabbit, who always was a lazy little bugger, and he said he wouldn't dig. So the animals all said, "Very well, Mr. Rabbit, if you won't help dig this well, you shan't have one drop of water to drink." But the rabbit just laughed and said, as smart as you please, "Never mind, you dig the well and I'll get a drink all right."

Now the animals all worked very hard, all except the rabbit, and soon they had the well so deep that they struck water, and they all got a drink and went away to their homes in the forest. But the very next morning what should they find but the rabbit's footprints in the mud at the mouth of the well, and they knew he had come in the night and stolen some water. So they all began to think how they could keep that lazy little rabbit from getting a drink, and they all talked and talked and talked, and after a while they decided that someone must watch the well, but no one seemed to want to stay up to do it. Finally the bear said, "I'll watch the well the first night. You just go to bed, and I'll show old Mr. Rabbit that he won't get any water while I'm around."

So all the animals went away and left him, and the bear sat down by the well. By and by the rabbit came out of the thicket on the hillside, and there he saw the old bear guarding the well. At first he didn't know what to do. Then he sat down and began to sing:

"Cha ra ra, will you, will you, can you?
Cha ra ra, will you, will you, can you?"

Presently the old bear lifted up his head and looked around. "Where's all that pretty music coming from?" he said. The rabbit kept on singing:

"Cha ra ra, will you, will you, can you?
Cha ra ra, will you, will you, can you?"

This time the bear got up on his hind feet. The rabbit kept on singing:

"Cha ra ra, will you, will you, can you?
Cha ra ra, will you, will you, can you?"

Then the bear began to dance, and after a while he danced so far away that the rabbit wasn't afraid of him any longer, and so he climbed down into the well and got a drink and ran away into the thicket.

Now when the animals came the next morning and found the rabbit's footprints in the mud, they made all kinds of fun of old Mr. Bear. They said, "Mr. Bear, you are a fine person to watch a well. Why, even Mr. Rabbit can outwit you." But the bear said, "The rabbit had nothing to do with it. I was sitting here wide-awake, when suddenly the most beautiful music came right down out of the sky. At least I think it came down out of the sky, for when I went to look for it, I could not find it, and it must have been while I was gone that Mr. Rabbit stole the water." "Anyway," said the other animals, "we can't trust you any more. Mr. Monkey, you had better watch the well tonight, and mind you, you'd better be pretty careful or old Mr. Rabbit will fool you." "I'd like to see him do it," said the monkey. "Just let him try." So the animals set the monkey to watch the well.

Presently it grew dark, and all the stars came out; and then the rabbit slipped out of the thicket and peeped over in the direction of the well. There he saw the monkey. Then he sat down on the hillside and began to sing:

"Cha ra ra, will you, will you, can you?
Cha ra ra, will you, will you, can you?"

Then the monkey peered down into the well. "It isn't the water," said he. The rabbit kept on singing:

"Cha ra ra, will you, will you, can you?
Cha ra ra, will you, will you, can you?"

This time the monkey looked into the sky. "It isn't the stars," said he. The rabbit kept on singing. This time the monkey looked toward the forest. "It must be the leaves," said he. "Anyway, it's too good music to let go to waste." So he began to dance, and after a while he danced so far away that the rabbit wasn't afraid, so he climbed down into the well and got a drink and ran off into the thicket.

Well, the next morning, when all the animals came down and found the footprints again, you should have heard them talk to that monkey. They said, "Mr. Monkey, you are no better than Mr. Bear; neither of you is of any account. You can't catch a rabbit." And the monkey said, "It wasn't old Mr. Rabbit's fault at all that I left the well. He had nothing to do with it. All at once the most beautiful music that you ever heard came out of the woods, and I went to see who was making it." But the animals only laughed at him. Then they tried to get someone else to watch the well that night. No one would do it. So they thought and thought and thought about what to do next. Finally the fox spoke up. "I'll tell you what let's do," said he. "Let's make a tar man and set him to watch the well." "Let's do," said all the other animals together. So they worked the whole day long building a tar man and set him to watch the well.

That night the rabbit crept out of the thicket, and there he saw the tar man. So he sat down on the hillside and began to sing:

"Cha ra ra, will you, will you, can you?
Cha ra ra, will you, will you, can you?"

But the tar man never heard. The rabbit kept on singing:

"Cha ra ra, will you, will you, can you?
Cha ra ra, will you, will you, can you?"

But the tar man never heard a word. The rabbit came a little closer.

"Cha ra ra, will you, will you, can you?
Cha ra ra, will you, will you, can you?"

The tar man never spoke. The rabbit came a little closer yet.

"Cha ra ra, will you, will you, can you?
Cha ra ra, will you, will you, can you?"

The tar man never spoke a word.

The rabbit came up close to the tar man. "Look here," he said, "you get out of my way and let me down into that well." The tar man never moved. "If you don't get out of my way, I'll hit you with my fist," said the rabbit. The tar man never moved a finger. Then the rabbit raised his fist and struck the tar man as hard as he could, and his right fist stuck tight in the tar. "Now you let go of my fist or I'll hit you with my other fist," said the rabbit. The tar man never budged. Then the rabbit struck him with his left fist, and his left fist stuck tight in the tar. "Now you let go of my fists or I'll kick you with my foot," said the rabbit. The tar man never budged an inch. Then the rabbit kicked him with his right foot, and his right foot stuck tight in the tar. "Now you let go of my foot or I'll kick you with my other foot," said the rabbit. The tar man never stirred. Then the rabbit kicked him with his left foot, and his left foot stuck tight in the tar. "Now you let me go or I'll butt you with my head," said the rabbit. And he butted him with his head, and there he was; and there the other animals found him the next morning.

Well, you should have heard those animals laugh. "Oh, ho, Mr. Rabbit," they said. "Now we'll see whether you steal any more of our water or not. We're going to lay you across the log and cut your head off." "Oh, please do," said the rabbit. "I've always wanted to have my head cut off. I'd rather die that way than any other way I know." "Then we won't do it," said the other animals. "We are not going to kill you any way you like. We are going to shoot you." "That's better," said the rabbit. "If I had just stopped to think, I'd have asked you to do that in the first place. Please shoot me." "No, we'll not shoot you," said the other animals; and then they had to think and think for a long time.

"I'll tell you what we'll do," said the bear. "We'll put you into a cupboard and let you eat and eat and eat until you are as fat as butter, and then we'll throw you up into the air and let you come down and burst." "Oh, please don't!" said the rabbit. "I never wanted to die that way. Just do anything else, but please don't burst me." "Then that's exactly what we'll do," said all the other animals together.

So they put the rabbit into the cupboard and they fed him pie and cake and sugar, everything that was good; and by and by he got just as fat as butter. And then they took him out on the hill-side, and the lion took a paw, and the fox took a paw, and the bear took a paw, and the monkey took a paw; and then they swung him back and forth, and back and forth, saying, "One for the money, two for the show, three to make ready, and four to go." And up they tossed him into the air, and he came down and lit on his feet and said:

"Yip, my name's Molly Cottontail;
Catch me if you can."

And off he ran into the thicket.

Contributed by Miss Dora Lee Newman to *Marion County in the Making* (West Virginia: privately printed, 1918), and reprinted in the *Journal of American Folklore*, Vol. 47 (1934).

DICEY AND ORPUS

DAT WAR eber so long ago, 'cause my granmammy tell me so. It h'aint no white-folks yarn—no sah. Gall she war called Dicey, an' she war borned on de plantation. Whar Jim Orpus kum from, granmammy she disremember. He war a boss-fiddler, he war, an' jus' that powerful, dat when de mules in de cotton field listen to um, dey no budge in de furrer. Orpus he neber want no mess of fish, ketched wid a angle. He just take him fiddle an' fool along de branch, an' play a tune, an' up dey comes, an' he cotch 'em in his hans. He war mighty sot on Dicey, an' dey war married all proper an' reg'lar. Hit war so long ago, dat de railroad war a bran-new spick an' span ting in dose days. Dicey once she lounge 'round de track, 'cause she tink she hear Orpus a fiddlin' in de fur-fur-away. Onyways de hengine smash her. Den Jim Orpus he took on turrible, an' when she war buried, he sot him down on de grave, an' he fiddle an' he fiddle till most yo' heart was bruk.

An' he play so long dat de groun' crummle [crumble] an' sink, an' nex' day, when de peoples look for Jim Orpus, dey no find um; oney big-hole in de lot, an' nobody never see Jim Orpus no mo'. An' dey do say, dat ef yo' go inter a darkey's burial groun', providin' no white man been planted thar, an' yo' clap yo' ear to de groun', yo' can hear Jim's fiddle way down deep belo', a folloin' Dicey fru' de lan' of de Golden Slippah.

From *The Book of Romance*, edited by Andrew Lang (New York: Longmans, Green and Company, 1902).

THE MAN AND HIS BOOTS

"ONE TIME," Uncle Remus said, "dey wuz a man what hear talk er some er Brer Rabbit's doin's—how he lay down in de road whiles a man wuz g'wine 'long wid some fishes in a waggin, en how he run 'roun' en lay down ag'in; en keep on doin' dat twel bimeby de man went back atter de fust rabbit he seed, en den Brer Rabbit had a chance fer ter git de fishes—I done mos' fergit dat ar tale off'n my min'. But howsomever hit wuz, de man done hear tell 'bout it, en he 'low ter hisse'f dat he des ez smart ez what Brer Rabbit is.

"So, one day, he got 'im a bran new pa'r er boots wid red tops on um, en whiles he settin' side er de road lookin' at um, he hear somebody comin' 'long in a waggin. He know'd who de somebody wuz, kaze he seed um on de rise er de hill.

"De man in de waggin had some calico fer ter make his wife a dress, en some blue chany ware fer ter put in de cubberd. De man what had de boots, he tuck'n flung one un um in de road, en hid hisse'f in de bushes fer ter see what de tudder man gwine do.

"Well, suh, de man in de waggin, he come 'long, en he see de boot in de road. He holler at his hoss for ter 'w'o, dar!' en he look at de boot right hard, like he studyin'.

"He 'low, 'Ef dey wuz two un you, I'd take you, but one boot ain't gwine do nobody no good, 'ceppin hit's a wooden-legged man.'

"So he driv on, en de man what lay de boot dar, he put out en went on ahead en flung de yuther boot in de road. De man in de waggin, he come 'long, he did, en he see de yuther boot.

"He 'low, 'Heyo! dish yer boot makes tudder boot good. W'o, dar, hoss! I'll go back en git 'er.'

"Wid dat, he drapt de lines on de dashboard en went back atter de odd boot. Whiles he gone, de man what had de boots tuck de calico en de crockery en made off wid um.

"He hid um in de underbresh, en den he come back en lissen fer ter see what de yuther man gwine do. Well, suh, de yuther man come back wid de boot, en den he had two. Time he clum in de waggin he seed dat somebody done steal his calico en his crockery, but he ain't say nothin'. He des look at de boots an laugh.

"De man in de bushes ain't know what ter make er dis. He stood dar, he did, en scratch his head en study. He watch de yuther man, en fur ez he kin see him he wuz lookin' at de boots en laughin'. De man in de bushes say he gwineter see what de matter wid dem ar boots, when de yuther man in de waggin kin swap off calico en crockery fer um en still feel good 'nuff fer ter laugh. So de man in de bushes he run 'roun' en head de yuther man off, en met 'im in de road. He come drivin' 'long, still lookin' at de boots en laughin'. Look like when he see de man in de road it make 'im laugh wusser dan befo'.

"De man in de road 'low, 'You mus' be havin' a mighty heap er fun all by yo'self.'

"De man in de waggin laugh like he gwine ter bus' wide open. All he kin say is, 'Lawsy massy! deze boots! deze boots! deze boots!' De man in de road 'low, 'What de matter wid de boots, dat dey er so mighty funny? Dey ain't look funny ter me.'

"De man in de waggin look like he choke wid laughin'. When he ketch his breff he holler, 'Oh, deze boots! deze boots!'

"Man in de road 'low, 'You ain't gwine crazy, is you?'

"Man in de waggin say, 'You'd be crazy too ef somebody had 'a' come 'long en drapt deze boots whar you could git um. Lawsy massy! deze boots!'

"Man in de road 'low, 'What kinder doin's is deze? You better lemme git up dar en take you home ter yo' fambly!'

"Man in de waggin say, 'My folks'll laugh too, when dey know what I knows; en you'd laugh yo'se'f ef yo'd 'a' been comin' 'long de road en fin' deze boots what got red in de top.'

"Man in de road say, 'I had a pair des like um, en dey ain't make me laugh.'

"Man in de waggin say, 'You'd laugh wusser dan me ef you'd er pick deze boots up in de road en foun' one ten dollar bill in one un um, en anudder ten dollar bill in tudder one.'

"Man in de road 'low, 'Lemme see dem boots! Dey er mine!

Han' um here! I tuck'n los' um yistiddy whiles I comin' fum town. Gi' me de money!'

"Man in de waggin shet his eye. He say, 'You right sho dey er yone?'

"Man in de road 'low, 'Yes dey is, en I got de proof un it!'

"Man in de waggin say, 'Well en good! Git up here en go along wid me, en show de proof.'

"Man in de road jump up on de wheel, but 'fo' he kin set down de man in de waggin flung 'im back in de waggin body en jump on 'im en tie 'im, en tuck 'im off ter de calaboose. Dar dey make 'im tell what he done wid de calico en de chany ware, en dey kep' 'im, I dunner how long; en 'fo' dey turn him loose dey tuck 'im out en hit 'im thirty-nine on de naked hide.

"Co'se," continued Uncle Remus, seeing a shade of perplexity on the little boy's face, "de man in de waggin ain't fin' no money in de boots. He des puttin' on, so he kin fin' de man what drap um, kaze he know dat right whar he fin' de man dat drap um, right dar he'll fin' de man what stoled his calico and crockery. Dat what make I say dat folks ain't got no business mockin' de way de creeturs does. Dey er bound ter git cotch up wid, en right den dey er in deep trouble. Creeturs kin take what ain't dern, en tell fibs, en dey don't no harm come fum it; but when folks tries it, dey er bleedz ter come ter some bad end. Now, you des watch um."

From "The Man and His Boots" in *Uncle Remus and His Friends*, by Joel Chandler Harris (Boston: Houghton Mifflin Company, 1892).

BIG JOHN THE CONQUEROR

Every night Big John used to go up to the Big House and stand in the chimney corner and listen to what Old Massa talked about. That way he learned a lot about what was goin' to happen. If he heard Old Massa say he was gonna kill hogs the next day, Big John would slip back to the quarters and tell the other niggers, "Tomorrow we kills hogs."

"How you know that?" they asked him.

"I can tell fortunes, that's how," said Big John. "Ain't nothin' hid from me."

And the next mornin' when Old Massa come out and told all the niggers to get ready for a big hog killin', they decided Big John was a fortuneteller for true. From then on they believed anything he told 'em.

One day when Big John was hangin' around the back door of the Big House, he seen his Mistress throw the water out of her wash basin, and in it he saw her diamond ring. But before he could pick it up, a turkey gobbler gobbled it down.

Soon the whole house was raisin' a ruckus lookin' for the lost ring, so Big John went to Old Massa and told him he knew where it was. Old Massa promised him if he could find the ring he would

make him a present of a fine fat shoat. So Big John told him to kill the gobbler and he would find the ring. At first Old Massa didn't want to kill his prize gobbler, and he told Big John that if he was foolin' him he would kill him sure. But when he killed the gobbler, there was the ring. From then on Old Massa thought Big John was a fortuneteller too.

One day Old Massa was braggin' to some white folks that he had a nigger who could tell fortunes. One man disputed his word, so Old Massa said, "I'll bet you forty acres of good bottomland my nigger can tell fortunes!"

"If you so sure, what you spuddin' for?" asked the man. "Why don't you make a real bet? I'll bet you my whole plantation."

"Since you really wants to make a bettin' thing outa my statement," said Old Massa, "let's make it worth my time. I'm a fightin' dog and my hide is worth money. We'll bet our whole plantations and every horse and mule and hog and nigger on the place."

So they agreed on it, and decided to prove the thing out a week from that day. Old Massa took Big John aside and told him about the bet, and said, "I bet everything I got in this world on you, and if you make me lose I'll kill you!"

The provin' day came, and Old Massa was up bright and early. He was up so early he had to saddle his own horse and then go wake up Big John. Big John climbed on a mule, and off they rode to the provin' ground. When they got there it looked like everybody and their brother was on hand to see the sight. The other bettin' man had the privilege of fixin' the proof, so Big John was led away a little piece. Then they brought him back and showed him a great big old black iron washpot turned upside down, and they asked him what was under it.

Everybody knew but Big John. Old Massa told him he better think good if he wanted to live. Everybody kept quiet waitin' to hear what Big John would say. He looked hard at the pot and walked around it three or four times, but he didn't have the least idea what was under it. He began to sweat and scratch his head, and Old Massa looked at him and began to sweat too. At last Big John decided he might just as well give up and get the killin' over with.

"You got the old coon," he said.

When he said that Old Massa throwed his hat up in the air and let out a whoop, and everybody else was yellin' with surprise, cause that's what was under the pot—a big old coon. So Old Massa went off to Philadelphia to celebrate, but before he left he gave Big John his freedom and a hundred dollars and left him in charge of the plantation.

Old Massa and Old Miss had no sooner got on the train than Big John sent word to the niggers on all the plantations, "Massa is gone to Philamayork and won't be back for three weeks. He done left me in charge of everything. Come on over to the Big House for a big time." While the invite was bein' carried around, he told some of the hands to go into Massa's lot and kill hogs till you could walk on 'em.

That night Big John really spread a scrumptious table. Everybody that could get hold of white folks' clothes had 'em on. Big John, he opened up the whole house and took Old Massa's big rockin' chair and put it on top of Massa's bed. Then he climbed up and sat down in it to call the figures for the dance. He was sittin' in his high seat with a box of Massa's cigars under his arm and two in his mouth when he seen a couple of poor-lookin' white folks come in.

"Take them poor folks out of here and carry them back to the kitchen where they belongs," Big John said. "Don't allow 'em back up front again. Nothin' but quality up here."

He didn't know that they was Old Massa and Miss, who had slipped back to see how he would behave while they was gone. They washed the dirt off their faces and came back up front where Big John was still sittin'.

"John," said Old Massa, "after I trusted you with my place you done smoked up my fine cigars and killed all my hogs and let all these niggers in my house to act like they was crazy. Now I'm gon take you out to the persimmon tree and hang you. You is entitled to a good hangin', and that's what you gon get."

While Old Massa was gone to fetch a rope, Big John called his friend Ike to one side and said, "Ike, Ole Massa is gonna take me out and hang me to the persimmon tree. Now I want you to hurry out to that tree and climb up in it. Take a box of matches with you, and every time you hear me ask God for a sign, you strike a match."

After a while here come Old Massa with the rope, and he led Big John out to the tree. He tied a noose in the rope and put it around Big John's neck and then threw the other end of the rope over a limb.

"I got just one favor to ask of you, Old Massa," said Big John. "Let me pray before I die."

"All right," said Old Massa, "but hurry up and get it over with, cause I never been so anxious to hang a nigger in my life."

So Big John kneeled down under the tree and prayed, "O Lord, if you mean for Massa not to hang me, give me a sign."

When he said that, Ike struck a match, and Old Massa seen it and began to shake. Big John kept on prayin', "O Lord, if you mean to strike Massa dead if he hangs me, give me a sign." Ike struck another match, and Old Massa said, "Never mind, John, you done prayed enough—the hangin's off!" But Big John prayed right on, "O Lord, if you means to put Old Massa and all his family to death unless he turns us niggers loose, give me a sign." This time Ike struck a whole handful of matches, and Old Massa lit out from there as fast as he could run.

And that's how the slaves were freed.

From *Palmetto Country*, by Stetson Kennedy (New York: Duell, Sloan & Pearce, Inc., 1942).

WHY WOMEN ALWAYS TAKE ADVANTAGE OF MEN

YOU SEE in de very first days, God made a man and a woman and put 'em in a house together to live. 'Way back in them days de woman was just as strong as de man and both of 'em did de same things. They useter get to fussin' 'bout who gointer do this and that and sometime they'd fight, but they was even balanced and neither one could whip de other one.

One day de man said to hisself, "B'lieve Ah'm gointer go see God and ast Him for a li'l mo' strength so Ah kin whip dis 'oman and make her mind. Ah'm tired of de way things is." So he went on up to God.

"Good mawnin', Ole Father."

"Howdy, man. Whut you doin' 'round my throne so soon dis mawnin'?"

"Ah'm troubled in mind, and nobody can't ease mah spirit 'ceptin' you."

God said, "Put yo' plea in de right form and Ah'll hear and answer."

"Ole Maker, wid de dawnin' stars glitterin' in yo' shinin' crown, wid de dust from yo' footsteps makin' worlds upon worlds, wid de blazin' bird we call de sun flyin' out of yo' right hand in de mawnin' and consumin' all day de flesh and blood of stump-black darkness, and comes flyin' home every evenin' to rest on yo' left hand, and never once in all yo' eternal years, mistood de left hand for de right, Ah ast you *please* to give me mo' strength than dat woman you give me, so Ah kin make her mind. Ah knows you don't want to be always comin' down way past de moon and stars to be straightenin' her out and it's got to be done. So give me a li'l mo' strength, Ole Maker, and Ah'll do it."

"All right, man, you got mo' strength than woman."

So de man run all de way down de stairs from Heben till he got home. He was so anxious to try his strength on de woman dat he couldn't take his time. Soon's he got in de house he hollered, "Woman! Here's yo' boss. God done tole me to handle you in which ever way Ah please. Ah'm yo' boss."

De woman flew to fightin' 'im right off. She fought 'im frightenin', but he beat her. She got her wind and tried 'im agin but he whipped her agin. She got herself together and made de third try on him vigorous, but he beat her every time. He was so proud he could whip 'er at last, dat he just crowed over her and made her do a lot of things she didn't like. He told her, "Long as you obey me, Ah'll be good to yuh, but every time yuh rear up Ah'm gointer put plenty wood on yo' back and plenty water in yo' eyes."

De woman was so mad she went straight up to Heben and stood befo' de Lawd. She didn't waste no words. She said, "Lawd, Ah come befo' you mighty mad t'day. Ah want back my strength and power Ah useter have."

"Woman, you got de same power you had since the beginnin'."

"Why is it, then, dat de man kin beat me now and he useter couldn't do it?"

"He got mo' strength than he useter have. He come and ast me for it and Ah give it to 'im. Ah gives to them that ast, and you ain't never ast me for no mo' power."

"Please suh, God, Ah'm astin' you for it now. Jus' gimme de same as you give him."

God shook his head. "It's too late now, woman. What Ah give, Ah never takes back. Ah give him mo' strength than you, and no matter how much Ah give, he'll have mo'."

De woman was so mad she wheeled round and went on off. She went straight to de devil and told him what had happened.

He said, "Don't be dis-incouraged, woman. You listen to me and you'll come out mo' than conqueror. Take dem frowns out yo' face and turn round and go right on back to Heben and ast God to give you dat bunch of keys hangin' by de mantel-piece. Then you bring 'em to me and Ah'll show you what to do wid 'em."

So de woman climbed back up to Heben again. She was mighty tired, but she was more out-done that she was tired so she climbed all night long and got back up to Heben again. When she got befo' de throne, butter wouldn't melt in her mouf.

"O Lawd and Master of de rainbow, Ah know yo' power. You never made two mountains without you put a valley in between. Ah know you kin hit a straight lick wid a crooked stick."

"Ast for whut you want, woman."

"God, gimme dat bunch of keys hangin' by yo' mantel-piece."

"Take 'em."

So de woman took de keys and hurried on back to de devil wid 'em. There was three keys on de bunch. Devil say, "See dese three keys? They got mo' power in 'em than all de strength de man kin ever git if you handle 'em right. Now dis first big key is to de do' of de kitchen, and you know a man always favor his stomach. Dis second one is de key to de bedroom, and he don't like to be shut out from dat neither, and dis last key is de key to de cradle, and he don't want to be cut off from his generations at all. So now you take dese keys and go lock up everything and wait till he come to you. Then don't you unlock nothin' until he use his strength for yo' benefit and yo' desires."

De woman thanked 'im and tole 'im, "If it wasn't for you, Lawd knows whut us po' womenfolks would do."

She started off, but de devil halted her. "Jus' one mo' thing: don't go home braggin' 'bout yo' keys. Jus' lock up everything and say nothin' until you git asked. And then don't talk too much."

De woman went on home and did like de devil tole her. When de man come home from work she was settin' on de porch singin' some song 'bout "Peck on de wood make de bed go good."

When de man found de three doors fastened what useter stand wide open, he swelled up like pine lumber after a rain. First thing he tried to break in, cause he figgered his strength would overcome all obstacles. When he saw he couldn't do it, he ast de woman, "Who locked dis do'?"

She tole 'im, "Me."

"Where did you git de key from?"

"God give it to me."

He run up to God and said, "God, woman got me locked 'way from my vittles, my bed, and my generations, and she say you give her de keys."

God said, "I did, man, Ah give her de keys, but de devil showed her how to use 'em!"

"Well, Ole Maker, please gimme some keys jus' lak 'em so she can't git de full control."

"No, man, what Ah give Ah give. Woman got de key."

"How kin Ah know 'bout my generations?"

"Ast de woman."

So de man come on back and submitted hisself to de woman, and she opened de doors.

He wasn't satisfied but he had to give in. 'Way after while he said to de woman, "Le's us divide up. Ah'll give you half of my strength if you lemme hold de keys in my hands."

De woman thought dat over so de devil popped and tol' her, "Tell 'im, naw. Let 'im keep his strength and you keep yo' keys."

So de woman wouldn't trade wid 'im, and de man had to mortgage his strength to her to live. And dat's why de man makes and de woman takes. You men is still braggin' 'bout yo' strength, and de women is sittin' on de keys and lettin' you blow off till she git ready to put de bridle on you.

From *Mules and Men*, by Zora Neale Hurston (Philadelphia: J. B. Lippincott Company, 1935).

DAVY CROCKETT: SUNRISE IN HIS POCKET

As Davy Crockett was drifting downstream, asleep on his log pillow, he was wakened by bumping into something. Before him was a strange equipage for river travel. In the center of a log three kegs had been fastened one on top of another, and on the topmost keg was sitting a fat little man wearing a snug tarpaulin hat that looked as bright as a new dollar. His trousers were of sailcloth, his shoes thin and light with ribbons on them. He wore a big black patch over one eye.

"Well, stranger," said Crockett, "you must have robbed a peddler and got off with all his flashy trumpery."

"Why," said the fat little man, "the critter's got the lingo of a Christian. I thought I had spoke to a catfish. I've plowed salt water for forty year and I've seen porpoises and dolphins and mermaids, and I've took many a Nantucket sleigh ride, but you're the queerest looking sea craft I ever come across, on sounding or off. Where are you cruising, old rusty bottom?"

The little man's voice grew deeper and rougher as he spoke. He had a voice so rough it couldn't be written down but would have to be shown in a picture.

"You infernal heathen!" said Crockett. "I suppose you're new down this way, but I'll tell you I'm a snorter by birth and education, and if you don't go floating along and leave me to finish my nap I'll give you a taste of my breed, beginning with the snapping turtle!"

At this rejoinder the fat little stranger looked as mad as a shovel full of hot coals. He took a string of tobacco out of his pocket and bit into it savagely. He bit off a string long and big enough to hang a buffalo with and roared out, "I'll shiver your mizzen, you landlubber! You rock crab! You deck sweeper!"

Crockett's steam was up. "I'll double you up like a spare shirt. My name is Crockett–"

With this the stranger roared with laughter, and his laugh was as rough and noisy as his talk. Stooping down, he reached out his hand. "Give us your flipper. I wouldn't hurt a hair of your head for all the world. I've been cruising up and down this river a-looking for you. Hurrah for Davy Crockett!"

The stranger explained that his name was Ben Hardin and that he was a man who had seen great times. "My business is seeing," he said jovially, and added that he had been told he could see more with the black patch over one eye than any other man could see with it off. He said he had been captain of ships that had turned bottom upward and sailed along to their destinations on their masts. He said that he had leaned his back against a hurricane. He said that he drank bitters made out of whisky and rusty cannon balls, and slept coiled up like a cable. The last time he counted he was going on into his ninety-ninth year.

As Hardin was talking a noise was heard like low thunder, then a distant roaring, like the voice of old Niagara.

"Hello," said Crockett, "there's a storm coming."

"No, it's a steamer," said Ben Hardin.

"Maybe it's the echo of our voices," said Crockett.

The noise grew louder, the water began to squirm about, and

Crockett's log and Hardin's little craft began playing seesaw. Then came a sudden roaring blast that would have made Niagara sound like a kitten. The trees on shore walked out by the roots and danced about. Houses came apart. Two boats on the river crashed into each other, and their ribs were stove in to the boilers. Crockett and Hardin thought it was time to be off.

When a streak of lightning glanced by, Crockett seized it by the fork and sprang upon it. For a man who had leaned his back against a hurricane Ben seemed in a hurry to leave. He gave a leap and seized Crockett's hair. Crockett greased the lightning with some rattlesnake oil he happened to have along, and the way they left the tornado behind and slid across the land was astonishing to all nature.

When this feat became known people talked about greased lightning. They still do. "Quick as greased lightning."

When this adventure was over Crockett landed with his new friend in the woods, and he felt as good-natured as a soaped eel. He invited Hardin to come along to his cabin, where he promised him a bear steak, and the two went along through the woods as good friends as a tame hawk and a blind rooster.

Ben Hardin told Crockett that he was a whole squall and a hurricane at a frolic. Old sailors used to say that he could dance all the girls in all the seaports from Cadiz to Cape Cod out of their stockings. He danced till he wore away the stone steps in front of Crockett's cabin.

"Well, old salt-rope," said Crockett, "I'll give you a frolic that'll last you for a seven years' cruise."

Now Ben had said that Crockett's daughter was as pretty as a dolphin. "I've seen dolphins and mermaids too," he added. The story was that she had once been captured by Indians who carried her away and tied her to a tree, and meant to kindle a fire about her. But while they were gone for wood, panthers came and gnawed the ropes and set her free, and gathered about her as she ran through the forest and escorted her most of the way home.

"Anyway she's the true grit," said Crockett, "and she can dance anything from an earthquake reel to a square-toed double-trouble shiver."

They all went to the Asphaltum Flats, where lightning couldn't strike because the Flats were so hard. An old man with a hemlock fiddle played new tunes that went so fast a hummingbird's wing couldn't keep time with them. Crockett set Ben and the girl at it, and away they went, and the Asphaltum Flats looked like a prairie on fire. "After the first three tunes," Crockett said, "Old Ben began to grunt like a saw going through a pine knot. Then he staggered. My girl said nothing but kept on leading out every new tune. After the hundred and fifteenth tune Ben began to roll like a ship in a sea storm and finally he fell over and curled up in his pigtail. But my girl was ready to go on."

Strange tales were told of Crockett's hunting exploits in the wild country of the Northwest and of his encounters with the Indians. One evening about dark Crockett and Hardin came to the great Indian Rock, which was the hardest stone in all creation.

"It was so 'tarnal high and so all flinty hard," said Crockett, "that it would turn off a common ordinary everyday streak of lightning and make it point down and look flat as a cow's tail."

They got under a shelf of this great rock, and Crockett struck a little fire from it with his knuckles to light their pipes, and they began puffing. They looked up, and the whole stone around and on both ends was alive and red with Indians, all with guns and tomahawks. Ben reached for his flintlock, but Crockett saw that lightning would be the only thing, so he rubbed himself against the shelf of the rock and struck his left eye two or three times. Then he stepped back and with a single wink sent such a blasting streak of hot lightning into the great rock that it parted into forty thousand pieces. There were red Indians shooting up into the sky like rockets and landing way out on the prairie. "We cut stick in such a shower of red Indians as was never seen before," said Crockett.

Another time Crockett and Ben Hardin were having a feast of roasted buffalo with some friendly Indians near one of their lodges. Afterward Crockett danced a breakdown on a great flat rock near by. He rattled off some clear music as he danced, and all the Indians came out and sat around in a circle to watch him—all but the Indian chief, who began a regular Indian war dance in opposition. The Indians began to shout and whoop. Crockett went at it harder and danced until the old rock began to snap and smoke like a hemlock back log. Fire began to fly about, the Indian chief's feet began to singe, and the blankets of the others were all in a light blaze. Just as the Indians were all going to run off Crockett finished with a regular old "Grind the Bottle," and stamped the whole fire out again.

They say that once Crockett went bear hunting in the fall up on Whangdoodle Knob. At sundown he was tired out, so he lay down under a big old dead cedar tree and went to sleep. In his sleep he rolled over and nearly broke his powder horn. Above him was a little curved yellow branch, and he hung his horn on it. The next morning the horn was gone, and he couldn't find the branch. That night he came back to the Knob, and soon the little crescent moon came up, riding low over the mountain. It came so close and looked so yellow it nearly blinded him, and there was his powder horn hanging from the tip. He reached it down and went along home to his cabin.

In a last story Crockett is portrayed as stronger than the sun, and he appears once more in the hunting country of Tennessee.

This story belongs to the Winter of the Big Snow, the winter of 1835, when Crockett set out for Texas, when snow fell early through the wide stretches of the North, crept farther and farther down through the hard wood forests of Michigan, then through the soft wood forests, through the long valleys of Wisconsin, down upon the prairie country of Illinois, into Kentucky and Tennessee. The story was told as if Crockett himself related it.

"On one of those winter mornings it was all-screwen cold," said Crockett. "The forest trees were so stiff they couldn't shake, and the very daybreak froze fast as it was trying to dawn. The tinder-box in my cabin would no more catch fire than a sunk raft at the bottom of the sea. All creation was in a fair way for freezing fast, so I thought I must strike a little fire from my fingers and travel out a few leagues and see what I could do about it. I brought my knuckles together like two thunderclouds, but the sparks froze up before I could collect 'em, so out I walked and tried to keep myself unfrozen by going along at a frolic gait, whistling the tune of 'Fire in the Mountains' and keeping going at three double-quick time. Well, after I had walked about a hundred miles up Daybreak Hill, I reached Peak o' Day, and there I discovered what was the matter. The earth had actually frozen fast on her axis and couldn't turn round, and the sun had got jammed between two cakes of ice under the wheels, and there he had been shining and working to get loose till he was frozen fast in his cold sweat.

" 'C-R-E-A-T-I-O-N,' thought I, 'this is the toughest sort of suspension, and it mustn't be endured—something must be done or human creation is done for!' It was so premature and antediluvian cold on top of Peak o' Day that my upper and lower teeth were all collapsed together as tight as a frozen oyster. So I took a big bear off my back that I'd picked up on my road and threw him down on the ice, and soon there was hot sweet bear oil on all sides. I took and squeezed him over the earth's axis until I'd thawed it loose, and I poured about a ton of sweet bear oil over the sun's face. Then I gave the earth's cog wheel one kick backward till I got the sun free and whistled 'Push Along, Keep Moving.' In about fifteen seconds the earth gave a grunt and began to roll around easy, and the sun walked up most beautiful, saluting me with such a wind of gratitude it made me sneeze.

"I lit my pipe by the blaze of his topknot and walked home, introducing people to the fresh daylight with a piece of sunrise in my pocket."

From *Davy Crockett*, by Constance Rourke (New York: Harcourt, Brace & Co., 1934).

PAUL BUNYAN'S BIG GRIDDLE

ONCE the king of Sweden drove all the good farmers out of the country and a senator from North Dakota he wanted all the fine upstanding timber cleared off the whole state so as to make room for them, so he asked Paul Bunyan for to do the job, and Paul he took the contract. Paul cut lumber out in North Dakota at the rate of a million foot a hour, and he didn't hardly know how to feed his men, he had so many in the camp. The worst trouble was with his hot-cake griddle. It weren't near big enough though it were a pretty good size. The cookees used to grease it with telephone poles with bunches of gunny sacks on the end, but it weren't near big enough. Paul knew where he could get a bigger griddle but he didn't hardly know how to get it to the camp. When it was got up on one aidge it made a track as wide as a wagon road and it were pretty hard to lift. So Paul he thought, and finally he hitched up his mule team. That mule team could travel so fast when they had their regular feed of seven bushels of wheat apiece that nobody couldn't hold them, and Paul had to drive them to a flat-bottomed wagon without no wheels. This time Paul hitched a couple of these here electromagnets on the back, and he drove off to where the griddle was, and he swung them magnets round till he got the griddle on its aidge, and then he drove off lippity-cut to the camp, and he got the griddle a-goin' round so fast he didn't hardly know how to stop it, but he got her near the place where he wanted it, and then he let her go by herself, and she went round and round and round and round, gittin' nearer and nearer the center, and finally she gouged out a hole big enough for a furnace and settled down on top. Then Paul he built a corral around the griddle and put a diamond-shaped roof over it, and built some grain elevators alongside, and put in eight of the biggest concrete mixers he could find. Long in the afternoon every day they'd begin to fill the elevators and start the mixers, and then the cookees would grease the griddle. They all had slabs of bacon on their feet, and they each had their routes. Paul he fixed up a fence of chicken wire round the aidge, in case some cookees didn't get off quick enough when the batter began to roll down, so's they'd have some place to climb to. When the batter was all ready somebody on the aidge used to blow a whistle, and it took four minutes for the sound to get across. Then they'd trip the chute, and out would roll a wave of hot-cake batter four feet high, and any poor cookee that was overtook was kinda out of luck.

Paul's cook shanty was so big that he had to have lunch counters all along the wall so's the hands could stop and get something to eat before they found their places or else they'd get faint a-lookin' for them. Paul he had the tables arranged in three decks, with the oldest hands on the top; and the men on the second deck wore tin hats like a fireman's, with little spouts up the back, and away from the third deck Paul ran a V-flume to the pigpen, for Paul he did hate waste. The problem was how to get the grub to the crew fast enough, because the cookees had so far to go from the cook shanty that it all got cold before they could get it onto the table. So Paul he put up a stop-clock ten foot across the face so as he could see it any place in the eatin' shanty, and he got in one of these here efficiency experts, and they got it all timed down to the plumb limit how long it ought to take to get that food hot to the table. Then Paul he decided to put in some Shetland ponies on roller skates for to draw the food around, and everything seemed fine. But them ponies was trotters, and they couldn't take the corners with any speed, and Paul he had to learn 'em how to pace, and a whole lot of victuals was wasted while he was a-learnin' of them, and Paul was losin' time and he knowed it. So finally he done away with the ponies and put in a train of grub cars with switches and double track and a loop at the end back to the main line, so that when the cars got started proper they came back by themselves. And Paul put in a steel tank especial for the soup, with an air-compressor cupola, six hundred pounds to the square inch, and they used to run the soup down to the men through a four-inch fire hose which the feller on top used to open up as he came through.

From "Paul Bunyon" by Constance Rourke, in the *New Republic*, July 2, 1920. (In this selection the standard spelling of Bunyan's name has been substituted for that used by Constance Rourke.)

PAUL'S CORNSTALK

WELL, when Paul had logged all the trees off North Dakota and pounded all the stumps down and got the land all cleared and smooth, he thought he was done and finished with the job. But then this other letter from the king of Sweden come. The king wrote over and wanted to know if the soil was fertile, and he said he wouldn't let the contract be called finished till Paul had proved that to his satisfaction. It wouldn't be no use to send his people over, he said, unless the soil was good, so's they could raise enough to eat and not have to starve to death or come back, which, like he'd said the other time, of course, he didn't want 'em to do.

And so Paul didn't hardly know what to do.

Course he himself knowed the soil was fertile—couldn't hardly help but be with a stand of timber on it like that—but how to prove that to the king, that was another kind of a job, and he was pretty considerably worried—for Paul, that is. And what the king asked was reasonable enough too, Paul thought, even though it wasn't really in the contract, and he wanted to do it up right, a little more if anything rather than a little less—that was the way with Paul always. And so he had to figgur up something else to do about it.

Course he might of sent Ole over with a sample—he carried enough around on his shoes generally—and let the king try it, but then Ole was needed right where he was. Babe might need shoein' for one thing, and Ole was the only man in camp that could shoe him, and then besides there was Teeny—Paul didn't want him to get away from Teeny just then. Paul was tryin' to get Ole for a son-in-law, because Ole was about the best man he had, and he figgured if he could get him in the family that way he could always be sure of him and wouldn't have to raise his wages none to keep him. And so he didn't care to send him to a foreign country just then, where there might be pretty Swede girls around; but he had to think up some other way, if he could.

Well, what he finally figgured out was, he'd get some people to swear to affidavits for him. He'd plant something, and then they'd watch it grow and swear to how far it growed the first day, and how far the second day, and how far the third day, and so on, all legal, and then they'd send the papers and the measurements to the king, and that ought to satisfy him.

So then when he'd got this all planned out and ready, Paul took a kernel of corn and went out and planted it.

Well, Paul, like I said, knowed that the soil there was fertile, but not even he had any good idea of how fertile it was. And he hadn't no more'n turned around to go back to the camp to get Ole and the other men that was goin' to watch it, till that corn was up out of the ground and higher'n his knee already—and Paul'd planted it a good four foot deep in the hole he'd made with his little finger. And when him and Ole and Charley Nordstrom come runnin' out there, it'd grew clean out of sight so you couldn't see the top at all no more.

Paul sent Ole up right away to cut the top off so it wouldn't grow no higher, but it wasn't but a minute till Ole was pretty near clean out of sight too.

"Cut the top off so it'll branch out!" Paul yells up to where he thought Ole ought to be by that time. "Hurry up. Be quick."

"Can't do it, Paul!" Ole yells back. "Top no bin har. He grows so fast I cannint see him."

And Paul knowed it wasn't no use, for pretty soon they couldn't hardly see Ole no more, and Paul yells, "Come on down then, Ole. Come on down!"

But Ole couldn't do that neither, because every foot he'd try to slide down, the cornstalk would carry him up three, it was growin' so fast, and so he kept goin' up and up all the time—good-by, Ole—and he would of starved to death if Paul hadn't of got his gun and shot him up some doughnuts and biscuits after a while.

And then Paul got his ax and tried to chop it down, but he couldn't do that neither, because he couldn't never chop twice in the same place, the cornstalk was growin' so fast, and so he seen that wouldn't do.

Charley skooted back to camp and got two of the sawyers to come out and bring a saw and a couple of springboards—that was the first time springboards was used in the woods—but they couldn't do it with that neither. They got the springboards in all right, but by the time they got ready to get up on 'em they was too high, and they'd forgot to bring the top air extensions to their ladders, so that was no good.

And Paul was sure what you'd call up a tree, only it wasn't him that was up the tree but Ole, and that's what made Paul feel the worst. Teeny would take on pretty hard if she heard how Ole was goin' out of sight. Course he could comfort her with that he was goin' in the right direction anyway, but that wouldn't do her much good, for she'd rather have him on earth. And then besides there was his future loggin' operations to take into consideration, for Ole he pretty near had to have for his loggin'. I think Paul dropped a tear out of the corner of one eye just about then, but it fell near the foot of the cornstalk and only made it grow faster.

So then Paul thought he maybe might get the Blue Ox and try to pull the corn out by the roots, but he remembered he'd have to put the chain around the stem and it might grow tight to the stem, and then when Babe'd begin to pull it might carry him up with it, and he'd lose his Ox too, besides his blacksmith and maybe son-in-law. And so then he didn't hardly know what to do.

And just about that time one of them government inspectors happened to come along.

"This your cornstalk?" he says to Paul.

"Well, I planted it," Paul says.

"You planted it. Well, then?"

"I planted it," says Paul, "but I didn't make it grow."

"No matter," says the inspector. "It's your cornstalk. You will have to remove it."

"Uh-huh," grunted Paul.

"Law of Public Nuisances," explains the inspector. "This cornstalk of yourn is found to be a Public Nuisance. Agricultural farmers in lower Illinois and Iowa complains of shortage of water for their crops. Something, they say, is sucking away the water from under the soil and leaving their wheat crops high and dry. Not only that, but steamboatmen on the Mississippi reports that the river has lowered six foot in the last six hours–"

"Well, I'll be darned," says Paul.

"Furthermore," says the inspector, puttin' on a legal way, like they do, "it is my duty to inform you that your cornstalk has to be cut down. For investigation has proved that it is that same cornstalk that is causing the disturbance complained of."

"Yah!" kind of snappily from Paul.

"And the said owner of the said cornstalk is therefore directed to chop it down."

But at that Paul gets mad. "That's what I been tryin' to do for the last six hours, you fool," he said. "Can't you see nothin'?"

"Law of Public Nuisances," keeps on the inspector. "I being the lawfully constituted–"

But he didn't get no further, for by the time he got that big mouthful out of his mouth he was flyin' out over the edge of the field at the end of Paul's shoe. And Paul turns back to the cornstalk again.

"I got an idea," he says after a minute, after he'd been lookin' around for a little while.

What he done was, the Great Northern had been layin' a railroad through there not so very far away, and Paul got some of them railroad rails Jim Hill had left, and that's what he done it with. There was a big pile of them steel rails layin' there alongside the right-of-way, and Paul just picks up a handful of 'em and brings 'em over to the cornstalk. He ties 'em all together in a long string and then, with the help of the Blue Ox that Charley had fetched, he swings 'em round the trunk of the corn and ties 'em in a knot.

With that, naturally, the corn begins to cut into itself, and it wasn't long before, growin' so fast, it'd cut itself clean through. With that steel rope around its neck, that cornstalk just naturally committed suicide, that's what it done.

And when it finally fell it took three days fallin', and made such a wind that the Mississippi Valley's been full of windstorms and cyclones ever since.

Paul grubbed out the main part of the stump, and you can see the hole standin' up three thousand feet in the air to this day. One of the ears of corn that was pretty near ripe struck into the ground when it fell down, and they burnt out the cob afterward and had a well two hundred foot down lined on all sides with roasted corn, just like they got a corn-beef mine somewheres over in Montana too, that maybe you've heard of.

Well, Ole, when he seen the cornstalk was beginnin' to fall, climbed out on one of the blades, and when he was pretty near the ground he just swung himself down like little boys swing down on saplings, and naturally he wasn't hurt at all. He told Teeny afterward she needn't to of worried none about his goin' clean through the sky and not bein' able to get back, because he had good suspenders on and they would of kept him from goin' clean through to the other side.

And the affidavits, and the king of Sweden. Well, Paul didn't get no affidavits, because nobody'd had time to take down any measurements, and there wasn't none that could be took down anyway, but a reporter on a Kansas paper wrote up the story, and Paul sent the clipping from the paper to the king. The Swede king believed the newspaper story all right because it was in print, you know, and so he sent all the money that was comin' to Paul, and then he sent his Swedes to North Dakota and there's where they are yet, a lot of 'em.

From *Paul Bunyan*, by Esther Shephard (New York: Harcourt, Brace & Co., 1924).

JOHN HENRY AND THE MACHINE IN WEST VIRGINIA

FROM his birth, it was clear that John Henry's life would be out of the ordinary. The day before, there was a rainbow, and a coal black preacher rode by the Henry cabin on a gray mule. The night was black, with a round red moon and no stars. Near by a cock crowed, a hound bayed, and somewhere in the forest panthers screamed. A great black cloud came from the southwest to cover the moon, and rain and forked lightning darted out of the cloud. And the thunder made a hammer of itself that pounded the earth till the trees quivered.

Then John Henry was born.

And the cloud went away, the moon shone white and bright, the stars came out, and the nightbirds started their singing. But in the moonlight a coal black preacher rode by the cabin again, and he was riding on a gray mule.

First thing John Henry knew, someone was saying, "He weigh thirty-three pound!" Next thing he knew, someone else was saying, "My, my, see them great big shoulders!"

"Course I weigh thirty-three pounds," says John Henry. "Course I got big shoulders. And I got me a voice that's deep and strong. And I got me a cravin' in my soul. What's more, I's hungry."

"My, my," John Henry's pappy said. "John Henry's talkin' already. What you aim to eat, son? Want a little old milk, son?"

"Milk's for babies," John Henry answered him back, "and already I's a natural boy, and soon I'll be a natural man. And I's hollow as an old dry well, sure as you born. So bring me seven hawg jowls and three kettle full of black-eyed peas. Bring me seven ham bones and three pot full of giant cabbage sloshed around in gravy. Bring me a bait of turnip greens that's higher than my woolly head, and a like amount of ash cake to soak in the pot-likker."

"Lawd, Lawd," says John Henry's mammy. "Sound like we got a bragful son on our weary hands. Pappy, maybe if we start right now and learn him his eyes is bigger than his stomach, it'll start him on a good life."

So, with the help of the neighbors, they got all those mountains of food together. And there wasn't room for all the food in the fireplace room, so they had to set it forth on seven tables in the yard.

When John Henry's pappy looked at all that food, he grinned from ear to ear. Then he went to that newborn son of his, and he said, "It's all there, son, set forth on seven tables. If you can eat it, it's steamin' in the moonlight."

John Henry walked to the tables, and he started to eat. The food began to fly, and everybody that watched him grinned to see the way he prized his food. Of course, they expected that he'd stop after the first or second table.

But soon every table was clean as a hound dog's tooth, and John Henry was untying his napkin from around his neck.

"My, my," his pappy said. "He done et up all that food."

"Course I did," says John Henry. "I told you I was hungry."

"We thought you was just a bragful son," his mammy said.

"No," John Henry told her. "I's not bragful and I's not humble. I's a natural boy, and what I says, I means. And now I's goin' to sleep for nine hours."

Nine hours after he went to sleep—nine hours on the dot—John Henry woke up. "I got me a cravin' in my soul, and I's hungry," he said. "Bring me thirteen possums with sweet taters piled treetop high around them. Bring me ninety-nine slices of fried razorback ham and the red gravy. Bring me three gallons of hominy grits to put gravy onto. And bring me thirty-three buttermilk biscuits and tree-sweetnin' for them, for to finish off with."

Knowing, by now, that the boy meant business, they brought what he asked and served it forth on nine tables. He ate it, easy as could be, untied his napkin from around his neck, and went back to bed.

And it went like that for quite a few months, while John Henry grew and grew. By good luck, that was back in the slave days before the war, so Ole Massa had to furnish all that food.

But John Henry grew fast, and his strength grew likewise.

He wasn't many weeks old when he got hold of a piece of steel and his pappy's five-pound hammer when the family was at meeting one fine Sunday morning.

When the family was a good piece from the cabin—"Lawd, Lawd," says John Henry's mammy. "Hear that hammer ringin'. It sounds like the meetin'-house bells when they's tollin' for a buryin'."

When the family came to the house, they found John Henry had gone out with that piece of steel and that hammer. He'd found every big stone he could find, and he'd used the steel and the five-pound hammer to break the big stones. He was working away on the biggest stone of the lot now, hammering the steel and singing in time:

> If I die (WHAM!)
> A railroad man, (WHAM!)
> Go bury me (WHAM!)
> Under the sand, (WHAM!)

With a pick and shovel (WHAM!)
At my head and feet, (WHAM!)
And a twenty-pound hammer (WHAM!)
In my hand. (WHAM!)

With the last wham the rock broke in two, just as clean as if it'd been sawed, and John Henry stood up, grinning, his white teeth shining in his dark face.

"Hello, folkses," says he. "Look like I's found what I want to do —swing a hammer and make the steel ring like a bell. Never been so happy in all my born days, and I's seven weeks old come Thursday. Seem like when I swings this old hammer, I don't have a cravin' in my soul—don't have a cravin' any more."

"My, my," his pappy said. "Look like our son was goin' to be a steel-drivin' man."

. . . John Henry was the best steel-driving man in the world. He could sink a hole down or he could sink it sideways, in soft rock or hard—it made no difference. When he worked with two twenty-pound hammers, one in each hand, it sounded as if the Big Bend Tunnel was caving in, the ring of the steel was so loud.

And John Henry and his sweet Polly Ann were as happy as singing birds, for their roaming days were over, and they felt they'd found a home.

Everything was going fine until a man came along and tried to peddle his steam drill to Captain Tommy. This man had pictures of the steam drill in a book, and he had a wagging tongue in his head. "This steam drill of mine," he said, "will out-drill any twenty men. It doesn't have to rest or eat either, so it'll save you lots of money."

"Hm, maybe," Captain Tommy said, "*maybe*. But I've got one steel-driving man here that's the finest in the world, and I'm mighty fond of big John Henry. So I'll tell you what I think we might do. We might have a race between the steam drill and this man of mine. If the steam drill wins, I'll buy it. But if John Henry wins, you give me the steam drill and five hundred dollars."

"I heard about John Henry, all right, and I know he's good," the man said. "But I know a man is nothing but a man. So I'll have that race, the way you say."

"Fine," says Captain Tommy, "except for one thing: I've got to ask John Henry, but I know pretty well what he'll say." So he went to John Henry, and asked him if he'd race that drill for a favor and a hundred dollars to boot.

John Henry said, "Course I'll race it, and course I'll beat it. For I's a natural-born steel-drivin' man that can beat any nine men or any of the traps that ever drove steel. I don't want any old machine to take my place at the happiest work I's ever found. So before I let that steam drill beat me, I'll die with my hammer in my hand."

The day of the race, country folks and all the steel-driving gangs in the whole section came to see whether John Henry meant what he said. The race was to be outside the mouth of the tunnel—out there by the blacksmith shops where the steels were sharpened and the hammers were fixed—a place where everybody could see. The steam drill, with a boiler about twenty feet long to make the steam, was on the right-hand corner, and the spot where John Henry was to drive was on the left. The crowd was sprinkled all around the edges of the quarry.

At the time the race was to start, the blacksmiths had sharpened piles of drills, the steam drill had its steam up, and the carriers were ready with pads on their shoulders to carry the sharpened steels from the shop and the dull ones back to be sharpened. When there was one minute to go, the steam drill whistled, and John Henry lifted one of his twenty-pound hammers. Then Captain Tommy dropped his hat, and the race started.

Says John Henry to Li'l Bill, the shaker, "Boy, you'd better pray. Cause if I miss this piece of steel, tomorrow be your buryin' day, sure as you born."

Then the steam drill was chugging, and John Henry was swinging and singing—singing "Oh, My Hammer," "Water Boy, Where Is You Hidin'," "If I Die a Railroad Man," and other hammer songs he could keep time to. The steel rang like silver, the carriers trotted to and from the blacksmith shops, and the crowd watched with all its might and main.

It wasn't long after the start that John Henry took the lead. The steam-drill salesman wasn't worried though—or if he was his talk didn't show it. "That man's a mighty man," he said. "But when he hits the hard rock, he'll weaken." Then when John Henry hit the hard rock, and kept driving fast as ever, the salesman said, "He can't keep it up."

John Henry did keep it up though, swinging those two hammers and driving down the steel, stopping only once an hour, maybe, to take a drink of water from the dipper Polly Ann had carried in her slender little hands. Six hours—seven hours—eight hours of that nine-hour race he made his hammer ring like gold. And though Li'l Bill got plumb played out and a new shaker had to take his place, all through the eighth hour John Henry was going strong as ever, with the rhythm in every muscle and joint helping him wham the steel.

It wasn't until the ninth hour that John Henry showed any signs of getting tired. Then, when Captain Tommy came up to ask him how things were going, he answered him back, "This rock is so hard and this steel is so tough, I feel my muscles givin' way. But," he went on to say, "before I let that machine beat me, I'll die with my hammer in my hand."

After that, the crowd that was watching could see signs that John Henry was a weary man—very, very tired and weary.

And John Henry wasn't singing any more. All you could hear was the ring of the hammer on the steel and the chug-chug of the steam drill.

When Captain Tommy, at the end of the ninth hour, looked at his watch and yelled, "The race is over," and when the drills stopped going down, everything was as still as a graveyard. Captain Tommy was looking at the holes. Then, when Captain Tommy said, "John Henry won—three holes ahead of the steam drill," everybody cheered, everybody, that is, excepting the salesman and the steam-drill crew—and John Henry.

When the crowd looked at John Henry, they saw the great man was lying on the ground, and his loving Polly Ann was holding his head. John Henry was moaning, and he sort of mumbled, "Before I let that steam drill beat me, I'll die with my hammer in my hand." (Sure enough, he had *two* hammers in his big black hands.)

Then he said, "Give me a cool drink of water 'fore I die."

Polly Ann was crying when she gave him the water.

Then John Henry kissed his hammer and he kissed his loving Polly Ann. She had to stoop down so he could kiss her. Then he lay very still, and Polly Ann cried harder than ever—sounded mighty loud in that quiet quarry.

Just at that minute, there was the sound of hoofs, and a coal black preacher came riding up on a gray mule. "You got troubles, sister?" he said to Polly Ann. "Can I help you?"

"Only way you can help," she answered him back, "is to read the buryin' service for my lovin' John Henry. Cause his home ain't here no more."

So the coal black preacher read the burying services. They buried John Henry on a hillside—with a hammer on each hand, a rod of steel across his breast, and a pick and shovel at his head and feet. And a great black cloud came out of the southwest to cover the copper sun.

From *Tall Tale America: A Legendary History of Our Humorous Heroes*, by Walter Blair (New York: Coward-McCann, Inc., 1944).

American Indian

The Rabbit Huntress

DESPITE the many differences in the customs and beliefs of the hundreds of Indian tribes that were once scattered from the tip of Florida to the Alaskan straits, there were many fundamental similarities in the tales they told. Generally speaking, theirs was a civilization of hunters and fishers, close to nature but without being bound to the soil (except, perhaps, for the pueblo-dwelling Zuñis), and this remained their condition to the end of their independent history. It is therefore not surprising that so many of their stories were woven around the phenomena of sky and earth and animal life.

Especially numerous are their creation myths. These range from accounts of the genesis of the universe, of man, light, darkness, wind, and stars, to such "just so" explanations as that of the origin of the crow's color in the conclusion of "The Hermit Mítsina." For the Indian the line between a grass plant, an animal, man, and the stars was very thin. The plant possessed a soul, beasts could speak, men changed into stars, and stars became men. Everywhere in nature there were spirits, both good and bad, who took an active, and occasionally, as in "The Rabbit Huntress," crucial, part in human affairs. Everywhere, too, there were animal powers. Sometimes, as in the Blackfoot tale, "The Raven Brings Light," the culture hero of the tribe is a bird. At other times, as in "The Creation of Man," he is a coyote; and when, in fact, Coyote behaves like a traditional character in animal fable, we may begin to suspect European influence.

These transatlantic influences were considerable, probably going back as far as the first French *voyageurs* and Spanish explorers. How quickly and completely an old European tale could become a part of the folklore of an American Indian tribe—or, to go further, how easily a story can pass from any culture to any other culture—is perfectly illustrated by an experience related by Frank Hamilton Cushing, who studied the Indians in the latter part of the nineteenth century. On one occasion Cushing told the old folk tale "The Cock and the Mouse," in a version from T. F. Crane's *Italian Popular Tales*, to a group that include several Zuñi storytellers. A year later he heard one of those storytellers retell the tale in a form five times its original length and completely adapted to the environment and modes of thought of an Indian tribe of the Southwest. The storyteller indicated that the story concerned a far-off people, the *Italia-kwe*, but the reference was already blurred, and there was little doubt that in a short time the tale would be as Indian as though Zuñis had been telling it for a thousand years.

THE CREATION OF MAN

A MIWOK LEGEND

AFTER the coyote had finished all the work of the world and the inferior creatures, he called a council of them to deliberate on the creation of man. They sat down in an open space in the forest all in a circle, with the lion at the head. On his right sat the grizzly bear, next the cinnamon bear, and so on around according to rank, ending with the little mouse, which sat at the lion's left.

The lion was the first to speak, and he declared he should like to see man created with a mighty voice like himself, wherewith he could frighten all animals. For the rest he would have him well covered with hair, terrible fangs in his claws, strong talons, etc.

The grizzly bear said it was ridiculous to have such a voice as his neighbor, for he was always roaring with it, and scared away the very prey he wished to capture. He said the man ought to have prodigious strength, and move about silently, but very swiftly if necessary, and be able to grip his prey without making a noise.

The buck said the man would, in his way of thinking, look very foolish unless he had a magnificent pair of antlers on his head to fight with. He also thought it very absurd to roar so loudly, and he would pay less attention to a man's throat than he would to his ears and his eyes, for he would have the first like a spider's web, and the second like fire.

The mountain sheep protested he never could see what sense there was in such antlers branching every way only to be caught in the thickets. If the man had horns, mostly rolled up, they would be like a stone on each side of his head, giving it weight and enabling him to butt a great deal harder.

When it came to the coyote's turn to speak, he declared all these were the stupidest speeches he had ever heard, and that he could hardly keep awake while listening to such a pack of noodles and nincompoops. Every one of them wanted to make the man like himself. They might just as well take one of their own cubs and call it a man. As for himself, he knew he was not the best animal that could be made, and he could make one better than himself or any other. Of course the man would have to be like himself in having four legs, five fingers, etc. It was well enough to have a voice like the lion, only the man need not roar all the while with it. The grizzly bear also had some good points, one of which was the shape of his feet, which enabled him easily to stand erect; and he was in favor, therefore, of making the man's feet nearly like the grizzly's. The grizzly, also, was happy in having no tail, for he had learned from his own experience that that organ was only a harbor for fleas. The buck's eyes and ears were pretty good, perhaps better than his own. Then there was the fish, which was naked, and which he envied, because hair was a burden most of the year; and he, therefore, favored a man without hair. His claws ought to be as long as the eagle's, so that he could hold things in them. But after all, with all their separate gifts, they must acknowledge that there was no animal besides himself that had wit enough to supply the man, and he should be obliged, therefore, to make him like himself in that respect also—cunning and crafty.

After the coyote had made an end, the beaver said he never heard such nonsense and twaddle in his life. No tail, indeed! He would make a man with a broad, flat tail, so he could haul mud and sand on it.

The owl said all the animals seemed to have lost their senses, none of them wanted to give the man wings. For himself, he could not see of what use anything on earth could be to himself without wings.

The mole said it was perfect folly to talk about wings, for with them the man would be certain to bump his head against the sky. Besides that, if he had wings and eyes both, he would get his eyes burned out by flying too near the sun; but without eyes he could burrow in the cool, soft earth and be happy.

Last of all the little mouse squeaked out that he would make a man with eyes, of course, so that he could see what he was eating; and as for burrowing in the ground, that was absurd.

So the animals disagreed among themselves, and the council broke up in a row. The coyote flew at the beaver and nipped a piece out of his cheek; the owl jumped on top of the coyote's head and commenced lifting his scalp, and there was a high time. Every animal set to work to make a man according to his own ideas, and taking a

lump of earth each one commenced molding it like himself, but the coyote began to make one like he had described in the council. It was so late before they fell to work that nightfall came on before anyone had finished his model, and they all lay down and fell asleep. But the cunning coyote stayed awake and worked hard on his model all night. When all the other animals were sound asleep, he went around and threw water on their models, and so spoiled them. In the morning early he finished his model, and gave it life, long before the others could make new models. And thus it was that man was made by the coyote.

From *The Folk-Lore Record*, Vol. V (London, 1882).

THE PLEIADES

A LONG time ago a party of Indians went through the woods toward a good hunting ground, which they had long known. They traveled several days through a very wild country, going at a leisurely pace and camping by the way. At last they reached Kan-ya-ti-yo, "the beautiful lake," where the gray rocks were crowned with great forest trees. Fish swarmed in the waters, and at every jutting point the deer came down from the hills around to bathe in or drink of the lake. On the hills and in the valleys were huge beech and chestnut trees, where squirrels chattered and bears came to take their morning and evening meals.

The chief of the band was Hah-yah-no, "Tracks in the Water," and he halted his party on the lake shore that he might return thanks to the Great Spirit for their safe arrival at this good hunting ground. "Here will we build our lodges for the winter, and may the Great Spirit, who has prospered us on our way, send us plenty of game and health and peace."

The pleasant autumn days passed by. The lodges had been built and the hunting had prospered, when the children took a fancy to dance for their own amusement. Having little to do, they were becoming bored, and so they began to meet daily in a quiet spot by the lake to have what they called their jolly dance. They had been doing this for a long time, when one day a very old man came to them. They had seen no one like him before. He was dressed in white feathers, and his white hair shone like silver. His appearance was strange and his words were unpleasant. He told them they must stop their dancing, or evil things would happen to them. Little did the children heed, for they were intent on their sport, and again and again the old man appeared, repeating his warning.

The dances did not afford all the enjoyment the children wished, so one little boy, who liked a good dinner, suggested a feast the next time they met. But the feast had to come from their fathers and mothers, so each child had to ask his parents for food when he returned home.

UNIVERSITY
of
PENNSYLVANIA
LIBRARIES

"You will waste and spoil good victuals," said one parent.

"You can eat at home as you should," said another.

So the children got nothing at all. Sorry as they were about this, they met and danced as before. A little to eat after each dance would have made them happy indeed. It is hard to be joyful on an empty stomach.

Their heads became so light with hunger that one day, as they danced, they found themselves rising little by little into the air. How this happened they did not know, but one said, "Do not look back, for something strange is taking place." One woman saw them rise, and called them back, but it had no effect on them, and they continued to rise slowly above the earth. The woman ran to the camp, and everyone came rushing out with food of every kind, but the children would not return, though their parents called piteously after them. But one child dared to look back, and he became a falling star. The others reached the sky, and are now what we call the Pleiades, and the Onondagas call Oot-kwa-tah. Every falling or shooting star recalls the story, and the seven stars shine on, a band of children dancing eternally in the sky.

Based on "An Onondaga Tale of the Pleiades," contributed by W. M. Beauchamp to the *Journal of American Folklore*, Vol. III (1900).

THE RAVEN BRINGS LIGHT

AN ALASKAN INDIAN TALE

IN THE first days there was light. Then the sun and the moon disappeared, and people were left with no light but the shining of the stars. The shamans made their strongest charms, but the darkness continued.

At this time in a village of the lower Yukon there lived an orphan boy who always sat upon the bench with the humble people over the entranceway to the *kashim*. The people of the village thought he was a foolish boy, and he was despised and ill treated by everyone. But after the shamans had tried very hard to bring back the sun and the moon and had failed, the boy began to mock them, saying, "What fine shamans you must be, not to be able to bring back the light. Even I could do it."

At this the shamans became very angry and beat the boy and drove him out of the *kashim*. Now it happened that this poor orphan was like any other boy until he put on a black coat which he had. Then he was at once magically transformed into a raven, and kept that form until he took off the coat again.

When the shamans drove the boy away, he went to the house of his aunt and told her what he had said and how he had been beaten and driven out. Then he asked her to tell him where the sun and the moon had gone, for he wished to go after them. At first she was loath to tell him, but after a long time he prevailed upon her, and she said to him, "Well, if you wish to find the light you must take off your snowshoes and go far to the south, to a place you will recognize as the right place when you get there."

The Raven boy at once took off his snowshoes and set out for the south. He traveled for many days, but everywhere the darkness was the same. At last, when he had gone a very great distance, he saw far off in front of him a ray of light, and felt encouraged. As he hurried on, the light showed up again, plainer than before, and then vanished and appeared at intervals. At last he came to a large hill, one side of which was in bright light while the other was lost in the blackness of night. In front of him and close to the hill the boy saw a hut, with a man shoveling snow from in front of it. The man was tossing the snow high into the air, and each time he did so the light was obscured, thus causing the alternations of light and darkness the boy had seen as he approached. Close beside the house he saw the light he had come in search of, looking like a great ball of fire. Then the boy paused and began to plan how to get the light and the shovel away from the man.

After a time he walked up to the man and said, "Why are you throwing up the snow and cutting off the light from our village?" The man stopped, looked up, and said, "I am only cleaning away the snow from my door; I am not hiding the light. But who are you, and whence did you come?" "It is so dark in our village that I did not want to live there," said the boy, "so I came here to live with you." "What–all the time?" asked the man. "Yes," replied the boy.

The man then said, "It is well. Come into the house with me." He dropped his shovel on the ground, and, stooping down, led the way through the underground passage, letting the curtain fall over the doorway as he passed, thinking the boy was close behind him. The moment the door flap fell behind the man, the boy caught up the ball of light and put it in the turned-up flap of his fur coat; then, picking up the shovel, he fled away to the north. He ran until his feet became tired. Then by means of his magic coat he changed into a raven and flew as fast as wings could carry him. Behind him he heard the frightful shrieks and cries of the old man who pursued him. At last, when the old man saw that he could not overtake the raven, he cried out, "Never mind; you may keep the light, but give me my shovel."

To this Raven answered, "No, you made our village dark and you may not have your shovel," and he left the old man behind.

As Raven traveled homeward he broke off a piece of the light and threw it away, thus making day. He went on for a long time through the darkness before he broke off another piece of light and made day again. This he continued to do at intervals until he reached the outside of the *kashim* in his own village, when he threw away the last piece. Then he went into the *kashim* and said, "See, you good-for-nothing shamans, I have brought back the light. Now there will be light and then dark, and we will have day and night." And the shamans could not answer him.

Thereafter in Raven's village day and night followed each other as he told them it would, but the length of each varied, for sometimes Raven had traveled a long time without throwing out any light, and at other times he had thrown out the light at frequent intervals, so that sometimes the nights are very short and sometimes they are very long.

Adapted from a story in the *Eighteenth Annual Report of the Bureau of American Ethnology* (Washington, D. C., 1899).

THE DISCONTENTED GRASS PLANT

A BERING STRAIT ESKIMO TALE

ONCE a stalk of grass grew near the mouth of the Yukon River. It thought itself most unlucky in not being something else than a grass plant.

Late every fall, just before winter came, the Indian women would go out from the village and gather great piles of this tall, slender grass. It was used for making baskets and braided mats and pads for the soles of skin boots. The women cut the grass close to the ground and carried bundles of it home on their backs. But they never touched the discontented grass plant.

It grew more and more dissatisfied with its lot. So it looked about. Almost at first glance it spied a bunch of herbs, small and scarcely noticeable. The grass plant said to itself, "I wish I were an herb."

The wish was no more than made when the grass became an herb. It had leaves instead of blades, and a branching stalk. For a while it was content, and days of quiet passed.

But before long the women came back to the riverside carrying sharp-pointed picks. They began to dig up the herbs and to eat some of the roots. Others they put in baskets and carried home. The herb that had been the grass plant was not dug up. When the women went home in the evening they left it growing on the riverbank.

Then it was filled with fear and no longer wished to be an herb. Looking about again, it saw a group of plants with tubers at their roots. "I wish I could be one of those," it said.

Scarcely had this second wish been made when a second change took place, and it was no longer an herb, but a plant with tubers at its roots.

Then one evening a little tundra mouse ran swiftly through the grass and began digging up the tubers. He held them in his fore-paws one at a time and nibbled at them. Then he ran away without touching the grass plant.

"To be safe, I must be a mouse," it thought.

At once, by wishing, it became a mouse. It scampered off, happy to have four feet and to be able to run about. Now and then it would stop to dig up and nibble at one of the tubers, just as the other mouse had done. Or it would sit up on its hind legs and look at the new things it could see all around.

Traveling nimbly along, the mouse was aware of a strange white bird coming near. The bird would fly a short distance, drop to the ground to eat something, then fly a bit farther.

As the bird came close the mouse could see that it was a big white owl. The owl saw the mouse and swooped down to eat it; but the mouse was lucky enough to escape by darting into a hole. So the big owl flew away. When the mouse came out of its shelter,

its heart beat painfully from the dreadful fright. "I want to be an owl," it thought. "Then I will surely be safe."

Again by wishing, its form was changed—this time into a beautiful white owl with slow, noiseless wings that swept the land and sea. It set off toward the north, pausing every now and then to eat a mouse.

After a long flight the owl, which had once been the unhappy little grass plant, saw an island in the distance and flew toward it. Far from home its untried wings grew very weary, so that it was scarcely able to keep from falling into the water. When at last the owl reached the shore, it perched on a piece of driftwood sticking upright in the sand. In a little while two young men passed by, and the old feeling of discontent arose again.

"I want to be a man," thought the owl. With a single flap of its wings it stood upon the ground, and was changed immediately into a man, though without clothing.

Soon night came over the earth, and the man sat down with his back against the stick of wood on which he had perched as an owl. He slept there till morning.

All this happened in the far north country where the nights are very cold, and where spring and autumn and winter are not bright summertime. When the man was awakened by the early light, he was stiff and lame from sitting in the chill night air. He hunted about until he found some grass, which he wove into a cloak to help keep out the cold.

Soon he saw some reindeer grazing not far away and felt a sudden desire to kill and eat one of them. He crept close on his hands and knees and, springing suddenly upon the animal nearest, he seized it by the horns and broke its neck with a single effort. He threw it over his shoulder and returned to the place where he had slept. Tossing the dead animal on the ground, he felt all over its body and discovered that his fingers could not pierce the skin.

For a long time he tried to think of what to do. Finally he found a sharp-edged stone with which he cut and removed the hide. But he had no fire to cook the meat. Looking about again, he saw two round white stones on the beach. He struck them together and they gave out sparks. With some dry grass which he gathered along the shore he made a fire, roasted a little of the meat, and ate it.

Another very cold night passed, and in the morning the man caught another reindeer, and on the next day another. Each time he threw the dead animal over his shoulder, carried it to his camping place on the shore, and skinned it. He wrapped himself from head to foot in the hides. But the nights grew colder and colder. So he gathered a great deal of driftwood and made himself a rude hut which was comfortable.

After finishing his house, he was walking over the hills one day when he saw a strange black animal eating among the blueberry bushes. It was a bear. He caught it by one of its hind legs. With an angry growl it turned and faced him, showing its teeth. In an instant he grabbed its coarse hair firmly and raised the animal over his head. He brought it to the ground with such force that the bear lay dead. Then he threw it across his shoulders and went home.

While the man was skinning the bear, he found enough fat to make oil which would light his house; until then it had been dark and hard to move about in. On the beach he picked up a large flat stone with a hollow place on one side and poured the oil into it. Then he lighted a moss wick and put it in the oil. He hung the bear-skin in the doorway to keep out the cold wind which had often chilled him during the night. In this way he lived many days, until he began to feel lonely.

Then he remembered the two young men he had seen when he perched on the shore as an owl. He thought, "It can't be far to where other people live. I will go seek them." So he went in search of people.

He wandered along the coast for some time and at last saw two fine new boats, with spears, lines, floats, and fishing tackle in them.

The man examined everything very curiously. Next he saw a path leading to the top of a hill. This he followed.

On the top of the hill were two houses, and on the ground in front were some freshly killed white whales, with the skulls of many others lying around. He crept with noiseless steps to the door of the nearest house. Cautiously lifting a corner of the skin that hung at the entrance, he looked in.

Opposite the door sat a young man who was working on some arrows, with a bow lying beside him. The man at the door dropped the skin curtain and stood quite still, fearing he might be shot. Then he said to himself, "If I enter and say, 'I have come, brother,' he will not hurt me." So he raised the curtain quickly, entered, and said, "I have come, brother." The young man cried out with delight, "Are you my brother? Come, sit beside me." The man who once was a grass plant did so eagerly.

"I am glad to see you," said the younger man. "I have always believed I had a brother somewhere, but I could not find him. Where have you lived? How did you grow up?"

So they talked of life by the seashore, of living alone, and of killing game for food.

In one of the houses on the hill there were many rich furs, and in the other an abundance of seal oil and food.

Finally the brothers fell asleep. At daybreak they arose, and, after eating, the one with the bow and arrows went out by himself to kill game. The other stayed at home to cook their meals.

They lived in this way a long time, but the man who had once been the discontented grass plant got tired of staying at home and cooking. One day he said to his brother, "Why can't I go out hunting with you?" But he was refused. The young hunter started off alone, but the other man soon crept up behind him softly and grabbed his foot. Turning, the hunter said angrily, "What do you mean by following me? You can kill nothing without a bow and arrows."

"I can kill game with my hands alone," said the man. But his brother said scornfully, "Go home and tend to the cooking."

Instead, the man crept up on a herd of reindeer and killed two with his bare hands, as he had done while living by himself. Then he stood up and waved for his brother to come. The young hunter was astonished and angry, for even with his arrows he had killed nothing.

The man who had once been the grass stalk lifted the two reindeer on his shoulders and carried them home. The brother followed with darkening brow and evil thoughts in his heart. Jealousy and anger took the place of all the kindly feelings he had known before. Great fear arose within him because he had seen his brother display such strength.

During all the evening he sat silent and moody, scarcely tasting the food before him. Finally his suspicions and angry thoughts aroused the same feelings in the other man's mind. They kept watching each other, fearing treachery.

The day following was calm and bright, and the men paddled two boats far out to sea. When the shore was quite distant they turned back, still discontented and unhappy.

"Now let us see who can reach the shore first," said the hunter.

Lightly the two boats darted away, first one, then the other, seeming to lead. With a final effort the two rivals ran the boats ashore and sprang on the beach at the same instant. With scowling brow the one said, "You are no more my brother. You go that way, I will go this." They turned their backs on each other and separated in anger.

The one was changed into a wolverine; the other into a gray wolf. To this very day they are found wandering in the same country, never together, both of them always discontented and unhappy.

From the *Eighteenth Annual Report of the Bureau of American Ethnology* (1899), as adapted by Caroline Cunningham in *The Talking Stone* (New York: Alfred A. Knopf, Inc., 1939).

THE SHINING LODGE

A BLACKFOOT TALE

IT WAS thousands of moons ago when Soatsaki, a young Indian girl whose name means Feather Lady, wakened very early one morning among the tall prairie grasses. She and her older sister had been sleeping outside their tepee because it was very warm.

"Oh, sister, look at the lovely Morning Star! I shall never marry any man here on earth. That bright beautiful star is going to be my husband," said Feather Lady, enchanted.

The sister did not like being roused so early, and, being annoyed, she ran into the camp and told the people what a foolish thing Feather Lady had said. Even though her tribesmen believed in magic stories of giants and spirits and winged canoes, they laughed at Feather Lady's idea.

Feather Lady herself soon forgot what she had said.

A few days later she and her sister went into the forest to gather wood. When they had their packs made and were lifting them up to their shoulders by the pack-straps, Feather Lady's strap broke. Every time she made up her pack and tried to lift it, the strap would break again. Her sister, who was standing beside her with her load of wood on her back, began to grow weary. She said, "I am going home with my bundle. You can follow."

When Feather Lady was left alone, she heard a voice say, "Feather Lady, I am Morning Star." She trembled and looked up. A bright youth stood in the river path. He was tall and straight, his hair long and glistening. He was dressed in a beaver-skin robe, and the fragrance of pine and sweet grass was around him. "Don't you remember? You wanted to marry me," he said to her. He took a long eagle feather and stuck it upright in her hair. He gave her a branch of juniper from which trailed two spiderwebs. Next he had her take hold of the upper strand and place her feet on the lower one. Then he told her to shut her eyes. In a second they were transported on the sparkling web to the roof of the world.

When she opened her eyes, Feather Lady found herself standing before a shining lodge with Morning Star beside her. This was the home of his father and mother, the Sun and the Moon.

The Sun was away on his daily journey across the sky. The Moon welcomed Feather Lady kindly and dressed the girl in a soft robe of buckskin trimmed with elk teeth.

When the Sun came home that night, he was pleased with Feather Lady and called her his daughter. So she was married to Morning Star. They all lived together very happily in the shining lodge, and after a while Feather Lady had a baby named Star Boy.

One day the Moon mother gave Feather Lady a root-digger and said, "You may go everywhere about sky land and dig up all kinds of roots. But you must never touch the great turnip that grows near our lodge. If you do, deep unhappiness will come to every one of us, for that turnip is medicine."

Day after day Feather Lady wandered about with Star Boy on her back, digging up roots. She often passed the great turnip, but never touched it.

Then one day she was curious to see what lay beneath. So she put Star Boy on the ground and began to dig. Her root-digger soon stuck in the side of the great turnip, and she could not pull it out.

Just then two beautiful snow-white loons from the far north flew overhead. She called to them for help. They sang a magic song, and the great turnip was uprooted.

Feather Lady looked down through the hole where the turnip had been. Far below she saw the camp on earth where she once had lived, the trees, the rivers, and the lodges of her people. Smoke was rising from the wigwams. She could hear the children laughing and playing and the women singing at their work. She was filled with homesickness and went back weeping to the shining lodge.

Morning Star looked at her very sorrowfully. "Alas, alas, my dear Feather Lady," he said, "you have uprooted the great turnip!"

The Sun and Moon were troubled. They loved Feather Lady dearly, but they knew she must now return to earth because of her curiosity and disobedience.

So Morning Star took Feather Lady sadly by the hand. He warned her not to let Star Boy touch the ground for fourteen days or he would return to the sky as a star. He told her to mark a sign on the back of her lodge on earth so she would be warned daily of her duty, but to tell no one.

Then he placed little Star Boy on her back and led her to the Spider Man who lived in sky land. Spider Man wove a beautiful web, glittering with dew, in the hole where the great turnip had been. They wrapped Feather Lady in an elk's hide and let her and her little boy gently down to earth upon the web. Feather Lady's people saw her coming like a falling star. Her path was the Milky Way, on which souls always go back and forth to heaven.

"Here is Feather Lady, who never came back with her wood," they said.

Her parents welcomed her and loved little Star Boy.

Feather Lady kept careful watch for thirteen days. Then her mother sent her for water. She cautioned her mother to keep the child on the pile of furs and not to let him touch the ground.

The grandmother wasn't so careful, because she didn't understand the reason for watching the child so closely. While her back was turned, the boy crawled off the furs onto the bare earth. When his grandmother saw him she grabbed him up and put him back as quickly as she could.

This seemed to make the child cross, for he pulled a robe up over his face. The grandmother paid no more attention to him.

When Star Boy's mother returned she looked around and said, "Where is my child?"

"Oh, he covered himself up with his robe," said the grandmother.

Feather Lady rushed to the pile of furs, pulled back the robe, and found nothing there. That evening she looked up into the sky. A new star glittered in the hole where she had pulled up the turnip. Then she knew what had become of her child.

So that is the way the North Star came to be. It is called "the Nail of the North," and always stands still. All the other stars move around it.

The half-circle of stars to the east of the North Star is the lodge of the Spider Man and is called "the Northern Crown." The bright stars just beyond, in the constellation of Hercules, the Indians believed to be his five fingers, with which he spun the web on which Feather Lady and her child, Star Boy, were let down to earth.

From "The Fixed Star," in the *Anthropological Papers of the American Museum of Natural History*, Vol. II (1909), as adapted by Caroline Cunningham in *The Talking Stone.*

THE HERMIT MÍTSINA

WHEN all was new, and the gods dwelt in the ancient places, long, long before the time of our ancients, many were the gods—some destined for good and some for evil or for the doing of things beneath understanding. And those of evil intent, so painfully bad were they to become that not in the company and council of the precious beloved of the *Kâkâ* (the Order of the Sacred Drama) could they be retained.

Thus it happened, in the times of our ancients, long, long ago, that there dwelt all alone in the Cañon of the Pines, southeast of Zuñi, Mítsina the Hermit. Of evil understanding he; therefore it had been said to him (by the gods), "Alone shalt thou dwell, being unwise and evil in thy ways, until thou hast, through much happening, even become worthy to dwell amongst us." Thus it was that Mítsina lived alone in his house in the Cañon of the Pines.

Sometimes when a young man, dressed in very fine apparel (wearing his collars of shell, and turquoise earrings, and other precious things which were plentiful in the days of our ancients), would be out hunting, and chanced to go through the Cañon of the Pines and near to the house of Mítsina, he would hear the sounds of gaming from within; for, being alone, the hermit whiled away his time in playing at the game of sacred arrows (or cane-cards).

Forever from the ceiling of his house there hung suspended his basket-drum, made of a large wicker bowl, over the mouth of which was stretched tightly a soft buckskin, even like the basket-drums which we use in the playing of cane-cards today, and which you know are suspended with the skin side downward from the ceilings of the gaming rooms in the topmost houses of our town. Though the one he had was no better than those we have today, save that it was larger and handsomer perhaps, yet he delighted to call it his cloud canopy, bethinking himself of the drum-basket of his former associates, the gods, which is even the rounded sky itself, with the clouds stretched across it. Forever upon the floor of his house there lay spread a great buffalo robe, the skin upward, dressed soft and smooth, as white as corn flour, and painted with the many-colored symbols and counting marks of the game, even as our own. But he delighted to call it his sacred terraced plain, bethinking himself of the robe-spread of the gods, which is even the outspread earth itself, bordered by terraced horizons, and diversified by mountains, valleys, and bright places, which are the symbols and game marks whereby the gods themselves count up the score of their game.

Hearing these sounds of the game in passing, the young man would naturally draw near and listen. Though all alone, every time he made a good throw Mítsina would exclaim, "*Her-r-r-r!*" And as the canes struck the skin of the drum-basket above, *tcha-le-le*, *tcha-le-le*, it would sound; and *ke-le-le* they would rattle as they fell on the robe below. "Ha! ha!" old Mítsina would exclaim, as if triumphantly to some opponent in the game, "*Kohakwa iyathtokyai!*" As much as to say, "Good for you, old fellow! The white-corn symbol fell uppermost!"

"Oh!" the young man would exclaim as he listened. "Oh!" And, wishing to learn more about the matter, he would stealthily climb up the ladder and peer down through the sky-hole. Old Mítsina would catch sight of him, be sure of that, and greet him most cordially, calling to him, "Come in, come in, my fine young fellow, come in! Let's have a game!"

Now he had practiced so long that he had acquired more skill than anyone else throughout the world—at least among mortals; so that when any of the young men chanced to play with him, he invariably lost, poor fellow! Hanging on the pole along the north side of Mítsina's house were the necklaces, embroidered mantles, and turquoises, and all sorts of treasures which he had won in this way; and as many on the western side, on the southern side as many, and on the eastern side also.

When the young man came in, Mítsina would continue, "My good friend, sit right down over there. Have you your canes to-day?" If the young man said, "Yes," he would say, "Ha! very well." Or, if he said, "No," "Never mind," Mítsina would say, "Here are some," producing a very fine set of polished canes. The young man, being thus pressed, would stake perhaps his necklace or his earrings, and the game would begin. Losing them, he would stake his clothing, his bows and arrows—in fact, everything he had about him. You know how it is with gamesters when they have lost a great deal and wish to get it back again? Well, so it was then. When the young man had lost everything, he would bow his head on his hand and sit thinking. Then old Mítsina, with a jolly, devil-may-care manner, would say, "Bet your left thigh. I'll put all you have lost and more, too, on that." The young man would say to himself, with a sigh of relief, "What an old fool you are!" and reply, "All right! I will take your bet." Alas! the one thigh he bet is lost; then the other goes the same way; then one of his sides and arms; losing which, he bet the other, and so on, until he had bet away his whole body, including his head. Then in utter despair he would exclaim, "Do with me as thou wilt. I am thy slave." And old Mítsina with the same devil-may-care manner would catch him up, take him out to the back of his house, and wring his neck that he might not go back and report his losses to his people.

Again, some other well-equipped young man would be passing that way, and, hearing the sound made by the solitary player, and being attracted thereby, would be drawn in the same way into the game, would lose everything, and old Mítsina would wring his neck and keep his treasures.

Thus it was in the days of the ancients. Great were the losses of the young men, and many of them perished.

Well, one day little Áhaiyúta and Mátsailéma—the war gods of peace times—who dwelt, as you know, where their shrine now stands on Face Mountain, with their old grandmother—went out hunting rabbits and prairie dogs. It chanced that in following the rabbits along the cliffs of a side cañon they came into the Cañon of the Pines, near where the house of Mítsina stood. Presently they heard the sound of his game. "Hu, hu!" the old fellow would exclaim as he cast his canes into the air. *Ke-le-le-le* they would rattle as they fell on the skin.

"Uh!" exclaimed Áhaiyúta, the elder. "Brother younger, listen."

The younger listened. "By my eyes!" exclaimed he, "it is someone playing at cane-cards. Let's go and have a peep at him." So they climbed the ladder and peered in through the sky-hole.

Presently old Mítsina espied them and called out, "Ha! my little fellows, glad to see you today! How are you? Come in, come in! I am dying for a game. I was playing here all by myself."

The two little war gods clambered down the ladder, and old Mítsina placed blankets for them, invited them most cordially to sit down, and asked if they would like to play a game. Nothing loath they, seeing all the fine things hanging round his room; so out from their girdles they drew their cane-cards, for those, as you know, they always carried with them.

Perhaps I have not told you that even the basket-drum old Mítsina played with was fringed with the handsome long turquoise earrings which he had won, and even under the robe on which he played there were piled one over another, in a great flat heap, the finest of necklaces gathered from those whom he had defeated in playing and then slain.

"What would you like to put up?" asked the old fellow, pointing around his room—particularly to the basket-drum fringed with turquoises—and lifting the robe and showing just enough of the necklaces underneath it to whet the appetites of the little war gods.

"We've nothing fine enough to bet for these things," said they ruefully.

"Oho!" cried Mítsina. "No matter, no matter at all, my boys. Bet your bows and arrows and clothing. If you like, bet everything you have on, and I'll put up that poleful there on the north side of my room."

"Good! Good! Tell him all right," whispered the younger brother to the elder.

So the elder agreed, chuckling to himself, for it was rarely that a man was found who could beat the little war gods in a game. And they began their playing. How the turquoises rattled as they threw their canes! How the canes jingled and jumped as they fell on the robe!

The game was merry and long and well played on both sides; but the poor little war gods lost. Their countenances fell; but old Mítsina, with a merry twinkle in his eyes, exclaimed, "Oh, pshaw! Never mind, never mind!"

"Yes," said the two war gods, "but how in the world are we ever going back to our grandmother in this plight?" glancing down over their bare bodies, for they had bet even the clothing off their backs. "What else can we bet? How can we win back what we have lost?"

"Bet your left thighs," said the old hermit.

They thought a moment and concluded they would do so. So the game was staked again and begun and the canes rattled merrily; but they lost again. Then old Mítsina suggested that they bet their other thighs. They did so and again lost. Then he suggested that they should bet their left sides, hoping forthwith to get hold of their hearts, but the young war gods were crafty. The elder one exclaimed, "All right!" but the younger one said, "Goodness! As for you, you can bet your left side if you want to, but I'll bet my right, for my heart is on my left side, and whoever heard of a man betting away his heart!"

"Just as you like," said Mítsina, "but if you'll bet your bodies up to your necks, I will stake all you have lost and all I have besides," said he, looking around on his fine possessions.

"Done!" cried the war gods. And again they played and again lost. They had nothing left but their heads and ears and eyes to bet. Finally they concluded to bet these also, for, said they to each other, "What good will our heads do us, even though they be the crown pieces of our being, without the rest?"

They played again, but the poor fellows lost their heads also. "Alas! Alas! Do as thou wilt with us," exclaimed the little war gods with rueful countenances.

Old Mítsina, locking them up in a small recess of his house, went out and gathered before his front door a great quantity of dry wood. Then he tied the little fellows hand and foot and laid them near by —not near enough to burn them up, but near enough so that they would scorch—and lighted the fire, to have the pleasure of roasting them. When they began to brown and sizzle a little they writhed and howled with pain, but they were tough and quite bad, as you know, and this did not kill them.

Who can hide a thing from the eyes of the gods? The elder brothers of these two foolish little war gods, Áhaiyúta and Mátsailéma, those who dwelt on Thunder Mountain, became aware of what was going on. "Come, brother younger," said the elder, strapping on his quiver and taking his bow in hand, "come, let us off to old Mítsina's house and teach him a lesson!" So, in a twinkling they were climbing down the mountain, speeding across the wide valley, and threading their way through the Cañon of the Pines.

Mítsina had grown tired of watching the poor little war gods and had gone in to have another little game, and there he was pitching his cane-cards and talking to himself, as usual. The two gods hauled their unfortunate brothers away from the fire, and, climbing the ladder, peered in. Mítsina espied them, and as usual invited them in to a game. With as jolly an air as his own they accepted his challenge and sat down. Mítsina offered to bet all his fine things hanging on the north side of the house. "What will you put up, my little fellows?" asked he.

"If you will include those ugly little devils that we saw sizzling before the fire when we came in, we will bet you everything we have with us," said they.

"Good! Good! Haul them in!" shouted Mítsina.

The war gods scrambled out of the house and, by no means gently, dragged their wretched little brothers in by the heels and dumped them down on the floor to show their indifference, sat down, and began to play. They bet their weapons, holding up the knife of war which they carried, the point of lightning itself fatal in power–splitter of mountains and overcomer of demons and men alike.

Old Mítsina, when told of the power of the weapons, became doubtful as to his company, but presently fell to and played with a will. He lost. Then he put up all the rest of his goods hanging on the other side of the room. Again he lost, and again, even the turquoises hanging from the basket-drum, the necklaces under his robe, and the things he played with; and getting wild with excitement, sure that his luck would return, followed out the plan he had so often suggested to others, and bet away his thighs, then his sides and arms, then his head and ears, excepting his eyes, and last of all his very eyes themselves. Each time the young war gods won. The old gambler let his hands fall by his sides and dropped his head on his breast, sick with humiliation and chagrin.

"Now, my brother," said the elder to the younger, "what shall we do with this beast?"

"I don't know," said the other. "We can't kill him; yet, if we leave him to go his own way, he will gamble and gamble without ceasing and make no end of trouble. Suppose we make a good man of him."

"How?" asked the other.

"Pluck out his eyes."

"Capital!" exclaimed the first. "So, while one of them held the old fellow down, the other gouged out his eyes, and with pain and horror he utterly forgot in unconsciousness (swooned away).

The two elder war gods set their younger brothers on their feet, and all four of them joined in clearing out the treasures and magnificent possessions which Mítsina through all these years had won from his victims; and these they took away with them that by their sacred knowledge they might change them into blessings for the faithful of their children among men, and thus return, as it were, what had been lost. Then away they went, leaving old Mítsina, still as witless as a dead man, to his fate.

By and by the old man came to his senses and, raising himself up, tried to look around, but, forsooth, he could not see.

"What in the world has happened? What a fearful pain I have in my temples!" said he. "What is the matter? Is it night?"

Then gradually his situation came to him. He uttered a groan of pain and sorrow and, putting out his hand, felt the wall and raised himself by it. Then he crept along, feeling his way to the window, not yet quite certain whether he had been dreaming all this and it was still night, or whether he had really lost everything and been bereft of his eyes by those midgets. When he put his hand into the window, however, he felt the warm sunlight streaming in, and knew that it was still day, and that it was all true.

In feeling there he chanced to touch a little package of pitch which had been laid in the window. He felt it all over with both hands, but could not quite tell what it was. Then he put it against his cheek, but was still uncertain; then he rubbed it, and smelled of it. "Pitch! pitch! as I live!" said he. "I have often lighted this when it was dark and been able to see. Now, maybe, if I light it this time, I shall be able to see again." He felt his way all round the room to the fireplace, and after burning his fingers two or three times in feeling for coals, he found a sliver and held it in the coals and ashes until he heard it begin to sputter and crackle. Then he lighted the pitch with it. Eyeless though he was, the fumes from this medicine of the woodlands restored to him a kind of vision. "Good!" cried the old fellow, "I see again!" But when he looked around he saw nothing as it had been formerly; and his thoughts reverted to the great City of the Gods (*Kothluellakwin*); and, as it were, he could see the way thither. So he turned toward his door and with a sigh gave up his old place of abode, relinquished all thought of his possessions, gave up his former bad inclinations, and turned westward toward the City of the Gods and Souls.

As he went along holding his light before him and following it, he sang a mournful song. The birds, hearing this song, flocked around him, and as he went on singing, exclaimed to one another, "Ha! ha! the old wretch! He has lost his eyes! Served him right! Let's put out his light for him."

Now, before that time, strange as it may seem, the eagles and even the crows were as white as the foam on warring waters. The

eagles were so strong that they thrust the other birds away and began to pounce down on Mítsina's light, trying to blow it out with their wings. *Thluh! thluh!* they would flap into the light; but still it would not go out; and they only singed their feathers and blackened their wings and tails with smoke. In looking at one another they saw what a sad plight they were in. "Good gracious, brothers!" exclaimed some of them to the others, "we have made a fine mess of our white plumage!" And they gave it up.

Then the crows rushed in and flapped against the light, but they could not put it out; and although they grew blacker and blacker, they would not give it up. So they became as black as crows are now; and ever since then eagles have been speckled with brown and black, and crows have been black, even to the tips of their beaks. And whenever in the Sacred Drama Dance of our people old Mítsina appears, he sings the doleful song and carries the light of pitch pine. He goes naked, with the exception of a wretched old cloth at his loins; and he wears a mask with deep holes for eyes, blood streaming from them.

Thus shortens my story.

From *Zuñi Folk Tales,* by Frank Hamilton Cushing (New York: Alfred A. Knopf, Inc., 1931).

THE RABBIT HUNTRESS

IT WAS long ago, in the days of the ancients, that a poor maiden lived at K'yawana Tehua-Tsana (Little Gateway of Zuñi River). You know there are black stone walls of houses standing there on the tops of the cliffs of lava, above the narrow place through which the river runs, to this day.

In one of these houses there lived this poor maiden alone with her feeble old father and her aged mother. She was unmarried, and her brothers had all been killed in wars or had died gently; so the family lived there helplessly, so far as many things were concerned, from the lack of men in their house.

It is true that in making the gardens—the little plantings of beans, pumpkins, squashes, melons, and corn—the maiden was able to do very well; and thus mainly on the products of these things the family were supported. But, as in those days of our ancients we had neither sheep nor cattle, the hunt was depended upon to supply the meat; or sometimes it was procured by barter of the products of the fields to those who hunted mostly. Of these things this little family had barely enough for their own subsistence; hence they could not procure their supplies of meat in this way.

Long before, it had been a great house, for many were the brave and strong young men who had lived in it; but the rooms were now empty, or at best contained only the leavings of those who had lived there, much used and worn out.

One autumn day, near wintertime, snow fell, and it became very cold. The maiden had gathered brush and firewood in abundance, and it was piled along the roof of the house and down underneath the ladder which descended from the top. She saw the young men issue forth the next morning in great numbers, their feet protected by long stockings of deerskin, the fur turned inward, and they carried on their shoulders and stuck in their belts stone axes and rabbit sticks. As she gazed at them from the roof, she said to herself, "O that I were a man and could go forth, as do these young men, hunting rabbits! Then my poor old mother and father would not lack for flesh with which duly to season their food and nourish their lean bodies." Thus ran her thoughts, and before night, as she saw these same young men coming in, one after another, some of them bringing long strings of rabbits, others short ones, but none of them empty-handed, she decided that, woman though she was, she would set forth on the morrow to try what luck she might find in the killing of rabbits herself.

It may seem strange that, although this maiden was beautiful and young, the youths did not give her some of their rabbits. But their feelings were not friendly, for no one of them would she accept as a husband, although one after another of them had offered himself for marriage.

Fully resolved, the girl that evening sat down by the fireplace and, turning toward her aged parents, said, "O my mother and father, I see that the snow has fallen, whereby rabbits are easily tracked, and the young men who went out this morning returned long before evening heavily laden with strings of this game. Behold, in the other rooms of our house are many rabbit sticks, and there hang on the walls stone axes, and with these I might perchance strike down a rabbit on his trail, or, if he run into a log, split the log and dig him out. So I have thought during the day, and have decided to go tomorrow and try my fortunes in the hunt, woman though I be."

"*Naiya*, my daughter," quavered the feeble old mother, "you would surely be very cold, or you would lose your way, or grow so tired that you could not return before night, and you must not go out to hunt rabbits, woman as you are."

"Why, certainly not," insisted the old man, rubbing his lean knees and shaking his head over the days that were gone. "No, no; let us live in poverty rather than that you should run such risks as these, O my daughter."

But, say what they would, the girl was determined. And the old man said at last, "Very well! You will not be turned from your course. Therefore, O daughter, I will help you as best I may." He hobbled into another room and found there some old deerskins covered thickly with fur; and drawing them out, he moistened and carefully softened them, and cut out for the maiden long stockings, which he sewed up with sinew and the fiber of the yucca leaf. Then he selected for her from among the old possessions of his brothers and sons, who had been killed or perished otherwise, a number of rabbit sticks and a fine, heavy stone ax. Meanwhile the old woman busied herself in preparing a lunch for the girl, which was composed of little cakes of corn meal, spiced with pepper and wild onions, pierced through the middle, and baked in the ashes. When she had made a long string of these by threading them like beads on a rope of yucca fiber, she laid them down not far from the ladder on a little bench, with the rabbit sticks, the stone ax, and the deerskin stockings.

That night the maiden planned and planned, and early on the following morning, even before the young men had gone out from the town, she had put on a warm, short-skirted dress, knotted a mantle over her shoulder and thrown another and larger one over her back, drawn on the deerskin stockings, had thrown the string of corn cakes over her shoulder, stuck the rabbit sticks in her belt, and, carrying the stone ax in her hand, sallied forth eastward through the Gateway of Zuñi and into the plain of the valley beyond, called the Plain of the Burned River, on account of the black, roasted-looking rocks along some parts of its sides. Dazzlingly white, the snow stretched out before her—not deep, but unbroken—and when she came near the cliffs with many little cañons in them, along the northern side of the valley, she saw many a trail of rabbits running out and in among the rocks and between the bushes.

Warm and excited by her unwonted exercise, she did not heed a coming snowstorm, but ran about from one place to another, following the trails of the rabbits, sometimes up into the cañons, where the forest of piñon and cedar stood, and where here and there she had the good fortune sometimes to run two, three, or four rabbits into a single hollow log. It was little work to split these logs, for they were small, as you know, and to dig out the rabbits and slay them by a blow of the hand on the nape of the neck, back of the ears; and as she killed each rabbit she raised it reverently to her lips, and breathed from its nostrils its expiring breath, and, tying its legs together, placed it on the string, which after a while began to grow heavy on her shoulders. Still she kept on, little heeding the snow which was falling fast; nor did she notice that it was growing darker and darker, so intent was she on the hunt, and so glad was she to capture so many rabbits. Indeed, she followed the trails until they were no longer visible, as the snow fell all around her, thinking all the while, "How happy will be my poor old father and mother that they shall now have flesh to eat! How strong will they grow! And when this meat is gone, that which is dried and preserved of it also, lo! another snowstorm will no doubt come, and I can go out hunting again."

At last the twilight came, and, looking around, she found that the snow had fallen deeply, there was no trail, and she had lost her way. True, she turned about and started in the direction of her home, as she supposed, walking as fast as she could through the soft, deep snow. Yet she reckoned not rightly, for instead of going eastward along the valley, she went southward across it, and entering the mouth of the Descending Plain of the Pines, she went on and on, thinking she was going homeward, until at last it grew dark and she knew not which way to turn.

"What harm," thought she, "if I find a sheltered place among the rocks? What harm if I remain all night, and go home in the morning when the snow has ceased falling, and by the light I shall know my way?"

So she turned about to some rocks which appeared, black and dim, a short distance away. Fortunately, among these rocks is the cave which is known as Taiuma's Cave. This she came to, and, peering into that black hole, she saw in it, back some distance, a little glowing light. "Ha, ha!" thought she; "perhaps some rabbit hunters like myself, belated yesterday, passed the night here and left the fire burning. If so, this is greater good fortune than I could have looked for." So, lowering the string of rabbits which she carried on her shoulder and throwing off her mantle, she crawled in, peering well into the darkness, for fear of wild beasts; then, returning, she drew in the string of rabbits and the mantle.

Behold! there was a bed of hot coals buried in the ashes in the very middle of the cave, and piled up on one side were fragments of broken wood. The girl, happy in her good fortune, issued forth and gathered more sticks from the cliffside, where dead piñons are found in great numbers, and bringing them in little armfuls one after another, she finally succeeded in gathering a store sufficient to keep the fire burning brightly all the night through. Then she drew off her snow-covered stockings of deerskin and the bedraggled mantles, and, building a fire, hung them up to dry and sat down to rest herself. The fire burned up and glowed brightly, so that the whole cave was as light as a room at night when a dance is being celebrated. By and by, after her clothing had dried, she spread a mantle on the floor of the cave by the side of the fire, and, sitting down, dressed one of her rabbits and roasted it, and, untying the string of corn cakes her mother had made for her, feasted on the roasted meat and cakes.

She had just finished her evening meal and was about to recline and watch the fire for a while when she heard away off in the distance a long, low cry of distress—"*Ho-o-o-o thlaia-a!*"

"Ah!" thought the girl, "someone, more belated than myself, is lost; doubtless one of the rabbit hunters." She got up and went nearer to the entrance of the cavern.

"*Ho-o-o thlaia-a!*" sounded the cry, nearer this time. She ran out, and, as it was repeated again, she placed her hand to her mouth and cried, woman though she was, as loudly as possible, "*Li-i thlaia-a!*" ("Here!")

The cry was repeated near at hand, and presently the maiden, listening first, and then shouting, and listening again, heard the clatter of an enormous rattle. In dismay and terror she threw her hands into the air and, crouching down, rushed into the cave and retreated to its farthest limits, where she sat shuddering with fear, for she knew that one of the Cannibal Demons of those days, perhaps the renowned Atahsaia of the east, had seen the light of her fire through the cave entrance, with his terrible staring eyes, and, assuming it to be a lost wanderer, had cried out, and so led her to guide him to her place of concealment.

On came the Demon, snapping the twigs under his feet and shouting in a hoarse, loud voice, "*Ho lithlsh tâ ime!*" ("Ho, there! So you are in here, are you?") *Kothl!* clanged his rattle, while, almost fainting with terror, closer to the rock crouched the maiden.

The old Demon came to the entrance of the cave and bawled out, "I am cold! I am hungry! Let me in!" Without further ado, he stooped and tried to get in; but, behold! the entrance was too small for his giant shoulders to pass. Then he pretended to be wonderfully civil and said, "Come out and bring me something to eat."

"I have nothing for you," cried the maiden. "I have eaten my food."

"Have you no rabbits?"

"Yes."

"Come out and bring me some of them."

But the maiden was so terrified that she dared not move toward the entrance.

"Throw me a rabbit!" shouted the old Demon.

The maiden threw him one of her precious rabbits at last, when she could rise and go to it. He clutched it with his long, horny hand, gave one gulp, and swallowed it. Then he cried out, "Throw me another!" She threw him another, which he also immediately swallowed; and so on until the poor maiden had thrown all the rabbits to the voracious old monster. Every one she threw him he caught in his huge yellow-tusked mouth, and swallowed, hair and all, at one gulp.

"Throw me another!" cried he when the last had already been thrown to him.

So the poor maiden was forced to say, "I have no more."

"Throw me your overshoes!" cried he.

She threw the overshoes of deerskin, and these like the rabbits he speedily devoured. Then he called for her moccasins, and she threw them; for her belt and she threw it; and finally, wonderful to tell, she threw even her mantles, and blanket, and her overdress, until, behold! she had nothing left.

Now, with all he had eaten, the old Demon was swollen hugely at the stomach, and, though he tried and tried to squeeze himself through the mouth of the cave, he could not by any means succeed. Finally, lifting his great flint ax, he began to shatter the rock about the entrance to the cave, and slowly but surely he enlarged the hole, and the maiden now knew that as soon as he could get in he would devour her also, and she almost fainted at the sickening thought. Pound, pound, pound, pound, went the great ax of the Demon as he struck the rocks.

In the distance the two war gods were sitting in their home at Thla-uthla (the Shrine amid the Bushes) beyond Thunder Moun tain, and, though far off, they heard thus in the middle of the night the pounding of the Demon's hammer ax against the rocks. And of course they knew at once that a poor maiden, for the sake of her father and mother, had been out hunting, that she had lost her way and, finding a cave where there was a little fire, entered it, rebuilt the fire, and rested herself; that, attracted by the light of her fire, the Cannibal Demon had come and besieged her retreat, and only a little time hence would he so enlarge the entrance to the cave that he could squeeze even his great overfilled paunch through it and come at the maiden to destroy her. So, catching up their wonderful weapons, these two war gods flew away into the darkness and in no time they were approaching the Descending Plain of the Pines.

Just as the Demon was about to enter the cavern, and the maiden had fainted at seeing his huge face and gray shock of hair and staring eyes, his yellow, protruding tusks, and his horny, taloned hand, they came upon the old beast, and, each one hitting him a welt with his war club, they "ended his daylight," and then hauled him forth into the open space. They opened his huge paunch and withdrew from it the maiden's garments, and even the rabbits which had been slain. The rabbits they cast away among the soap-weed plants that grew on the slope at the foot of the cliff. The garments they spread out on the snow, and by their knowledge cleansed and made them perfect, even more perfect than they had been before. Then, flinging the huge body of the giant Demon down into the depths of the cañon, they turned them about and, calling out gentle words to the maiden, entered and restored her; and she, seeing in them not their usual ugly persons, but handsome youths (as like to one another as are two deer born of the same mother), was greatly comforted; and bending low, and breathing upon their hands, thanked them over and over for the rescue they had brought her. But she crouched herself low with shame that her garments were but few, when, behold! the youths went out and brought in to her the garments they had cleaned by their knowledge, restoring them to her.

Then, spreading their mantles by the door of the cave, they slept there that night, in order to protect the maiden, and on the morrow wakened her. They told her many things, and showed her many things which she had not known before, and counseled her thus: "It is not fearful that a maiden should marry; therefore, O maiden, return unto thy people in the Village of the Gateway of the River of Zuñi. This morning we will slay rabbits unnumbered for you, and start you on your way, guarding you down the snow-covered valley, and when you are in sight of your home we will leave you, telling you our names."

So, early in the morning, the two gods went forth; and flinging their sticks among the soap-weed plants, behold! as though the soap-weed plants were rabbits, so many lay killed on the snow before these mighty hunters. And they gathered together great numbers of these rabbits, a string for each one of the party; and when the Sun had risen clearer in the sky, and his light sparkled on the snow around them, they took the rabbits to the maiden and presented them, saying, "We will carry each one of us a string of these rabbits." Then, taking her hand, they led her out of the cave and down the valley, until, beyond on the high black mesas at the Gateway of the River of Zuñi, she saw the smoke rise from the houses of her village. Then turned the two war gods to her, and they told her their names. And again she bent low and breathed on their hands. Then, dropping the strings of rabbits which they had carried close beside the maiden, they swiftly disappeared.

Thinking much of all she had learned, she continued her way to the home of her father and mother; and as she went into the town, staggering under her load of rabbits, the young men and the old men and women and children beheld her with wonder; and no hunter in that town thought of comparing himself with the Maiden Huntress of K'yawana Tehua-tsana. The old man and the old woman, who had mourned the night through and sat up anxiously watching, were overcome with happiness when they saw their daughter returning; and as she laid the rabbits at their feet, she said, "Behold! my father and my mother, foolish have I been, and much danger have I passed through, because I forgot the ways of a woman and assumed the ways of a man. But two wondrous youths have taught me that a woman may be a huntress and yet never leave her own fireside. Behold! I will marry, when some youth comes to me, and he will hunt rabbits and deer for me, for my parents and my children."

So, one day, when one of those youths who had seen her come in laden with rabbits, and who had admired her time out of mind, presented himself with a bundle at the maiden's fireside, behold! she smilingly and delightedly accepted him. And from that day to this, when women would hunt rabbits or deer, they marry, and behold, the rabbits and deer are hunted.

Thus shortens my story.

From *Zuñi Folk Tales.*

THE DECEIVED BLIND MEN

THERE was a large settlement on the shore of a lake, and among its people were two old blind men. It was decided to remove these men to the opposite side of the lake, where they might live in safety, as the settlement was exposed to the attack of enemies, when they might easily be captured and killed. So the relations of the old men got a canoe, some food, a kettle, and a bowl and started across the lake, where they built for them a wigwam in a grove some distance from the water. A line was stretched from the door of the wigwam to a post in the water, so that they would have no difficulty in helping themselves. The food and vessels were put into the wigwam, and after the relations of the old men promised them that they would call often and keep them provided with everything that was needful, they returned to their settlement.

The two old blind men now began to take care of themselves. On one day one of them would do the cooking while the other went for water, and on the next day they would change about in their work, so that their labors were evenly divided. As they knew just how much food they required for each meal, the quantity prepared was equally divided, but was eaten out of the one bowl which they had.

Here they lived in contentment for several years; but one day a Raccoon, which was following the water's edge looking for crawfish, came to the line which had been stretched from the lake to the wigwam. The Raccoon thought it rather curious to find a cord where he had not before observed one, and wondered to himself, "What is this? I think I shall follow this cord to see where it leads." So he followed the path along which the cord was stretched until he came to the wigwam. Approaching very cautiously, he went up to the entrance, where he saw the two old men asleep on the ground, their heads at the door and their feet directed toward the heap of hot coals within. The Raccoon sniffed about and soon found there was something good to eat within the wigwam; but he decided not to enter at once for fear of waking the old men; so he retired a short distance to hide himself and to see what they would do.

Presently the old men awoke, and one said to the other, "My friend, I am getting hungry; let us prepare some food." "Very well," replied his companion, "you go down to the lake and fetch some water while I get the fire started."

The Raccoon heard this conversation and, wishing to deceive the old man, immediately ran to the water, untied the cord from the post, and carried it to a clump of bushes, where he tied it. When the old man came along with his kettle to get water, he stumbled around the brush until he found the end of the cord; then he began to dip his kettle down upon the ground for water. Not finding any, he slowly returned and said to his companion, "We shall surely die, because the lake is dried up and the brush is grown where we used to get water. What shall we do?"

"That cannot be," responded his companion, "for we have not been asleep long enough for the brush to grow upon the lake bed. Let me go out to try if I cannot get some water." So, taking the kettle from his friend, he started off.

So soon as the first old man had returned to the wigwam, the Raccoon took the cord back and tied it where he had found it, then waited to see the result.

The second old man now came along, entered the lake, and getting his kettle full of water returned to the wigwam, saying as he entered, "My friend, you told me what was not true. There is water enough; for here, you see, I have our kettle full." The other could not understand this at all and wondered what had caused the deception.

The Raccoon approached the wigwam and entered to await the cooking of the food. When it was ready, the pieces of meat, for there were eight of them, were put into the bowl, and the old men sat down on the ground facing each other, with the bowl between them. Each took a piece of meat, and they began to talk of various things and were enjoying themselves.

The Raccoon now quietly removed four pieces of meat from the bowl and began to eat them, enjoying the feast even more than the old blind men. Presently one of them reached into the bowl to get another piece of meat and, finding that only two pieces remained, said, "My friend, you must be very hungry to eat so rapidly. I have had but one piece, and there are but two pieces left."

The other replied, "I have not taken them, but suspect you have eaten them yourself." Whereupon the other replied more angrily than before. Thus they argued, and the Raccoon, desiring to have more sport, tapped each of them on the face. The old men, each believing the other had struck him, began to fight, rolling over the floor of the wigwam, upsetting the bowl and the kettle, and causing the fire to be scattered. The Raccoon then took the two remaining pieces of meat and made his exit from the wigwam, laughing, ha, ha, ha, ha; whereupon the old men instantly ceased their strife, for they now knew they had been deceived. The Raccoon then remarked to them, "I have played a nice trick on you; you should not find fault with each other so easily." Then the Raccoon continued his crawfish hunting along the lake shore.

From "The Menomini Indians," by Walter James Hoffman, in *Report of the Bureau of American Ethnology*, Vol. XIV (1896). See also *Tales of the North American Indians*, selected by Stith Thompson.

Arabian and Turkish

What Happened to Hadji

ALTHOUGH Arabian tales had been filtering into Europe for centuries, Europe was not really delivered over to the spell of "The Arabian Nights" until in 1704 Antoine Galland published the first translation in a European language of *The Thousand Nights and a Night.*

According to the book's framework narrative, the tales were told by the lovely Shahrazad to King Shahryar to beguile him from his unsocial habit of marrying a maiden each night and beheading her in the morning. Serenely ignoring the fact that the tales are supposed to have been told by a woman, a woman who is, moreover, desperately defending her virtue, many of them hinge on the infidelity of womankind. Actually the *Nights* was an anthology of the romances, fables, jests, and moral—or not so moral—tales current throughout the Near East during the Middle Ages, and was perhaps more representative of the taste of city people than of country folk. European readers were understandably dazzled by its vivid hues, its mingling of unbridled fancy, sensuality, and vigorous incident. Singlehandedly it made the name of Baghdad synonymous with exotic adventure and amatory intrigue and gave the realm of fantasy such marvelous presences as Caliph Harun al-Raschid, Sindbad the Seaman, Aladdin (or Ala al-Din), the Forty Thieves, and the Barmecides.

As for English translations of the *Nights*, they did not appear until the nineteenth century, and then in bowdlerized versions. As a reaction, Sir Richard Burton, maverick among Victorians, produced a translation that made the erotic almost as much of a fetish as other editions had made it a taboo. But it also gave the impression that it had caught, as fully as any, the prodigal variety and richness of the original.

"The Woman of the Well" is an example of the Arabian folk tales told among the people of Iraq today. The jinn are still active, but the glamorous manner of the *Nights* has given way to a much less ornate kind of storytelling.

This is also true of modern Turkish tales, many of which seem closer to European traditions than to those of the East. Of such tales in the following pages, most come from the coffee-houses of Constantinople, but tales of Nasr-ed-Din Hodja can be found wherever Turkish is spoken. The Hodja—a title given a teacher and prayer-leader—is supposed to have lived in the early fifteenth century, about the time Tamerlane was master of southern Asia and the Near East. The Hodja is a foolish-wise, ignorant-shrewd, good-natured fellow on whom Turkish-speaking peoples have hung all the jests and droll stories they have invented or borrowed. Even at the Hodja's grave, we are told, the people laugh, for the grave is protected by an iron gate, carefully locked, but without a surrounding fence.

THE FIRST KALANDAR'S TALE

KNOW, O my lady, that the cause of my beard being shorn and my eye being out-torn was as follows:

My father was a king and he had a brother who was a king over another city; and it came to pass that I and my cousin, the son of my paternal uncle, were both born on one and the same day. And years and days rolled on; and, as we grew up, I used to visit my uncle every now and then and to spend a certain number of months with him. Now my cousin and I were sworn friends; for he ever entreated me with exceeding kindness; he killed for me the fattest sheep and strained the best of his wines, and we enjoyed long conversing and carousing.

One day when the wine had gotten the better of us, the son of my uncle said to me, "O my cousin, I have a great service to ask of thee; and I desire that thou stay me not in whatso I desire to do!" And I replied, "With joy and goodly will." Then he made me swear the most binding oaths and left me; but after a little while he returned leading a lady veiled and richly appareled with ornaments worth a large sum of money. Presently he turned to me (the woman being still behind him) and said, "Take this lady with thee and go before me to such a burial ground"—describing it, so that I knew the place—"and enter with her into such a sepulcher and there await my coming." The oaths I swore to him made me keep silence and suffered me not to oppose him; so I led the woman to the cemetery and both I and she took our seats in the sepulcher; and hardly had we sat down when in came my uncle's son, with a bowl of water, a bag of mortar, and an adze somewhat like a hoe. He went straight to the tomb in the midst of the sepulcher and, breaking it open with the adze, set the stones on one side; then he fell to digging into the earth of the tomb till he came upon a large iron plate, the size of a wicket door; and on raising it there appeared below it a staircase vaulted and winding. Then he turned to the lady and said to her, "Come now and take thy final choice!" She at once went down by the staircase and disappeared; then quoth he to me, "O son of my uncle, by way of completing thy kindness, when I shall have descended into this place, restore the trap-door to where it was and heap back the earth upon it as it lay before; and then of thy goodness mix this unslaked lime which is in the bag with this water which is in the bowl and, after building up the stones, plaster the outside so that none looking upon it shall say, 'This is a new opening in an old tomb.' For a whole year have I worked at this place whereof none knoweth but Allah, and this is the need I have of thee"; presently adding, "May Allah never bereave thy friends of thee nor make them desolate by thine absence, O son of my uncle, O my dear cousin!" And he went down the stairs and disappeared forever. When he was lost to sight I replaced the iron plate and did all his bidding till the tomb became as it was before; and I worked almost unconsciously, for my head was heated with wine.

Returning to the palace of my uncle, I was told that he had gone forth a-sporting and hunting; so I slept that night without seeing him; and, when the morning dawned, I remembered the scenes of the past evening and what happened between me and my cousin. I repented of having obeyed him when penitence was of no avail. I still thought, however, that it was a dream. So I fell to asking for the son of my uncle; but there was none to answer me concerning him; and I went out to the graveyard and the sepulchers and sought for the tomb under which he was, but could not find it; and I ceased not wandering about from sepulcher to sepulcher, and tomb to tomb, all without success, till night set in. So I returned to the city, yet I could neither eat nor drink; my thoughts being engrossed with my cousin, for that I knew not what was become of him; and I grieved with exceeding grief and passed another sorrowful night, watching until the morning. Then I went a second time to the cemetery, pondering over what the son of mine uncle had done; and, sorely repenting my hearkening to him, went round among all the tombs, but could not find the tomb I sought. I mourned over the past, and remained in my mourning seven days, seeking the place and ever missing the path.

Then my torture of scruples grew upon me till I well-nigh went mad, and I found no way to dispel my grief save travel and return to my father. So I set out and journeyed homeward; but as I was entering my father's capital a crowd of rioters sprang upon me and pinioned me. I wondered thereat with all wonderment, seeing that I was the son of the sultan, and these men were my father's subjects, and amongst them were some of my own slaves. A great fear fell upon me, and I said to my soul, "Would heaven I knew what hath happened to my father!" I questioned those that bound me of the cause of their doing, but they returned me no answer. However, after a while one of them said to me (and he had been a hired servant of our house), "Fortune hath been false to thy father; his troops betrayed him, and the wazir who slew him now reigneth in his stead, and we lay in wait to seize thee by the bidding of him." I was well-nigh distraught and felt ready to faint on hearing of my father's death; when they carried me off and placed me in presence of the usurper.

Now between me and him there was an olden grudge, the cause of which was this: I was fond of shooting with the stone bow, and it befell one day as I was standing on the terrace roof of the palace that a bird lighted on the top of the wazir's house when he happened to be there. I shot at the bird and missed the mark; but I hit the wazir's eye and knocked it out as fate and fortune decreed. Now when I knocked out the wazir's eye he could not say a single word, for that my father was king of the city, but he hated me ever after and dire was the grudge thus caused between us twain.

So when I was set before him hand-bound and pinioned, he straightway gave orders for me to be beheaded. I asked, "For what crime wilt thou put me to death?" Whereupon he answered, "What crime is greater than this?" pointing the while to the place where his eye had been. Quoth I, "This I did by accident not of malice prepense"; and quoth he, "If thou didst it by accident, I will do the like by thee with intention." Then cried he, "Bring him forward," and they brought me up to him, when he thrust his finger into my left eye and gouged it out; whereupon I became one-eyed as ye see me. Then he bade bind me hand and foot, and put me into a chest, and said to the sworder, "Take charge of this fellow, and go off with him to the waste lands about the city; then draw thy scimitar and slay him, and leave him to feed the beasts and birds."

So the headsman fared forth with me, and when he was in the midst of the desert he took me out of the chest (and I with both hands pinioned and both feet fettered) and was about to bandage my eyes before striking off my head. But I wept with exceeding weeping until I made him weep with me, and, looking at him, I began to recite these couplets:

I deemed you coat-o'-mail that should withstand
The foeman's shafts; and you proved foeman's brand;
I hoped your aidance in mine every chance,
Though fail my left to aid my dexter hand:
Aloof you stand and hear the railer's gibe
While rain their shafts on me the giber-band:
But an ye will not guard me from my foes
Stand clear, and succor neither these nor those!

When the headsman heard my lines (he had been sworder to my sire and he owed me a debt of gratitude) he cried, "O my lord, what can I do, being but a slave under orders?" presently adding, "Fly for thy life and nevermore return to this land, or they will slay thee and slay me with thee."

Hardly believing in my escape, I kissed his hand and thought the loss of my eye a light matter in consideration of my escaping from being slain. I arrived at my uncle's capital; and, going in to him, told him of what had befallen my father and myself; whereat he wept and said, "Verily thou addest grief to my grief, and woe to my woe; for thy cousin hath been missing these many days; I wot not what hath happened to him, and none can give me news of him." And he wept till he fainted. I sorrowed and condoled with him; and he would have applied certain medicaments to my eye, but he saw that it was become as a walnut with the shell empty. Then said he, "O my son, better to lose eye and keep life!" After that I could no longer remain silent about my cousin, who was his only son and one dearly loved, so I told him all that had happened.

He rejoiced with extreme joyance to hear news of his son and said, "Come now and show me the tomb." But I replied, "By Allah, O my uncle, I know not its place, though I sought it carefully full many times, yet could not find the site." However, I and my uncle went to the graveyard and looked right and left, till at last I recognized the tomb, and we both rejoiced with exceeding joy. We entered the sepulcher and loosened the earth about the grave; then, upraising the trap-door, descended some fifty steps till we came to the foot of the staircase, when lo! we were stopped by a blinding smoke. Thereupon said my uncle that saying whose sayer shall never come to shame, "There is no Majesty and there is no Might, save in Allah, the Glorious, the Great!" and we advanced till we suddenly came upon a saloon, whose floor was strewed with flour and grain and provisions and all manner of necessaries; and in the midst of it stood a canopy sheltering a couch. Thereupon my uncle went up to the couch and, inspecting it, found his son and the lady who had gone down with him into the tomb, lying in each other's embrace; but the twain had become black as charred wood; it was as if they had been cast into a pit of fire. When my uncle saw this spectacle, he spat in his son's face and said, "Thou hast thy deserts, O thou hog! this is thy judgment in the transitory world, and yet remaineth the judgment in the world to come, a durer and a more enduring"—

And Shahrazad perceived the dawn of day and ceased saying her permitted say. When it was the 12th night, she continued,

It hath reached me, O auspicious King, that the Kalandar thus went on with his story before the lady and the Caliph and Ja'afar:

My uncle struck his son with his slipper as he lay there, a black heap of coal. I marveled at his hardness of heart and, grieving for my cousin and the lady, said, "By Allah, O my uncle, calm thy wrath: dost thou not see that all my thoughts are occupied with this misfortune, and how sorrowful I am for what hath befallen thy son, and how horrible it is that naught of him remaineth but a black heap of charcoal? And is not that enough but thou must smite him with thy slipper?"

Answered he, "O son of my brother, this youth from his boyhood was madly in love with his own sister, and often and often I forbade him from her, saying to myself, 'They are but little ones.' However, when they grew up sin befell between them; and, although I could hardly believe it, I confined him and chided him and threatened him with the severest threats; and the eunuchs and servants said to him, 'Beware of so foul a thing which none before thee ever did, and which none after thee will ever do; and have a care lest thou be dishonored and disgraced among the kings of the day, even to the end of time.' And I added, 'Such a report as this will be spread abroad by caravans, and take heed not to give them cause to talk, or I will assuredly curse thee and do thee to death.' After that I lodged them apart and shut her up; but the accursed girl loved him with passionate love, for Satan had got the mastery of her as well as of him and made their foul sin seem fair in their sight. Now when my son saw that I separated them, he secretly built this subterranean place and furnished it and transported to it victuals, even as thou seest; and, when I had gone out a-sporting, came here with his sister and hid from me. Then His righteous judgment fell upon the twain and consumed them with fire from heaven; and verily the last judgment will deal them durer pains and more enduring!"

Then he wept, and I wept with him; and he looked at me and said, "Thou art my son in his stead." And I bethought me awhile of the world and of its chances, how the wazir had slain my father and had taken his place and had put out my eye; and how my cousin had come to his death by the strangest chance: and I wept again, and my uncle wept with me. Then we mounted the steps and let down the iron plate and heaped up the earth over it; and, after restoring the tomb to its former condition, we returned to the palace.

But hardly had we sat down ere we heard the tomtoming of the kettledrum and tantara of trumpets and clash of cymbals; and the rattling of warmen's lances; and the clamors of assailants and the clanking of bits and the neighing of steeds; while the world was canopied with dense dust and sand-clouds raised by the horses' hoofs. We were amazed at sight and sound, knowing not what could be the matter; so we asked, and were told us that the wazir who usurped my father's kingdom had marched his men; and that after levying his soldiery and taking a host of wild Arabs into service, he had come down upon us with armies like the sands of the sea; their number none could tell, and against them none could prevail. They attacked the city unawares; and the citizens, being powerless to oppose them, surrendered the place: my uncle was slain, and I made for the suburbs saying to myself, "If thou fall into this villain's hands he will assuredly kill thee."

On this wise all my troubles were renewed; and I pondered all that had betided my father and my uncle and I knew not what to do; for if the city people or my father's troops had recognized me they would have done their best to win favor by destroying me; and I could think of no way to escape save by shaving off my beard and my eyebrows. So I shore them off and, changing my fine clothes for a Kalandar's rags, I fared forth from my uncle's capital and made for this city; hoping that peradventure someone would assist me to the presence of the Prince of the Faithful, and the Caliph who is the Viceregent of Allah upon earth.

Thus have I come hither that I might tell him my tale and lay my case before him. I arrived here this very night, and was standing in doubt whither I should go, when suddenly I saw this second Kalandar; so I salaam'd to him, saying, "I am a stranger!" And he answered, "I too am a stranger!" And as we were conversing, behold! up came our companion, this third Kalandar, and saluted us, saying, "I am a stranger!" And we answered, "We too be strangers!" Then we three walked on and together till darkness overtook us and Destiny drave us to your house. Such, then, is the cause of the shaving of my beard and mustachios and eyebrows; and the manner of my losing my right eye.

From *The Thousand Nights and a Night,* translated by Richard F. Burton (London: privately printed, 1885–1888).

THE BARBER'S TALE OF HIS SIXTH BROTHER

My sixth brother, O Commander of the Faithful, Shakashik, or Many-clamors, the shorn of both lips, was once rich and became poor; so one day he went out to beg somewhat to keep life in him. As he was on the road he suddenly caught sight of a large and handsome mansion, with a detached building wide and lofty at the entrance, where sat sundry eunuchs bidding and forbidding. My brother inquired of one of those idling there, and he replied, "The palace belongs to a scion of the Barmaki house"; so he stepped up to the doorkeepers and asked an alms of them. "Enter," said they, "by the great gate, and thou shalt get what thou seekest from the wazir our master."

Accordingly he went in and, passing through the outer entrance, walked on a while and presently came to a mansion of the utmost beauty and elegance, paved with marble, hung with curtains, and having in the midst of it a flower garden whose like he had never seen. My brother stood awhile as one bewildered, not knowing whither to turn his steps; then, seeing the farther end of the sitting-chamber tenanted, he walked up to it and there found a man of handsome presence and comely beard. When this personage saw my brother he stood up to him and welcomed him and asked him of his case; whereto he replied that he was in want and needed charity.

Hearing these words, the grandee showed great concern and, putting his hand to his fine robe, rent it, exclaiming, "What! am I in a city, and thou here an-hungered? I have not patience to bear such disgrace!" Then he promised him all manner of good cheer and said, "There is no help but that thou stay with me and eat of my salt." "O my lord," answered my brother, "I can wait no longer; for I am indeed dying of hunger." So he cried, "Ho, boy! bring basin and ewer"; and, turning to my brother, said, "O my guest, come forward and wash thy hands." My brother rose to do so, but he saw neither ewer nor basin; yet his host kept washing his hands with invisible soap in imperceptible water and cried, "Bring the table!" But my brother again saw nothing. Then said the host, "Honor me by eating of this meat and be not ashamed." And he kept moving his hand to and fro as if he ate and saying to my brother, "I wonder to see thee eating thus sparely: do not stint thyself for I am sure thou art famished."

So my brother began to make as though he were eating, whilst his host kept saying to him, "Fall to, and note especially the excellence of this bread and its whiteness!" But still my brother saw nothing. Then said he to himself, "This man is fond of poking fun at people," and replied, "O my lord, in all my days I never knew aught more winsome than its whiteness or sweeter than its savor." The Barmecide said, "This bread was baked by a handmaid of mine whom I bought for five hundred dinars." Then he called out, "Ho, boy, bring in the meat-pudding for our first dish, and let there be plenty of fat in it"; and, turning to my brother, said, "Oh my guest, Allah upon thee, hast ever seen anything better than this meat-pudding? Now by my life, eat and be not abashed." Presently he cried out again, "Ho, boy, serve up the marinated stew with the fatted sand grouse in it"; and he said to my brother, "Up and eat, O my guest, for truly thou art hungry and needest food." So my brother began wagging his jaws and made as if champing and chewing, whilst the host continued calling for one dish after another and yet produced nothing save orders to eat. Presently he cried out, "Ho, boy, bring us the chickens stuffed with pistachio nuts"; and said to my brother, "By thy life, O my guest, I have fattened these chickens upon pistachios; eat, for thou hast never eaten their like." "O my lord," replied my brother, "they are indeed first-rate." Then the host began motioning with his hand as though he were giving my brother a mouthful; and ceased not to enumerate and expatiate upon the various dishes to the hungry man whose hunger waxed still more violent, so that his soul lusted after a bit of bread, even a barley scone.

Quoth the Barmecide, "Didst thou ever taste anything more delicious than the seasoning of these dishes?" And quoth my brother, "Never, O my lord!" "Eat heartily and be not ashamed," said the host, and the guest, "I have eaten my fill of meat." So the entertainer cried, "Take away and bring in the sweets"; and, turning to my brother, said, "Eat of this almond conserve for it is prime, and of these honey fritters; take this one, by my life, the syrup runs out of it." "May I never be bereaved of thee, O my lord," replied the hungry one and began to ask him about the abundance of musk in the fritters. "Such is my custom," he answered: "they put me a dinar weight of musk in every honey fritter and half that quantity of ambergris."

All this time my brother kept wagging head and jaws till the master cried, "Enough of this. Bring us the dessert!" Then said he to him, "Eat of these almonds and walnuts and raisins; and of this and that (naming divers kinds of dried fruits), and be not abashed." But my brother replied, "O my lord, indeed I am full: I can eat no more." "O my guest," repeated the host, "if thou have a mind to these good things eat. Allah! Allah! do not remain hungry." But my brother rejoined, "O my lord, he who hath eaten of all these dishes how can he be hungry?"

Then he considered and said to himself, "I will do that shall make him repent of these pranks." Presently the entertainer called out, "Bring me the wine"; and, moving his hands in the air, as though they had set it before them, he gave my brother a cup and said, "Take this cup and, if it please thee, let me know." "O my lord," he replied, "it is notable good as to nose, but I am wont to drink wine some twenty years old." "Knock then at this door," quoth the host, "for thou canst not drink of aught better." "By thy kindness," said my brother, motioning with his hand as though he were drinking. "Health and joy to thee," exclaimed the house master, and feigned to fill a cup and drink it off; then he handed another to my brother, who quaffed it and made as if he were drunken. Presently he took the host unawares; and, raising his arm till the white of his armpit appeared, dealt him such a cuff on the nape of his neck that the palace echoed to it. Then he came down upon him with a second cuff, and the entertainer cried aloud, "What is this, O thou

scum of the earth?" "O my lord," replied my brother, "thou hast shown much kindness to thy slave and admitted him into thine abode and given him to eat of thy victual; then thou madest him drink of thine old wine till he became drunken and boisterous; but thou art too noble not to bear with his ignorance and pardon his offense."

When the Barmaki heard my brother's words he laughed his loudest and said, "Long have I been wont to make mock of men and play the madcap among my intimates, but never yet have I come across a single one who had the patience and the wit to enter into all my humors save thyself: so I forgive thee, and thou shalt be my boon companion in very sooth and never leave me." Then he ordered the servants to lay the table in earnest, and they set on all the dishes of which he had spoken in sport; and he and my brother ate till they were satisfied; after which they removed to the drinking-chamber, where they found damsels like moons who sang all manner songs and played on all manner instruments. There they remained drinking till their wine got the better of them, and the host treated my brother like a familiar friend, so that he became as it were his brother, and bestowed on him a robe of honor and loved him with exceeding love.

From *The Thousand Nights and a Night.*

TALE OF THE DEVOUT ISRAELITE

THERE was once a devout man of the Children of Israel, whose family spun cotton thread; and he used every day to sell the yarn and buy fresh cotton, and with the profit he laid in daily bread for his household. One morning he went out and sold the day's yarn as wont, when there met him one of his brethren, who complained to him of need; so he gave him the price of the thread and returned, empty-handed, to his family, who said to him, "Where is the cotton and the food?" Quoth he, "Such a one met me and complained to me of want; whereupon I gave him the price of the yarn." And they said, "How shall we do? We have nothing to sell." Now they had a cracked trencher and a jar; so he took them to the bazaar, but none would buy them of him. However, presently, as he stood in the market, there passed by a man with a fish—

And Shahrazad perceived the dawn of day and ceased saying her permitted say. When it was the 349th night, she said,

It hath reached me, O auspicious King, that the man took the trencher and jar to the bazaar, but none would buy them of him. However, there presently passed by a man with a fish which was so stinking and so swollen that no one would buy it of him, and he said to the Jew, "Wilt thou sell me thine unsalable ware for mine?" "Yes," answered the Jew; and, giving him the wooden trencher and jar, took the fish and carried it home to his family, who said, "What shall we do with this fish?" Quoth he, "We will broil it and eat it, till it please Allah to provide bread for us."

So they took it and, ripping open its belly, found therein a great pearl and told the head of the household who said, "See ye if it be pierced: if so, it belongeth to some one of the folk; if not, 'tis a provision of Allah for us." So they examined it and found it unpierced. Now when it was the morrow, the Jew carried it to one of his brethren which was an expert in jewels, and the man asked, "O such a one! whence haddest thou this pearl?" Whereto the Jew answered, "It was a gift of Almighty Allah to us," and the other said, "It is worth a thousand dirhams and I will give thee that; but take it to such a one, for he hath more money and skill than I." So the Jew took it to the jeweler, who said, "It is worth seventy thousand

dirhams and no more." Then he paid him that sum, and the Jew hired two porters to carry the money to his house. As he came to his door a beggar accosted him, saying, "Give me of that which Allah hath given thee." Quoth the Jew to the asker, "But yesterday we were even as thou: take thee half this money"; so he made two parts of it, and each took his half. Then said the beggar, "Take back thy money and Allah bless and prosper thee in it. I am a Messenger, whom thy Lord hath sent to try thee."

Quoth the Jew, "To Allah be the praise and the thanks!" and abode in all delight of life he and his household till death.

From *The Thousand Nights and a Night.*

KHUSRAU AND THE FISHERMAN

King Khusrau Shahinshah of Persia loved fish; and one day, as he sat in his saloon, he and Shirin his wife, there came a fisherman, with a great fish, and he laid it before the king, who was pleased and ordered the man four thousand dirhams. Thereupon Shirin said to the king, "Thou has done ill." Asked he, "And why?" And she answered, "Because if, after this, thou give one of thy courtiers a like sum, he will disdain it and say, 'He hath but given me the like of what he gave the fisherman.' And if thou give him less, the same will say, 'He despiseth me and giveth me less than he gave the fisherman.'" Rejoined Khusrau, "Thou art right, but it would dishonor a king to go back on his gift; and the thing is done." Quoth Shirin, "If thou wilt, I will contrive thee a means to get it back from him." Quoth he, "How so?" And she said, "Call back, if thou so please, the fisherman and ask him if the fish be male or female. If he say, 'Male,' say thou, 'We want a female,' and if he say, 'Female,' say, 'We want a male.'"

So the king sent for the fisherman, who was a man of wit and acuteness, and said to him, "Is this fish male or female?" Whereupon the fisherman kissed the ground and answered, "This fish is a hermaphrodite, neither male nor female." Khusrau laughed at this clever reply and ordered him four thousand dirhams. So the fisherman went to the treasurer and, taking his eight thousand dirhams, put them in a sack he had with him. Then, throwing it over his shoulder, he was going away, when he dropped a dirham; so he laid the bag off his back and stooped down to pick it up. Now the king and Shirin were looking on, and the queen said, "O King, didst thou note the meanness of the man, in that he must needs stoop down to pick up the one dirham, and could not bring himself to leave it for any of the king's servants?" When the king heard these words, he was exceeding wroth with the fisherman and said, "Thou art right, O Shirin!" So he called the man back and said to him, "Thou low-minded carl! Thou art no man! How couldst thou put the bag with all this money off thy back and bend thee groundward to pick up the one dirham and grudge to leave it where it fell?"

Thereupon the fisherman kissed the earth before him and answered, "May Allah prolong the King's life! Indeed, I did not pick up the dirham off the ground because of its value in my eyes; but I raised it off the earth because on one of its faces is the likeness of the King and on the other his name; and I feared lest any should unwittingly set foot upon it, thus dishonoring the name and presentment of the King, and I be blamed for this offense." The king wondered at his words and approved of his wit and shrewdness, and ordered him yet other four thousand dirhams. Moreover, he bade cry abroad in his kingdom, saying, "It behooveth none to be guided by women's counsel; for whoso followeth their advice, loseth, with his one dirham, other twain."

From *The Thousand Nights and a Night.*

THE RUINED MAN WHO BECAME RICH AGAIN THROUGH A DREAM

THERE lived once in Baghdad a wealthy man and made of money, who lost all his substance and became so destitute that he could earn his living only by hard labor. One night he lay down to sleep, dejected and heavyhearted, and saw in a dream a speaker who said to him, "Verily thy fortune is in Cairo; go thither and seek it."

So he set out for Cairo; but when he arrived there, evening overtook him and he lay down to sleep in a mosque. Presently, by decree of Allah Almighty, a band of bandits entered the mosque and made their way thence into an adjoining house; but the owners, being aroused by the noise of the thieves, awoke and cried out; whereupon the chief of police came to their aid with his officers. The robbers made off; but the wali entered the mosque and, finding the man from Baghdad asleep there, laid hold of him and beat him with palm rods so grievous a beating that he was well-nigh dead. Then they cast him into jail, where he abode three days; after which the chief of police sent for him and asked him, "Whence art thou?" and he answered, "From Baghdad." Quoth the wali, "And what brought thee to Cairo?" And quoth the Baghdadi, "I saw in a dream one who said to me, 'Thy fortune is in Cairo; go thither to it.' But when I came to Cairo the fortune which he promised me proved to be the palm rods thou so generously gavest me." The wali laughed till he showed his wisdom teeth and said, "O man of little wit, thrice have I seen in a dream one who said to me, 'There is in Baghdad a house in such a district and of such a fashion and its courtyard is laid out garden-wise, at the lower end whereof is a jetting fountain, and under the same a great sum of money lieth buried. Go thither and take it.' Yet I went not; but thou, of the briefness of thy wit, hast journeyed from place to place, on the faith of a dream, which was but an idle galimatias of sleep." Then he gave him money, saying, "Help thee back herewith to thine own country"—

And Shahrazad perceived the dawn of day and ceased to say her permitted say. When it was the 352nd night, she said,

It hath reached me, O auspicious King, that the wali gave the man some silver, saying, "Help thee back herewith to thine own country"; and he took the money and set out upon his homeward march. Now the house the wali had described was the man's own house in Baghdad; so the wayfarer returned thither and, digging underneath the fountain in his garden, discovered a great treasure. And thus Allah gave him abundant fortune; and a marvelous coincidence occurred.

From *The Thousand Nights and a Night.*

THE FIFTH VOYAGE OF SINDBAD THE SEAMAN

KNOW, O my brothers, that when I had been awhile on shore after my fourth voyage; and when, in my comfort and pleasures and merrymakings and in my rejoicing over my large gains and profits, I had forgotten all I had endured of perils and sufferings, the carnal man was again seized with longing to travel and see foreign countries and islands. Accordingly I bought costly merchandise suited to my purpose and, making it up into bales, repaired to Bassorah, where I walked about the river quay till I found a fine tall ship, newly builded, with gear unused and fitted ready for sea. She pleased me; so I bought her and, embarking my goods in her, hired a master and crew, over whom I set certain of my slaves and servants as inspectors. A number of merchants also brought their outfits and paid me freight and passage money; then, after reciting the Fatihah, we set sail over Allah's pool in all joy and cheer, promising ourselves a prosperous voyage and much profit.

We sailed from city to city and from island to island and from sea to sea, viewing the cities and countries by which we passed, and selling and buying in not a few till one day we came to a great uninhabited island, deserted and desolate, whereon was a white dome of biggest bulk buried in the sands. The merchants landed to examine this dome, leaving me in the ship; and when they drew near, behold, it was a huge Rukh's egg. They fell a-beating it with stones, knowing not what it was, and presently broke it open, whereupon much water ran out of it, and the young Rukh appeared within. So they pulled it forth of the shell and cut its throat and took of it great store of meat. Now I was in the ship and knew not what they did; but presently one of the passengers came up to me and said, "O my lord, come and look at the egg that we thought to be a dome." So I looked and, seeing the merchants beating it with stones, called out to them, "Stop, stop! do not meddle with that egg, or the bird Rukh will come out and break our ship and destroy us." But they paid no heed to me and gave not over smiting upon the egg, when, behold, the day grew dark and dun and the sun was hidden from us, as if some great cloud had passed over the firmament. So we raised our eyes and saw that what we took for a cloud was the Rukh poised between us and the sun, and it was his wings that darkened the day. When he came and saw his egg broken, he cried a loud cry, whereupon his mate came flying up and they both began circling about the ship, crying out at us with voices louder than thunder. I called to the Rais and crew, "Put out to sea and seek safety in flight, before we be all destroyed."

So the merchants came on board, and we cast off and made haste from the island to gain the open sea. When the Rukhs saw this they flew off, and we crowded all sail on the ship, thinking to get out of

their country; but presently the two reappeared and flew after us and stood over us, each carrying in its claws a huge boulder which it had brought from the mountains. As soon as the he-Rukh came up with us, he let fall upon us the rock he held in his pounces; but the master put about ship, so that the rock missed her by some small matter and plunged into the waves with such violence that the ship pitched high and then sank into the trough of the sea and the bottom of the ocean appeared to us. Then the she-Rukh let fall her rock, which was bigger than that of her mate, and as Destiny had decreed, it fell on the poop of the ship and crushed it, the rudder flying into twenty pieces; whereupon the vessel foundered, and all

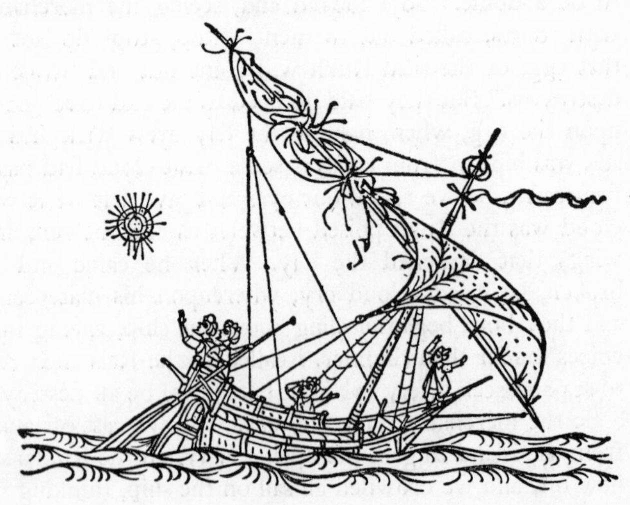

and everything on board were cast into the main. As for me, I struggled for sweet life, till Almighty Allah threw in my way one of the planks of the ship, to which I clung and, bestriding it, fell a-paddling with my feet.

Now the ship had gone down hard by an island in the midst of the main, and the winds and waves bore me on till, by permission of the Most High, they cast me up on the shore of the island, at the last gasp for toil and distress and half dead with hunger and thirst. So I landed more like a corpse than a live man and, throwing myself down on the beach, lay there awhile, till I began to revive and recover spirits, when I walked about the island and found it as it were one of the garths and gardens of paradise. Its trees, in abundance dight, bore ripe yellow fruit for freight; its streams ran clear and bright; its flowers were fair to scent and to sight; and its birds warbled with delight the praises of Him to whom belong permanence and all-might. So I ate my fill of the fruits and slaked my thirst with the water of the streams till I could no more, and I returned thanks to the Most High and glorified Him—

And Shahrazad perceived the dawn of day and ceased saying her permitted say. When it was the 557th night, she said,

It hath reached me, O auspicious King, that Sindbad the Seaman continued: So when I escaped drowning and reached the island which afforded me fruit to eat and water to drink, I returned thanks to the Most High and glorified Him; after which I sat till nightfall, hearing no voice and seeing no inhabitant. Then I lay down, well-nigh dead for travail and trouble and terror, and slept without surcease till morning, when I arose and walked about under the trees, till I came to the channel of a draw-well fed by a spring of running water, by which well sat an old man of venerable aspect, girt about with a waist-cloth made of the fiber of palm fronds. Quoth I to myself, "Haply this shaykh is one of those who were wrecked in the ship and hath made his way to this island."

So I drew near to him and saluted him, and he returned my salaam by signs, but spoke not; and I said to him, "O nuncle mine, what causeth thee to sit here?" He shook his head and moaned and signed me with his hand as who should say, "Take me on thy shoulders and carry me to the other side of the well channel." And quoth I in my mind, "I will deal kindly with him and do what he desireth; it may be I shall win me a reward in heaven, for he may be a paralytic." So I took him on my back and, carrying him to the place whereat he pointed, said to him, "Dismount at thy leisure." But he would not get off my back and wound his legs around my neck. I looked at them and, seeing that they were like a buffalo's hide for blackness and roughness, was affrighted and would have cast him off; but he clung to me and gripped my neck with his legs till I was well-nigh choked, the world grew black in my sight, and I fell senseless to the ground like one dead. But he still kept his seat and, raising his legs, drummed with his heels and beat harder than palm rods my back and shoulders, till he forced me to rise for excess of pain. Then he signed to me with his hand to carry him hither and thither among the trees which bore the best fruits; and if ever I refused to do his bidding or loitered or took my leisure, he beat me with his feet more grievously than if I had been beaten with whips. He ceased not to signal with his hand wherever he was minded to go; so I carried him about the island, like a captive slave, and he dismounted not night nor day; and whenas he wished to sleep he wound his legs about my neck and leaned back and slept awhile, then arose and beat me; whereupon I sprang up in haste, unable to gainsay him because of the pain he inflicted on me.

And indeed I blamed myself and sore repented me of having taken compassion on him and continued in this condition, suffering fatigue not to be described, till I said to myself, "I wrought him a weal and he requited me with my ill; by Allah, nevermore will I do any man a service so long as I live!" And again and again I besought the Most High that I might die, for stress of weariness and misery; and thus I abode a long while till, one day, I came with him to a place wherein was abundance of gourds, many of them dry. So I took a great dry gourd and, cutting open the head, scooped out the inside and cleaned it; after which I gathered grapes from a vine which grew hard by and squeezed them into the gourd, till it was full of the juice. Then I stopped up the mouth and set it in the sun, where I left it for some days, until it became strong wine; and every day I used to drink of it, to comfort and sustain me under my fatigues with that forward and obstinate fiend; and as often as I drank myself drunk, I forgot my troubles and took new heart.

One day he saw me drinking and signed to me with his hand, as who should say, "What is that?" Quoth I, "It is an excellent cordial, which cheereth the heart and reviveth the spirits." Then, being heated with wine, I ran and danced with him among the trees, clapping my hands and singing and making merry; and I staggered under him by design. When he saw this, he signed to me to give him the gourd that he might drink, and I feared him and gave it him. So he took it, and, draining it to the dregs, cast it to the ground, whereupon he grew frolicsome and began to clap hands and jig to and fro on my shoulders. But presently the fumes of the wine rising to his head, he became helplessly drunk, and his side muscles and limbs relaxed, and he swayed to and fro on my back. When I saw that he had lost his senses for drunkenness, I put my hand to his legs and, loosing them from my neck, stooped down well-nigh to the ground and threw him at full length—

And Shahrazad perceived the dawn of day and ceased to say her permitted say. When it was the 558th night, she said,

It hath reached me, O auspicious king, that Sindbad the Seaman continued: So I threw the devil off my shoulders, hardly crediting my deliverance from him and fearing lest he should shake off his drunkenness and do me a mischief. Then I took up a great stone from among the trees and, coming up to him, smote him therewith on the head with all my might and crushed in his skull as he lay dead drunk. Thereupon his flesh and fat and blood being in a pulp, he died and went to his deserts, the Fire, no mercy of Allah be upon him! I then returned with a heart at ease to my former station on the seashore and abode in that island many days, eating of its fruits and drinking of its waters and keeping a lookout for passing ships; till one day, as I sat on the beach, recalling all that had befallen me and saying, "I wonder if Allah will save me alive and restore me to my home and family and friends!" behold, a ship was making for the island through the dashing sea and clashing waves. Presently it cast anchor and the passengers landed; so I made for them, and when they saw me all hastened up to me and, gathering round me, questioned me of my case and how I came thither. I told them all that had betided me, whereat they marveled with exceeding marvel and said, "He who rode on thy shoulder is called the Shaykh al-Bahr, or Old Man of the Sea, and none ever felt his legs on neck and came off alive but thou; and those who die under him he eateth. So praised be Allah for thy safety!"

Then they set somewhat of food before me, whereof I ate my fill, and gave me somewhat of clothes, wherewith I clad myself anew and covered my nakedness; after which they took me up into the ship, and we sailed days and nights, till fate brought us to a place called the City of Apes, builded with lofty houses, all of which gave upon the sea, and it had a single gate studded and strengthened with iron nails. Now every night, as soon as it is dusk, the dwellers in this city used to come forth of the gates and, putting out to sea in boats and ships, pass the night upon the waters in their fear lest the apes should come down on them from the mountains. Hearing this, I was sore troubled, remembering what I had before suffered from the ape-kind. Presently I landed to solace myself in the city, but meanwhile the ship set sail without me and I repented of having gone ashore, and, calling to mind my companions and what had befallen me with the apes, first and after, I sat down and fell a-weeping and lamenting.

Presently one of the townsfolk accosted me and said to me, "O my lord, meseemeth thou art a stranger in these parts?" "Yes," answered I, "I am indeed a stranger and a poor one, who came hither in a ship which cast anchor here, and I landed to visit the town; but when I would have gone on board again, I found they had sailed without me." Quoth he, "Come and embark with us, for if thou lie the night in the city, the apes will destroy thee." "Hearkening and obedience," replied I, and, rising, straightway embarked with him in one of the boats, whereupon they pushed off from the shore and, anchoring a mile or so from the land, there passed the night. At daybreak they rowed back to the city and, landing, went each about his business. Thus they did every night, for if any tarried in the town by night the apes came down on him and slew him. As soon as it was day the apes left the place and ate of the fruits of the gardens, then went back to the mountains and slept till nightfall, when they again came down upon the city.

Now this place was in the farthest part of the country of the blacks, and one of the strangest things that befell me during my sojourn in the city was on this wise. One of the company with whom I passed the night in the boat asked me, "O my lord, thou art apparently a stranger in these parts; has thou any craft whereat thou canst work?" And I answered, "By Allah, O my brother, I have no trade nor know I any handicraft, for I was a merchant and a man of money and substance and had a ship of my own, laden with great store of goods and merchandise; but it foundered at sea, and all were drowned excepting me who saved myself on a piece of plank which Allah vouchsafed to me of His favor." Upon this he brought me a cotton bag and, giving it to me, said, "Take this bag and fill it with pebbles from the beach and go forth with a company of the townsfolk to whom I will give a charge respecting thee. Do as they do, and belike thou shalt gain what may further thy return voyage to thy native land." Then he carried me to the beach, where I filled my bag with pebbles large and small, and presently we saw a company of folk issue from the town, each bearing a bag like mine, filled with pebbles. To these he committed me, commanding me to their care, and saying, "This man is a stranger, so take him with you and teach him how to gather, that he may get his daily bread, and you will earn your reward and recompense in Heaven." "On our head and eyes be it!" answered they and, bidding me welcome, fared on with me till we came to a spacious wadi, full of lofty trees with trunks so smooth that none might climb them.

Now sleeping under these trees were many apes, which when they saw us rose and fled from us and swarmed up among the branches; whereupon my companions began to pelt them with what they had in their bags, and the apes fell to plucking of the fruit of the trees and casting them to the folk. I looked at the fruits they cast at us and found them to be Indian or cocoa-nuts; so I chose out a great tree, full of apes, and, going up to it, began to pelt them with stones, and they in return pelted me with nuts, which I collected, as did the rest; so that even before I had made an end of my bagful of pebbles, I had gotten great plenty of nuts; and as soon as my companions had in like manner gotten as many nuts as they could carry, we returned to the city, where we arrived at the fag end of day.

Then I went to the kindly man who had brought me in company with the nut-gatherers and gave him all I had gotten, thanking him for his kindness; but he would not accept them, saying, "Sell them and make profit by the price"; and presently he added (giving me the key of a closet in his house), "Store thy nuts in this safe place and go thou forth every morning and gather them as thou hast done today, and choose out the worst for sale and supplying thyself; but lay up the rest here, so haply thou mayst collect enough to serve thee for thy return home." "Allah requite thee!" answered I and did as he advised me, going out daily with the cocoa-nut gatherers, who commended me to one another and showed me the best-stocked trees.

Thus did I for some time, till I had laid up a great store of excellent nuts, besides a large sum of money, the price of those I had sold. I became thus at my ease and bought all I saw and had a mind to, and passed my time pleasantly, greatly enjoying my stay in the city, till, as I stood on the beach, one day, a great ship steering through the heart of the sea presently cast anchor by the shore and landed a company of merchants, who proceeded to sell and buy and barter their goods for cocoa-nuts and other commodities. Then I went to my friend and told him of the coming of the ship and how I had a mind to return to my own country; and he said, "'Tis for thee to decide." So I thanked him for his bounties and took leave of him; then, going to the captain of the ship, I agreed with him for my passage and embarked my cocoa-nuts and what else I possessed. We weighed anchor—

And Shahrazad perceived the dawn of day and ceased saying her permitted say. When it was the 559th night, she said,

It hath reached me, O auspicious King, that Sindbad the Seaman continued: So I left the City of the Apes and embarked my cocoa-nuts and what else I possessed. We weighed anchor the same day and sailed from island to island and sea to sea; and whenever we stopped I sold and traded with my cocoa-nuts, and the Lord requited me more than I erst had and lost. Amongst other places, we came to an island abounding in cloves and cinnamon and pepper; and the country people told me that by the side of each pepper-bunch groweth a great leaf which shadeth it from the sun and casteth the water off it in the wet season; but when the rain ceaseth the leaf turneth over and droopeth down by the side of the bunch. Here I took in great store of pepper and cloves and cinnamon, in exchange for cocoa-nuts, and we passed thence to the Island of Al-Usirát, whence cometh the Comorin aloes-wood and thence to another island, five days' journey in length, where grows the Chinese lign-aloes, which is better than the Comorin; but the people of this island are fouler of condition and religion than those of the other, for that they love fornication and wine-bibbing, and know not prayer nor call to prayer. Thence we came to the pearl fisheries, and I gave the divers some of my cocoa-nuts and said to them, "Dive for my luck and lot!" They did so and brought up from the deep bight great store of large and priceless pearls; and they said to me, "By Allah, O my master, thy luck is a lucky!" Then we sailed on, with the blessing of Allah (whose name be exalted!); and ceased not sailing till we arrived safely at Bassorah. There I abode a little and then went on to Baghdad, where I entered my quarter and found my house and foregathered with my family and saluted my friends, who gave me joy of my safe return, and I laid up all my goods and valuables in my storehouses. Then I distributed alms and largesse and clothed the widow and the orphan and made presents to my relations and comrades; for the Lord had requited me fourfold that I had lost. After which I returned to my old merry way of life and forgot all I had suffered in the great profit and gain I had made. Such, then, is the history of my fifth voyage and its wonderments.

From *The Thousand Nights and a Night.*

THE KING AND HIS WAZIR'S WIFE

THERE was once a king of the kings, a potent man and a proud, who was devoted to the love of women; and one day, being in the privacy of his palace, he espied a beautiful woman on the terrace roof of her house and could not contain himself from falling consumedly in love with her. He asked his folk to whom the house and the damsel belonged, and they said, "This is the dwelling of the wazir such a one, and she is his wife." So he called the minister in question and dispatched him on an errand to a distant part of the kingdom, where he was to collect information and to return; but, as soon as he obeyed and was gone, the king contrived by a trick to gain access to his house. When the wazir's wife saw him, she knew him and, springing up, kissed his hands and feet and welcomed him. Then she stood afar off, busying herself in his service, and said to him, "O our lord, what is the cause of thy gracious coming? Such an honor is not for the like of me." Quoth he, "The cause of it is that love of thee has moved me to this." Whereupon she kissed the ground before him a second time and said, "By Allah, O our lord, indeed I am not worthy to be the handmaid of one of the King's servants; whence, then, have I the great good fortune to be in such high honor and favor with thee?" Then the king put out his hand to her, when she said, "This thing shall not escape us; but take patience, O my King, and abide with thy handmaid all this day, that she may make ready for thee somewhat to eat and drink."

So the king sat down on his minister's couch, and she went in haste and brought him a book wherein he might read whilst she made ready the food. He took the book and, beginning to read, found therein moral instances and exhortations such as restrained him from adultery and broke his courage to commit sin and crime. After a while she returned and set before him some ninety dishes of different kinds of colors, and he ate a mouthful of each and found that, while the number was many, the taste of them was one. At this he marveled with exceeding marvel and said to her, "O damsel, I see these meats to be manifold and various, but the taste of them is simple and the same." "Allah prosper the King!" replied she. "This is a parable I have set for thee, that thou mayst be admonished thereby." He asked, "And what is its meaning?" And she answered, "Allah amend the case of our lord the King! In thy palace are ninety concubines of various colors, but their taste is one." When the king heard this, he was ashamed and, rising hastily, went out without offering her any affront and returned to his palace; but, in his haste and confusion, he forgot his signet ring and left it under the cushion where he had been sitting, and albeit he remembered it he was ashamed to send for it.

Now hardly had he reached home when the wazir returned and, presenting himself before the king, kissed the ground and made his report to him of the state of the province in question. Then he repaired to his own house and sat down on his couch, and chancing to put his hand under the cushion, behold, he found the king's seal ring. So he knew it, and taking the matter to heart, held aloof in great grief from his wife for a whole year, not going in unto her nor even speaking to her, whilst she knew not the reason of his anger. At last, being weary of the longsome neglect, she sent for her sire and told him the case—

And Shahrazad perceived the approach of day and ceased saying her permitted say. When it was the 579th night, she resumed her story, saying,

It hath reached me, O auspicious King, that the wazir held aloof from his wife, whilst she knew not the cause of his wrath. At last, being weary of the longsome neglect, she sent for her sire and told him the case; whereupon quoth he, "I will complain of him to the King, at some time when he is in the presence." So, one day, he went in to the king and, finding the wazir and the kazi of the army before him, complained thus, saying, "Almighty Allah amend the

King's case! I had a fair flower garden, which I planted with mine own hand and thereon spent my substance till it bore fruit; and its fruitage was ripe for plucking when I gave it to this thy wazir, who ate of it what seemed good to him, then deserted it and watered it not, so that its bloom wilted and withered and its sheen departed and its state changed."

Then said the wazir, "O my King, this man saith sooth. I did indeed care for and guard the garden and keep it in good condition and ate thereof, till one day I went thither and I saw the trail of the lion there, wherefore I feared for my life and withdrew from the garden." The king understood him that the trail of the lion meant his own seal ring, which he had forgotten in the woman's house; so he said, "Return, O Wazir, to thy flower garden and fear nothing, for the lion came not near it. It hath reached me that he went thither; but, by the honor of my fathers and forefathers, he offered it no hurt." "Hearkening and obedience," answered the minister and, returning home, sent for his wife and made his peace with her and thenceforth put faith in her chastity.

From *The Thousand Nights and a Night.*

THE WOMAN OF THE WELL

In ancient times there was an old man who was very poor, and who lived in a village at some distance from Mosul. All his life he had worked and nothing had prospered; indeed, he and his wife were often forced to beg. To add to his misery, his wife was a very shaitan, whose tongue afflicted him from morning to night. For his misfortunes she had nothing but railing, and for his poverty she did nothing but upbraid him.

One day it happened that they had nothing in the house to eat or to sell, and as soon as the day dawned she began to scold and abuse him.

"Here we are starving, and you look for no work! Never was a woman cursed with such a vagabond as you!"

By her stinging words she forced him to rise and go out to seek employment, and he went from one place to another, but no man would employ him, for the harvest was over and work was scant. So, not knowing where else to go, he seated himself by the roadside in heaviness of spirit and thought how sorely his wife would use him when he came back with nothing more in his pocket than a morsel of bread which a charitable soul had given him. It was then full noon, and as he sat and watched the wheelmarks and footmarks that flowed away over the hill like a stream, for the road led to Mosul, "Mosul is a fair city," said he, his thoughts following the track, "and if Allah so willed it, it might be that wealth and fortune would await me, if my wife and I set out thither." And then he considered, and, reflecting that even with wealth his life would be a burden if she continued to plague him, he changed his thought and said, "Why should I not journey alone to Mosul?"

And his heart grew light, and, drawing the bread from his pocket, he rose up and set off upon the road, eating as he went. He walked until the sun was nearing the horizon, and then, seeing a well and a shady tree by the wayside, he turned aside, and after he had refreshed his thirst, he seated himself on the edge of the well to rest.

He had rested but a little while when he saw on the brow of the hill a cloud of dust. It came nearer and nearer, and then he saw that it was caused by a woman, moving swiftly, and his heart became water within him, for he knew that it was his wife who had followed him. As soon as she was within hearing, she began to scream and abuse him for deserting her, calling him a dog and the son of a dog, the child of iniquity, an eater of filth, and a doer of evil. He answered nothing, for his conscience accused him, and they sat together on the edge of the well, she reviling and he listening, until, losing patience, he struck her with his elbow and she fell into the well below.

Rising affrighted, he went again on his way, regardless of her screams, and after he had gone an hour or two his mind began to rest, and he thought that after all, what had happened was ordained, and that now, by the favor of heaven, he was a free man. It was sunset, and he stopped to prepare himself for prayer by the wayside. But as he turned, lo, in the distance he saw a cloud of dust. It came nearer and nearer, and his heart turned to water within him. But when he could perceive clearly who was approaching, he saw that it was not his wife, but a jinni, who approached him with angry looks and said, "I am come to slay thee!"

The old man fell on his knees and said, "What have I done to you, O Amir of the Jinn, that you should require my life? Give me but time to say my prayers, and tell me the reason of your anger."

"Have I not reason for anger?" said the jinni. "For forty years I have slumbered peacefully in my well, and this day you have cast into it a woman whose tongue is a plague and her screaming like the screaming of peacocks."

"O Amir of the Jinn," said the old man, "for forty years you have had peace and quietness and for only two hours a woman's tongue. But what of my unhappy lot? For forty years I have had my woman's tongue, and but two hours have I had peace and quietness. Consider and be merciful!"

"Your lot has indeed been hard," said the jinni, "but what of the woman in my well?"

"O Amir of the Jinn, leave her in the well and travel the world with me."

The jinni was pleased with the words of the old man and traveled with him until they got to Mosul, where they entered a khan and ordered the best that could be provided for them.

"I will pay," said the jinni, and the next day he took a large house with many servants, male and female, where he and the old man lived together, entertaining the notables and rich people of the town and spending much money in pleasure and hospitality. But this life did not suit the jinni, who began to thirst after mischief, and after a while he said to the old man, "If I continue to live with you, I shall do you a harm. Better is it that we part now."

"Alas! Without money what shall I do?" asked the old man.

"I will tell you how to win fame and fortune," said the jinni. "It is my fancy to enter folk and make them mad, and when I leave you, I shall enter into the daughter of the grand wazir of Baghdad. He will reward highly the man who can cure the possessed girl, and that man will be yourself."

"But how shall I cure her?"

"I will tell you upon one condition—that you do not again employ exorcism against me. If you do, I will enter into you and never leave you, but keep you in torment." And with that he taught the old man the exorcism.

Thereafter he disappeared, and the old man left Mosul and traveled to Baghdad. Shortly after he had taken up his abode in the city, he heard the news that the grand wazir's daughter was grievously ill; that a jinni had entered into her and was tormenting her with all the pains of hell. And he went to the grand wazir's house and asked to see him, saying that he was a skilled physician with special skill in curing those possessed.

The wazir received him with honor and asked him if indeed he could cure his daughter. The old man said, "Sir, I can cure her, but not without reward."

"What is your price?" asked the wazir. "Name it, and I will pay it though it be large."

The old man answered, "My price is two thousand dinars."

When he heard the exorbitance of the sum, the wazir was angry. "This is indeed beyond reason," said he. "Are there no physicians in Baghdad beside you?" And he sent him away.

But day by day his daughter's malady increased, and all the doctors and exorcists of the town tried their skill upon her in vain. She was conducted to the shrine of Abdul Qāder al Gilāni and left there for three days and nights; she was chained to the grill at the tomb of the two Kādhims for yet another such period; the Qurān was read over her, she was anointed by magic balms and salves, and she was beaten to the point of death, but all was useless.

Then the old man went again to the wazir and told him that he was able to cure his daughter.

"Cure her," cried the wazir, "and I will pay thy price, even the two thousand dinars."

"Sir," said the old man, "my price has increased. It is now the half of thy possessions."

Then the wazir was enraged and swore that he would not give it. He said, "This day comes a wise man from Al Hind, and if God wills, he will cure her."

"If God wills," said the old man, and he went out. But the wise man from Al Hind was not able to cure the wazir's daughter.

Then the wazir sent for the old man and said to him, "O old man, cure my daughter, and I will give thee half I possess."

"Sir," said the old man, "my price has increased. It is now half thy possessions and the hand of thy daughter."

"Take what thou askest if the cure be perfect, or thou wilt leave me nothing. But if there is no cure, look to it, for I will order my servants to beat thee soundly."

"Fear not," said the old man, and they took him to the room

where the wazir's daughter, a very pearl of beauty, was bound down with ropes and bonds.

When he was left alone with her, he pronounced the word of power which the jinni had taught him, and with a loud scream the evil spirit departed from her. The maiden blushed at coming to herself and finding that she was alone with a man, but when she knew that he was her deliverer and promised husband, she greeted him with kindness and permitted him to loose her bonds. Then they went to her father, who was overjoyed at her recovery.

So there were marriage rejoicings for seven days and seven nights, and the old man renewed his youth in his beautiful bride, and lived happily with her for a period of three months.

At the end of that time there came to the old man as he was sitting in the harem with his wife a message from his father-in-law, bidding him come at once to his house. He went, and the wazir, greeting him affectionately, said to him, "The Commander of the Faithful has ordered me to bring thee to the palace without delay; the cause being the illness of his favorite daughter, who is possessed by a terrible jinni."

The old man was much alarmed, for he suspected that the jinni who had taken possession of the princess was the jinni of the well. He began to excuse himself from accompanying the wazir, but the wazir would not hear him and insisted that they must obey the commands of the khalīfa. When they had arrived in the presence of the khalīfa, the old man kissed the ground, and when he received the order to visit the princess, he said, "O Commander of the Faithful, I am the least of thy slaves, and my knowledge of healing is insignificant. Send for thy physicians and let them heal the princess, for are they not skilled men and worthier than I?"

The khalīfa frowned and said, "What is this and why art thou unwilling to exercise upon my daughter the skill which thou hast proven upon the family of my wazir?"

And the old man said, "Not from unwillingness but from incapacity, O Commander of the Faithful."

"Thou liest!" cried the khalīfa. "Does not all Baghdad know thee for a skilled exorcist, for didst thou not succeed in expelling a demon from the daughter of my wazir when all else had failed and every physician in the kingdom had tried his craft in vain. Why these evasions and excuses? Cure my daughter, or, by Allah, I will hand thee over to the executioner to meet a death befitting such reluctance to serve thy sovereign."

And he ordered his attendants to take the old man to the apartment of the princess and to strike off his head if he either attempted escape or failed in his exorcism.

As the old man was conducted through the palace toward the women's quarters, he beat his breast and wept bitterly. "Alas, woe is me! What man can escape from his fate? It is the destiny of one to be born to sorrow and another to fortune. I have now but the choice between a miserable death and a life of torture."

So complaining, he was led to the apartment of the princess, who lay upon her bed exhausted and like one beaten. As he gazed upon her, with the hand of the executioner on his shoulder, he thought upon the bride he had just left, and upon all the deceptions and disappointments of his life, beginning with his first marriage. And suddenly he bit on his hand and cried, "What an owl am I!" And hope, which a moment before had flown him, returned to his breast.

Boldly approaching the princess, he pronounced the word of power.

In a moment the evil jinni leaped from her body and, appearing to the old man in a frightful aspect, he laid hold of him, crying, "Thou old fool! what did I tell thee! Now I shall enter into thy body and torment thee until the end of thy life!"

"O Amir of the Jinn," answered the old man, "one torment is not worse than the other. Enter into my miserable body—but know that my wife has escaped from the well and is even now waiting without for me."

"What!" shrieked the jinni. "Live beside thy wife and listen to her revilings? Never, never!" And with a loud cry he flew to the window and leaped from it into the air and was never seen or heard of in those parts afterward.

And this is the end of the story of the Woman of the Well.

From *Folk-Tales of Iraq*, set down and translated from the Arabic by E. S. Stevens (Oxford: The Clarendon Press, 1931).

THE LADY AND THE UNJUST JUDGE

NOW IT came to pass that a certain chöpdji, or dust collector, had, in the course of five years of labor, amassed the sum of five hundred piasters. He was afraid to keep this money by him; so, hearing the cadi of Stamboul highly and reverently spoken of, he decided to entrust his hard-earned savings to the judge's keeping.

Going to the cadi, he said, "O learned and righteous man, for five long years have I labored, carrying the dregs and dross of rich and poor alike, and I have saved a sum of five hundred piasters. With the help of Allah, in another two years I shall have saved a further sum of at least one hundred piasters, when, *Inshallah!* I shall return to my country and clasp my wife and children in my arms again. In the meantime you will grant a boon to your slave if you will consent to keep this money for me until the time for my departure has come."

The cadi replied, "Thou hast done well, my son. I swear on penalty of having to divorce my wife that this money will be kept faithfully and returned unto thee when required."

The poor chöpdji departed, well satisfied. But after a very short time he learned that several of his friends were about to return to their *memleket* [province] and he decided to join them, thinking that his five hundred piasters were ample for the time being. "Besides," said he, "who knows what may or may not happen in the next two years?" So he decided to depart with his friends at once.

He went to the cadi, explained that he had changed his mind, that he was going to leave for his country immediately, and asked for his money. The cadi called him a dog and ordered him to be whipped out of the place by his servants. Alas! what could the poor chöpdji do? He wept in impotent despair as he counted the number of years he must yet work before he beheld his loved ones.

One day, while removing the refuse from the konak of a wealthy pasha, his soul uttered a sigh which reached the ears of the hanoum, and from the window she asked him why he sighed so deeply.

He replied that he sighed for something that could in no way interest her. The hanoum's sympathy was excited, however; and finally, with tears in his eyes, the chöpdji consented, after much coaxing, to tell her of his great misfortune. The hanoum thought for a few minutes and then told him to go the following day to the cadi at a certain hour and again ask for the money as if nothing had happened.

The hanoum in the meantime gathered together a quantity of jewelry and, instructing her favorite and confidential female slave to come with her to the cadi, she told her to remain outside whilst she went in. She also told the slave that when she saw the chöpdji come out with his money, she, the slave, was to enter the cadi's room hurriedly and say to her mistress, "Your husband has arrived from Egypt and is waiting for you at the konak."

The hanoum then went to the cadi, carrying in her hand a bag containing the jewelry. With a profound salaam she said, "O cadi, my husband, who is in Egypt and who has been there for several years, has at last asked me to come and join him there. These jewels are, however, of great value, and I hesitate to take them with me on so long and dangerous a journey. If you would kindly consent to keep them for me until my return, I will think of you with lifelong gratitude. And in case I never return, you may keep them in token of my esteem."

The hanoum then began displaying the rich jewelry. Just at that moment the chöpdji entered and, bending low, said, "O master, your slave has come for his savings in order that he may proceed to his country."

"Ah, welcome!" said the cadi. "So you are going already!" And immediately he ordered the treasurer to pay the five hundred piasters to the chöpdji.

"You see," said the cadi to the hanoum, "what confidence the people have in me. This money I have held for some time without receipt or acknowledgment; but directly it is asked for it is paid."

No sooner had the chöpdji gone out of the door than the hanoum's slave came rushing in. "Hanoum effendi! Hanoum effendi!" she cried, "your husband has arrived from Egypt and is anxiously awaiting you at the konak."

On hearing this, the hanoum, in well-feigned excitement, gathered up her jewelry, and, wishing the cadi a thousand years of happiness, departed.

The cadi was thunderstruck and, caressing his beard with grave affection, thoughtfully said to it, "For forty years have I been a judge, but never before, by Allah, has a cause been pleaded here in this fashion."

From *Tales from Turkey*, collected and translated by Allan Ramsay and Francis McCullagh (London: Simpkin, Marshall, Hamilton, Kent and Co., Ltd., 1914).

CHAPKIN THE SCAMP

In Balata there lived, some years ago, two scapegraces called Chapkin Halid and Pitch Osman. Those two young rascals lived by their wits and at the expense of their neighbors. But they often had to lament the ever-increasing difficulties they encountered in procuring the few piasters they needed daily for bread and the coffee-house. They had tried several schemes in their own neighborhood, with exceptionally poor results, and were almost disheartened, when Chapkin Halid conceived an idea that seemed to offer them every chance of success. He explained to his friend Osman that Balata was played out, at least for a time, and that they must go elsewhere to satisfy their needs. Halid's plan was to go to Stamboul, and feign death in the principal street, while Osman was to collect the funeral expenses from the shocked and sympathetic onlookers.

Arriving in Stamboul, Halid stretched himself on his back on the pavement and covered his face with an old sack, while Osman sat himself down beside the supposed corpse, and every now and then bewailed the hard fate of the stranger who had met with death on the first day of his arrival. The corpse prompted Osman whenever the coast was clear, and the touching tale told by Osman soon brought contributions for the burial of the stranger. Osman had collected about thirty piasters, and Halid was seriously thinking of a resurrection, when the approach of a procession made it necessary for him to remain dead for some time longer. The procession was the suite of the grand vizier, who, catching sight of Halid, inquired why the man lay on the ground in that fashion. Being told that the body was that of a stranger who had died in the street, the grand vizier gave instructions to an imam, who happened to be at hand, to bury the unknown and to come afterward for the funeral expenses to the Sublime Porte.

Halid was reverently carried off to the mosque, and Osman thought that it was time to leave the corpse to take care of itself. The imam laid Halid on the marble floor and prepared to wash him prior to interment. He had taken off his turban and long cloak and got ready the water, when he remembered that he had no soap and immediately went out to purchase some. No sooner had the imam disappeared than Halid jumped up and, donning the imam's turban and long cloak, repaired to the Sublime Porte. Here he asked for admittance to the presence of the grand vizier, but he was told that his request could not be granted until he had told the nature of his business. Halid said he was the imam who, in compliance with the verbal instructions received from His Highness, had buried a stranger, and that he had now come for the payment which had been promised to him. The grand vizier sent five gold pieces (one hundred piasters) to the supposed imam, and Halid made off as fast as possible.

No sooner had Halid departed than the imam arrived without his cloak and in breathless haste. He explained that he was the imam who had received instructions from the grand vizier to bury a stranger, but that the supposed corpse had disappeared, and so had his own cloak and turban. Witnesses having proved this man to be undoubtedly the imam of the quarter, the grand vizier gave orders to his chief detective to capture, within three days, on pain of death, and bring to the Sublime Porte, this fearless evildoer.

The chief detective was soon on the track of Halid; but the latter was on the lookout. With the aid of the money he had received from the grand vizier to defray his own burial expenses, he successfully evaded the clutches of the chief detective, who was very angry at being thus frustrated. On the second day the detective again got on the scent of Halid, and determined to follow him till an opportunity offered for his capture. Halid knew that he was being followed, and, of course, he divined the intentions of his pursuer. As he was passing a pharmacy he noticed there several young men, so he entered and, handing the druggist one of the gold pieces he had received from the grand vizier, he said that his uncle, who would come in presently, was not right, alas! in his mind, but that, if the druggist could manage to shower his head and back with cold water, he would regain sanity. No sooner did the chief detective enter the shop than, at a word from the apothecary, the young men seized him, and, by means of a large squirt, did their utmost to give him the salutary shower which his nephew had recommended.

The more the detective protested, the more the apothecary soothingly explained that the shower would soon be over and that he would feel much better after it. The shopkeeper also told of numerous similar cases which he had cured in a like manner. The detective saw that it was useless to struggle, so he abandoned himself to the treatment; and in the meantime Halid made off. The chief detective was so disheartened by this experience that he went to the grand vizier and begged for instant decapitation, as death, said he, was preferable to the annoyance he had received and might still receive at the hands of Chapkin Halid. The grand vizier was both furious and amused, so he spared the chief detective and gave orders that guards should be placed at the twenty-four gates of the city and that Halid should be seized at the first opportunity. A reward was further promised to the person who would bring him to the Sublime Porte. Meanwhile, however, Halid lived quietly in the old Tower of Galata.

Halid was finally caught one night as he was going out of the Top-Kapou [Cannon Gate]. He had gone into the great subterranean palace of Yèrè-Batan-Seraï and traversed a secret passage which would bring him, he thought, outside the walls of the city. But it brought him into a pile of ruins close by a guardhouse, the soldiers of which took him at first for the devil. But having recognized him after a while, they rejoiced in their capture, and also in the prospect of now getting a little rest after their watch. As a result of considerable discussion, they decided to bind their prisoner to a large tree close to the guardhouse. By doing so they would avoid the loss of sleep and the anxiety of watching over so desperate a character. They carried out their scheme, and Halid now thought that his case was indeed hopeless. Toward dawn, however, he perceived a man with a lantern walking toward the Armenian church, and rightly concluded that it was the beadle going to make ready for the early morning service. So he called out in a loud voice, "Beadle! Brother! Beadle! Brother! Come here quickly!"

Now it happened that the beadle was a poor hunchback, and no sooner did Halid perceive this than he said, "Quick, quick, Beadle! look at my back and see if it has gone!"

"See if what has gone?" asked the beadle, carefully looking behind the tree.

"Why, my hump, of course," answered Halid.

The beadle made a close inspection and declared that he could see no hump.

"A thousand thanks!" fervently exclaimed Halid. "Then please undo the rope."

The beadle set about the work of liberating Halid, earnestly begging him at the same time to tell how he had got rid of his hump, so that he, the beadle, might also free himself of his deformity. Halid agreed to tell his rescuer the cure, provided he had not yet broken his fast, and provided also that he was prepared to pay a certain small sum of money for the secret. The beadle satisfied Halid

on both of these points, whereupon Halid immediately proceeded to bind the hunchback to the tree, telling him meanwhile to repeat sixty-one times the words "Esserti! Pesserti! Sersepeti!" Halid left the poor beadle earnestly repeating those nonsensical words.

The guards were very much surprised when they found tied to the tree, not Halid, but a stranger, who took no notice of them and continued to repeat very rapidly words which they could not understand.

"Who is this hunchback and what is he saying?" asked a soldier. "He is mad. He is talking nonsense."

"Therefore it is," quoth the bimbashi [major], who was a very holy man, having been on the hajj [pilgrimage], "therefore it is that he may be a prophet. Is it not the same in the Koran? Does not

'*Al Arof*' begin with four letters whose meaning is known neither to men nor to angels, but only to Allah alone?"

But soon the Armenian priest came on the scene and, recognizing the beadle, begged the soldiers to liberate him. The soldiers were furious as they began to unbind the captive, and what made them the more furious was the fact that the only answer they could get to their questions was "Esserti, Pesserti, Sersepeti!" As the knots were loosened the despairing voice of the beadle rose louder and louder as he called out the charmed words. No sooner was the beadle freed than he asked Allah to bring down calamity on the destroyers of the charm that was to remove his hump. On hearing the beadle's tale, the guards understood how their prisoner had secured his liberty and sent word to the chief detective. This gentleman then repaired once more to the grand vizier and, having prostrated himself at the feet of that dignitary, told this latest instance of the notorious Chapkin's cunning. The grand vizier was amused and also very anxious to see this Chapkin Halid, so he sent criers all over the city, announcing the grant of a full pardon to Halid on condition that he would come to the Sublime Porte and confess in person to the grand vizier. Halid obeyed the summons, and came to kiss the hem of the grand vizier's garment, and His Excellency was so favorably impressed by him that he there and then appointed him to be his chief detective.

From *Tales from Turkey*.

WHAT HAPPENED TO HADJI

HADJI was a merchant in the Great Bazaar of Stamboul. Being a pious Mohammedan, he was of course a married man, but even so he was not invulnerable to the charms of women. It happened one day that a charming hanoum came to his shop to purchase some spices. After the departure of his fair visitor, Hadji, do what he might, could not drive her image from his mind's eye. Furthermore, he was greatly puzzled by a tiny black bag containing twelve grains of wheat, which the hanoum had evidently forgotten.

Till a late hour that night did Hadji remain in his shop, in the hope that either the hanoum or one of her servants would come for the bag and thus give him the means of seeing her again, or at least of learning where she lived. But Hadji was doomed to disappointment; and, much preoccupied, he returned to his house. There he sat, plunged in thought, unresponsive to his wife's conversation.

Hadji remained downcast day after day, but at last, giving way to his wife's entreaties, he told what had happened and admitted that ever since that fatal day his soul had been in bondage to the fair unknown.

"Oh, husband," replied his wife, "and do you not understand what that black bag containing the twelve grains of wheat means?"

"Alas, no," replied Hadji.

"Why, my husband, it is plain; plain as if it had been told. She lives in the Wheat Market, at house No. 12, with a black door."

Much excited, Hadji rushed off and found that there was a No. 12 in the Wheat Market, with a black door, so he promptly knocked. The door opened, and whom should he behold but the lady in question! Instead of speaking to him, however, she threw a basin of water out into the street and then shut the door. Hadji did not know what to think of this. Having lingered about the doorway for a time, he at length returned home. He greeted his wife more pleasantly than he had done for many days and told her of his adventure.

"Why," said his wife, "don't you understand what the basin of water thrown out of the door means?"

"Alas, no," said Hadji.

"*Veyh! Veyh!*" she exclaimed pityingly, "it means that at the back of the house there is a running stream, and that you must go to her that way."

Off rushed Hadji, and found that his wife was right; there *was* a running stream at the back of the house, so he knocked at the back door. The hanoum, however, instead of opening it, came to the window, showed a mirror, reversed it, and then disappeared. Hadji lingered at the back of the house for a long time, but, seeing no further sign of life, he returned to his own home much dejected. On entering the doorway, his wife greeted him with, "Well, was it not as I told you?"

"Yes," said Hadji. "You are truly a wonderful woman! But I do not know why she came to the window and showed me a mirror, both front and back, instead of opening the door."

"Oh," said his wife, "that is very simple; she means that you must go when the face of the moon has reversed itself—about ten o'clock." The hour arrived, Hadji hurried off, and so did his wife; the one to see his love, and the other to inform the police.

Whilst Hadji and his charmer were talking in the garden the police seized them and carried them both off to prison; and Hadji's wife, having accomplished her mission, returned home.

The next morning she baked a quantity of *lokma* cakes, and, taking them to the prison, begged entrance of the guards, and permission to distribute those cakes to the prisoners, for the repose of the souls of her dead. This being a request which could not be denied, she was allowed to enter. Finding the cell in which the lady who had attracted her husband was confined, she offered to save her the disgrace of the exposure, provided she would consent never again to cast loving eyes upon Hadji the merchant. Those conditions were gratefully accepted, and Hadji's wife changed places with the prisoner.

When they were brought before the judge, Hadji was thunderstruck to see his wife, but, being a wise man, he held his peace and let her do the talking, which she did most vigorously. Vehemently did she protest against the insult inflicted on both her and her husband. What right had the police to bring them to prison because they chose to converse in a garden, seeing that they were lawfully wedded people? To witness that they were man and wife she called upon the watchman and the priest of the district and several of her neighbors.

Poor Hadji was dumfounded, as, accompanied by his wife, he soon after left the prison where he had expected to stay at least a year or two. "Truly thou art a wonderful woman!" was all he was able to say.

From *Tales from Turkey*.

NASR-ED-DIN HODJA IN THE PULPIT

NASR-ED-DIN HODJA one day addressed his congregation from the pulpit in the following words: "I beseech you to tell me truly, O brethren! O true believers! if what I am going to say to you is already known to you."

And the answer came, as in one voice, from his congregation, that they did not know, and that it was not possible for them to know, what the Hodja was going to say to them. "Then," quoth the preacher, "of what use to you or to me is an unknown subject?" And he descended from the pulpit and left the mosque.

On the following Friday his congregation, instead of having decreased, had greatly increased, and their anxiety to hear what he was going to say was felt in the very atmosphere.

The Hodja ascended the pulpit and said, "O brethren! O true believers! I beseech you to tell me truly if what I am going to say to you is already known to you."

The answer that came to the Hodja was so spontaneous as to suggest prearrangement. They all shouted, "Yes, Hodja, we do know what you are going to say to us."

"That being the case," quoth the Hodja, "there is no need either of you wasting your time or of me wasting my time." And, descending from the pulpit, he left the mosque. His congregation, having prayed, also left gradually, one by one and in groups.

On the following Friday Nasr-el-Din Hodja again mounted the pulpit, and saw that his mosque was so crowded that not a nook or corner in it was empty. He addressed his congregation in exactly the same manner. "O brethren! O true believers!" said he, "I ask you to tell me truly if what I am going to say is already known to you?"

And again the answer of his numerous congregation had evidently been prepared beforehand, for one half of them rose and said, "Yes, Hodja, we do know what you are going to say to us," and the other half rose and said, "O Hodja effendi, how could we poor ignorant people know what you intend to say to us?"

The Hodja answered, "It is well said; and now if the half that knows what I am going to say would explain to the other half what it is, I would be deeply grateful, for, of course, it will be unnecessary for me to say anything."

Whereupon he descended from the pulpit and left the mosque.

From *Tales from Turkey*.

THE HODJA AND THE CALDRON

Being once in need of a caldron, the Hodja went to one of his neighbors and borrowed a large copper caldron which answered his requirements so well that he had no wish to part with it. Instead of returning the borrowed utensil on the promised day, he went to his neighbor and handed him in a somewhat dejected manner a much smaller caldron resembling in shape the one which he had borrowed.

The owner looked at it suspiciously and asked, "What is this?" Whereunto the Hodja answered, "Your caldron has given birth to a little one and is far too unwell for me to return it today. Take its offspring instead, I beseech you."

The owner of the caldron was much surprised, but he was at the same time not a little gratified at this unexpected fertility, and when his wife soundly abused him for having thus allowed himself to be put upon, he testily advised the good dame to have patience and not to ask any questions for a day or two.

The Hodja's need of the caldron having come to an end, he brought it back and said, "Here, take your caldron back again, for now it is quite well." The neighbor and his family rejoiced, and the fame of the Hodja was much increased.

Some days later the Hodja again required the caldron, and this time his neighbor was so pleased to lend it to him that he even helped to carry it to the Hodja's house. After a considerable time had elapsed without any baby caldron appearing on the scene, the neighbor called on Nasr-ed-Din Hodja to inquire when he might expect his caldron to return. He was polite and profusely apologetic, but he said that his wife wanted it.

The Hodja seemed very much surprised that his neighbor had not heard the news—the sad news that the caldron had died. The manner and tone of the obliging neighbor now underwent an instant change, and he remonstrated loudly. Indeed, he created such an uproar that a crowd speedily assembled round the house; but, so far as the Hodja was concerned, the large caldron was dead for all time, and he advised his neighbor to return home quietly, and break the news to the baby caldron which he had claimed as his. "For it stands to reason," quoth Nasr-ed-Din Hodja, "that anything or anyone that can give birth to young can also die."

The crowd agreed and said that verily he spake well and truly. It was *hak* [just].

From *Tales from Turkey.*

THE HODJA AND THE BURGLAR

ONE NIGHT the holy but poor Hodja heard someone moving cautiously about his room, and, far from becoming alarmed, he cordially greeted the unknown and earnestly begged him to strike a light. The thief was so startled at this unusual request that he betrayed himself and asked in astonishment why the Hodja wished him to strike a light.

"Oh, fear nothing," said the Hodja in a reassuring tone. "I only wished to see your face that I might worship it, for truly you must be a very great man when you attempt to find in the dark what I am unable to find in the daytime, though I am constantly looking for it."

From *Tales from Turkey.*

THE HODJA VISITS HALIL

"HURRY! You will be late for the banquet at Halil's house!" One person after another called this advice to Nasr-ed-Din Hodja as he jogged home from a day's work in his vineyard.

"They are right," the Hodja finally admitted. The sun was almost touching the horizon. "I will be late for the dinner unless I go now—just as I am."

He turned his reluctant donkey's head about and was soon at Halil's house. He tied his donkey in Halil's courtyard and walked confidently into the house, where the feast was soon to begin. Always sure of a welcome, he spread his smiles and his jokes to right and to left. He was so happy talking that he did not notice for some time a very strange thing. He was talking to backs instead of to faces. Not a single man was listening to him! Soon an even stranger thing happened. When the soup was brought in, Halil ushered other men to seats at the low table, but he had no word for Nasr-ed-Din Hodja.

The Hodja cleared his throat noisily. Halil did not notice. He coughed loudly. Halil paid no attention.

"Oh, Halil effendi!" called Nasr-ed-Din Hodja cheerily. "I noticed a fine crop of fruit in your vineyard today."

Halil, busy with his well-dressed guests, did not hear.

"Oh, Halil effendi!" The Hodja's voice was even louder this time. "Your smallest grapes are twice as big as the best in my vineyard."

Still Halil seemed unable to hear or to see the one guest who stood alone in his shabby, dirty working clothes.

The Hodja looked thoughtfully at the other guests. Each man was scrubbed till he glistened. Each man was wearing his best clothes. Then the Hodja looked at his own brown hands, caked with the honest dirt of the vineyards. He looked at his own clothes with their patches upon patches, and with the day's new holes which the patient Fatima would mend that night.

Very quietly Nasr-ed-Din Hodja slipped out of the door, untied his willing donkey, and jogged home.

"Hot water, Fatima!" he ordered. "Soap, Fatima! My new shoes! My best turban! My new coat!"

Fatima bustled and fluttered about. Soon Nasr-ed-Din Hodja looked like a new man. He preened himself before the admiring Fatima, who had not seen her husband so completely well dressed in years. He strutted out of the house. Little boys spoke to him respectfully as he swaggered back along the street to Halil's house. Women peered from behind their veils at the grand gentleman who walked with such an air.

A bowing servant ushered him into the banquet room at Halil's house. A beaming Halil hurried to meet him and escort him to the best seat in the room. Men smiled and nodded. Halil heaped his plate with goodies. Questions and stories were directed toward Nasr-ed-Din Hodja.

When he felt that all eyes were upon him, the Hodja picked up the choicest piece of meat on his plate. He did not raise it to his lips. Instead, he opened his coat and placed it in a pocket which was hidden inside.

"Eat, coat, eat!" said the Hodja.

A handful of pilaf, a square of cheese, a pickle, and a fig followed the meat into the coat.

"Eat, coat, eat!" said the Hodja as he put in each tidbit. The guests stopped eating to watch the Hodja feed his coat.

Finally Halil could hold in no longer. "Tell me, Hodja effendi, what you mean by telling your coat to eat."

"Why, surely, you wish the coat to eat." The Hodja raised innocent eyes to Halil. "When I came in my old clothes, there was no place at the table for me. When I come in my new clothes, nothing is too good for me. That shows it was the coat, not me, that you invited to your banquet."

From a story called "A Guest for Halil" in *Once the Hodja*, by Alice Geer Kelsey (New York: Longmans, Green & Co., 1943).

Chinese

The Sorcerer of the White Lotus Lodge

POPULAR conceptions of China's isolation notwithstanding, Chinese folk tales have been no more free of international influence than those of Europe or America. Coming mostly from India through the medium of Buddhism, but also from the Near East, many familiar themes, including those of Cinderella, the Master Thief, and the trapping of a jinni in a bottle, appear in Chinese folklore. But the national temperament asserts itself in many ways. Ripened by centuries of a religious philosophy that makes for serenity, the Chinese have lent their stories many distinctive qualities: a gentle whimsicality, fantasy, pathos, the uncanny, a quiet resignation to fate.

Among their greatest favorites are tales of supernatural beings—whether Immortals or wizards or simply spirits—who are moved to take part in human affairs or those of their fellows. Their motives vary greatly: in "Planting a Pear Tree" the bonge materializes for the purpose of teaching a stingy man a lesson; in "The Thunder God" the deity treats an ordinary mortal to a flight among the stars; the sorcerer of the White Lotus Lodge plagues folks with black magic; the Taoist priest plays a prank on a pair of nosy citizens; and in "The Cinnamon Tree in the Moon" the Immortals mete out punishment to a weak-willed brother. Often Chinese tales seem to get closer to the lineaments of poetry than is common in folk story. This is partly due to the fact that most of these tales have so far been published in rewritten and apparently literary versions. But even if we discount the consciously poetic elements in the translation of some of these tales there is evident in them an unusual feeling for the charming fancy, the imaginative turn. As for the fatalism we call Oriental, it may be noted that "Women" is a typical *Arabian Nights* tale of unfaithful womankind—except that not only does the woman's deception succeed, but the husband accepts it as inevitable.

PLANTING A PEAR TREE

A COUNTRY man was one day selling his pears in the market. They were unusually sweet and fine flavored, and the price he asked was high. A Taoist priest in rags and tatters stopped at the barrow and begged one of them. The country man told him to go away, but when he did not do so the country man began to curse and swear at him. The priest said, "You have several hundred pears on your barrow; I ask for a single one, the loss of which, sir, you would not feel. Why then get angry?"

The lookers-on told the country man to give the man an inferior one and let him go, but this he obstinately refused to do. Thereupon the beadle of the place, finding the commotion too great, purchased a pear and handed it to the priest. The latter received it with a bow and, turning to the crowd, said, "We who have left our homes and given up all that is dear to us are at a loss to understand selfish, niggardly conduct in others. Now I have some exquisite pears which I shall do myself the honor to put before you."

Here somebody asked, "Since you have pears yourself, why don't you eat those?"

"Because," replied the priest, "I wanted one of these pips to grow them from." So saying, he munched the pear; and when he had finished took a pip in his hand, unstrapped a pick from his back, and proceeded to make a hole in the ground, several inches deep, wherein he deposited the pip, filling in the earth as before. He then asked the bystanders for a little hot water to water it with, and one among them who loved a joke fetched him some boiling water from a neighboring shop. The priest poured this over the place where he had made the hole, and every eye was turned upon him when sprouts were seen shooting up and gradually growing larger and larger. By and by there was a tree with branches sparsely covered with leaves; then flowers, and last of all fine, large, sweet-smelling pears hanging in great profusion. These the priest picked and handed round to the assembled crowd until all were gone, whereupon he took his pick and hacked away for a long time at the tree, finally cutting it down. This he shouldered, leaves and all, and sauntered quietly away.

Now, from the very beginning, our friend the country man had been amongst the crowd, straining his neck to see what was going on and forgetting all about his business. At the departure of the priest he turned round and discovered that every one of his pears was gone. He then knew that those the old fellow had been giving away so freely were really his own pears. Looking more closely at the barrow, he also found that one of the handles was missing, evidently having been newly cut off. Boiling with rage, he set out in pursuit of the priest, but just as he turned the corner he saw the lost barrow handle lying under the wall, being in fact the very pear tree the priest had cut down. But there were no traces of the priest—much to the amusement of the crowd in the market place.

From *Strange Stories from a Chinese Studio*, translated by Herbert A. Giles (London: Thomas De La Rue & Co., Ltd., 1880).

A TAOIST PRIEST

ONCE upon a time there was a Mr. Han, who belonged to a wealthy family and was fond of entertaining people. A man named Hsü, of the same town, frequently joined him over the bottle; and on one occasion when they were together a Taoist priest came to the door with his alms bowl in his hand. The servants threw him some money and food, but the priest would not accept them, neither would he go away; and at length the servants took no more notice of him. Mr. Han finally heard the noise of the priest knocking his bowl and asked his servants what was the matter; and they had hardly told him when the priest himself walked in. Mr. Han begged him to be seated; whereupon the priest bowed to both gentlemen and took his seat.

On making the usual inquiries, they found that he lived in an old tumble-down temple to the east of the town, and Mr. Han expressed regret at not having heard sooner of his arrival, so that he might have shown him the proper hospitality of a resident. The priest said that he had only recently arrived and had no friends in the place; but hearing that Mr. Han was a jovial fellow, he had been very anxious to take a glass with him. Mr. Han then ordered wine, and the priest soon distinguished himself as a hard drinker; Mr. Hsü treated him with a certain amount of disrespect in consequence of his shabby appearance, but Mr. Han made allowances for him as being a traveler. When he had drunk over twenty large cups of wine, the priest took his leave, returning subsequently whenever any jollification was going on, no matter whether it was eating or drinking. Even Han began to tire a little of him; and on one occasion Hsü said to him in raillery,

"Good priest, you seem to like being a guest; why don't you play the host sometimes for a change?"

"Ah," replied the priest, "I am much the same as yourself—a mouth carried between a couple of shoulders."

This put Hsü to shame, and he had no answer to make; so the priest continued, "But although that is so, I have been revolving the question with myself for some time, and when you visit me I shall do my best to repay your kindness with a cup of my own poor wine."

When they had finished drinking, the priest said he hoped he should have the pleasure of their company the following day at noon; and at the appointed time the two friends went together, not expecting, however, to find anything ready for them. But the priest was waiting for them in the street; and, passing through a handsome courtyard, they beheld long suites of elegant apartments stretching away before them. In great astonishment, they remarked to the priest that they had not visited this temple for some time and asked when it had been thus repaired; to which he replied that the work had been only lately completed. They then went inside, and there was a magnificently decorated apartment, such as would not be found even in the houses of the wealthy. This made them begin to feel more respect for their host; and no sooner had they sat down than wine and food were served by a number of boys, all about sixteen years of age, and dressed in embroidered coats, with red shoes. The drink and the food were delicious, and very nicely served; and when the dinner was taken away, so many rare fruits were put on the table that it would be impossible to mention the names of all of them. They were arranged in dishes of crystal and jade, the brilliancy of which lighted up the surrounding furniture; and the goblets in which the wine was poured were of glass, and more than a foot in circumference.

The priest here cried out, "Call the Shih sisters," whereupon one of the boys went out and in a few moments two elegant young ladies walked in. The first was tall and slim like a willow wand; the other was short and very young. Both were exceedingly pretty. Being told to sing while the company were drinking, the younger beat time and sang a song, while the elder accompanied her on the flageolet. They acquitted themselves admirably; and, when the song was over, the priest, holding his goblet bottom upward in the air, challenged his guests to follow his example, bidding his servants pour out more wine all round. He then turned to the girls and, remarking that they had not danced for a long time, asked if they were still able to do so; upon which a carpet was spread by one of the boys, and the two young ladies proceeded to dance, their long robes waving about and perfuming the air around. The dance concluded, they leaned against a painted screen, while the two guests gradually became more and more befuddled and were at last completely drunk.

The priest took no notice of them; but when he had finished drinking, he got up and said, "Pray, go on with your wine; I am going to rest awhile and will return by and by." He then went away and lay down on a splendid couch at the other end of the room; at which Hsü was very angry and shouted out, "Priest, you are a rude fellow," at the same time making toward him with a view to rousing him. The priest then ran out, and Han and Hsü lay down to sleep, one at each end of the room, on elaborately carved couches covered with beautiful mattresses.

When they woke up they found themselves lying in the road, Mr. Hsü with his head in a dirty drain. Hard by were a couple of rush huts; but everything else was gone.

From *Strange Stories from a Chinese Studio.*

THE THUNDER GOD

YO YÜN-HAO and Hsia P'ing-tzŭ lived as boys in the same village, and when they grew up read with the same tutor, becoming the firmest of friends. Hsia was a clever fellow and had acquired some reputation even at the early age of ten. Yo was not a bit envious, but rather looked up to him, and Hsia in return helped his friend very much with his studies, so that he too made considerable progress. This increased Hsia's fame, though try as he would he could never succeed at the public examinations; and by and by he sickened and died. His family was so poor they could not find money for his burial, whereupon Yo came forward and paid all expenses, besides taking care of his widow and children.

Every peck or bushel he would share with them, the widow trusting entirely to his support; and thus he acquired a good name in the village, though not being a rich man himself he soon ran through all his own property. "Alas!" cried he, "where talents like Hsia's failed, can I expect to succeed? Wealth and rank are matters of destiny, and my present career will only end by my dying like a dog in a ditch. I must try something else." So he gave up book-learning and went into trade, and in six months he had a trifle of money in hand.

One day when he was resting at an inn in Nanking he saw a great big fellow walk in and seat himself at no great distance in a very melancholy mood. Yo asked him if he was hungry, and, on receiving no answer, pushed some food over toward him. The stranger immediately set to feeding himself by handfuls, and in no time the whole had disappeared. Yo ordered another supply, but that was quickly disposed of in like manner; and then he told the landlord to bring a shoulder of pork and a quantity of boiled dumplings. Thus, after eating enough for half a dozen, his appetite was appeased and he turned to thank his benefactor, saying, "For three years I haven't had such a meal." "And why should a fine fellow like you be in such a state of destitution?" inquired Yo. To which the other only replied, "The judgments of heaven may not be discussed." Being asked where he lived, the stranger replied, "On land I have no home, on the water no boat; at dawn in the village, at night in the city."

Yo then prepared to depart, but his friend would not leave him, declaring that he was in imminent danger and that he could not forget the late kindness Yo had shown him. So they went along together, and on the way Yo invited the other to eat with him; but this he refused, saying that he took food only occasionally. Yo marveled more than ever at this.

Next day when they were on the river a great storm arose and capsized all their boats, Yo himself being thrown into the water along with the others. Suddenly the gale abated, and the stranger bore Yo on his back to another boat, plunging at once into the water and bringing back the lost vessel, upon which he placed Yo, bidding him remain quietly there. He then returned once more, this time carrying in his arms a part of the cargo, which he replaced in the vessel, and so he went on until it was all restored.

Yo thanked him, saying, "It was enough to save my life; but you have added to this the restoration of my goods." Nothing, in fact, had been lost, and now Yo began to regard the stranger as something more than human. The latter here wished to take his leave, but Yo pressed him so much to stay that at last he consented to remain. Then Yo remarked that after all he had lost a gold pin, and immediately the stranger plunged into the water again, rising at length to the surface with the missing article in his mouth, and presenting it to Yo with the remark that he was delighted to be able to fulfill his commands. The people on the river were all much astonished at what they saw.

Meanwhile Yo went home with his friend, and there they lived together, the big man eating only once in ten or twelve days, but then displaying an enormous appetite. One day he spoke of going away, to which Yo would by no means consent; and as it was just then about to rain and thunder, Yo asked him to tell him what the clouds were like, what thunder was, and how he could get up to the sky and have a look, so as to set his mind at rest on the subject.

"Would you like to take a ramble among the clouds?" asked the stranger, as Yo was lying down to take a nap. On awaking, Yo felt himself spinning along through the air, and not at all as if he were lying on a bed. Opening his eyes he saw he was among the clouds, and around him was only fleecy atmosphere. Jumping up in great alarm, he felt as giddy as if he had been at sea, and underneath his feet he found a soft, yielding substance unlike the earth. Above him were the stars, and this made him think he was dreaming; but, looking up, he saw that they were set in the sky like seeds in the cup of a lily, varying from the size of the biggest bowl to that of a small basin. On raising his hand, he discovered that the large stars were all tightly fixed; but he managed to pick a small one, which he concealed in his sleeve; and then, parting the clouds beneath him, he looked through and saw the sea glittering like silver below. Large cities appeared no bigger than beans. Just at this moment, however, he bethought himself that if his foot were to slip, what a tremendous fall he would have.

He now beheld two dragons writhing their way along and drawing a cart with a huge vat in it, each movement of their tails sounding like the crack of a bullock driver's whip. The vat was full of water, and numbers of men were employed in ladling it out and sprinkling it on the clouds. These men were astonished at seeing Yo; however, a big fellow among them called out, "All right, he's my friend," and then they gave him a ladle to help them throw the water out. Now it happened to be a very dry season, and when Yo got hold of the ladle he took good care to throw the water so that it should all fall on and around his own home. The stranger then told him that he was an assistant to the God of Thunder, and that he had just returned from a three years' punishment inflicted on him in consequence of some neglect of his in the matter of rain. He added that they must now part; and, taking the long rope which had been used as reins for the cart, he bade Yo grip it tightly, that he might be let down to earth. Yo was afraid of this, but on being told there was no danger, he did so, and in a moment whish-h-h-h-h away he went, and found himself safe and sound on terra firma.

He discovered that he had descended outside his native village, and then the rope was drawn up into the clouds and he saw it no more. The drought had been excessive; for three or four miles around very little rain had fallen, though in Yo's own village the watercourses were all full. On reaching home, he took the star out of his sleeve and put it on the table. It was as dull looking as an ordinary stone; but at night it became very brilliant and lighted up the whole house. This made him value it highly, and he stored it carefully away, bringing it out only when he had guests, to light them at their wine. It was always thus dazzling bright, until one evening, when his wife was sitting with him doing her hair, the star began to diminish in brilliancy and to flit about like a firefly. Mrs. Yo sat gaping with astonishment, when all of a sudden it flitted into her mouth and ran down her throat. She tried to cough it up, but couldn't, to the very great amazement of her husband.

That night Yo dreamed that his old friend Hsia appeared before him and said, "I am the Shao-wei star. Your friendship is still cherished by me, and now you have brought me back from the sky. Truly our destinies are knitted together, and I will repay your kindness by becoming your son." Now Yo was thirty years of age, but without sons; however, after this dream his wife bore him a male child, and they called him Star. He was extraordinarily clever, and at sixteen years of age took his master's degree.

From *Strange Stories from a Chinese Studio.*

RETRIBUTION

ONCE upon a time there was a boy named Ma, whose father taught him at home. The window of the upper story looked out on the rear upon a terrace belonging to Old Wang, who had a garden of chrysanthemums there. One day Ma rose early and stood leaning against the window, watching the day dawn. And out came Old Wang from his terrace and watered his chrysanthemums. When he had just finished and was going in again, along came a water-carrier, bearing two pails on his shoulders, who seemed to want to help him. But the old man grew annoyed and motioned him off. Yet the water-carrier insisted on mounting the terrace. So they pulled each other about on the terrace edge. It had been raining, the terrace was slippery, its border high and narrow, and when the old man thrust back the water-carrier with his hand, the latter lost his balance, slipped, and tumbled down the slope. Then the old man hastened down to pick him up; but the two pails had fallen on his chest, and he lay there with feet outstretched. The old man was extremely frightened. Without uttering a sound, he took hold of the water-carrier's feet and dragged him through the back door to the bank of the stream which flowed by the garden. Then he fetched the pails and set them down beside the corpse. After that he went home, locked the door, and went to bed again.

Little Ma, in spite of his youth, thought it would be better to say nothing about an affair of this kind, in which a human life was involved. He shut the window and withdrew. The sun rose higher, and soon he heard a clamor without: "A dead man is lying on the riverbank!" The constable gave notice, and in the afternoon the judge came up to the beating of gongs, and the inspector of the dead knelt down and uncovered the corpse; yet the body showed no wound. So it was said: "He slipped and fell to his death!" The judge questioned the neighbors, but the neighbors all insisted that they knew nothing of the matter. Thereupon the judge had the body placed in a coffin, sealed it with his seal, and ordered that the relatives of the deceased be found. And then he went his way.

Nine years passed by, and young Ma had reached the age of twenty-one and attained a baccalaureate. His father had died, and the family was poor. So it came about that in the same room in which he had formerly studied his lessons, he now gathered a few pupils about him, to instruct them.

The time for examinations drew near. Ma had risen early, in order to work. He opened the window and there, in the distant valley, he saw a man with two pails gradually drawing nearer. When he looked more closely, it was the water-carrier. Greatly frightened, he thought that the man had returned to repay Old Wang. Yet he passed the old man's door without entering it. Then he went a few steps farther to the house of the Lis, and there went in. The Lis were wealthy people, and since they were near neighbors, the Mas and they were on a friendly footing. The matter seemed strange to Ma, and he got up and followed the water-carrier.

At the door of Li's house he met an old servant who was just coming out and who said, "Heaven is about to send a child to our mistress! I must go buy incense to burn to the gods in order to show our gratitude!"

Ma asked, "Did not a man with two pails of water on his shoulders just go in?"

The servant said there had not, but before he had finished speaking a maid came from the house and said, "You need not go to buy incense, for I have found some. And, through the favor of heaven, the child has already come to us." Then Ma realized that the water-carrier had returned to be born again into the life of earth, and not to exact retribution. He wondered, though, for what merit of his the former water-carrier happened to be reborn into so wealthy a family. So he kept the matter in mind, and from time to time inquired as to the child's well-being.

Seven more years went by, and the boy gradually grew up. He did not show much taste for learning, but he loved to keep birds. Old Wang was still strong and healthy. And though he was by this time more than eighty years old, his love for his chrysanthemums had only increased with age.

One day Ma once more rose early and stood leaning against his window. And he saw Old Wang come out upon his terrace and begin to water his chrysanthemums. Little Li sat in the upper story of his house, flying his pigeons. Suddenly some of the pigeons flew down to the railing of the flower garden. The boy was afraid they might fly off and he called them, but the pigeons did not move. The boy did not know what to do: he picked up stones and threw them at the birds. By mistake one of them struck Old Wang. The old man started, slipped, and fell from the terrace. Time passed and he did not rise. He lay there with his feet outstretched. The boy was very much frightened. Without uttering a sound he softly closed his window and went away. The sun gradually rose higher, and the old man's sons and grandsons all came out to look for him. They found him and said, "He slipped and fell to his death!" And they buried him according to the custom.

From *The Chinese Fairy Book*, edited by R. Wilhelm and translated by Frederick H. Martens (Philadelphia: J. B. Lippincott Co., 1921).

THE SORCERER OF THE WHITE LOTUS LODGE

ONCE upon a time there was a sorcerer who belonged to the White Lotus Lodge. He knew how to deceive the multitude with his black arts, and many who wished to learn the secret of his enchantment became his pupils.

One day the sorcerer wished to go out. He placed a bowl, covered with another bowl, in the hall of his house and ordered his pupils to watch it. But he warned them against uncovering the bowl to see what might be in it.

No sooner had he gone than the pupils uncovered the bowl and saw that it was filled with clear water. And floating on the water was a little ship made of straw, with real masts and sails. They were surprised and pushed it with their fingers till it upset. Then they quickly righted it again and once more covered the bowl. By that time the sorcerer was already standing among them. He was angry and scolded them, saying, "Why did you disobey my command?"

The pupils rose and denied that they had done so.

But the sorcerer answered, "Did not my ship turn turtle at sea, and yet you try to deceive me?"

On another evening he lit a giant candle in his room and ordered his pupils to watch it lest it be blown out by the wind. The second watch of the night came and the sorcerer had not yet returned. The pupils grew tired and sleepy, so they went to bed and gradually fell asleep. When they woke again the candle had gone out. So they rose quickly and relit it. But the sorcerer was already in the room, and again he scolded them.

"Truly we did not sleep! How could the light have gone out?"

Angrily the sorcerer replied, "You let me walk fifteen miles in the dark, and still you can talk nonsense!"

Then his pupils were very much frightened.

In the course of time one of his pupils insulted the sorcerer. The latter made note of the insult but said nothing. Soon after he told the pupil to feed the swine, and no sooner had he entered the sty than his master turned him into a pig. The sorcerer then at once called in a butcher, sold the pig to the man, and he went the way of all pigs who go to the butcher.

One day this pupil's father turned up to ask after his son, for he had not come back to his home for a long time. The sorcerer told him that his son had left him long ago. The father returned home and inquired everywhere for his son—without success. But one of his son's fellow pupils, who knew of the matter, informed the father. So the father complained to the district mandarin. The latter, however, feared that the sorcerer might make himself invisible. He did not dare to have him arrested, but informed his superior and begged for a thousand well-armed soldiers. These surrounded the sorcerer's home and seized him, together with his wife and child. All three were put into wooden cages to be transported to the capital.

The road wound through the mountains, and in the midst of the hills up came a giant as large as a tree, with eyes like saucers, a mouth like a plate, and teeth a foot long. The soldiers stood there trembling and did not dare to move.

Said the sorcerer, "That is a mountain spirit. My wife will be able to drive him off."

They did as he suggested, unchained the woman, and she took a spear and went to meet the giant. The latter was angered, and he swallowed her, tooth and nail. This frightened the rest all the more.

The sorcerer said, "Well, if he has done away with my wife, then it is my son's turn!"

So they let the son out of his cage. But the giant swallowed him in the same way. The rest all looked on without knowing what to do.

The sorcerer then wept with rage and said, "First he destroys my wife, and then my son. If only he might be punished for it! But I am the only one who can punish him!"

And, sure enough, they took him out of his cage too, gave him a sword, and sent him out against the giant. The sorcerer and the giant fought with each other for a time, and at last the giant seized the sorcerer, thrust him into his maw, stretched his neck, and swallowed him. Then he went his way contentedly.

And then, when it was too late, the soldiers realized that the sorcerer had tricked them.

From *The Chinese Fairy Book.*

THE CINNAMON TREE IN THE MOON

On a clear night, when not the softest breeze is stirring the heavens, one can see shadows in the moon, shivering to and fro like the branches of a tree. They are the shadows of the cinnamon tree in the moon.

I have heard that in former times this tree did not exist; instead there were fields of lovely flowers in which bewitching Immortals used to play. All of them, except Wu Kang, who guarded the dragon, were women and maidens. Wu Kang was so lazy that he often allowed the dragon to run away, while he amused himself and drank wine.

One day he went past Mount K'un Lun on his way back from the seas with the dragon. He met a large number of his friends there, and soon he was tossing down cup after cup of wine, composing poems, and throwing dice. He drank till he was completely tipsy, and even at sunset no idea of returning entered his head. During the night he felt gayer and gayer, and when he found some other Immortals playing chess he joined them with a shout of joy. The others all advised him to return home, but Wu Kang paid not the slightest attention and insisted on joining their game. The gamblers were loath to have such a poor devil as a player, because they were playing for marvel-

ous treasures, but Wu Kang proudly struck his chest and said, "I have a dragon pearl. I will wager that."

A few moves later the jewel was already lost, but he thought to himself that, since he could not drive the dragon home without it, he might as well continue the game and stake the dragon itself. But once again luck was against him, and he lost the dragon too. Now he had nothing more and had to crawl home shamefacedly.

The Immortals were furious when they learned of the loss and immediately sowed a pearl in the earth, out of which grew a tall cinnamon tree. They gave Wu Kang an ax and told him to hack off the branches; if he could manage to do this before the branches grew again, they would forgive him. He was very strong and easily cut off all the branches; but as soon as he had done so new ones sprouted out of the wounds and became stronger and bigger than before. If he was ever lazy the tree would grow so quickly that he never dared to rest for a moment. He is there to this day, and his beard has grown down to his waist. Day and night he cuts off the branches, and the trembling shadows are the branches falling down.

From *Chinese Fairy Tales and Folk Tales,* collected and translated by Wolfram Eberhard (New York: E. P. Dutton & Co., 1938).

WOMEN

AFTER he was married, Chang the Third no longer wanted to go to work. He sat at home the whole day and played with his wife. He gazed endlessly at her beautiful face, and the longer he looked the less he wanted to go out. Finally he gave up his job and remained night and day with his wife. He went on in this way for six months, and then for a year; but even the largest fortune is soon exhausted if one does nothing, and Chang had merely lived on his earnings. In two years all his wife's jewels, the chairs, the tables, the linen, the clothes, in fact everything they had, was pawned or sold, and they were left without a penny.

His wife was really unusually beautiful, but she thought to herself, "Since his marriage my husband has never left the house. Day and night he sits around doing nothing but eat. In a short while we shall no longer have the wherewithal to live." So she upbraided him, saying, "You really can't stay at home all day. All men must go to work." But Chang saw her beauty and he thought anxiously, "If I went out another man could come and make love to her." And instead of listening to her words he remained at home, preferring to eat the most miserable food.

But eventually their poverty became unbearable. They could no longer live if he did not work. Finally, one morning, he said good-by to his wife and decided to go to a village. On his way he met a fine-looking man of about fifty years, who said to him, "Which is the way to such and such a village?" Chang answered, "I am going there myself, so we can go together." During their walk Chang told the stranger his story. "I am so unhappy at leaving my wife," he said. "But I must look for work to enable us to live."

The stranger replied, "The simplest thing is to bottle up your wife. I will give you the bottle, and every day, when you leave, you will only need to look at your wife and blow into the bottle, and she will vanish inside at once. As you can always take it with you, you will never lose your wife. I must now take another road, so farewell." Then he handed Chang a large three-inch bottle from his bag and disappeared. Chang dropped the bottle into his bag, noting what the man had said, and set off gaily for the village. The next day he tried the gift. As his wife was combing her hair before the mirror he secretly blew into the bottle. The woman saw in the mirror the reflection of her husband blowing into a bottle, but then she lost consciousness and woke up to find herself inside the bottle. Chang put the bottle in his pocket and went off to his work in the village. He was quite contented, for now no other man could flirt with his wife. In the evening he tipped the bottle, and his beautiful wife stood before him as before.

One day, however, he was forced to leave his wife at home to do the washing. He begged her not to leave the house when the washing was finished, and then set off to the village, forgetting to take the bottle with him.

After her husband's departure the wife went down to the river to wash the clothes. While she was rinsing a shirt she suddenly felt a long, hard thing between her fingers. She took it out and looked at it carefully. "It's a bottle," she said to herself. "Every morning my husband blows into it and I vanish inside. Why has he forgotten it today?" While she was pondering over the matter, a handsome young man passed by on the other bank. She looked up at him, and without thinking what she was doing blew into the bottle, whereupon the young man disappeared. When she had finished the washing she replaced the bottle in her husband's clothes.

When the man arrived home he immediately asked for the bottle he had left behind, and his wife handed it to him without a word. The next day when he went out he blew into the bottle as usual, and his wife disappeared, and again he flattered himself that she was safe from the caresses of other men.

That evening on his return he tipped the bottle, but this time two people appeared, his wife and a handsome young man. He was very much surprised and said to himself, "How strange! I thought my wife was quite safe shut up in the bottle, but now she has got a man with her! How odd it is! And how impossible it is to keep a beautiful wife to oneself."

From *Chinese Fairy Tales and Folk Tales.*

Egyptian

The Shipwrecked Sailor

All the tales in this section are older than the fifth century B.C., and "The Shipwrecked Sailor" is generally believed to be about three thousand and seven hundred years old. As such, the survivor's description of his casting away on a disappearing island presided over by a serpent who is all kingly gold and lazuli and prophesies like a wizard prince—indeed like a Prospero—is perhaps the prototype of all tales of enchanted islands and of princes in the shape of serpents. Similarly, "The Doomed Prince," ascribed to the late 18th Dynasty (or about 1400 B.C.), is an amazingly early treatment—unfortunately a fragment—of such familiar folk-tale themes as the child granted to parents by the gods but subject to a dire prophecy, or the maiden imprisoned in a tower from which only the bravest prince can release her.

But early and relatively simple as such stories may be, the narratives are far from primitive and possess passages of color and imagination that are notable even when measured by literary standards. This is especially true of the best known of them, the 19th Dynasty account of the brothers Anpu and Bata. It opens as a realistic tale of a young man slandered by his older brother's wife because he has rejected her advances, but then abruptly becomes a welter of magic transformations and marvels. The earlier part is, of course, essentially the same as the Biblical story of young Joseph and Potiphar's wife, and since the Hebrew account is also set in Egypt of roughly the same period, it is hard to believe that both were not originally one and the same story.

"The Treasures of Rhampsinitus" is a legend that Herodotus, earliest of Greek historians, heard from Egyptian priests during his travels in Africa about 450 B.C. If not the original of the Master Thief stories found in folklore all over the world (a Scandinavian version is given on page 676), it is undoubtedly one of the earliest versions.

ANPU AND BATA

Once there were two brethren, of one mother and one father; Anpu was the name of the elder, and Bata was the name of the younger. Now, as for Anpu, he had a house and he had a wife. But his little brother was to him as it were a son; he it was who made for him his clothes; he it was who followed behind his oxen to the fields; he it was who did the plowing; he it was who harvested the corn; he it was who did for him all the matters that were in the field. Behold, his younger brother grew to be an excellent worker, there was not his equal in the whole land; behold! the spirit of a god was in him.

Now after this the younger brother followed his oxen in his daily manner; and every evening he turned again to the house, laden with all the herbs of the field, with milk and with wood, and with all things of the field. And he put them down before his elder brother, who was sitting with his wife; and he drank and ate, and he lay down in his stable with the cattle. And at the dawn of day he took bread which he had baked, and laid it before his elder brother; and he took with him his bread to the field, and he drove his cattle to pasture in the fields. And as he walked behind his cattle, they said to him, "Good is the herbage which is in that place"; and he listened to all that they said, and he took them to the good place which they desired. And the cattle which were before him became exceeding excellent, and they multiplied greatly.

Now at the time of plowing his elder brother said unto him, "Let us make ready for ourselves a goodly yoke of oxen for plowing, for the land has come out from the water, it is fit for plowing. Moreover, do thou come to the field with corn, for we will begin the plowing in the morrow morning." Thus said he to him; and his younger brother did all things as his elder brother had spoken unto him to do them.

And when the morn was come, they went to the fields with their things; and their hearts were pleased exceedingly with their task in the beginning of their work. And it came to pass after this that as they were in the field they stopped for corn, and he sent his younger brother, saying, "Haste thou, bring to us corn from the farm." And the younger brother found the wife of his elder brother, as she was sitting tiring her hair. He said to her, "Get up and give to me corn, that I may run to the field, for my elder brother hastened me; do not delay." She said to him, "Go, open the bin, and thou shalt take to thyself according to thy will, that I may not drop my locks of hair while I dress them."

The youth went into the stable; he took a large measure, for he desired to take much corn; he loaded it with wheat and barley; and he went out carrying it. She said to him, "How much of the corn is wanted, is that which is on thy shoulder?" He said to her, "Three bushels of barley, and two of wheat, in all, five; these are what are upon my shoulder": thus said he to her. And she conversed with him, saying, "There is great strength in thee, for I see thy might every day." And her heart knew him with the knowledge of youth. And she arose and came to him, and conversed with him, saying, "Come, stay with me, and it shall be well for thee, and I will make for thee beautiful garments." Then the youth became like a panther of the south with fury at the evil speech which she had made to him; and she feared greatly. And he spake unto her, saying, "Behold, thou art to me as a mother, thy husband is to me as a father, for he who is elder than I has brought me up. What is this wickedness that thou hast said to me? Say it not to me again. For I will not tell it to any man, for I will not let it be uttered by the mouth of any man." He lifted up his burden, and he went to the field and came to his elder brother; and they took up their work, to labor at their task.

Now afterward, at eventime, his elder brother was returning to his house; and the younger brother was following after his oxen, and he loaded himself with all the things of the field; and he brought his oxen before him, to make them lie down in their stable which was in the farm. And behold, the wife of the elder brother was afraid for the words which she had said. She took a parcel of fat, she became like one who is evilly beaten, desiring to say to her husband, "It is thy younger brother who has done this wrong." Her husband returned in the even, as was his wont of every day; he came unto his house; he found his wife ill of violence; she did not give him water upon his hands as he used to have, she did not make a light before him, his house was in darkness, and she was lying very sick.

Her husband said to her, "Who has spoken with thee?" Behold, she said, "No one has spoken with me except thy younger brother. When he came to take for thee corn he found me sitting alone; he said to me, 'Come, let us stay together, tie up thy hair': thus spake he to me. I did not listen to him, but thus spake I to him, 'Behold, am I not thy mother, is not thy elder brother to thee as a father?' And he feared, and he beat me to stop me from making report to thee, and if thou lettest him live I shall die. Now, behold, he is coming in the evening; and I complain of these wicked words, for he would have done this even in daylight."

And the elder brother became as a panther of the south; he sharpened his knife; he took it in his hand; he stood behind the door of his stable to slay his younger brother as he came in the evening to bring his cattle into the stable.

Now the sun went down, and he loaded himself with herbs in his daily manner. He came, and his foremost cow entered the stable, and she said to her keeper, "Behold thou thy elder brother standing before thee with his knife to slay thee. Flee from before him." He heard what his first cow had said; and the next entering, she also said likewise. He looked beneath the door of the stable; he saw the feet of his elder brother; he was standing behind the door, and his knife was in his hand. He cast down his load to the ground and betook himself to flee swiftly; and his elder brother pursued after him with his knife. Then the younger brother cried out unto Ra Harakhti, saying, "My good Lord! Thou art He who divides the evil from the good." And Ra stood and heard all his cry; and Ra made a wide water between him and his elder brother, and it was full of crocodiles; and the one brother was on one bank, and the other on the other bank; and the elder brother smote twice on his hands at not slaying him. Thus did he. And the younger brother called to the elder on the bank, saying, "Stand still until the dawn of day; and when Ra ariseth, I shall judge with thee before Him, and He discerneth between the good and the evil. For I shall not be with thee any more forever; I shall not be in the place in which thou art; I shall go to the valley of the acacia."

Now when the land was lightened, and the next day appeared, Ra Harakhti arose, and one looked unto the other. And the youth spake with his elder brother, saying, "Wherefore camest thou after me to slay me in craftiness, when thou didst not hear the words of my mouth? For I am thy brother in truth, and thou art to me as a father, and thy wife even as a mother: is it not so? Verily, when I was sent to bring for us corn, thy wife said to me, 'Come, stay with me'; for behold, this has been turned over unto thee in another wise." And he caused him to understand of all that happened with him and his wife. And he swore an oath by Ra Harakhti, saying, "Thy coming to slay me by deceit with thy knife was an abomination." Then the youth took a knife, and cut off his flesh, and cast it into the water, and the fish swallowed it. He failed; he became faint; and his elder brother cursed his own heart greatly; he stood weeping for him afar off; he knew not how to pass over to where his younger brother was, because of the crocodiles. And the younger brother called unto him, saying, "Whereas thou hast devised an evil thing, wilt thou not also devise a good thing, even like that which I would do unto thee? When thou goest to thy house thou must look to thy cattle, for I shall not stay in the place where thou art; I am going to the valley of the acacia. And now as to what thou shalt do for me: it is even that thou shalt come to seek after me, if thou perceivest a matter, namely, that there are things happening unto me. And this is what shall come to pass, that I shall draw out my soul, and I shall put it upon the top of the flowers of the acacia, and when the acacia is cut down, and it falls to the ground, and thou comest to seek for it, if thou searchest for it seven years, do not let thy heart be wearied. For thou wilt find it, and thou must put it in a cup of cold water, and expect that I shall live again, that I may make answer to what has been done wrong. And thou shalt know of this, that is to say, that things are happening to me, when one shall give to thee a cup of beer in thy hand, and it shall be troubled; stay not then, for verily it shall come to pass with thee."

And the youth went to the valley of the acacia; and his elder brother went unto his house; his hand was laid on his head, and he cast dust on his head; he came to his house, and he slew his wife, he cast her to the dogs, and he sat in mourning for his younger brother.

Now many days after these things the younger brother was in the valley of the acacia; there was none with him; he spent his time in hunting the beasts of the desert, and he came back in the even to lie down under the acacia, which bore his soul upon the topmost flower. And after this he built himself a tower with his own hands, in the valley of the acacia; it was full of all good things, that he might provide for himself a home.

And he went out from his tower, and he met the Nine Gods, who were walking forth to look upon the whole land. The Nine Gods talked one with another, and they said unto him, "Ho! Bata, bull of the Nine Gods, art thou remaining alone? Thou hast left thy village for the wife of Anpu, thy elder brother. Behold, his wife is slain. Thou hast given him an answer to all that was transgressed against thee." And their hearts were vexed for him exceedingly. And Ra Harakhti said to Khnumu, "Behold, frame thou a woman for Bata, that he may not remain alive alone." And Khnumu made for him a mate to dwell with him. She was more beautiful in her limbs than any woman who is in the whole land. The essence of every god was in her. The seven Hathors came to see her: they said with one mouth, "She will die a sharp death."

And Bata loved her very exceedingly, and she dwelt in his house; he passed his time in hunting the beasts, and brought and laid them before her. He said, "Go not outside, lest the sea seize thee; for I cannot rescue thee from it, for I am a woman like thee; my soul is placed on the head of the flower of the acacia; and if another find it, I must fight with him." And he opened unto her his heart in all its nature.

Now after these things Bata went to hunt in his daily manner. And the young girl went to walk under the acacia which was by the side of her house. Then the sea saw her and cast its waves up after her. She betook herself to flee from before it. She entered her house. And the sea called unto the acacia, saying, "Oh, would that I could seize her!" And the acacia brought a lock from her hair, and the sea carried it to Egypt and dropped it in the place of the fullers of Pharaoh's linen. The smell of the lock of hair entered into the clothes of Pharaoh; and they were wroth with the fullers of Pharaoh, saying, "The smell of ointment is in the clothes of Pharaoh." And the people were rebuked every day, they knew not what they should do. And the chief fuller of Pharaoh walked by the bank, and his heart was very evil within him after the daily quarrel with him. He stood still, he stood upon the sand opposite to the lock of hair, which was in the water, and he made one enter into the water and bring it to him; and there was found in it a smell, exceeding sweet. He took it to Pharaoh; and they brought the scribes and the wise men, and they said unto Pharaoh, "This lock of hair belongs to a daughter of Ra Harakhti: the essence of every god is in her, and it is a tribute to thee from another land. Let messengers go to every strange land to seek her: and as for the messenger who shall go to the valley of the acacia, let many men go with him to bring her." Then said his majesty, "Excellent exceedingly is what has been said to us"; and they sent them. And many days after these things the people who were sent to strange lands came to give report unto the king: but there came not those who went to the valley of the acacia, for Bata had slain them, but let one of them return to give a report to the king. His majesty sent many men and soldiers, as well as horsemen, to bring her back. And there was a woman amongst them, and to her had been given in her hand beautiful ornaments of a woman. And the girl came back with her, and they rejoiced over her in the whole land.

And his majesty loved her exceedingly and raised her to high estate; and he spake unto her that she should tell him concerning her husband. And she said, "Let the acacia be cut down, and let one chop it up." And they sent men and soldiers with their weapons to cut down the acacia; and they came to the acacia, and they cut the flower upon which was the soul of Bata, and he fell dead suddenly. And when the next day came, and the earth was lightened, the acacia was cut down. And Anpu, the elder brother of Bata, entered his house and washed his hands; and one gave him a cup of beer, and it became troubled; and one gave him another of wine, and the smell of it was evil. Then he took his staff, and his sandals, and likewise his clothes, with his weapons of war; and he betook himself forth to the valley of the acacia. He entered the tower of his younger brother, and he found him lying upon his mat, he was dead. And he wept when he saw his younger brother verily lying dead. And he went out to seek the soul of his younger brother under the acacia tree, under which his younger brother lay in the evening. He spent three years in seeking for it, but found it not. And when he began the fourth year, he desired in his heart to return into Egypt; he said, "I will go tomorrow morn"; thus spake he in his heart.

Now when the land lightened, and the next day appeared, he was walking under the acacia; he was spending his time in seeking it. And he returned in the evening and labored at seeking it again. He found a seed. He returned with it. Behold, this was the soul of his younger brother. He brought a cup of cold water, and he cast the seed into it; and he sat down, as he was wont. Now when the night came Bata's soul sucked up the water; he shuddered in all his limbs, and he looked on his elder brother; his soul was in the cup.

Then Anpu took the cup of cold water, in which the soul of his younger brother was; Bata drank it, his soul stood again in its place, and he became as he had been. They embraced each other, and they conversed together.

And Bata said to his elder brother, "Behold, I am to become as a great bull, which bears every good mark; no one knoweth its history, and thou must sit upon my back. When the sun arises I shall be in the place where my wife is, that I may return answer to her; and thou must take me to the place where the king is. For all good things shall be done for thee; for one shall lade thee with silver and gold, because thou bringest me to Pharaoh, for I become a great marvel, and they shall rejoice for me in all the land. And thou shalt go to thy village."

And when the land was lightened, and the next day appeared, Bata became in the form which he had told to his elder brother. And Anpu sat upon his back until the dawn. He came to the place where the king was, and they made his majesty to know of him; he saw him, and he was exceeding joyful with him. He made for him great offerings, saying, "This is a great wonder which has come to pass." There were rejoicings over him in the whole land. They presented unto him silver and gold for his elder brother, who went and stayed in his village. They gave to the bull many men and many things, and Pharaoh loved him exceedingly above all that is in this land.

And after many days after these things the bull entered the purified place; he stood in the place where the princess was; he began to speak with her, saying, "Behold, I am alive indeed." And she said to him, "And, pray, who art thou?" He said to her, "I am Bata. I perceived when thou causedst that they should destroy the acacia of Pharaoh, which was my abode, that I might not be suffered to live. Behold, I am alive indeed, I am as an ox." Then the princess feared exceedingly for the words that her husband had spoken to her. And he went out from the purified place.

And his majesty was sitting, making a good day with her: she was at the table of his majesty, and the king was exceeding pleased with her. And she said to his majesty, "Swear to me by God, saying, 'What thou shalt say, I will obey it for thy sake.'" He hearkened unto all that she said, even this. "Let me eat of the liver of the ox, because he is fit for naught": thus spake she to him. And the king was exceeding sad at her words, the heart of Pharaoh grieved him greatly. And after the land was lightened, and the next day appeared, they proclaimed a great feast with offerings to the ox. And the king sent one of the chief butchers of his majesty to cause the ox to be sacrificed. And when he was sacrificed, as he was upon the shoulders of the people, he shook his neck, and he threw two drops of blood over against the two doors of his majesty. The one fell upon the one side, on the great door of Pharaoh, and the other upon the other door. They grew as two great Persea trees, and each of them was excellent.

And one went to tell unto his majesty, "Two great Persea trees have grown, as a great marvel of his majesty, in the night by the side of the great gate of his majesty." And there was rejoicing for them in all the land, and there were offerings made to them.

And when the days were multiplied after these things, his majesty was adorned with the blue crown, with garlands of flowers on his neck, and he was upon the chariot of pale gold, and he went out from the palace to behold the Persea trees: the princess also was going out with horses behind his majesty. And his majesty sat beneath one of the Persea trees, and it spake thus with his wife, "Oh, thou deceitful one, I am Bata, I am alive, though I have been evilly entreated. I knew who caused the acacia to be cut down by Pharaoh at my dwelling. I then became an ox, and thou causedst that I should be killed."

And many days after these things the princess stood at the table of Pharaoh, and the king was pleased with her. And she said to his majesty, "Swear to me by God, saying, 'That which the princess shall say to me I will obey it for her.' " And he hearkened unto all she said. And he commanded, "Let these two Persea trees be cut down, and let them be made into goodly planks." And he hearkened unto all she said. And after this his majesty sent skillful craftsmen, and they cut down the Persea trees of Pharaoh; and the princess, the royal wife, was standing looking on, and they did all that was in her heart unto the trees. But a chip flew up, and it entered into the mouth of the princess; she swallowed it, and after many days she bore a son. And one went to tell his majesty, "There is born to thee a son." And they brought him, and gave to him a nurse and servants; and there were rejoicings in the whole land. And the king sat making a merry day, as they were about the naming of him, and his majesty loved him exceedingly at that moment, and the king raised him to be the royal son of Kush.

Now after the days had multiplied after these things, his majesty made him heir of all the land. And many days after that, when he had fulfilled many years as heir, his majesty flew up to heaven. And the heir said, "Let my great nobles of his majesty be brought before me, that I may make them to know all that has happened to me." And they brought also before him his wife, and he judged with her before him, and they agreed with him. They brought to him his elder brother; he made him hereditary prince in all his land. He was thirty years king of Egypt, and he died, and his elder brother stood in his place on the day of burial.

From *Egyptian Tales*, edited by W. M. Flinders Petrie (London: Methuen & Co., 1895).

THE SHIPWRECKED SAILOR

THE WISE servant said, "Let thy heart be satisfied, O my lord, for that we have come back to the country; after we have long been on board, and rowed much, the prow has at last touched land. All the people rejoice and embrace us one after another. Moreover, we have come back in good health, and not a man is lacking; although we have been to the ends of Wawat, and gone through the land of Senmut, we have returned in peace, and our land—behold, we have come back to it. Hear me, my lord; I have no other refuge. Wash thee, and turn the water over thy fingers; then go and tell the tale to the majesty."

His lord replied, "Thy heart continues still its wandering words! but although the mouth of a man may save him, his words may also cover his face with confusion. Wilt thou do then as thy heart moves thee? This that thou wilt say, tell quietly."

The sailor then answered, "Now I shall tell that which has happened to me, to my very self. I was going to the mines of Pharaoh, and I went down on the sea on a ship of one hundred and fifty cubits long and forty cubits wide, with one hundred and fifty sailors of the best of Egypt, who had seen heaven and earth, and whose hearts were stronger than lions. They had said that the wind would not be contrary, or that there would be none. But as we approached the land the wind arose, and threw up waves eight cubits high. As for me, I seized a piece of wood; but those who were in the vessel perished, without one remaining. A wave threw me on an island, after that I had been three days alone, without a companion beside my own heart. I laid me in a thicket, and the shadow covered me. Then stretched I my limbs to try to find something for my mouth. I found there figs and grapes, all manner of good herbs, berries and grain, melons of all kinds, fishes and birds. Nothing was lacking. And I satisfied myself; and left on the ground that which was over, of what my arms had been filled withal. I dug a pit, I lighted a fire, and I made a burned offering unto the gods.

"Suddenly I heard a noise as of thunder, which I thought to be that of a wave of the sea. The trees shook, and the earth was

moved. I uncovered my face, and I saw that a serpent drew near. He was thirty cubits long, and his beard greater than two cubits; his body was as overlaid with gold, and his color as that of true lazuli. He coiled himself before me.

"Then he opened his mouth, while I lay on my face before him, and he said to me, 'What has brought thee, what has brought thee, little one, what has brought thee? If thou sayest not speedily what has brought thee to this isle, I will make thee know thyself; as a flame thou shalt vanish if thou tellest me not something I have not heard, or which I knew not, before thee.'

"Then he took me in his mouth and carried me to his resting place and laid me down without any hurt. I was whole and sound, and nothing was gone from me. Then he opened his mouth against me, while I lay on my face before him, and he said, 'What has brought thee, what has brought thee, little one, what has brought thee to this isle which is in the sea, and of which the shores are in the midst of the waves?'

"Then I replied to him, and, holding my arms low before him, I said to him, 'I was embarked for the mines by the order of the majesty, in a ship; one hundred and fifty cubits was its length, and the width of it forty cubits. It had one hundred and fifty sailors of the best of Egypt, who had seen heaven and earth, and the hearts of whom were stronger than lions. They said that the wind would not be contrary, or that there would be none. Each of them exceeded his companion in the prudence of his heart and the strength of his arm, and I was not beneath any of them. A storm came upon us while we were on the sea. Hardly could we reach to the shore when the wind waxed yet greater, and the waves rose even eight cubits. As for me, I seized a piece of wood, while those who were in the boat perished, without one being left with me for three days. Behold me now before thee, for I was brought to this isle by a wave of the sea.'

"Then said he to me, 'Fear not, fear not, little one, and make not thy face sad. If thou hast come to me, it is God who has let thee live. For it is He who has brought thee to this isle of the blest, where nothing is lacking, and which is filled with all good things. See now, thou shalt pass one month after another, until thou shalt be four months in this isle. Then a ship shall come from thy land with sailors, and thou shalt leave with them and go to thy country, and thou shalt die in thy town.

" 'Converse is pleasing, and he who tastes of it passes over his misery. I will therefore tell thee of that which is in this isle. I am here with my brethren and my children around me; we are seventy-five serpents, children, and kindred; without naming a young girl who was brought unto me by chance, and on whom the fire of heaven fell and burned her to ashes.

" 'As for thee if thou art strong, and if thy heart waits patiently, thou shalt press thy infants to thy bosom and embrace thy wife. Thou shalt return to thy house which is full of all good things, thou shalt see thy land, where thou shalt dwell in the midst of thy kindred.'

"Then I bowed, in my obeisance, and I touched the ground before him. 'Behold now that which I have told thee before. I shall tell of thy presence unto Pharaoh, I shall make him to know of thy greatness, and I will bring to thee of the sacred oils and perfumes, and of incense of the temples with which all gods are honored. I shall tell, moreover, of that which I do now see (thanks to him), and there shall be rendered to thee praises before the fullness of all the land. I shall slay asses for thee in sacrifice, I shall pluck for thee the birds, and I shall bring for thee ships full of all kinds of the treasures of Egypt, as is comely to do unto a god, a friend of men in a far country, of which men know not.'

"Then he smiled at my speech, because of that which was in his heart, for he said to me, 'Thou art not rich in perfumes, for all that thou hast is but common incense. As for me, I am prince of the land of Punt, and I have perfumes. Only the oil which thou saidst thou wouldst bring is not common in this isle. But, when thou shalt depart from this place, thou shalt never more see this isle; it shall be changed into waves.'

"And, behold, when the ship drew near, according to all that he had told me before, I got me up into a high tree, to strive to see those who were within it. Then I came and told to him this matter; but it was already known unto him before. Then he said to me, 'Farewell, farewell, go to thy house, little one, see again thy children, and let thy name be good in thy town; these are my wishes for thee.'

"Then I bowed myself before him, and held my arms low before him, and he, he gave me gifts of precious perfumes, of cassia, of sweet woods, of kohl, of cypress, an abundance of incense, of ivory tusks, of baboons, of apes, and all kind of precious things. I embarked all in the ship which was come, and, bowing myself, I prayed God for him.

"Then he said to me, 'Behold, thou shalt come to thy country in two months, thou shalt press to thy bosom thy children, and thou shalt rest in thy tomb.' After this I went down to the shore unto the ship, and I called to the sailors who were there. Then on the shore I rendered adoration to the master of this isle and to those who dwelt therein.

"When we shall come, in our return, to the house of Pharaoh, in the second month, according to all that serpent has said, we shall approach unto the palace. And I shall go in before Pharaoh, I shall bring the gifts which I have brought from this isle into the country.

Then he shall thank me before the fullness of all the land. Grant then unto me a follower, and lead me to the courtiers of the king. Cast thy eye upon me, after I am come to land again, after I have both seen and proved this. Hear my prayer, for it is good to listen to people. It was said unto me, 'Become a wise man, and thou shalt come to honor,' and behold I have become such."

This is finished from its beginning unto its end, even as it was found in a writing. It is written by the scribe of cunning fingers Ameni-amen-aa; may he live in life, wealth, and health!

From *Egyptian Tales.*

THE DOOMED PRINCE

THERE once was a king to whom no son was born; and his heart was grieved, and he prayed for himself unto the gods around him for a child. They decreed that one should be born to him. And his wife, after her time was fulfilled, brought forth a son. Then came the Hathors to decree for him a destiny; they said, "His death is to be by the crocodile, or by the serpent, or by the dog." Then the people who stood by heard this, and they went to tell it to his majesty. Then his majesty's heart sickened very greatly. And his majesty caused a house to be built upon the desert; it was furnished with people and with all good things of the royal house, that the child should not go abroad. And when the child was grown, he went up upon the roof, and he saw a dog; it was following a man who was walking on the road. He spoke to his page, who was with him, "What is this that walks behind the man who is coming along the road?" He answered him, "This is a dog." The child said to him, "Let there be brought to me one like it." The page went to repeat this to his majesty. And his majesty said, "Let there be brought to him a little pet dog, lest his heart be sad." And behold, they brought to him the dog.

Then when the days increased after this, and when the child became grown in all his limbs, he sent a message to his father, saying, "Come, wherefore am I kept here? Inasmuch as I am fated to three evil fates, let me follow my desire. Let God do what is in His heart."

They agreed to all he said, and gave him all sorts of arms, and also his dog to follow him, and they took him to the east country, and said to him, "Behold, go thou whither thou wilt." His dog was with him, and he went northward, following his heart in the desert, while he lived on all the best of the game of the desert. He went to the chief of Naharaina.

And behold, there had not been any born to the chief of Naharaina except one daughter. Behold, there had been built for her a house; its seventy windows were seventy cubits from the ground. And the chief caused to be brought all the sons of the chiefs of the land of Khalu, and said to them, "He who reaches the window of my daughter, she shall be to him for a wife."

And many days after these things, as they were in their daily task, the youth rode by the place where they were. They took the youth to their house, they bathed him, they gave provender to his horses, they brought all kinds of things for the youth, they perfumed him, they anointed his feet, they gave him portions of their own food; and they spake to him, "Whence comest thou, goodly youth?" He said to them, "I am son of an officer of the land of Egypt; my mother is dead, and my father has taken another wife. And when she bore children, she grew to hate me, and I have come as a fugitive from before her." And they embraced him and kissed him.

And after many days were passed he said to the youths, "What is it that ye do here?" And they said to him, "We spend our time in this: we climb up, and he who shall reach the window of the daughter of the chief of Naharaina, to him will be given her to wife." He said to them, "If it please you, let me behold the matter, that I may come to climb with you." They went to climb, as was their daily wont: and the youth stood afar off to behold; and the face of the daughter of the chief of Naharaina was turned to them. And another day the sons came to climb, and the youth came to climb with the sons of the chiefs. He climbed, and he reached the window of the daughter of the chief of Naharaina. She kissed him, she embraced him in all his limbs.

And one went to rejoice the heart of her father and said to him, "One of the people has reached the window of thy daughter." And the prince inquired of the messenger, saying, "The son of which of the princes is it?" And he replied, "It is the son of an officer, who has come as a fugitive from the land of Egypt, fleeing from before his stepmother when she had children." Then the chief of Naharaina was exceeding angry; and he said, "Shall I indeed give my daughter to the Egyptian fugitive? Let him go back whence he came." And one came to tell the youth, "Go back to the place thou camest from." But the maiden seized his hand; she swore an oath by God, saying, "By the being of Ra Harakhti, if one takes him from me, I will not eat, I will not drink, I shall die in that same hour." The messenger went to tell unto her father all that she said. Then the prince sent men to slay the youth, while he was in his house. But the maiden said, "By the being of Ra, if one slay him I shall be dead ere the sun goeth down. I will not pass an hour of life if I am parted from him." And one went to tell her father. Then the prince made them bring the youth with the maiden. The youth was seized with fear when he came before the prince. But he embraced him, he kissed him all over, and said, "Oh, tell me who thou art; behold, thou art to me as a son." He said to him, "I am a son of an officer of the land of Egypt; my mother died, my father took to him a second wife; she came to hate me, and I fled a fugitive from before her." He then gave to him his daughter to wife; he gave also to him a house, and serfs, and fields, also cattle and all manner of good things.

But after the days of these things were passed, the youth said to his wife, "I am doomed to three fates—a crocodile, a serpent, and a dog." She said to him, "Let one kill the dog which belongs to thee." He replied to her, "I am not going to kill my dog, which I have brought up from when it was small." And she feared greatly for her husband and would not let him go alone abroad.

And one went with the youth toward the land of Egypt, to travel in that country. Behold, the crocodile of the river, he came out by the town in which the youth was. And in that town was a mighty man. And the mighty man would not suffer the crocodile to escape. And when the crocodile was bound, the mighty man went back to the house; and he did so every day, during two months of days.

Now when the days passed after this, the youth sat making a good day in his house. And when the evening came he lay down on his bed, sleep seized upon his limbs; and his wife filled a bowl of milk and placed it by his side. Then came out a serpent from his hole, to bite the youth; behold, his wife was sitting by him, she lay not down. Thereupon the servants gave milk to the serpent, and he drank, and was drunk, and lay upside down. Then his wife made it to perish with the blows of her dagger. And they woke her husband, who was astonished; and she said unto him, "Behold, thy God has given one of thy dooms into thy hand; He will also give thee the others." And he sacrificed to God, adoring Him, and praising His spirits from day to day.

And when the days were passed after these things, the youth went to walk in the fields of his domain. He went not alone, behold, his dog was following him. And his dog ran aside after the wild game, and he followed the dog. He came to the river, and entered the river behind his dog. Then came out the crocodile, and took him to the place where the mighty man was. And the crocodile said to the youth, "I am thy doom, following after thee. . . ."

(Here the papyrus breaks off.)

From *Egyptian Tales*.

THE TREASURES OF RHAMPSINITUS

THERE was once a king of Egypt who was called Rhampsinitus. He was very rich and greedy. He tried to get as much money as he could from his people; but the more he had, the more he wanted. His house was full of gold and silver; and his servants every day brought him more, until he was puzzled to know where he should put it. For a long time he thought how he might hide it, for he could hardly rest by day or sleep by night for fear that thieves might come and take away some of his riches. At last he sent for a mason and told him to build a great and strong room, which should have no windows and only a single door, fastened with iron bars and with strong bolts and locks. So the room was built in a corner of the palace, and the outer wall faced the roadway. When the house was finished, Rhampsinitus carried all his silver and gold secretly into it; and the whole room was filled with his riches. There were jars full of gold round the walls, and others full of diamonds, and pearls, and rubies, and jaspers; and in the middle of the room there was a great heap of coins, which shone so brightly that they almost made that dismal place look cheerful. Then King Rhampsinitus thought himself a happier man, and he went to sleep more soundly, because he fancied that no one would be able to steal his money.

Not long after this the old mason who had built the treasure house fell ill, and he called his two sons to his bedside and said to them, "I am so weak and ill that I know I shall soon die; but I do not wish to leave you without telling you the secret of the house where King Rhampsinitus has hoarded up his money. I have little to give you myself, for the king tried to make me work hard and to give me as little as he could for all my trouble. But I know a way in which you may get money when you are in need of it. The king does not know that I have placed a mark on one of the stones in the wall of his treasure house on the side which faces the road. This stone can be easily taken out and put back again by two men, or even by one, and his money can be taken without moving the bolts or touching the locks."

Soon after he had told them this secret the old mason died; and not long afterward his two sons began to think about the treasures of King Rhampsinitus, for the money which the old mason left them was soon wasted in eating and drinking with their friends. But they did not care, for they knew that when they wanted it they could get plenty of money from the treasures of King Rhampsinitus. So one night, when the moon was shining high up in the sky, they went very softly to the house where the money was hid; and after looking about for a little while, they found the stone, and they put it aside and went into the room. They were afraid to stay there long; but they filled their clothes with as much gold and silver as they could carry, and when they had put back the stone carefully, they went home and showed their mother all the money which they had stolen from the king. The next night they went again; and for many nights they kept on going, till at last King Rhampsinitus began to think that some of the heaps of money were smaller than they used to be; and every day when he went into the treasure house he looked at the heaps, and rubbed his eyes, and looked at them again, for he could not make out how it was that they seemed to grow smaller and smaller. And he said, "This is very odd. What can it be that takes away my money? The locks of the treasure house are not touched, and the bolts and bars have not been moved; and still my heaps of gold and silver seem every day to become smaller than they were." Then he thought that perhaps it might be his own fancy, until he put a heap of coins on purpose in one part of the room; and very soon these were taken away. Then he knew that some thief had found out a way to come in without unlocking the door. But King Rhampsinitus did not care much about it, for he said, "I think I know how to catch the thief who comes to steal my money." So he got a large trap which was big enough to hold a man's leg and put it in the treasure house.

In a day or two after this the sons of the old mason came again, and the younger one went in first and presently stepped into the trap. His leg was terribly hurt, but he did not scream or make any noise, because he was afraid that King Rhampsinitus might hear him. Then he called to his brother who was standing outside, and showed him how he was caught in the trap, and that he could not get his leg out of it; and he said, "Make haste, brother, and cut off my head, and carry it away. You must do this; for if you do not, the king will come and see who I am, and then he will have your head cut off as well as mine."

His brother was very sorry, but there seemed to be no help for it. So he cut off his head and took it home with him; and when King Rhampsinitus came in the morning to look at his gold and silver, he started back and held up his hands in great wonder; for he saw that two men had come in and that one had carried away the dead man's head, and he knew that there was someone else still alive who might come and rob him of his money. Then he thought of a way to find him out, and he told his servants to take the body out of the trap and hang it upon a wall, and ordered the soldiers to watch and if they saw anyone crying or weeping near it, to take him and bring him before the king.

Now when the mason's elder son got home, he was obliged to tell his mother that his brother had been caught in the trap and that he had cut off his head and brought it away with him; and his mother was very sorry and very angry too, and she said that he must go and get the body and bury it along with the head. And she was still more angry when in the morning the soldiers hung the body of her son high up on the wall; and she called her elder son and said to him that she would go and tell King Rhampsinitus all that had been done unless he went and brought his brother's body to her. At first her son was greatly troubled and could not think what to do; but presently he started up from his seat, and went out, and got five or six asses, and on their backs he placed large leather sacks full of wine, which he had bought with the money of King

Rhampsinitus. Then he drove the asses by the wall on which his brother's body was hung up; and when he came near the soldiers who were guarding it, he loosened the string which was round the mouth of two or three of the sacks, and the wine began to trickle down upon the ground. Then he cried out with a loud voice for all the guards to hear, and tore his hair, and ran about the road as if he did not know which sack to tie up first. Quickly the soldiers came up, and there was such a pushing as was never seen before. Instead of helping him to tie up the leather bottles, they ran for cups to catch up the wine as it streamed out on the ground, and they drank it up as fast as their cups were filled. Then the mason's son began to scold them and pretended to be dreadfully angry; but the soldiers tried to coax and soothe him, until at last he drove his asses off the road and began to put the sacks right again.

Then the guards came round him and began to talk and laugh with him; and by and by he gave them one of the bottles of wine to drink. But they said that they would not drink it unless he drank some of it with them. So they poured the wine out into the cups, and they drank and made merry together. Then he gave them another bottle, and another, and another, till all the soldiers fell down on the ground fast asleep. They had been so long drinking and laughing together that it was now night; and it was so dark that nobody could see what he was doing. Then the mason's son went softly to the wall and took down his brother's body which was hanging on it, and afterward he went to all the soldiers, one by one, and shaved off the whiskers and beard from one side of their faces; and then he returned home to his mother and gave her the body of his brother.

When the morning came the soldiers woke up from their heavy sleep. They felt very dull and stupid, but when they looked at the wall they saw that there was no dead body hanging on it; and when they looked at each other, they knew what a trick the mason's son had played them. They were dreadfully angry and terribly afraid; but there was no help except to go and tell the king. As they went, a crowd of people gathered round them, and everyone shouted with laughter to see the soldiers who had half their whiskers and beards shaved off. But when King Rhampsinitus heard what the mason's son had done he was quite furious, and he said, "What can I do to find out the man who has done these very wicked and very clever things?"

So he sent a herald all through the country and told him to say with a loud voice that the king would not punish the man who had stolen the money, but would give him his daughter for a wife, if he would only tell him how he had got into his treasure house. Then the son of the old mason came and told Rhampsinitus all the story, and the king looked at him earnestly and said, "I believe that the Egyptians are cleverer than all other men; but you are cleverer than all the Egyptians."

From *Tales of Ancient Greece*, by Sir George W. Cox (London: Longmans, Green and Company, 1868).

English

Jack and the Beanstalk

It is probable, as Andrew Lang, Joseph Jacobs, and others have suggested, that tales from the Continent displaced many of England's native folk stories before the latter-day collectors came on the scene. But this applies—as Lang noted—rather to the area south of the Scottish and east of the Welsh marches than to the more isolated regions of the North and the Southwest. It applies not at all to narratives in verse, for English-Scottish ballads were gathered as early as the mid-seventeenth century and represent as rich, and richly local, a store of folk narrative as can be found in any form anywhere. One is even tempted to suggest that the British people have poured so much of their genius for narrative into ballad verse that there has not been nearly enough to sustain the prose, particularly against the encroachments of Perrault, Grimm, Andersen, and the like.

Of the tales still circulating in central England in the nineteenth century and preserved in compilations made in the last quarter of the century, several, such as "Jack and the Beanstalk," "Jack the Giant-Killer," and the Robin Hood legends, may lay claim to being essentially British. But others, including some of the most popular, owe much of their machinery to older traditions. Dick Whittington is as British as can be, but the story of his cat is antique; and "The Master and His Pupil" (cousin to the Scandinavian magic quern and Finnish magic sampo) is probably descended through "sorcerer's apprentice" tales from Lucian's "The Lie Fancier."

From the lonely headlands of Cornwall in the Southwest come some delightfully fanciful and detailed accounts of the little people, there called piskeys, and of some sadly human giants—all of them with a flavor that reminds us that Cornwall is very much in the Celtic orbit. In the same orbit are most of the tales J. F. Campbell of Islay collected almost a century ago in the Scottish Highlands. They were in fact translated from Scottish Gaelic. But whatever the local affiliations of the style in which it is told, the motif of "The

Widow and Her Daughters" belongs to that international tradition whose most popular representative is "Bluebeard."

Although Robin Hood is best known from the numerous ballads about him, he occasionally appears in chapbook tales, and so it is possible to include several prose accounts of his adventures in the pages that follow. But "Get Up and Bar the Door" and "Our Goodman," those rollicking comments on woman's obstinacy and deceitfulness, appear in all their vigor only in verse, and thus verse forces itself into this company of prose tales despite every effort to exclude it.

THE HEDLEY KOW

THERE was once an old woman who earned a poor living by going errands and such like for the farmers' wives round about the village where she lived. It wasn't much she earned by it; but with a plate of meat at one house, and a cup of tea at another, she made shift to get on somehow, and always looked as cheerful as if she hadn't a want in the world.

Well, one summer evening as she was trotting away homeward she came upon a big black pot lying at the side of the road.

"Now *that*," said she, stopping to look at it, "would be just the very thing for me if I had anything to put into it! But who can have left it here?" And she looked round about, as if the person it belonged to must be not far off. But she could see no one.

"Maybe it'll have a hole in it," she said thoughtfully. "Ay, that'll be how they've left it lying, hinny. But then it'd do fine to put a flower in for the window. I'm thinking I'll just take it home, anyways." And she bent her stiff old back and lifted the lid to look inside.

"Mercy me!" she cried and jumped back to the other side of the road. "If it isn't brim full o' gold *pieces!*"

For a while she could do nothing but walk round and round her treasure, admiring the yellow gold and wondering at her good luck, and saying to herself about every two minutes, "Well, I *do* be feeling rich and grand!" But presently she began to think how she could best take it home with her; and she couldn't see any other way than by fastening one end of her shawl to it, and so dragging it after her along the road.

"It'll certainly be soon dark," she said to herself, "and folk'll not see what I'm bringing home with me, and so I'll have all the night to myself to think what I'll do with it. I could buy a grand house and all, and live like the queen herself, and not do a stroke of work all day, but just sit by the fire with a cup of tea; or maybe I'll give it to the priest to keep for me, and get a piece as I'm wanting; or maybe I'll just bury it in a hole at the garden-foot, and put a bit on the chimney, between the chiney teapot and the spoons—for ornament like. Ah! I feel so grand, I don't know myself rightly!"

And by this time, being already rather tired with dragging such a heavy weight after her, she stopped to rest for a minute, turning to make sure that her treasure was safe.

But when she looked at it, it wasn't a pot of gold at all, but a great lump of shining silver!

She stared at it, and rubbed her eyes, and stared at it again; but she couldn't make it look like anything but a great lump of silver. "I'd have sworn it was a pot of gold," she said at last, "but I reckon I must have been dreaming. Ay, now, that's a change for the better; it'll be far less trouble to look after, and none so easy stolen; yon gold pieces would have been a sight of bother to keep 'em safe. Ay, I'm well quit of them; and with my bonny lump I'm as rich as rich!"

And she set off homeward again, cheerfully planning all the grand things she was going to do with her money. It wasn't very long, however, before she got tired again and stopped once more to rest for a minute or two.

Again she turned to look at her treasure, and as soon as she set eyes on it she cried out in astonishment. "Oh, my!" said she, "now it's a lump of iron! Well, that beats all; and it's just real convenient! I can sell it as easy as easy, and get a lot o' penny pieces for it. Ay, hinny, an' it's much handier than a lot o' yer gold and silver as'd have kept me from sleeping o' nights thinking the neighbors were robbing me—an' it's a real good thing to have by you in a house, ye niver can tell what ye mightn't use it for, an' it'll sell—ay, for a real lot. Rich? I'll be just rolling!"

And on she trotted again, chuckling to herself on her good luck, till presently she glanced over her shoulder, "just to make sure it was there still," as she said to herself.

"Eh, my!" she cried as soon as she saw it, "if it hasn't gone and turned itself into a great stone this time! Now, how could it have known that I was just *terrible* wanting something to hold my door open with? Ay, if that isn't a good change! Hinny, it's a fine thing to have such good luck."

And, all in a hurry to see how the stone would look in its corner by her door, she trotted off down the hill and stopped at the foot, beside her own little gate.

When she had unlatched it, she turned to unfasten her shawl from the stone, which this time seemed to lie unchanged and peaceably on the path beside her. There was still plenty of light, and she could see the stone quite plainly as she bent her stiff back over it to untie the shawl end; when, all of a sudden, it seemed to give a jump and a squeal, and grew in a moment as big as a great horse; then it threw down four lanky legs, and shook out two long ears, flourished a tail, and went off, kicking its feet into the air and laughing like a naughty, mocking boy.

The old woman stared after it, till it was fairly out of sight.

"*Well!*" she said at last, "I *do* be the luckiest body hereabouts! Fancy me seeing the Hedley Kow all to myself, and making so free with it too! I can tell you, I *do* feel that *grand!*"

And she went into her cottage and sat down by the fire to think over her good luck.

From *More English Fairy Tales*, collected and edited by Joseph Jacobs (New York: G. P. Putnam's Sons, n.d.).

COAT O' CLAY

Once on a time, in the parts of Lindsey, there lived a wise woman. Some said she was a witch, but they said it in a whisper, lest she should overhear and do them a mischief, and truly it was not a thing one could be sure of, for she was never known to hurt anyone, which, if she were a witch, she would have been sure to do. But she could tell you what your sickness was, and how to cure it with herbs, and she could mix rare possets that would drive the pain out of you in a twinkling; and she could advise you what to do if your cows were ill, or if you'd got into trouble, and tell the maids whether their sweethearts were likely to be faithful.

But she was ill pleased if folks questioned her too much or too long, and she sore misliked fools. A many came to her asking foolish things, as was their nature, and to them she never gave counsel—at least of a kind that could aid them much.

Well, one day, as she sat at her door paring potatoes, over the stile and up the path came a tall lad with a long nose and goggle eyes and his hands in his pockets.

"That's a fool, if ever was one, and a fool's luck in his face," said the wise woman to herself with a nod of her head, and threw a potato skin over her left shoulder to keep off ill chance.

"Good day, missis," said the fool. "I be come to see thee."

"So thou art," said the wise woman. "I see that. How's all in thy folk this year?"

"Oh, fairly," answered he. "But they say I be a fool."

"Ay, so thou art," nodded she, and threw away a bad potato. "I see that too. What wouldst o' me? I keep no brains for sale."

"Well, see now. Mother says I'll ne'er be wiser all my born days; but folks tell us thou canst do everything. Can't thee teach me a bit, so they'll think me a clever fellow at home?"

"Hout-tout!" said the wise woman. "Thou'rt a bigger fool than I thought. Nay, I can't teach thee naught, lad; but I tell thee summat. Thou'lt be a fool all thy days till thou gets a coat o' clay; and then thou'lt know more than me."

"Hi, missis, what sort of a coat's that?" said he.

"That's none o' my business," answered she. "Thou'st got to find out that."

And she took up her potatoes and went into her house.

The fool took off his cap and scratched his head. "It's a queer kind of coat to look for, sure-*ly*," said he. "I never heard of a coat o' clay. But then I be a fool, that's true."

So he walked on till he came to the drain near by, with just a pickle of water and a foot of mud in it.

"Here's muck," said the fool, much pleased, and he got in and rolled in it, spluttering. "Hi, yi!" said he, for he had his mouth full, "I've got a coat o' clay now to be sure. I'll go home and tell my mother I'm a wise man and not a fool any longer." And he went on home.

Presently he came to a cottage with a lass at the door.

"Morning, fool," said she. "Hast thou been ducked in a horse pond?"

"Fool, yourself," said he. "The wise woman says I'll know more'n she when I get a coat o' clay, and here it is. Shall I marry thee, lass?"

"Ay," said she, for she thought she'd like a fool for a husband, "when shall it be?"

"I'll come and fetch thee when I've told my mother," said the fool, and he gave her his lucky penny and went on.

When he got home his mother was on the doorstep. "Mother, I've got a coat o' clay," said he.

"Coat o' muck," said she. "And what of that?"

"Wise woman said I'd know more than she when I got a coat o' clay," said he, "so I down in the drain and got one, and I'm not a fool any longer."

"Very good," said his mother. "Now thou canst get a wife."

"Ay," said he, "I'm going to marry so-an'-so."

"What!" said his mother, "*that* lass? No, and that thou'lt not. She's naught but a brat, with ne'er a cow or a cabbage o' her own."

"But I gave her my luck penny," said the fool.

"Then thou'rt a bigger fool than ever, for all thy coat o' clay!" said his mother, and banged the door in his face.

"Dang it!" said the fool and scratched his head, "that's not the right sort o' clay sure-*ly*."

So back he went to the highroad and sat down on the bank of

the river close by, looking at the water, which was cool and clear. By and by he fell asleep, and before he knew what he was about—plump!—he rolled off into the river with a splash, and scrambled out, dripping like a drowned rat.

"Dear, dear," said he, "I'd better go and get dry in the sun." So up he went to the highroad and lay down in the dust, rolling about so that the sun should get at him all over.

Presently, when he sat up and looked down at himself, he found that the dust had caked into a sort of skin over his wet clothes till you could not see an inch of them, they were so well covered. "Hi, yi!" said he, "here's a coat o' clay ready made, and a fine one. See now, I'm a clever fellow this time sure-*ly*, for I've found what I wanted without looking for it! Wow, but it's a fine feeling to be so smart!"

And he sat and scratched his head and thought about his own cleverness. But all of a sudden, round the corner came the squire on horseback, full gallop, as if the boggles were after him; but the fool had to jump even though the squire pulled his horse back on his haunches.

"What the dickens," said the squire, "do you mean by lying in the middle of the road like that?"

"Well, master," said the fool, "I fell into the river and got wet, so I lay down in the road to get dry; and I lay down a fool an' got up a wise man."

"Ah, ah!" laughed the squire, "whoever heard of a wise man lying in the middle of the highroad to be ridden over? Lad, take my word for it, you are a bigger fool than ever," and he rode on, laughing.

"Dang it!" said the fool as he scratched his head. "I've not got the right sort of coat yet, then." And he choked and spluttered in the dust that the squire's horse had raised.

So on he went in a melancholy mood till he came to an inn, and the landlord at his door smoking.

"Well, fool," said he, "thou'rt fine and dirty."

"Ay," said the fool, "I be dirty outside an' dusty in, but it's not the right thing yet." And he told the landlord all about the wise woman and the coat o' clay.

"Hout-tout!" said the landlord with a wink. "I know what's wrong. Thou'st got a skin o' dirt outside and all dry dust inside. Thou must moisten it, lad, with a good drink, and then thou'lt have a real all-over coat o' clay."

"Hi," said the fool, "that's a good word."

So down he sat and began to drink. But it was wonderful how much liquor it took to moisten so much dust; and each time he got to the bottom of the pot he found he was still dry. At last he began to feel very merry and pleased with himself.

"Hi, yi!" said he. "I've got a real coat o' clay now, outside and in–what a difference it do make, to be sure. I feel another man now–so smart."

And he told the landlord he was certainly a wise man now, though he couldn't speak overdistinctly after drinking too much. So up he got and thought he would go home and tell his mother she hadn't a fool for a son any more. But just as he was trying to get through the inn door, which would scarcely keep still long

enough for him to find it, up came the landlord and caught him by the sleeve.

"See here, master," said he, "thou hasn't paid for thy score. Where's thy money?"

"Haven't any!" said the fool and pulled out his pockets to show they were empty.

"What!" said the landlord, and swore, "Thou'st drunk all my liquor and haven't got naught to pay for it with!"

"Hi!" said the fool. "You told me to drink so as to get a coat o' clay; but as I'm a wise man now I don't mind helping thee along in the world a bit, for though I'm a smart fellow I'm not too proud to my friends."

"Wise man! Smart fellow!" said the landlord. "And help me

along, wilt thee? Dang it! thou'rt the biggest fool I ever saw, and it's I'll help *thee* first—out o' this!"

And he kicked him out of the door into the road and swore at him.

"Hum," said the fool as he lay in the dust, "I'm not so wise as I thought. I guess I'll go back to the wise woman and tell her there's a screw loose somewhere."

So up he got and went along to her house and found her sitting at the door.

"So thou'rt come back," said she with a nod. "What dost thou want with me now?"

So he sat down and told her how he'd tried to get a coat o' clay, and he wasn't any wiser for all of it.

"No," said the wise woman, "thou'rt a bigger fool than ever, my lad."

"So they all say," sighed the fool. "But where can I get the right sort of coat o' clay, then, missis?"

"When thou'rt done with this world, and thy folk put thee in the ground," said the wise woman. "That's the only coat o' clay as'll make such as *thee* wise, lad. Born a fool, die a fool, and be a fool thy life long, and that's the truth!"

And she went into the house and shut the door.

"Dang it," said the fool. "I must tell my mother she was right after all, and that she'll never have a wise man for a son!"

And he went off home.

Contributed by M. C. Balfour to *Longman's Magazine* and reprinted in *Folk-Lore* (London, 1890).

THE KING O' THE CATS

ONE WINTER'S evening the sexton's wife was sitting by the fire-side with her big black cat, Old Tom, on the other side, both half asleep and waiting for the master to come home. They waited and they waited, but still he didn't come, till at last he came rushing in, calling out, "Who's Tommy Tildrum?" in such a wild way that both his wife and his cat stared at him to know what was the matter.

"Why, what's the matter?" said his wife, "and why do you want to know who Tommy Tildrum is?"

"Oh, I've had such an adventure. I was digging away at old Mr. Fordyce's grave when I suppose I must have dropped asleep, and only woke up by hearing a cat's *miaou*."

"*Miaou!*" said Old Tom in answer.

"Yes, just like that! So I looked over the edge of the grave, and what do you think I saw?"

"Now, how can I tell?" said the sexton's wife.

"Why, nine black cats all like our friend Tom here, all with a white spot on their chestesses. And what do you think they were carrying? Why, a small coffin covered with a black velvet pall, and

on the pall was a small coronet all of gold, and at every third step they took they cried all together, *miaou*–"

"*Miaou!*" said Old Tom again.

"Yes, just like that!" said the sexton. "And as they came nearer and nearer to me I could see them more distinctly, because their eyes shone out with a sort of green light. Well, they all came toward me, eight of them carrying the coffin, and the biggest cat of all walking in front for all the world like–but look at our Tom, how he's looking at me. You'd think he knew all I was saying."

"Go on, go on," said his wife, "never mind Old Tom."

"Well, as I was a-saying, they came toward me slowly and solemnly, and at every third step crying all together, *miaou*–"

"*Miaou!*" said Old Tom again.

"Yes, just like that, till they came and stood right opposite Mr. Fordyce's grave, where I was, when they all stood still and looked straight at me. I did feel queer, that I did! But look at Old Tom—he's looking at me just like they did."

"Go on, go on," said his wife, "never mind Old Tom."

"Where was I? Oh, they all stood still looking at me, when the one that wasn't carrying the coffin came forward and, staring straight at me, said to me—yes, I told 'ee, *said* to me, with a squeaky voice, 'Tell Tom Tildrum that Tim Toldrum's dead,' and that's why I asked you if you know who Tom Tildrum was, for how can I tell Tom Tildrum Tim Toldrum's dead if I don't know who Tom Tildrum is?"

"Look at Old Tom, look at Old Tom!" screamed his wife.

And well he might look, for Tom was swelling, and Tom was staring, and at last Tom shrieked out, "What—old Tim dead! then I'm king o' the Cats!" and rushed up the chimney and was nevermore seen.

From *More English Fairy Tales.*

THE MASTER AND HIS PUPIL

THERE was once a very learned man in the north country who knew all the languages under the sun and who was acquainted with all the mysteries of creation. He had one big book bound in black calf and clasped with iron, and with iron corners, and chained to a table which was made fast to the floor; and when he read out of this book, he unlocked it with an iron key, and none but he read from it, for it contained all the secrets of the spiritual world. It told how many angels there were in heaven, and how they marched in their ranks, and sang in the choirs, and what were their several functions, and what was the name of each great angel of might. And it told of the devils of hell, how many of them there were, and what were their several powers, and their labors, and their names, and how they might be summoned, and how tasks might be imposed on them, and how they might be chained to be as slaves to man.

Now the master had a pupil who was but a foolish lad, and acted as servant to the great master, but never was he suffered to look into the black book, hardly to enter the private room.

One day the master was out, and then the lad, impelled by curiosity, hurried to the chamber where his master kept his wondrous apparatus for changing copper into gold, and lead into silver, and where was his mirror in which he could see all that was passing in the world, and where was the shell which when held to the ear whispered all the words that were being spoken by anyone the master desired to know about. The lad tried in vain with the crucibles to turn copper and lead into gold and silver; he looked long and vainly into the mirror—smoke and clouds fleeted over it, but he saw nothing plain; and the shell to his ear produced only indistinct murmurings, like the breaking of distant seas on an unknown shore. "I can

do nothing," he said, "as I don't know the right words to utter, and they are locked up in this book." He looked round, and, see! the book was unfastened; the master had forgotten to lock it before he went out. The boy rushed to it and unclosed the volume. It was written with red and black ink, and much that was in it he could not understand; but he put his finger on a line and spelled it through.

At once the room was darkened, and the house trembled; a clap of thunder rolled through the passage of the old mansion, and there stood before the terrified youth a horrible form, breathing fire, and with eyes like burning lamps. It was the Evil One, Beelzebub, whom he had called up to serve him.

"Set me a task!" he said with a voice like the roaring of an iron furnace.

The boy only trembled and his hair stood up.

"Set me a task, or I shall strangle you!"

But the lad could not speak. Then the evil spirit stepped toward him and, putting forth his hands, touched his throat. The fingers burned his flesh. "Set me a task."

"Water that flower," cried the boy in despair, pointing to a geranium which stood in a pot on the floor.

Instantly the spirit left the room, but in another instant he returned with a barrel on his back and poured its contents over the flower; and again and again he went and came, and poured more and more water, till the floor of the room was ankle-deep.

"Enough, enough!" gasped the lad; but the Evil One heeded him not; the lad didn't know the words by which to dismiss him, and still he fetched water.

It rose to the boy's knees, and still more water was poured. It mounted to his waist, and Beelzebub still kept on bringing barrels full. It rose to his armpits, and he scrambled to the tabletop. And now the water in the room stood up to the window and washed against the glass and swirled around his feet on the table. It still rose; it reached his breast. In vain he cried; the evil spirit would not be dismissed. And to this day he would have been pouring water, and would have drowned all Yorkshire, but the master remembered on his journey that he had not locked his book, and therefore returned, and at the moment when the water was bubbling about the pupil's chin rushed into the room and spoke the words which cast Beelzebub back into his fiery home.

Contributed by the Rev. S. Baring-Gould to *Notes on the Folk Lore of the Northern Counties,* by William Henderson (London: Longmans, Green & Co., 1866).

DICK WHITTINGTON

One Richard Whittington, supposed to have been an outcast, for he did not know his parents, they either dying or leaving him to the parish of Taunton Dean, in Somersetshire; but as he grew up, being displeased with the cruel usage of the nurse, he ran away from her at seven years of age and traveled about the country, living upon the charity of well-disposed persons, till he grew up to be a fine sturdy youth; when at last, being threatened to be whipped if he continued in that idle course of life, he resolved to go to London, having heard that the streets were paved with gold. Not knowing the way, he followed the carriers, and at night, for the little service he did them in rubbing the horses, they gave him a supper. When he arrived in this famous city, the carriers, supposing he would be a troublesome hanger-on, told him plainly he must leave the inn and immediately seek out some employment, and gave him a groat. With this he wandered about, but, not knowing anyone, and being in tattered garb, some pitied him as a forlorn wretch, but few gave him anything.

What he had got being soon spent, his stomach craved supply; but not having anything to satisfy it, he resolved rather to starve than steal. After two hungry days, and lying on the hulks at night, weary and faint, he got to a merchant's house in Leadenhall Street, where he made many signs of his distressed condition; but the ill-natured cook was going to kick him from the door, saying, "If you tarry here, I will kick you into the kennel." This put him almost into despair, so he laid him down on the ground, being unable to go any farther. In the meantime, Mr. Fitz-Warren, whose house it was, came from the Royal Exchange, and, seeing him there in that condition, demanded what he wanted and sharply told him if he did not immediately depart he would cause him to be sent to the House of Correction, calling him a lazy, idle fellow. On this he got up, and, after falling two or three times through faintness for want of food, and making a bow, told him he was a poor country fellow in a starving condition, and if that he might be put in a way, he would refuse no labor, if it was only for his victuals. This raised a Christian compassion in the merchant toward him, and then, wanting a scullion, he immediately ordered one of his servants to take him in, and gave orders how he should be employed; and so he was feasted to his great refreshment.

This was the first step of Providence to raise him to what in time made him to be the City's glory and the nation's wonder. But he met with many difficulties, for the servants made sport of him, and the ill-natured cook told him, "You are to come under me, so look sharp; clean the spit and the dripping-pan, make the fires, wind up the jack, and nimbly do all other scullery work that I may set you about, or else I will break your head with my ladle, and kick you about like a football."

This was cold comfort, but better than starving; and what gave him a beam of hope was Mrs. Alice, his master's daughter, who, hearing her father had entertained a new servant, came to see him, and ordered that he should be kindly used. After she had discussed with him about his kindred and method of life, and found his answers ingenuous, she ordered him some cast-off garments, and that he should be cleaned, and appear like a servant in the house. Then she went to her parents and gave them her opinion of this stranger, which pleased them well, saying, "He looks like a serviceable fellow to do kitchen drudgery, run on errands, clean the shoes, and do such other things as the rest of the servants think beneath them." By this he was confirmed in his place, and a flock bed prepared in the garret for him. These conditions pleased him, and he showed great diligence in the work, rising early and sitting up late, leaving nothing undone that he could do. But his being mostly under the cook-maid, she gave him sour sauce to these little sweets; for she, being of a morose temper, used her authority beyond reason, so that to keep in the family he had many a broken head, bearing it patiently; and the more he tried with good words to dissuade her from her cruelty, the more she insulted him, and not only abused him, but frequently complained against him, endeavoring to get him turned out of his service. But Mrs. Alice, hearing of her usage, interposed in his favor, so that she should not prevail against him.

This was not the only misery he suffered, for, lying in a place for a long time unfrequented, such abundance of rats and mice had bred there that they were almost as troublesome by night as the cook was by day, running over his face and disturbing him with their squeaking, so that he knew not what to think of his condition, or how to mend it. After many disquieting thoughts, he at last comforted himself with the hope that the cook might soon marry, or die, or quit her service; and as for the rats and mice, a cat would be an effectual remedy against them. Soon after, a merchant came to dinner, and when it rained exceedingly, stayed all night. Whittington having cleaned his shoes and presented them at his chamber door, he gave him a penny. This stock the boy improved, when, going along the street of an errand, he saw a woman with a cat under her arm; so he desired to know the price of it. The woman praised it for a good mouser and told him sixpence; but he declaring that a penny was all his stock, she let him have it. He brought it home and kept it in a box all day, lest the cook should kill it if it strayed into the kitchen; and at night he set it to work for its living. Puss delivered him from one plague, but the other remained, though not for many years.

It was the custom with the worthy merchant, Mr. Hugh Fitz-Warren, that God might give him a greater blessing to his endeavors, to call all his servants together when he sent out a ship and cause everyone to venture something in it, to try their fortune, for which they were to pay nothing for freight or custom.

Now all but Whittington appeared, and brought things according to their abilities; but Mrs. Alice being by, and supposing that poverty made him decline coming, she ordered him to be called, on which he made several excuses. However, being constrained to come, he fell upon his knees, desiring them not to jeer at a poor simple fellow, in expectation that he was going to turn merchant, since all that he could lay claim to as his own was but a poor cat, which he had bought for one penny that had been given him for cleaning shoes, and which had much befriended him in keeping the rats and mice from him. Upon this Mrs. Alice proffered to lay something down for him; but her father told her the custom, it must be his own which he ventured, and ordered him to fetch his cat, which he did, but with great reluctance, fancying nothing could come of it, and with some tears delivered the animal to the master of the ship, which was called the *Unicorn*, and was to sail down to Blackwall, in order to proceed on her voyage.

The cook-maid, who little thought how advantageous Whittington's cat would prove, when she did not scold at him, would jeer him about his grand adventure, and led him such a life that he grew weary of enduring it, and, little expecting what ensued, resolved rather to try Dame Fortune than live in such great torment; and so, having packed up his bundle over night, got out early on All Hallows' Day, intending to ramble the country. But as he went through Moorfields, he began to have pensive thoughts, and his resolutions began to fail. However, on he went to Holloway, and sat down to consider the matter, when, on a sudden, Bow Bells began to ring a merry peal. He, listening, fancied they called him back from his intended journey and promised him good fortune, imagining they expressed–

Turn again, Whittington
Lord Mayor of London.

This was a happy thought for him, as it made so great an impression on him that, finding it early, and that he might be back before the family were stirring, he delayed not; and all things answered his expectation, for, having left the door ajar, he crept softly in and got to his usual drudgery.

During this time the ship in which the cat was, by contrary winds, was driven on the coast of Barbary, inhabited by the Moors, unknown to the English; but finding the people courteous, the Master and Factor traded with them; so, bringing their wares of sundry sorts upon deck and opening them, they pleased them so well that the news was carried to the king, who sent for patterns, with which he was so pleased that he sent for the Factor to come to his palace. Their entertainment, according to custom, was on the floor, covered with carpets interwoven with gold and silver, whereon they sat cross-legged. This kind of table was no sooner covered with various dishes but the scent drew together a great number of rats and mice, who devoured all that came in the way; which surprised the Factor, who asked the nobles if these vermin were not offensive.

"Oh," said they, "His Majesty would give half his revenue to be freed from them, for they are not only offensive at his table, but his chamber and bed are so troubled with them that he is always watched for fear of mischief." The Factor then, remembering Whittington's cat, and rejoicing at the occasion, told them that he had an English beast in the ship that would rid all the Court of them quickly. The king, overjoyed at the good news, and being anxious to be freed from those mice which so much spoiled his pleasure, desired to see this surprising creature, saying, "For such a thing I will load your ship with gold, diamonds, and pearls."

This large offer made the Master endeavor the more to enhance the cat's merits, saying, "She is the most admirable creature in the world, and I cannot spare her, for she keeps my ship clear of them, otherwise they would destroy all my goods." But His Majesty would take no denial, saying, "No price shall part us." The cat being sent for, and the tables spread, the mice came as before. Then, she being set on the table, she fell to immediately and killed them all in a trice. Then she came purring and curling up her tail to the king and queen, as if she asked a reward for her service; whilst they admired her, protesting it was the finest diversion they had ever seen.

The Moorish king was so pleased with the cat, especially when the Master told him she was with young and would stock the whole country, that he gave ten times more for the cat than all the freight besides. So they sailed with a fair wind and arrived safe at Blackwall, being the richest ship that ever came into England. The Master, taking the cabinet of jewels with him, they being too rich a prize to be left on board, presented his bill of lading to Fitz-Warren, who praised God for such a prosperous voyage. But when he called all his servants to give each his due, the Master showed him the cabinet of jewels and pearls, the sight of which much surprised him. But on being told it was all for Whittington's cat, he said, "God forbid that I should deprive him of one farthing of it." And so he sent for him by the title of Mr. Whittington, who was then in the kitchen cleaning pots and spits.

Being told he must come to his master, he made several excuses; but being urged to go, he at length came to the door, and there stood scringing and scraping, scrupling to enter, till the merchant commanded him in and ordered a chair to be immediately set for him; on which he, thinking they intended to make sport with him, fell on his knees, and with tears in his eyes besought them not to mock a simple fellow who meant none of them any harm. Mr. Fitz-Warren, raising him up, said, "Indeed, Mr. Whittington, we are serious with you, for in estate at this instant you are an abler man than myself"; and then gave him the vast riches, which amounted to three hundred thousand pounds.

At length, being persuaded to believe, he fell upon his knees and praised Almighty God, who had vouchsafed to behold so poor a creature in the midst of his misery. Then, turning to his master, he laid his riches at his feet; but he said, "No, Mr. Whittington, God forbid I should take so much as a ducat from you; may it be a comfort to you." Then he turned to Mrs. Alice, but she also refused it. Upon which, bowing low, he said unto her, "Madam, whenever you please to make choice of a husband, I will make you the greatest fortune in the world."

Upon this he began to distribute his bounty to his fellow servants, giving even his mortal enemy the cook one hundred pounds for her portion. When she said she had acted in passion, he freely forgave her. He also distributed his bounty very plentifully to all the ship's crew.

Upon this change, the haberdashers, tailors, and seamstresses were set to work to make Mr. Whittington's clothes, all things answerable to his fortune. Being dressed, he appeared a very comely person, insomuch that Mrs. Alice began to lay her eyes upon him. Now her father, seeing this, intended a match for them, looking upon him to be a fortunate man. He also took him to the Royal Exchange, to see the customs of the merchants, where he was no sooner known than they came to welcome him into their society. Soon after, a match was proposed between him and his master's daughter, when he excused himself on account of the meanness of his birth; but that objection being removed by his present worth, it was soon agreed on, and the Lord Mayor and Aldermen invited to the wedding.

After the honeymoon was over, his father-in-law asked him what employment he would follow. Whereupon he replied he should think of that of a merchant. So they joined together in partnership, and both grew immensely rich.

Though fortune had thus bountifully smiled on the subject of our history, he was far from proud, yet merry, which made his company and acquaintance courted by all. In a short time he was nominated Sheriff of London and thereafter Lord Mayor, in which office he behaved with such justice and prudence that he was chosen to it twice afterward.

From a chapbook, "History of Sir Richard Whittington," reprinted in *Sir Richard Whittington*, by Walter Besant and James Rice (New York: G. P. Putnam's Sons, 1881).

JACK AND THE BEANSTALK

THERE was once upon a time a poor widow who had an only son named Jack, and a cow named Milky-white. And all they had to live on was the milk the cow gave every morning, which they carried to the market and sold. But one morning Milky-white gave no milk, and they didn't know what to do.

"What shall we do, what shall we do?" said the widow, wringing her hands.

"Cheer up, mother, I'll go and get work somewhere," said Jack.

"We've tried that before, and nobody would take you," said his mother. "We must sell Milky-white, and with the money start shop or something."

"All right, mother," says Jack. "It's market day today, and I'll soon sell Milky-white, and then we'll see what we can do."

So he took the cow's halter in his hand and off he started. He hadn't gone far when he met a funny-looking old man, who said to him, "Good morning, Jack."

"Good morning to you," said Jack and wondered how he knew his name.

"Well, Jack, and where are you off to?" said the man.

"I am going to market to sell our cow here."

"Oh, you look the proper sort of chap to sell cows," said the man. "I wonder if you know how many beans make five."

"Two in each hand and one in your mouth," says Jack, as sharp as a needle.

"Right you are," says the man, "and here they are, the very beans themselves," he went on, pulling out of his pocket a number of strange-looking beans. "As you are so sharp," says he, "I don't mind doing a swop with you—your cow for these beans."

"Go along," says Jack, "wouldn't you like it?"

"Ah! you don't know what these beans are," said the man. "If you plant them overnight, by morning they grow right up to the sky."

"Really," said Jack, "you don't say so?"

"Yes, that is so, and if it doesn't turn out to be true you can have your cow back."

"Right," says Jack and hands him over Milky-white's halter and pockets the beans.

Back goes Jack home, and as he hadn't gone very far it wasn't dusk by the time he got to his door.

"Back already, Jack?" said his mother. "I see you haven't got Milky-white, so you've sold her. How much did you get for her?"

"You'll never guess, mother," says Jack.

"No, you don't say so? Good boy! Five pounds, ten, fifteen–no, it can't be twenty."

"I told you you couldn't guess. What do you say to these beans; they're magical, plant them overnight and–"

"What!" says Jack's mother, "have you been such a fool, such a dolt, such an idiot, as to give away my Milky-white, the best milker in the parish, and prime beef to boot, for a set of paltry beans? Take that! Take that! Take that! And as for your precious beans, here they go out of the window. And now off with you to bed. Not a sup shall you drink, and not a bit shall you swallow this very night."

So Jack went upstairs to his little room in the attic, and sad and sorry he was, to be sure, as much for his mother's sake as for the loss of his supper.

At last he dropped off to sleep.

When he woke up the room looked so funny. The sun was shining into part of it, and yet all the rest was quite dark and shady. So Jack jumped up and dressed himself and went to the window. And what do you think he saw? Why, the beans his mother had thrown out of the window into the garden had sprung up into a big beanstalk which went up and up and up till it reached the sky. So the man spoke truth after all.

The beanstalk grew up quite close past Jack's window, so all he had to do was to open it and give a jump onto the beanstalk, which ran up just like a big ladder. So Jack climbed, and he climbed and he climbed and he climbed and he climbed and he climbed and he climbed till at last he reached the sky. And when he got there he found a long broad road going as straight as a dart. So he walked along and he walked along and he walked along till he came to a great big tall house, and on the doorstep there was a great big tall woman.

"Good morning, mum," says Jack, quite polite-like. "Could you be so kind as to give me some breakfast?" For he hadn't had anything to eat, you know, the night before, and he was as hungry as a hunter.

"It's breakfast you want, is it?" says the great big tall woman. "It's breakfast you'll be if you don't move off from here. My man is an ogre and there's nothing he likes better than boys broiled on toast. You'd better be moving on or he'll soon be coming."

"Oh! please mum, do give me something to eat, mum. I've had nothing to eat since yesterday morning, really and truly, mum," says Jack. "I may as well be broiled as die of hunger."

Well, the ogre's wife was not half so bad after all. So she took Jack into the kitchen and gave him a chunk of bread and cheese and a jug of milk. But Jack hadn't half finished these when thump! thump! thump! the whole house began to tremble with the noise of someone coming.

"Goodness gracious me! It's my old man," said the ogre's wife. "What on earth shall I do? Come along quick and jump in here." And she bundled Jack into the oven just as the ogre came in.

He was a big one, to be sure. At his belt he had three calves strung up by the heels, and he unhooked them and threw them down on the table and said, "Here, wife, broil me a couple of these for breakfast. Ah! what's this I smell?

Fee-fi-fo-fum,
I smell the blood of an Englishman,
Be he alive, or be he dead
I'll have his bones to grind my bread."

"Nonsense, dear," said his wife, "you're dreaming. Or perhaps you smell the scraps of that little boy you liked so much for yesterday's dinner. Here, you go and have a wash and tidy up, and by the time you come back your breakfast'll be ready for you."

So off the ogre went, and Jack was just going to jump out of the oven and run away when the woman told him not. "Wait till he's asleep," says she. "He always has a doze after breakfast."

Well, the ogre had his breakfast, and after that he goes to a big chest and takes out of it a couple of bags of gold, and down he sits and counts till at last his head began to nod and he began to snore till the whole house shook again.

Then Jack crept out on tiptoe from his oven, and as he was passing the ogre he took one of the bags of gold under his arm, and off he pelters till he came to the beanstalk, and then he threw down the bag of gold, which of course fell into his mother's garden, and then he climbed down and climbed down till at last he got home and told his mother and showed her the gold and said, "Well, mother, wasn't I right about the beans? They are really magical, you see."

So they lived on the bag of gold for some time, but at last they came to the end of it, and Jack made up his mind to try his luck once more up at the top of the beanstalk. So one fine morning he rose up early, and got onto the beanstalk, and he climbed and he climbed and he climbed and he climbed and he climbed and he climbed till at last he came out on to the road again, and up to the great big tall house he had been to before. There, sure enough, was the great big tall woman a-standing on the doorstep.

"Good morning, mum," says Jack, as bold as brass, "could you be so good as to give me something to eat?"

"Go away, my boy," said the big tall woman, "or else my man will eat you up for breakfast. But aren't you the youngster who came here once before? Do you know, that very day my man missed one of his bags of gold?"

"That's strange, mum," said Jack. "I daresay I could tell you something about that, but I'm so hungry I can't speak till I've had something to eat."

Well, the big tall woman was so curious that she took him in and gave him something to eat. But he had scarcely begun munching it as slowly as he could when thump! thump! thump! they heard the giant's footstep, and his wife hid Jack away in the oven.

All happened as it did before. In came the ogre as he did before, said, "Fee-fi-fo-fum," and had his breakfast of three broiled oxen. Then he said, "Wife, bring me the hen that lays the golden eggs." So she brought it, and the ogre said, "Lay," and it laid an egg all of gold. And then the ogre began to nod his head and to snore till the house shook.

Then Jack crept out of the oven on tiptoe and caught hold of the golden hen and was off before you could say "Jack Robinson." But this time the hen gave a cackle which woke the ogre, and just as Jack got out of the house he heard him calling, "Wife, wife, what have you done with my golden hen?"

And the wife said, "Why, my dear?"

But that was all Jack heard, for he rushed off to the beanstalk and climbed down like a house on fire. And when he got home he showed his mother the wonderful hen and said "Lay" to it; and it laid a golden egg every time he said "Lay."

Well, Jack was not content, and it wasn't very long before he determined to have another try at his luck up there at the top of the beanstalk. So one fine morning he rose up early, and got onto the beanstalk, and he climbed and he climbed and he climbed and he climbed till he got to the top. But this time he knew better than to go straight to the ogre's house. And when he got near it, he waited behind a bush till he saw the ogre's wife come out with a pail to get some water, and then he crept into the house and got into the copper. He hadn't been there long when he heard thump! thump! thump! as before, and in come the ogre and his wife.

"Fee-fi-fo-fum, I smell the blood of an Englishman," cried the ogre. "I smell him, wife, I smell him."

"Do you, dearie?" says the ogre's wife. "Then, if it's that little rogue that stole your gold and the hen that laid the golden eggs, he's sure to have got into the oven." And they both rushed to the oven. But Jack wasn't there, luckily, and the ogre's wife said, "There you are again with your fee-fi-fo-fum. Why of course it's the boy you caught last night that I've just broiled for your breakfast. How forgetful I am, and how careless you are, not to know the difference between live and dead after all these years."

So the ogre sat down to the breakfast and ate it, but every now and then he would mutter, "Well, I could have sworn—" and he'd get up and search the larder and the cupboards and everything, only, luckily, he didn't think of the copper.

After breakfast was over the ogre called out, "Wife, wife, bring me my golden harp." So she brought it and put it on the table before him. Then he said, "Sing!" and the golden harp sang most beautifully. And it went on singing till the ogre fell asleep and commenced to snore like thunder.

Then Jack lifted up the copper lid very quietly and got down like a mouse and crept on hands and knees till he came to the table, when up he crawled, caught hold of the golden harp, and dashed with it toward the door. But the harp called out quite loud, "Master! Master!" and the ogre woke up just in time to see Jack running off with his harp.

Jack ran as fast as he could, and the ogre came rushing after, and would soon have caught him only Jack had a start and dodged him a bit and knew where he was going. When he got to the beanstalk the ogre was not more than twenty yards away when suddenly he saw Jack disappear, and when he came to the end of the road he saw Jack underneath climbing down for dear life. Well, the ogre didn't like trusting himself to such a ladder, and he stood and waited, so Jack got another start. But just then the harp cried out, "Master! Master!" and the ogre swung himself down onto the beanstalk, which shook with his weight. Down climbs Jack, and after him climbed the ogre. By this time Jack had climbed down and climbed down and climbed down till he was very nearly home. So he called out, "Mother! Mother! Bring me an ax, bring me an ax!" And his mother came rushing out with the ax in her hand, but when she came to the beanstalk she stood stock still with fright, for there she saw the ogre with his legs just through the clouds.

But Jack jumped down and got hold of the ax and gave a chop at the beanstalk which cut it half in two. The ogre felt the beanstalk shake and quiver, so he stopped to see what was the matter. Then Jack gave another chop with the ax, and the beanstalk was cut in two and began to topple over. Then the ogre fell down and broke his crown and the beanstalk came toppling after.

Then Jack showed his mother his golden harp, and what with showing that and selling the golden eggs Jack and his mother became very rich, and he married a great princess, and they lived happy ever after.

From *English Fairy Tales*, collected and edited by Joseph Jacobs (New York: G. P. Putnam's Sons, n. d.).

ROBIN HOOD AND THE BUTCHER

WALKING in the forest as was his daily custom, Robin Hood one day observed a butcher riding along the way, carrying good store of meat on his mare's back, which he was to sell in the market.

"Good morrow, good fellow," said Robin to the butcher.

"Good fellow," replied the butcher, "heavens keep me from Robin Good fellow, for if I meet with him, I may chance to fall short of my journey, and my meat of the market."

"I like thy company well. What hast thou to sell?" said Robin Hood.

"Flesh, master," said the butcher, "with which I am going to Nottingham market."

"What is the price of thy flesh," said Robin Hood, "and of thy mare that bears it? Tell me, for if thou wilt use me well, I will buy both."

"Four mark," said the butcher. "I cannot bate anything of it."

"Sit down then and tell thy money," said Robin Hood. "I will try for once if I can thrive by being a butcher."

The money being told, Robin Hood gets up on the mare, and away he rides with the meat to Nottingham market, where he made such good penniworths that he had sold all his meat by ten of the clock in the morn. He sold more meat for one penny than others could do for five. The butchers in the market, that had their stands near him, said one to another, "Certainly this man's meat is nought and putrefied, or else he hath stolen it. From whence comes he?"

Saith another, "I never did see him before."

"That will I tell you by and by," said a third butcher, and, stepping to Robin Hood, said unto him, "Brother, thou art the freest butcher that ever came to this market; we be all of one trade; come, let us dine together."

"Accurst be he that will deny a butcher so fair an invitation," said Robin Hood, and, going with him to the inn, the table was suddenly covered and furnished, and the best man in the company being to say grace, Robin Hood at the upper end of the table did put off his bonnet. He was no sooner sat, but he called for a cup of sack and drank to them all, desiring them to be merry, for if there were five pounds to pay, he would pay every farthing.

"Thou art the bravest blade," said the butchers, "that ever came to Nottingham market." Robin Hood still called for more wine, and the cups trouled up and down the table, insomuch that the sheriff, who had newly alighted and taken his chamber in the inn, hearing of it, said that he must be some prodigal that had sold his land and would now spend it all at once. This coming to Robin Hood's ear, he after dinner took the opportunity to speak with the sheriff.

Said the sheriff, "Good fellow, thou hast made a good market today; hast thou any more horned beasts to sell?"

"Yes, that I have," said Robin Hood to master sheriff. "I have two or three hundred, and a hundred acres of good land to keep them on as ever the crow flew over, which if you will buy of me, I will make you as good assurance of it as ever my father made me."

The sheriff, being a covetous man and persuading himself that he would make him Robin Hood's penniworths, commanded his horse to be brought forth, and, taking some money with him for the purchase, he rode with Robin Hood, who led him into the forest for a mile or two. The sheriff being laden with good store of gold, and surprised with the melancholy of the place, said he did wish himself at Nottingham again.

"And why so?" said Robin Hood.

"I tell thee plainly," said the sheriff, "I do not like thy company."

"No?" said Robin Hood. "Then I will provide you better."

"God keep me from Robin Hood," said the sheriff, "for this is the haunt he useth."

Robin Hood, smiling, observed a herd of three hundred gallant deer feeding in the forest close by him and demanded of the sheriff how he liked those horned beasts, assuring him that they were the best that he could show him. With that he blew his horn, whereupon Little John with fifty more of his associates came presently in, to whom Robin Hood imparted that he had brought with him the sheriff of Nottingham to dine with him.

"He is welcome," said Little John. "I know he hath store of gold and will honestly pay for his dinner."

"Ay, ay," said Robin Hood, "never doubt it." And taking off the sheriff's portmantle, he took to himself the three hundred pounds that was in it. Then leading the sheriff back through the forest, he desired him to remember him kindly to his wife, and so went laughing away.

From *Early English Prose Romances*, edited by William J. Thoms (London, 1828).

ROBIN HOOD AND THE BEGGAR

But Robin Hood took not any long delight in the mare which he bought of the butcher, but having now supplied himself with good store of money which he had gotten by the sheriff of Nottingham, he bought himself a stout gelding, and, riding one day toward Nottingham, it was his fortune to meet with a poor beggar. Robin

Hood was of good spirit, and no accepter of persons, but observing the beggar to have several sorts of bags which were fastened to his patched coat, he did ride up to him, and, giving him the time of the day, he demanded of him what countryman he was.

"A Yorkshireman," said the beggar, "and I would desire of you to give me something."

"Give thee!" said Robin Hood. "Why, I have nothing to give thee. I am a poor ranger in the forest, and thou seemest to be a lusty knave: shall I give thee a good bastinado over the shoulder?"

"Content, content," said the beggar. "I durst wager my coat and all my bags against a threaden point that thou wilt repent it." With that Robin Hood alighted, and the beggar and he fell to it, he with his sword and buckler, and the beggar with his long quarterstaff, who so well defended himself that let Robin Hood do what he could, he could not come within the beggar to flash him to a remembrance of his over-boldness. And nothing vexed him more than to find that the beggar's staff was as hard and as obdurate as iron itself, but so was not Robin Hood's head, for the beggar with all his force did let his staff descend with such a side blow that Robin Hood for all his skill could not defend it, but the blood came trickling down his face, which turning Robin Hood's courage into revenge and fury he let fly at him with his trusty sword and doubled blow on blow. But perceiving that the beggar did hold him so hard to it that one of his blows was but the forerunner of another and every blow was almost the postilion of Death, he cried out to him to hold his hand.

"That will I not do," said the beggar, "unless thou wilt resign unto me thy horse, and thy sword, and thy clothes, with all the money thou hast in thy pockets."

"The change is uneven," said Robin Hood, "but for once I am content."

So putting on the beggar's clothes, the beggar was the gentleman, and Robin Hood the beggar, who, entering into Nottingham town with his patched coat and several wallets, understood that three brethren were that day to suffer at the gallows, being condemned for killing the king's deer. He made no more ado but went directly to the sheriff's house, where a young gentleman, seeing him stand at the door, demanded of him what he would have. Robin Hood returned answer that he came to crave neither meat nor drink, but the lives of those three brothers who were condemned to die.

"That cannot be," said the young gentleman, "for they are all this day to suffer according to law for stealing the king's deer, and they are already conveyed out of town to the place of execution."

"I will be there with them presently," said Robin Hood, and, coming to the gallows, he found many making great lamentation for the three. Robin Hood did comfort them and assured them they would

not die, and blowing his horn, behold! on a sudden a hundred brave archers came unto him, by whose help having released the prisoners and killed the hangman and hurt many of the sheriff's officers, they took those who were condemned to die for killing the king's deer along with them, who being very thankful for the preservation of their lives, became afterward of the yeomanry of Robin Hood.

From *Early English Prose Romances.*

THE GIANTS OF CASTLE TREEN

It is not known what powerful magician raised the stronghold called Castle Treen, but according to tradition it must have been there before even Arthur and Merlin visited Cornwall. According to tradition, too, the earliest inhabitants of the castle were giants who protected the neighboring people in return for cattle and other necessities. So it came about that when one giant couple began to grow old without having any children their neighbors were much grieved and disappointed.

The giantess, having no household to think about, grew, as most unemployed women do, peevish and troublesome. The giant, having little or no work, grew fat and lazy. Quiet and good-tempered as he was, he was dreadfully tormented by his wife. She called him a useless old loon, and said he was too fat, and didn't take exercise enough. When he had nothing else to do she told him to get out and stretch his sinews and make his blood circulate, instead of dozing away all day and night in his chair.

"Swim over to the Dollar rocks," she would say, "it's only two miles or so; dive round them and catch me a few good big congers; I want their fat to make a cake. And the pollock and cod that feed thereabouts are excellent eating."

Sometimes he would take her advice, swim away, and, in an hour or two, bring home a string of fish a furlong long.

Then he would log [shake] Men Amber for a bit. This he could easily do with the tip of his finger, when standing on the grass below it; for the sacred stone is only thirty feet or so from the grass, and Treen giant stood at least forty feet high, without his boots. He was stout in proportion, and his strength was prodigious. Sometimes, with his staff, he kept the sacred stone in motion when seated in his chair, just opposite it. But often it happened that he fell asleep long ere the sand was down in his wife's hourglass. And then she would pelt her husband with rocks, heaps of which may still be seen lying about. He would wake up, with a sore head, to hear her say in a voice like a bellowing bull, "Stop thy snoring, thou confounded old fool, and work away, or I'll pommel thy noddle to browse [pulp]."

"What the deuce shall I do to stop her tongue and cure her temper? Can 'e tell me, my good people?" he would often say to Treen folks and others who visited him of a summer's evening. "She's the most troublesome woman I ever heard of! Why should she fret and fume for lack of children? And what need have you, either, in these peaceful times, to care whether we have descendants or no?"

Potent reasons were given both by the giantess and the people why they desired that their chief's race should be continued. Yet much time passed, and their rock-hewn cradle was still empty, when a happy thought struck a wise man of Treen. He advised that a baby should be stolen from the giant of Maen, who had a large family, and was, moreover, a very troublesome and aggressive neighbor. The giant and his wife were delighted with the sage man's advice. To steal a baby from the big man who was proud of his stronghold between Land's End and Black Stone Headland would be capital revenge on him and his.

"Then how nice it will be for me," said the giant's wife, "to sit on the Logan stone with the cheeld in my arms, of summer afternoons, when the waves sing lullaby, and my old man can rock us both till the dear baby falls asleep. Or he may dandle it in his arms atop of Castle Peak, or jump with it thence to Gamp-an-sees rocks and back again, whilst I skin an ox for our supper, and you, my good people, bring us down plenty of milk to nurse him on, that he may grow apace."

A witch of Treen, who could take any shape, was selected as the most likely person to execute the project without causing any trouble with the Maen giant, who was very fierce, and proud of his descent from old blustering Bellerus, who is said to have lived thereabouts in the old days.

One afternoon away went the witch, and, without being noticed on the road, reached Cairn-men-ellas, where she hid herself between rocks to watch. A little before sunset she saw a giant's child, of four years or so, coming that way with some common people's children, who wanted to show him how to play bob. Now the infant giant, though as big as an ordinary man, was still a baby in every feature, and he hadn't long been weaned; he still wore a bib, though he had outgrown his clothes, and his pinafore scarcely reached to his knees. The common boys and girls, from ten to a dozen years of age—like children in size compared to him—led him about and did with him just as they pleased.

The woman, seeing them place buttons on the bob, took from her basket a string of large bright ones, shook them before the giant baby, and said, "Now kiss me, dear, and I will give you all these." He kissed her again and again, delighted to have the buttons. After a while she said, "The tides are low, and I am on my way to get limpets and gweans [winkles] from Cowloe; will 'e go, dears?"

The elder ones said it was then too late—they must be all home to Treve before sundown, or their mammies would strap them soundly and send them to bed without supper. But the babe-giant said, "I'll go, for I want some gweans to play five-stones."

"Come along then, my turtle," said the witch as she took his hand and led him off.

On the way she took from her basket many toys and showed him how to play with them. This pleased him, so that he thought no more of Cowloe, and she led him away to Brew Moors. There, to divert him, she changed herself into the shape of a horse, and he trotted on her a mile or more; then she resumed her woman's form and led him into Castle Treen, where he was received with open arms by the mistress.

It would take long to tell how he was caressed by the childless pair and fed by their people.

At sunrise in summer the old giant delighted to carry him up to Castle Peak, where he placed the infant on the topmost stone and named to him all the places within ken. When the sun shone warm he took the baby down to the Castle Leas, near the Gap. From these rocks, at the water's edge, the giant, like a monstrous dolphin, stretched on the sea with the boy standing on his broad back and holding on by the hair of his head like bridle reins, would swim out and round to the rock that stands like an island under Haldynas. Having rested there a while and given the cheeld a few shags' eggs, limpets, mussels, and such-like dainties, back they would steer, but farther out, coasting all the seaboard of the castle.

When the boy was a few years older, the giant taught him to fish with rod and line, and how to make fish-hooks out of bones and croggan-rims. It wasn't much, however, that the giant could teach the youngster, for like so many of great bulk he had more strength than knowledge.

Meanwhile the giantess took care that the boy had an unlimited quantity of food. In a few years he was nearly equal in bulk to his Dadda, as he called the old giant.

All her care and attention were bestowed on the boy, and she neglected her old husband, so that he had to dive for fish, and skin oxen, or eat them skin, horns, and all. Sheep he could seldom get; they were dainties reserved for the young fellow. To add insult to injury, the giantess often taunted her aged spouse with his weakness, and cut him to the heart by making unfavorable comparisons between him and the pampered youth.

The poor old giant was slow to become jealous, till he found himself utterly forsaken by his spouse and adopted son, who always stole away by themselves to sunny glades between the carns. That would have passed, however, without notice—he rather liked to be left alone, to dose in his chair of afternoons—had not some Treen women, who were sharp in such things, spied what was going on and, out of envy, told the old giant. He became very surly, and one winter's day, when he was starting out to get provision, he told his wife and the youngster that one of them should meet him on his way back to assist in taking home whatever he might procure.

They promised to do so, but time passed so pleasantly with the couple that they thought little of their good old provider till they heard his footsteps and angry voice, about a quarter of a mile off, as he came stamping along Pedn-y-vounder cliff, vowing vengeance on his ungrateful wife and foster-son.

They became frightened, and the giantess prepared for the encounter by placing herself on the rocks west of the Gap, a dozen feet or so above the narrow path which the giant would have to pass. He came stamping along, an ox on his shoulders—its legs tied together and passed over his head—and on each arm he carried a sheep.

He roared louder than the stormy breakers when he entered his castle's inner enclosure and found that no one, even then, came to meet him. In his fury he bounced along without noticing his wicked wife, with her arm bared and fist clenched, awaiting his approach. As he came along the narrow ledge she dealt him a blow in the eyes that sent him, cattle and all, heels over head down the precipice.

When she beheld him falling, a remembrance of their early love, or something else, caused a sudden revulsion of feeling, which made her regret her rashness, and, unwilling to witness her husband's dying agony, she stepped back. There she cast her apron over her head that she might hear less of the giant's awful moans. Though the giant's skull was very thick, it was smashed on the boulders. Yet he didn't die until he had called on the Powers whom he served to avenge him. This they did instantly by changing his vile partner into stone where she stood, and where she may still be seen. Nothing more is known of the young giant, and but little of the other Titans that in that mythic age dwelt in Castle Treen.

Adapted from *Traditions and Hearthside Stories of West Cornwall*, by William Bottrell (London, 1873).

THE PISKEYS ON SELENA MOOR

ONE AFTERNOON in harvest time, in the days when the ancient family of Noy flourished in Buryan in Cornwall, Mr. Noy, with some of his men, were over to Baranhual to help his kinfolks, the Pendars. As more hands were required for the next day, which was to be the gulthise, or harvest home, he rode up to Church-town to get them, and to invite the parson, clerk, and sexton—the latter being particularly welcome to the harvest folk as he was generally a good fiddler and teller of drolls.

Soon after day-down Mr. Noy, followed by his dogs, left the public house intending to return to Baranhual, but he didn't arrive there that night or the next. The Pendars and their people thought he might have enjoyed himself at the Ship Inn till late and then have gone home to Pendrea. Mr. Noy had no wife or anybody else to be much alarmed about him, since he was a rather elderly bachelor. But next day when people from Church-town, Pendrea, and other farms came with their horses to help and feast at the gulthise, and nobody among them had seen or heard of Mr. Noy from the time he left the inn, they got somewhat uneasy. Yet they still supposed he might have gone to some corn-carrying down the lower side of Buryan.

As usual there was a great chase to bring home the corn in trusses; leaders and other helpers took their flowery-milk [hasty pudding] for breakfast, apple pies for dinner, just when and how they could, with beer and cider whenever they felt inclined, so they might keep the mowers always building, to have the corn under thatch before suppertime. As soon as all was secured in the mowhay, scores of all ages enjoyed roast and boiled beef, mutton, squab pies, rabbit and hare pies, pudding, and other substantial fare. Then drinking, singing, dancing, and other pastimes were kept up till late. In the meantime Dame Pendar had sent messengers round to all places where she thought Mr. Noy might have gone, but they returned, just as the feast was breaking up, without any tidings of him.

Then everyone became anxious, and as it was near daybreak they volunteered to disperse and search in every place they could think of before going to bed.

So away they went, some on horseback, others afoot, to examine millpools, stream works, cliffs, and other dangerous places, near and far. They returned at night, but nobody had seen or heard of the missing man. Next morning horsemen were dispatched to other parishes, and as Mr. Noy was well known and liked, there was a general turn out to hunt for him; but this day, too, was passed in a fruitless search.

On the third day, however, in the gray of the morning, a horse was heard to neigh and dogs were heard barking among thickets on a piece of dry ground almost surrounded with bogs and pools on Pendrea side of Selena Moor.

Now it happened that no one had thought of looking for Mr. Noy so near home, but when with much ado a score or so of men discovered a passable road into this sort of island in the bogs, they saw there Mr. Noy's horse and hounds. The horse had found plenty of pasture, but the dogs, poor things, were half starved. Horses and dogs showed their joy, and led the way through thorns, furze, and brambles till they came to the ruins of an old bowjey [cowshed] or some such building that no one had known about. Hunters never attempted in winter to cross the boggy ground that nearly surrounded these two or three acres of dry land, and in summer no one was curious enough to penetrate this wilderness of thickets which, like all such places, was swarming with adders.

The horse stopped at what had been a doorway, looked around and whinnied; the dogs, followed by several people, pushed through the brambles that choked the entrance, and within they found Mr. Noy lying on the ground fast asleep. It was a difficult matter to arouse him; at last he awoke, stretched himself, rubbed his eyes, and said, "Why, you are Baranhual and Pendrea folks; how are ye all come here? What parish am I in? How could 'e have found me?" He seemed like one dazed and all benumbed, so without staying to answer his questions, they gave him some brandy, lifted him on his horse, and let the animal pick its way out.

Though told he was less than half a mile from Baranhual, Mr. Noy couldn't make out the country till he crossed the running water that divides the farms. "But I am glad," said he, "however it came to pass, to have got back in time for the gulthise." When they told him how the corn had been carried three days before, he said they were joking, and wouldn't believe it till he had seen all in the mowhay under thatch and roped down, and all the harvest implements put away till next season.

Then, seated on a chimney stool by a blazing fire, he told his neighbors that when he had come to Cotnewilly, the night being clear, he thought he might as well make a short cut across the moor. But his horse, which was pretty much used to finding its own way when its master was tipsy, wanted to keep to the usual road, and its rider, to balk it, pulled farther off toward Pendrea side of the common. He went on in this way till he found himself in a part that was unknown to him, though he had been, as he thought, over every inch of it that man or beast could tread on. Becoming alarmed at the strange appearance of everything around him, he tried in vain to retrace his steps, then gave the horse its head and let it take its own course.

After wandering miles and miles, sometimes riding but oftener afoot, without seeing any habitation, he at last heard strains of lively music and spied lights glimmering through the trees and people moving about.

His dogs slunk back, and the horse wasn't willing to go on, so he tied it to a tree. Then he made his way through an orchard toward the lights and came to a meadow where he saw hundreds of people, some seated at tables eating and drinking with great enjoyment, others dancing reels to the music of a "crowd," or tambourine, played by a damsel dressed in white.

The revelers were all very smartly decked out, but they seemed to be a set of undersized mortals. The forms and tables, with the drinking vessels on them, were all in proportion to the little people. The dancers moved so fast that he couldn't count the number that footed jigs and reels together.

He noticed that the damsel who played the music was more like an ordinary woman in stature. He took her to be the master's daughter, because when one dance was ended she gave the crowd to a little fellow that stood near her, entered the house, fetched therefrom a blackjack, went round the tables and filled the cups and tankards that were handed to her.

Then, as she beat up a new tune for another set of dancers, Mr. Noy thought she cast a side glance toward him. The music, he recalled, was so charming and lively that to save his soul he couldn't refrain from going to join the dancers in a three-handed reel, but the girl, with a frown and look of alarm, made a motion with her head for him to withdraw round a corner of the house, out of sight. She beckoned to the same little old man, gave him the tambourine to play, and, leaving the company, went toward the orchard, signaling to Mr. Noy to follow her. In a clear spot where moonlight shone, she waited for him. He approached and was surprised to see that the damsel was no other than a farmer's daughter from Selena, one Grace Hutchens, who had been his sweetheart for a long while, until she had died three or four years before—at least he had mourned her as dead, and she had been buried in Buryan Churchyard as such.

When Mr. Noy came within a yard or so of her she said, "Thank the stars, my dear William, that I was on the lookout to stop ye, or

you would this minute be changed into the small people's state like I am—woe is me."

He was about to kiss her when she exclaimed, "Beware! Do not embrace me, nor touch flower nor fruit; for eating a tempting plum in this enchanted orchard was my undoing. You may think it strange, yet it was all through my love for you that I am come to this. People believed, and so it seemed, that I was found on the moor dead. What was buried for me, however, was only a changeling, or sham body, never mine I should think, for I feel much the same as when I lived to be your sweetheart."

As she said this several little voices squeaked, "Grace, Grace, bring us more beer and cider, and be quick!"

"Follow me into the garden and remain there behind the house; be sure you keep out of sight, and don't for your life touch fruit or flower," said she. "Await me here, I'll soon return. Sad is my lot to be stolen from the living and made housekeeper to these sprites," she murmured as she left him.

After a few minutes she returned, led him into a bowery walk, where the music and noise of merriment didn't drown out their voices, and said, "You know, my dear Willy, that I loved you much, but you never knew how dearly.

"Rest yourself on that seat," she continued, pointing to a stone, "whilst I tell ye what you never dreamed of." Mr. Noy seated himself as desired, and Grace related how one evening, about dusk, she was out on Selena Moor in quest of strayed sheep. Hearing him, in Pendrea ground, halloo and whistle to his dogs, she crossed over in the hope of falling in with him, but missed her way among ferns higher than her head and wandered on for hours amidst pools and bogs.

After rambling many miles, as it seemed to her, she waded a brook and entered an orchard. Then she heard music at a distance, and, proceeding toward it, passed into a beautiful garden with alleys all bordered by roses and many sweet flowers that she had never seen the like of. Apples and other tempting fruit dropped in the walks and hung overhead, bursting ripe.

This garden was so surrounded with trees and water that, like one led by piskeys, all her endeavors to find a way out of it were in vain. The music, too, seemed very near at times, but she could see nobody. Feeling weary and athirst, she plucked a plum that looked like gold in the clear starlight; her lips no sooner closed on the fruit than it dissolved to bitter water, which made her sick and faint. She then fell to the ground in a fit and remained insensible, she couldn't say how long. She awoke to find herself surrounded by hundreds of small people, who rejoiced to get her among them, as they very much wanted a tidy girl who knew how to bake and brew, one that would keep their habitation decent and nurse the changed-children.

At first she felt like one entranced and hardly knew how to "find herself" in such strange company; even after many years' experience, their mode of life remained somewhat unnatural to her, for everything among them seemed mere illusion and sham. They had no hearts, she believed, and but little feeling; what served them, in a way, as such, was merely the remembrance of whatever pleased them when they lived as mortals.

What appeared like ruddy apples and other delicious fruit were only sloes, hoggans [haws], and blackberries. The sweet-scented and rare flowers were no other than such as grow wild on every moor.

In answer to Mr. Hoy's inquiries about small people's diet, Grace told him how she sickened, at first, on their washy food of honey-dew and berries and how she often longed for a bit of salt fish. The only thing she relished was goat's milk, "for you must have often heard," said she, "that these animals are frequently seen on moors, or among carns and in other out-of-the-way places, miles from their homes. They are enticed away by small people to nourish their babes and changelings. There's a score or more of goats here at times. Those cunning old he-ones that often come among a flock—no one knows whence—and disappear with the best milkers, are the decoys, being small people in such shapes. One may often notice in these venerable longbeards a look of more than human craftiness and a sly witch-like glance cast from the corner of their eyes."

She also told him that she was the more content with her condition since she was enabled to take the form of any bird she pleased and thus gratify her desire to be near him. So that when he thought of her, she was usually hovering round him in the shape of some common small bird.

Mr. Noy wanted to know much more about these strange beings and was about to inquire when they again called, "Grace, Grace, where art thou so long? Bring us some drink quickly." She hastily entered the house, and that moment it came into his head that he, too, would have some liquor, disperse the small tribe, and save Grace.

Knowing that any garment turned inside out and cast among such sprites would make them flee, and happening to put his hand into his coat pocket, he felt there the gloves that he had worn in the afternoon. Quick as thought, he turned one inside out, put into it a small stone, and threw it among them. In an instant they all vanished with the house, Grace, and the furniture. He just had time to glance round, and see nothing but thickets and the roofless house, when he received a blow on his forehead that knocked him down.

Those to whom Mr. Noy related his story said that he had learned nothing new from Grace, for old folks always believed of the fairy people such things as she told him. It was said, too, that those who took animal forms got smaller and smaller with every change, till they were finally lost in the earth as muryans [ants], and that they passed the winter, for the most part, in underground habitations, entered from carns.

From the night that Mr. Noy strayed into the small people's habitation, he seemed to be a changed man. He talked of little else but what he had seen and heard there, and fancied that every redbreast, yellowhammer, wagtail, or other familiar small bird that came near him might be his departed love.

Often on moonlight nights he wandered around the moors in the hope of meeting Grace, and when he found his search was all in vain he became melancholy, neglected his farm, tired of hunting, and departed this life before the next harvest.

Adapted from ***Traditions and Hearthside Stories of West Cornwall.***

THE BAILIE'S DAUGHTER

THERE were at some time of the world two brothers in one farm, and they were very great friends, and they had each a son; and one of the brothers died, and he left his brother guardian. When the lad was near to be grown up, he was keeping the farm for his mother almost as well as his father could have done. One night he saw in a dream the most beautiful lady that there was in the world, and he dreamed of her three times, and he resolved to marry her and no other woman in the world; and he would not stay in the farm, and he grew pale, and his father's brother could not think what ailed him; and he was always asking him what was wrong with him. "Well, never mind," one day he said. "Brother of my father, I have seen in a dream the most beautiful woman that there is in the world, and I will marry no other but she; and I will now go out and search for her over the whole world till I find her."

Said the uncle, "Son of my brother, I have a hundred pounds; I will give them to thee, and go; and when that is spent, come back to me, and I will give thee another hundred."

So the lad took the hundred pounds, and he went to France, and then he went to Spain, and all over the world, but he could not find the lady he had seen in his sleep. At last he came to London, and he had spent all his money, and his clothes were worn, and he did not know what he should do for a night's lodging.

Well, as he was wandering about the streets, whom should he see but a quiet-looking, respectable old woman; and he spoke to her; and, from less to more, he told her all that had happened to him; and she was well pleased to see a countryman, and she said, "I, too, am a Highland woman, though I am in this town." And she took him to a small house that she had, and she gave him meat and clothes.

And she said, "Go out now and take a walk; maybe thou mayest see here in one day what thou mightest not see in a year."

The next day he was out taking a walk about the town, and he saw a woman at a window, and he knew her at once, for she was the lady he had seen in his sleep, and he went back to the old woman.

"How went it with thee this day, Gael?" said she.

"It went well," said he. "I have seen the lady I saw in my sleep." And he told her all about it.

Then the old woman asked about the house and the street; and when she knew—"Thou hast seen her," said she. "That is all thou wilt see of her. That is the daughter of the Bailie of London; but I am her foster mother, and I would be right glad if she would marry a countryman of my own. Now, do thou go out on the morrow, and I will give thee fine Highland clothes, and thou wilt find the lady walking in such a street: herself and three maidens will go out together; and do thou tread on her gown; and when she turns round to see what is the matter, do thou speak to her."

Well, the lad did this. He went out and he found the lady, and he set his foot on her dress, and the gown rent from the band; and when she turned round he said, "I am asking you much grace—it was an accident."

"It was not your fault; it was the fault of the dressmaker that made the dress so long," said she.

And she looked at him; and when she saw how handsome he was she said, "Will you be so kind as to come home with me to my father's house and take something?"

So the lad went and sat down, and before she asked him anything she set down wine before him and said, "Quicker is a drink than a tale."

When he had taken the wine he told her all that happened, and how he had seen her in his sleep, and when, and she was pleased.

"And I saw thee in my sleep on the same night," said she.

He went away that day, and the old woman he was lodging with asked him how he had got on, and he told her everything that had happened; and she went to the Bailie's daughter and told her all the good she could think of about the young lad; and after that he was often at the Bailie's house; and at last the daughter said she would marry him. "But I fear that will not do," said she. "Go home for a year, and when thou comest back I will contrive to marry thee," said she, "for it is the law of this country that no one must be married unless the Bailie himself gives her by the hand to the bridegroom," said she; and she left her blessing with him.

Well, the lad went home; and he told his father's brother all that had happened to him. And when the year was nearly out he set off for London again, and he had the second hundred with him, and some good oatmeal cakes.

On the road, whom should he meet but a Saxon gentleman who was going the same road, and they began to talk.

"Where art thou going?" said the Saxon.

"Well, I am going to London," said the Gael. "When I was last there I sowed lintseed [that is, set a net] in a street, and I am going to see if it is as I left it. If it is, well, I will take it with me; if not, I will leave it."

"Well," said the other, "that is a silly thing. How can lintseed be as thou hast left it? It must have grown up and been trodden down by ducks and geese and eaten by hens long ago. I am going to London, too; but I am going to marry the Bailie's daughter."

Well, they walked on together, and at long last the Saxon began to get hungry, and since he had no food with him, and there was no house near he said to the other, "Wilt thou give me some of thy food?"

"Well," said the Gael, "I have but poor food—oaten bread. I will give you some if you will take it, but if I were a gentleman like you I would never travel without my own mother."

"How can I travel with my mother?" said the Saxon. "She is dead and buried long ago and rotting in the earth. And why should I have her with me?" And he took the oat cake and ate it, and they went on their way.

They had not gone far when a heavy shower came on, and the Gael had a rough plaid to put about himself, but the Saxon had none, and he said, "Wilt thou lend me thy plaid?"

"I will lend you a part of it," said the Gael. "But if I were a gentleman like you, I would never travel without my house, and I would not be indebted to anyone for favors."

"Thou art a fool," said the Saxon. "My house is four stories high.

How could any man carry a house that is four stories high about with him?" But he wrapped the end of the Highlander's plaid about his shoulders, and they went on.

Well, they had not gone far till they came to a small river, and the water was deep after the rain, and there was no bridge, and in those days bridges were not so plentiful as they are now; and the Saxon would not wet his feet, so he said to the Highlander, "Wilt thou carry me over?"

"Well," said the Gael, "I don't mind if I do. But if I were a gentleman like you, I would never travel without my own bridge, and I would not be in any man's debt for favors."

"Thou art a silly fellow," said the Saxon. "How can any man travel about with a bridge that is made of stone and lime."

But he got on the back of his fellow traveler, and they went on till they got to London. Then the Saxon went to the house of the Bailie, and the other went to the little house of his old countrywoman who was the foster mother of the Bailie's daughter.

Well, the Saxon gentleman began to tell the Bailie all that had happened to him on the road; and he said, "I met with a Gael, and he was a perfect fool—the greatest booby that man ever saw. He told me that he had sown lintseed here a year ago in a street, and that he was coming to fetch it, if he should find it as he left it, but that if he did not, he would leave it. And how should he find that after a year? He told me I should never travel without my mother, and my house, and my bridge. And how could a man travel with all these things? But though he was nothing but a fool, he was a good-natured fellow, for he gave me some of his food, and lent me a bit of his plaid, and he carried me over a river."

"I know not but he was as wise as the man that was speaking to him," said the Bailie, for the Bailie was a wise man. "I'll tell you what he meant," said he.

"Well, I will show that he was a fool as great as ever was seen," said the Saxon.

"He has left a girl in this town," said the Bailie, "and he is come to see if she is still in the same mind as she was when he left her; if so, he will take her with him; if not, he will leave her; and so he has set a net," said he. "When he said that your mother nourished you, and a gentleman like you should have his own nourishment with him, he meant that you should not be dependent on him. The booby was the one that was with him," said the Bailie. "A gentleman like you should have his own shelter, and your house is your shelter when you are at home. A bridge is made for crossing a river, and a man should always be able to do that without help; and the man was right, and he was no fool, but a smart lad, and I should like to meet him," said the Bailie; "and I would go to fetch him if I knew where he was."

Well, the next day the Bailie went to the house where the lad was, and he asked him to come to dinner; and the lad came, and he told the Bailie that he had understood all that had been said.

"Now," said the Gael, "as it is the law that no man may be married here unless the Bailie gives him the bride by the hand, will you be so kind as to give me the girl that I have come to marry, if she is still in the same mind? I will have everything ready."

And the Bailie said, "I will do that, my smart lad, tomorrow, or whenever thou dost choose. I would go farther than that for such a smart boy."

When the morrow came the Bailie's daughter disguised herself, and she went to the house of the foster mother, and the Gael had a churchman there; and the Bailie came in, and he took his own daughter by the hand without knowing her.

"Give thy hand, girl," said the Bailie. "It is an honor for thee to marry such a smart lad." And he gave her to him, and they were married according to law.

Then the Bailie went home, and he was to give his daughter by the hand to the Saxon gentleman that day; but the daughter was not to be found.

"Well," said the Bailie, "I will lay a wager that Gael has got her, after all." And the Gael came in with the daughter, and he told them everything just as had happened, from beginning to the end, and how he had plenty of land in his own country.

And the Bailie said, "Well, since I myself have given thee my daughter by the hand, it is a marriage, and I am glad that she has got a smart lad like thee for a husband."

And they made a wedding that lasted a year and a day, and they lived happily ever after, and if they have not died since then they are alive yet.

Adapted from "Bailie Lunnain," in *Popular Tales of the West Highlands,* translated from the Gaelic by J. F. Campbell.

THE WIDOW AND HER DAUGHTERS

THERE was formerly a poor widow, and she had three daughters, and all she had to feed them was from a kail yard. But each day a great gray horse came to the yard to eat the kail.

Said the oldest of the daughters to her mother, "I will go into the yard today, and I will take the spinning wheel with me, and I will keep the horse out of the kail." "Do," said her mother. So the daughter went out, and when the horse came she took the distaff from the wheel and struck him with it. The distaff stuck to the horse, and her hand stuck to the distaff. Away went the horse till they reached a green hill, and he called out, "Open, open, oh, green hill, and let in the king's son; open, open, oh, green hill, and let in the widow's daughter." The hill opened, and they went in.

The horse that was a king's son warmed water for her feet, and made a soft bed for her limbs, and she lay down that night. Early on the morrow he rose and made ready to go to hunt. But first he gave her the keys to the whole house and said to her that she might open every chamber but one, but by all she ever saw not to open that one. And then he said that she should have his dinner ready when he came back, and that if she were a good woman he would marry her.

When he went away she began to open the doors of the chambers. Every chamber, as she opened it, was finer than the one before, till she came to the one that was forbidden. She wondered what might be in it that she might not open it too. So she opened it, and it was full of dead gentlewomen, and she went down to the knees in blood. Then she came out, and though she tried to cleanse her feet, still she could not take a bit of the blood off. Then a tiny cat came and said to her that if she would give it a little drop of milk it would clean her feet as clean as they were before.

"Thou! Ugly beast! be off! Dost thou suppose that I won't clean them better than thou?"

"Well, then, take thine own way. Thou wilt see what will happen to thee when himself comes home."

He came home, and she set the dinner on the board, and they sat down to it. But before they ate a bit he said to her, "Wert thou a good woman today?"

"I was," said she.

"Let me see thy foot, and I will tell whether thou wert or wert not." She let him see the one that was clean.

"Let me see the other one," said he. When he saw the blood, "Oho!" said he. He rose and took an ax and took her head off, and he threw her into the chamber with the other dead ones. He lay down that night, and early on the morrow he went to the widow's yard again.

Said the second one of the widow's daughters to her mother, "I will go out with my sewing today, and I will keep the gray horse out of the yard." She went out with her sewing. She struck the cloth she was sewing on the horse. The cloth stuck to the horse, and her hand stuck to the cloth. They reached the hill again. He called to the hill, the hill opened, and they went in. He warmed water for her feet, and made a soft bed for her limbs, and they lay down that night. Early in the morning he made ready to go to hunt, and he said to her that she should open every chamber but one, but by all she ever saw not to open that one.

She opened every chamber till she came to the one, and because she thought, "What may be in that one more than the rest that I may not open it?" she opened it, and it was full of dead gentlewomen, and her own sister amongst them. She went down to the knees in blood. She came out, and as she was cleaning herself the little cat came round about and said to her, "If thou wilt give me a tiny drop of milk I will clean thy foot as well as it ever was."

"Thou! Ugly beast! begone. Dost thou think that I will not clean it myself better than thou?"

"Thou wilt see," said the cat, "what will happen to thee when himself comes home."

When he came, she set down the dinner, and they sat down to it. Said he, "Wert thou a good woman today?"

"I was," said she.

"Let me see thy foot, and I will tell thee whether thou wert or wert not." She let him see the foot that was clean.

"Let me see the other one," said he. She let him see it. "Oho!" said he, and he took the ax and took her head off. He lay down that night.

Early on the morrow said the youngest one to her mother, as she wove a stocking, "I will go out with my stocking today, and I will watch the gray horse. I will see what happened to my two sisters, and I will return to tell you."

"Do," said her mother, "and see thou dost not stay away." The daughter went out, and the horse came. She struck the stocking on the horse. The stocking stuck to the horse, and the hand stuck to the stocking. They went away, and they reached the green hill. He called out as usual, and they went in. He warmed water for her feet, and made a soft bed for her limbs, and they lay down that night. On the morrow he was going to hunt, and he said to her that if she would behave herself as a good woman till he returned they would be married in a few days. He gave her the keys and said to her that she might open every chamber but one, but that she should not open that one.

She opened every one, and when she came to that one she thought, "What may be in it that I may not open it more than the rest?" and opened it, and she saw her two sisters lying there dead, and she went down to the knees in blood. She came out, and she cleaned her feet, but she could not take a bit of the blood off them. The tiny cat came and said to her, "Give me a tiny drop of milk, and I will clean thy feet as clean as they were before."

"I will give it, thou creature; I will give thee thy desire of milk if thou wilt clean my feet."

The cat licked her feet as clean as they were before. Then the king's son came home, and she set down his dinner, and they sat down to it. But before they ate a bit he said to her, "Wert thou a good woman today?"

"I was middlin'," said she. "I have no boast to make of myself."

"Let me see thy feet," said he. She let him see her feet.

"Thou wert a good woman," said he; "and if thou holdest on thus till the end of a few days, thyself and I will be married."

On the morrow he went away to hunt. After he had gone the little cat came. "Now, I will tell thee in what way thou canst be quickest married to him," said the cat. "There are a lot of old chests within. Thou shalt take out three of them and clean them. Thou shalt say to him that he must leave these three chests in thy mother's house, as they are of no use here. Thou shalt say to him that he must not open any of them on the road, and if he does, that thou wilt leave him; that thou wilt go up into a treetop and wilt be looking, and if he opens any of them that thou wilt see. Then when he goes hunting, thou shalt open the chamber and bring out thy two sisters. Thou shalt draw on them the magic club, and they will be as lively and whole as they were before; thou shalt cleanse them then, and thou shalt put one in each chest, and go thyself into the third one. Thou shalt put as much silver and gold in the chests as will keep thy mother and thy sisters right for their lives. When he has left the chests in thy mother's house and returned, he will fly into a wild rage: he will then go to thy mother's house in this fury and break in the door. Be thou behind the door, and take off his head with a bar. And then he will be a king's son, as precious as he was before, and he will marry thee.

"Say to thy sisters, if he attempts to open the chests by the way, to call out, 'I see thee, I see thee,' and he will think that thou art calling out from the tree."

When he came home he carried away the chests, one after one. And when he came to a glen where he thought she in the tree could not see him, he began to let each chest down to see what was in it, but she that was in the chest called out, "I see thee, I see thee!"

"Good luck be on thy pretty little head," said he, "if thou canst see so long a way!"

This was what happened on each journey, till he had left all the chests in her mother's house.

When he returned home on the last journey and saw that she was not there, he flew into a wild rage; he went back to the widow's house, and when he reached the door he drove it in before him. She was standing behind the door, and she took his head off with the bar. Then he became a king's son, as precious as ever was; and they were in great gladness. She and himself married, and they left enough gold and silver with her mother and sisters to keep them well for life.

Adapted from *Popular Tales of the West Highlands.*

GET UP AND BAR THE DOOR

IT FELL about the Martinmas time,
And a gay time it was then,
When our good wife got puddings to make,
And she's boild them in the pan.

The wind sae cauld blew south and north,
  And blew into the floor;
Quoth our goodman to our goodwife,
  "Gae out and bar the door."

"My hand is in my hussyfskap,[1]
  Goodman, as ye may see;
An it shoud nae be barrd this hundred year,
  It's no be barrd for me."

They made a paction tween them twa,
  They made it firm and sure,
That the first word whaeer[2] shoud speak
  Shoud rise and bar the door.

Then by there came two gentlemen,
  At twelve o'clock at night,
And they could neither see house nor hall,
  Nor coal nor candle-light.

"Now whether is this a rich man's house,
  Or whether is it a poor?"
But neer a word wad ane o them speak,
  For barring of the door.

And first they ate the white puddings,
  And then they ate the black;
Tho muckle thought the goodwife to hersel,
  Yet neer a word she spake.

Then said the one unto the other,
  "Here, man, tak ye my knife;
De ye tak aff the auld man's beard,
  And I'll kiss the goodwife."

"But there's nae water in the house,
  And what shall we do than?"
"What ails thee at the pudding-broo,
  That boils into the pan?"

[1] kneading-trough
[2] whoever

O up then started our goodman,
An angry man was he:
"Will ye kiss my wife before my een,
And scad me wi pudding-bree?"

Then up and started our goodwife,
Gied three skips on the floor:
"Goodman, you've spoken the foremost word,
Get up and bar the door."

From *The English and Scottish Popular Ballads*, collected and edited by F. J. Child (Boston: Houghton Mifflin Company, 1882–1898).

OUR GOODMAN

HAME came our goodman,
And hame came he,
And then he saw a saddle-horse
Where nae horse should be.

"What's this now, goodwife?
What's this I see?
How came this horse here,
Without the leave o me?"

Recitative. "A horse?" quo she.
"Ay, a horse," quo he.

"Shame fa your cuckold face,
Ill mat[1] ye see!
'Tis naething, but a broad sow,
My minnie[2] sent to me."

"A broad sow?" quo he.
"Ay, a sow," quo she.

[1] may [2] mother

"Far hae I ridden,
  And farer hae I gane,
But a saddle on a sow's back
  I never saw nane."

Hame came our goodman,
  And hame came he;
He spy'd a pair of jack-boots,
  Where nae boots should be.

"What's this now, goodwife?
  What's this I see?
How came these boots here,
  Without the leave o me?"

"Boots?" quo she.
"Ay, boots," quo he.

"Shame fa your cuckold face,
  And ill mat ye see.
It's but a pair of water-stoups,[3]
  My minnie sent to me."

"Water-stoups?" quo he.
"Ay, water-stoups," quo she.

"Far hae I ridden,
  And farer hae I gane,
But siller spurs on water-stoups
  I saw never nane."

Hame came our goodman,
  And hame came he,
And he saw a sword,
  Where a sword should na be.

"What's this now, goodwife?
  What's this I see?
How came this sword here,
  Without the leave o me?"

[3] pitchers

"A sword?" quo she.
"Ay, a sword," quo he.

"Shame fa your cuckold face,
Ill mat ye see!
It's but a porridge-spurtle,[4]
My minnie sent to me."

"A spurtle?" quo he.
"Ay, a spurtle," quo she.

"Far hae I ridden,
And farer hae I gane,
But siller-handed spurtles
I saw never nane."

Hame came our goodman,
And hame came he;
There he spy'd a powderd wig
Where nae wig should be.

"What's this now, goodwife?
What's this I see?
How came this wig here,
Without the leave o me?"

"A wig?" quo she.
"Ay, a wig," quo he.

"Shame fa your cuckold face,
And ill mat ye see!
'Tis naething but a clocken-hen,[5]
My minnie sent to me."

"Clocken hen?" quo he.
"Ay, clocken hen," quo she.

[4] stirrer
[5] clucking-hen

"Far hae I ridden,
  And farer hae I gane,
But powder on a clocken-hen
  I saw never nane."

Hame came our goodman,
  And hame came he,
And there he saw a muckle[6] coat,
  Where nae coat should be.

"What's this now, goodwife?
  What's this I see?
How came this coat here,
  Without the leave o me?"

"A coat?" quo she.
"Ay, a coat," quo he.

"Shame fa your cuckold face,
  Ill mat ye see!
It's but a pair of blankets,
  My minnie sent to me."

"Blankets?" quo he.
"Ay, blankets," quo she.

"Far hae I ridden,
  And farer hae I gane,
But buttons upon blankets
  I saw never nane."

Ben[7] went our goodman,
  And ben went he,
And there he spy'd a sturdy man,
  Where nae man should be.

"What's this now, goodwife?
  What's this I see?
How came this man here,
  Without the leave o me?"

[6] great
[7] into the inner room

"A man?" quo she.
"Ay, a man," quo he.

"Poor blind body,
And blinder mat ye be!
It's a new milking-maid
My mither sent to me."

"A maid?" quo he.
"Ay, a maid," quo she.

"Far hae I ridden,
And farer hae I gane,
But lang-bearded maidens
I saw never nane."

From *The English and Scottish Popular Ballads.*

Finnish

The Destruction of the Sampo

STIMULATED by an unusually strong sense of nationalism, Finnish story collectors (their Finno-Ugric tongue, it might be recalled, is neither Slavic nor Scandinavian but an independent language) have during the past century assembled upward of thirty thousand tales in their tiny land. Very few of these have been published and only a handful translated into English. But those few include the *Kalevala.* Although Elias Lönrot, who gathered the *Kalevala* stories in eastern Finland and Karelia more than a century ago, treated them as if they constituted a coherent national epic, they were actually a series of ballads (sung to the accompaniment of a rude form of harp called the kantele) celebrating the deeds of Vainamoinen, hero of heroes and oldest magician, and his brother Ilmarinen, the mighty smith, forger of the heavens. Most of their adventures result from their attempts to win the dazzling daughter of Louhi, sorceress of the North Country. In his effort to win the girl, Ilmarinen makes for old Louhi a magic mill that yields (like the quern in the Norwegian "Why the Sea Is Salt," or the barrel of the sorcerer's apprentice in the English story, "The Master and His Pupil") endless quantities of corn, salt, or coin. After Ilmarinen has won and lost the daughter, the brothers, together with another hero, Lemminkainen, attempt to carry off the sampo. Louhi pursues them and what then happens is here described in "The Destruction of the Sampo" and "The Last Adventure."

A few of Vainamoinen's adventures (for example, his visits to the Land of the Dead and his sojourn in the entrails of a giant) resemble episodes in other sagas, but everywhere there are vivid northland scenes and such striking descriptions of old Finnish customs as those dealing with Vainamoinen's powers as singer and kantele-player.

"Lippo and Tapio," with its account of a mighty Lapland hunter who woos the daughter of the forest god, is plainly from the same region and in the same tradition as the *Kalevala*, but "The Pig-Headed Wife" is the kind of folk tale that can be found wherever men think women are stubborn or husbands find fault with their wives.

THE KALEVALA

The Destruction of the Sampo

Old Louhi's first act was to summon all the warriors of the North Country. She armed them with bows and arrows and sharp swords, and then she fitted out a mighty warship. There were a hundred swordsmen on board, and a thousand men with crossbows in the tall ship. Old Louhi herself lifted the mast and spread the canvas. The mainsail was so wide that it hung like a cloud in heaven. Thus they set forth to give battle to old Vainamoinen and recapture the magic sampo.

Now lusty old Vainamoinen had already overcome many dangers, but he felt in his bones that he must be wary, and ever keep on guard against greater trouble. So he sent young Lemminkainen to the lookout to see what he could see.

Lemminkainen climbed up the masthead of the red ship, among the billowing sails, and looked east and west and northwest and south and over toward the dark and misty shores of the North Country.

"The horizon is clear before us," he called down, "but behind us in the north there is a cloud, a small cloud, off to the northwest."

"Nonsense," said old Vainamoinen. "There can be no cloud there. Look again."

Lemminkainen looked again more sharply. "I see an island in the distance," he called down. "A far away island, covered with trees. There are falcons and speckled grouse perched on the branches."

"Nonsense!" exclaimed old Vainamoinen. "There can be no falcons there and no speckled grouse. Look again."

So Lemminkainen looked over the waters a third time. "I see a ship!" he shouted, "a ship sailing from the North Country. There are a hundred men at the oars, and a thousand bowmen beside them."

"Row, brother smith!" cried Vainamoinen. "Row, Ilmarinen, as fast as you can! And you, Lemminkainen, climb down and pull at the oars. All of you, row as hard and as fast as you can!"

At once everybody in the red ship set to work and rowed mightily, straining at the pinewood oars. The prow dashed forward like a seal in flight, the waves boiled, and the foam flew. The heroes pulled at the oars as if they were rowing for a wager. They strove as though they were racing. But though they used all their strength, they did not widen the distance between them and the warship from the North Country.

Now they were indeed in serious trouble. Misfortune was on their tracks. Old Vainamoinen thought that doomsday was falling on his head. But he was not one to be daunted. He considered what it was best to do. It was not long before the oldest magician thought of a plan whereby he could outwit the Mistress of the North Country.

He took a small piece of tinder from his tinderbox and threw it over his left shoulder, and as it flew through the air he uttered a spell. Thanks to Vainamoinen's magic, the tinder no sooner struck the water than it grew up into a sharp cliff that jutted east and north. Old Louhi's ship, rushing forward at tremendous speed, dashed against this cliff, wedged against the rocks, and splintered. The masts crashed into the water, the sails were carried away by the wind. Vainly old Louhi tried to raise her ship. The ribs were staved in, the oarlocks were shattered.

But crafty old Louhi was not without magic of her own. She took five sharp scythes and six worn-out hoes and fashioned them into talons. Then she seized the broken planks of her ship and turned them into wings, and of the rudder she fashioned a tail. And the scythes and the hoes and the planks and the rudder became a mighty eagle. When all was finished, old Louhi herself took the shape of the eagle she had contrived. And under her wings she took a hundred of her swordsmen, and on her tail she carried a thousand archers.

Then she flew, flapping one wing against the clouds and trailing one wing in the water, to attack old Vainamoinen. She swept over the sea and perched on the masthead of his red ship. The boat lurched sideways with the weight of the eagle and of the fighters clinging to its wings and riding on its tail. Old Vainamoinen thought that his red ship would surely sink under the load.

He looked up at the masthead and hailed the terrible bird.

"I know that you want the sampo," he said. "And so do we heroes of the Land of Heroes. But the magic mill is big enough for all of us. Let us carry it to shore and divide it, half for the folk of the North Country and half for us of the Land of Heroes. Even a piece of the magic sampo will work well enough to give us great plenty."

"Never will I share the sampo!" cried old Louhi fiercely. And without further talk she swooped down to seize the magic mill by force.

Young Lemminkainen whipped out his sword and struck at the eagle, but to no purpose. Then old Vainamoinen lifted the rudder and smote with all his might. A hundred swordsmen dropped from the eagle's wings, a thousand archers tumbled from her tail. There was savage fighting on the red ship, and the warriors of the North Country were overwhelmed and drowned in the sea. Old Vainamoinen struck and struck again. At last the eagle dropped upon the deck. Vainamoinen's blows had broken every claw but one. Only the tiniest remained.

But old Louhi was firm in her purpose. With the single small claw that was left her she dragged at the sampo by its many-colored lid and pulled it out of the ship's hold, and cast it into the water. But small good this did her, for the magic sampo broke into fragments and the many-colored lid was smashed to splinters. The larger pieces were so heavy that they sank beneath the waves, where they have lain ever since, producing the wealth of the sea. The smaller pieces floated on the surface of the waters, rocked by the waves and wafted hither and yon by the winds.

Old Vainamoinen watched them tossing about and he rejoiced at the sight, for he could gather the fragments that floated to shore and bear them off to the Land of Heroes to create riches for all the folk of that country.

"Aha, old Louhi!" he cried. "You have done well for us. You have done very well. Even the pieces of the sampo are good magic. Our plowing and our sowing will prosper! Our crops will grow in the sunlight and shine like silver in the pleasant moonlight. Our cattle will feed in the sun, and in the pleasant moonlight they shall have increase."

But the eagle that was crafty old Louhi screamed vengefully, "You may have the better part of the sampo, but your crops will not prosper nor your cattle increase. I shall find ways to prevent it, if I must steal the lights out of the sky."

Then with her one remaining claw she seized a tiny piece of the sampo's many-colored lid and carried it back with her to the North Country, lamenting her loss as she flew. For this poor fragment of the magic mill could bring small blessings to those cold and misty regions, and it would be a starved life that her folk would lead there without the sampo. So, shrieking and wailing, she flew homeward.

But lusty old Vainamoinen paid little heed to old Louhi's threats. He too went back to his own country, carrying with him in his red ship many pieces of the magic sampo that he had picked up from the shore. When he reached home, he planted them in the earth, that they might grow and flourish and the land be rich in barley and the flowing ale that is brewed of the barley grain, and rich in rye and the crusty bread that is made of the rye flour.

The capture of so many pieces of the sampo and the thought of the harvest filled old Vainamoinen with joy. "Now is the time for music and pleasure. Now is the time for singing," he said. But then he sighed, for the kantele that he had wrought of the pike's head was sunk to the bottom of the sea.

Yet he would not despair. He summoned his brother the smith. "Go to your smithy, Ilmarinen," he said, "and forge me a rake of iron. Set the teeth close together and make the handle five hundred fathoms long. I must rake among the reeds of the lake and in the rocky caverns of the salmon and among the crooked paths of the fishes under the sea. I am going to rake the waves for my lost kantele."

Ilmarinen was glad to be of service. He too wanted to hear again the lovely strains of the kantele. So he forged a rake with a copper handle. The teeth were a hundred fathoms in length, and the copper handle full five hundred fathoms.

Vainamoinen took the rake and went down to the shore and stepped into a boat to sail in search of his lost treasure. He sailed here and there. He raked among the shore drift and the leaves of the water-lilies. He raked the shoals and the deeps as well, but his harp of pike-bone he did not find. Sadly he returned home, with his head bowed and his cap awry. He left his boat on the beach and his rake beside it, and he wandered on the edge of the woodland, wishing for his lost kantele.

He had not gone far when he heard a sound of weeping. It came from a speckled birch. Old Vainamoinen hurried to where the birch tree was standing. He was in a mood to sympathize with whatever mourned.

"What are you crying about?" he asked.

"Oh," wailed the birch tree, "I have cause enough to cry. There is no tree in the forest that is so cruelly used as I am. In the spring the children come with their sharp knives and cut me and carve me. In summer the wicked herdsmen strip my bark away to plait themselves berry baskets. Girls come to dance beneath my branches and pull off my crown for their whiskbrooms. The young men cut off my boughs to get faggots for burning. And in winter I shiver and shake, leafless and scarred and stripped, in the snow and the wind. There is no tree so hacked and hewed as I."

"Do not cry, little birch tree," said old Vainamoinen gently. "There is happiness in store for you. I will make you sing for pleasure."

Indeed he spoke truly. For of the tough birch wood old Vainamoinen fashioned the frame of a new kantele. It was firm and fine, and its curves were curves of beauty. Now he needed pegs for his harp. There was a splendid oak standing in the farmyard. On every branch hung an acorn, and on every acorn perched a cuckoo, and every cuckoo was sounding five clear notes, and as the notes sounded, silver and gold fell from their beaks upon the ground. Old Vainamoinen gathered the silver and gold for the pegs of his new kantele. But still he had no harp strings. Without five harp strings, the beautiful birch wood frame and the gold and silver pegs would never make music.

Lusty old Vainamoinen went wandering along the heath, thinking where he could find them. Now there was a young girl sitting on the heath, singing softly to herself while she waited for her sweetheart to come and meet her. Old Vainamoinen heard her singing, and he went up to her and spoke to her gently and begged her politely to give him a few strands of her hair. The girl was willing, and gave him five strands of her strong, lovely hair, and of these he wrought his harp strings.

Then old Vainamoinen sat down on a rock and propped the knob of his new kantele on his knee and turned the frame toward heaven, and adjusted the strings. And then with all his fingers he drew forth the most delicious music. The birch wood rang out joyfully, the pegs given by the golden cuckoos turned smoothly, and the hair of the young girl waiting for her sweetheart sang like a happy heart.

At the sound of Vainamoinen's new kantele the mountains trembled and the plains shook, the gravel stirred in the water, the pine trees rejoiced on the hill, and even the old stumps on the heath began to skip for pleasure. All the folk of the Land of Heroes came running to hear the music. Laughing girls and smiling mothers, men holding their caps in their fists, and old women with their hands at their sides, all trooped toward Vainamoinen, exclaiming over the wonderful kantele. The beasts of the forest rested on their paws to hear the melody, the birds perched on the branches near the harper, the fish swam to the surface of the sea to listen, and even the worms turned around in the earth and crept to the top of the soil to hear Vainamoinen's music.

He played for a whole day and for another day and for a third day, every morning right after breakfast. And he did not stop to put on a fresh girdle and he wore the same shirt for three days, because he did not want to pause in his playing to change it. Part of the time he played walking through the pine wood, and then every needle on the pines rejoiced to hear him. And part of the time he sat in his own house playing, and then the roof rang and the boards resounded and the ceilings sang and the doors creaked happily and the windows laughed, and even the stones of the hearth were stirred by the enchanting music of Vainamoinen's birch-wood kantele.

But while he had been fashioning his new harp and delighting all the folk of the Land of Heroes with his singing, old Louhi, the crafty Mistress of the North Country, had been brooding over the loss of the magic sampo. When finally the news reached her of how Vainamoinen had gathered the broken pieces of the sampo and planted them in the Land of Heroes, and of how they flourished there, old Louhi was filled with jealousy. And when she heard that Vainamoinen was traveling about playing the harp and singing songs about the prosperity of his country, then old Louhi was very angry indeed.

She called upon Ukko the Creator to send an iron hail or a deadly plague upon the folk of the Land of Heroes.

"Let the men die in the farmyard and the women die on the floor of the cowshed. Let the whole people perish!" cried old Louhi in her rage.

But she knew well enough that if her curse was to be effective, she herself must work her evil magic. And how she did this and what came of it, you shall hear.

The Last Adventure

Now it happened that the blackest and ugliest of the daughters of Tuoni, Lord of the Dead, had wandered to the North Country and there given birth to nine hideous children. And in the time of childbirth it was crafty old Louhi, the Mistress of the North Country, who had helped her and cared for her. The names of four of these children were Colic and Itch and Gout and Plague, and there were four more as ugly, but the ninth and nastiest was Envy. It was these horrid creatures that old Louhi sent forth to the Land of Heroes to destroy its people.

Great then was the misery in that country. The singing was changed to wailing and the laughter to tears. Lusty old Vainamoinen put aside his kantele and with fire and water he made magic against the dread diseases. Then he took his sharp sword and drove them to the Mount of Torments, where the stones would not weep for pain nor the rocks complain of aching. With eight soothing salves and nine magic drugs old Vainamoinen rubbed and anointed the sick till all were sound and hale. The diseases were sealed up in a barrel and locked fast in the Mount of Torments. And Envy was banished with them.

The folk of the Land of Heroes were full of gratitude to the oldest magician and to Ukko the Creator, who had helped him to dispel all these evils. But the news that her sorcery was in vain was not pleasing to old Louhi, when it came at last to her ears, and she set to work to devise another way of injuring those who possessed the pieces of the magic sampo. She awakened the Great Bear of the heath from his slumbers and drove him to the Land of Heroes to work ill among its people.

But old Vainamoinen called upon his brother the smith to forge him a new spear with a copper shaft and three cutting edges. Then with Ilmarinen's handiwork he went forth against the shaggy monster.

It was not long before the old huntsman returned victorious. Then great was the rejoicing. The honey-eater was stripped of his skin, and the flesh was cut up and placed in caldrons of copper and gilded kettles. There it simmered away, till the meat was sweet, and then it was heaped on brimming platters and carried to the tables beside great mugs of red ale. There was enough bear steak for an abundant feast, and more than enough to be salted away. It was evening before the feast was over, and then the time was come for singing. So lusty old Vainamoinen took his kantele and played so sweetly that the Moon came from his house and stood on a crooked birch tree to listen, and the Sun came from his castle and sat on a fir tree to hear.

But crafty old Louhi, the Mistress of the North Country, was ill content. Instead of destroying the folk of the Land of Heroes, the honey-eater had provided them with a fat feast. Still, she had not come to the end of her evil magic.

She set to work to capture the Sun from the top of the fir tree and to seize the Moon from the birch tree. She carried the lights of heaven home with her to the dark and misty regions of the North Country, and there she hid them in a mountain as hard as steel among rocks as strong as iron. The Land of Heroes was left in cold and darkness. The sky was filled with night, and the house of Ukko the Creator was as dismal as the lightless homes in Vainamoinen's country.

Ukko the Creator felt strange indeed without his Moon or his Sun, so he walked out in his blue stockings to the edge of the clouds and the borders of the heavens to seek them. But he could not find any sign of them. Then he took his sword and struck it against his fingernail, and a bright spark flew forth. Ukko gave the spark to one of the Maidens of the Air to tend, hoping to fashion a new sun of this brightness. But the stupid Maiden of the Air dropped it, and it fell flaming through the six spangled vaults of heaven and fell into a lake.

The waters of the lake boiled up. All the fishes rushed to seize the spark that was destroying their watery homes, and in the end it was swallowed by a herring. The unhappy creature swam up and down, tormented by the fiery spark, till a salmon trout, tired of its complaints, gulped it down. Now it was the salmon trout's turn to swim up and down in burning misery, until a great gray pike came forward and swallowed the salmon trout who had swallowed the herring who had swallowed the fiery spark.

Old Vainamoinen had seen the spark fall from the sky and he was eager to get hold of it, for he too hoped it would replace the light of the stolen Sun and Moon. He went out onto the lake where it had fallen, and there the fishes told him what had happened. But try as he might, Vainamoinen could not capture the gray pike.

At last he returned home and prepared a linen net of the fairest flax, a net of a hundred meshes. He placed this in his boat, and, taking along his brother Ilmarinen, he set forth once more. He cast the linen net into the water and drew it and dragged it, and many a perch and many a salmon trout and many a bream came to his net, but never the gray pike with the spark of fire in his belly. All Vainamoinen's labors were in vain.

But he had a friend, a dwarf, a very small hero, and the dwarf came down to the shore of the lake and lifted a pine tree from the bank and threshed the water with it till the fish swam by hundreds into Vainamoinen's net. The oldest magician urged his boat with its heavy load to the red bridge-end, and there he sorted out the fishes. Among them was the gray pike.

But Vainamoinen knew that it was a risky thing to take barehanded a fish with a spark of fire in its belly. For such a task he needed iron gloves or gauntlets of stone or perhaps copper mittens.

While he was reflecting what he had best do, the son of the Sun spoke to him and said, "Do not fret, old Vainamoinen. I will venture to take the gray pike in my own hands, for fire will not hurt me, and I will rip him up with the knife my father gave me. It has a golden haft and a silver blade."

With these words the son of the Sun dropped down beside old Vainamoinen and took his knife from his belt and ripped open the body of the gray pike. There was the salmon trout, and within it lay the smooth-skinned herring. The son of the Sun split open the herring and found a blue clew in the third fold of its entrails. He unwound it and found a red clew. In the middle of the red clew was the spark of fire itself.

"How shall I carry it to the cold, dark dwellings of the Land of Heroes?" Vainamoinen wondered.

But before he could think of a plan the spark flew up and singed

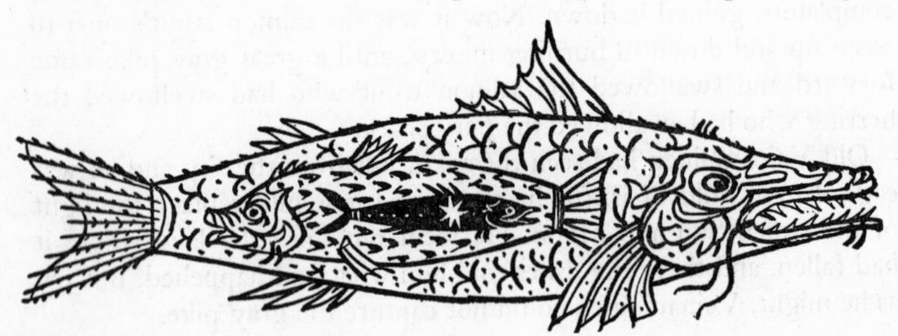

the hands of the son of the Sun and singed the beard of lusty old Vainamoinen. His brother the smith was standing beside him. The spark leaped up and singed the hands and scorched the cheeks of Ilmarinen so terribly that he had to run to the shore of the lake and cry to Ukko the Creator for ice and hoar frost with which to soothe his stinging burns.

But lusty old Vainamoinen was not to be daunted. He thrust the fiery spark into a piece of tinder and carried it to the hearths and kettles of his people to give light and heat for cooking.

Still, it was of no use as a substitute for the stolen Sun and Moon. The crops were consumed by frost. The cattle suffered. The birds of the air felt strange in this enduring night. And the folk of the Land of Heroes mourned in darkness. They never knew whether it was morning or evening. It was indeed hard to live without the lights of the sky.

They came to Ilmarinen the smith and begged him to forge them a new sun and a new moon out of silver and gold. He labored long at the task, and when the false sun and moon were finished, he lifted them and set them up, the one on the tip of a birch tree and the other on the summit of a fir. But though they were very beautiful, they did not shine like sunlight and like moonlight.

Then the oldest magician took counsel with himself and made magic with a handful of sticks from the boughs of the alder. He questioned the sticks, and they told him that the real Sun and Moon were hidden deep in the stone mountain in the dark and misty regions of the North Country.

So old Vainamoinen took ship and sailed for that place to demand the lights of heaven.

"You may have them," said old Louhi's warriors mockingly, "if you overcome us in open combat."

Now old Vainamoinen's sword was longer than theirs by only so much as a barley grain or perhaps the width of a cornstalk. But he sliced off their heads like turnip tops and went forthwith to the stone mountain to fetch what he had come for.

There were nine doors and a hundred bolts to the stone mountain. There were dreadful serpents guarding the stolen treasures. It was a trifle for the oldest magician to destroy the serpents. But not all his spells were sufficient to break the bolts and move the heavy doors.

Very much annoyed, he went home and sought out his brother the smith.

"You must forge me mighty spears and a dozen hatchets," he said. "You must give me a bunch of enormous keys to open the doors of the stone mountain. Otherwise I shall never be able to get at the Sun and Moon."

Ilmarinen set to work at once. He made a great bundle of spears, and he forged twelve strong hatchets, and then he began making a bunch of enormous keys. The noise in the smithy was so loud that it thundered far off in the cold and misty regions of the North Country. Old Louhi heard the clatter and the clamor. She was fearful of what it might mean. So she took the form of a hawk and came flying to the Land of Heroes.

She flew straight to Ilmarinen's smithy. She flew so fast that the smith thought a fierce wind was blowing. He went to the window of his smithy to see what he could see. But he found only the gray hawk that was old Louhi.

"What are you doing here outside my window, O bird of prey?" he inquired.

"I have come to watch you at work," answered crafty old Louhi. "You are indeed a marvelous smith. What skillful fingers you have, and what mighty arms!" she said, flattering him. "You are truly a wonderful craftsman."

"It is no wonder," answered Ilmarinen. "It was I who forged the heavens and I who welded the arch of the air."

"But what are you making now, O smith?" asked the hawk. "What are you forging this time?"

"I am forging a collar," replied Ilmarinen. "I am making a ring for the neck of the wicked Mistress of the North Country. When this work is done she will be firmly fettered forever to the side of a great mountain."

When old Louhi heard these words she felt her doom coming upon her. Filled with fear, she flew swiftly back to her own country. She did not stop until she had come to the place where she had hidden the lights of heaven. Quickly she freed the Sun and Moon from hiding. Then, taking the shape of a pigeon, she flew back to Ilmarinen's smithy.

"What are you doing here, O pigeon?" asked the smith. "Why are you perched on my threshold?"

"I have come to bring you news," said old Louhi. "The Moon has risen out of the stone. The Sun is freed from the rock."

Ilmarinen did not wait to see the bird depart for the North Country, nevermore to return. He hurried out of the dark smithy into the open and gazed anxiously at the sky. There he saw that the Moon was truly gleaming on high and the Sun was shining as before. At once he rushed to the house of his brother, old Vainamoinen.

"Come, brother!" he cried. "Here is something for a singer to see! The Moon is shining and the Sun is shining too. They have been restored to their places in the heavens. Come and look!"

Lusty old Vainamoinen hurried out into the open and lifted up his head, and there indeed he saw the Moon risen and the Sun beaming freely.

"Hail, fair-cheeked Moon!" he cried. "You are a silver dove in the heavens. And you, bright Sun, like a golden cuckoo! How good it is to see you again! Now you may travel on your accustomed ways, and bring us health and increase."

Now as never before was a time for singing. Lusty old Vainamoinen took his birch-wood kantele and sang sweetly and surely. He sang of the lights of heaven and of the prospering earth. He sang of the Land of Heroes and its people, their sorrows and their feasts and their great deeds. He sang the story of the magic sampo. He sang too of his own childhood and of his strange birth in the beginning of the beginning.

For it came to pass that the Virgin of the Air, tiring of her lonely life in the upper regions, descended to the surface of the sea. There she mated with the wind, and became the Mother of Waters, but it was long and long before she bore the child Vainamoinen. And as she swam restlessly back and forth, a teal came flying in search of a dwelling. Then the Mother of Waters lifted up her knee, and on her knee the teal made its nest and laid a great egg. The egg was so heavy a burden that the Mother of Waters moved her knee, and the egg fell into the water and broke. But it was not lost. The under half of the shell turned to solid earth, and the upper half to the arch of heaven. The yolk became the Sun and the white of the egg was the bright Moon. Then the Mother of Waters, swimming amid the waves, pointed with her finger and produced the rocky headlands, and stepped over the depths of the sea and left in her footprints the caves of the fishes. She set all Creation in order. But the child Vainamoinen had not yet been born. Long and long he rested in his mother's body, but it was a narrow room he found there, and he longed for freedom. He too wished to see the lights of heaven and the stars of the Great Bear. He begged them to help him come forth. But they could not help him to be born. At last by his own mighty efforts he issued forth and floated on the surface of the sea, admiring the Sun and Moon and the stars of the Great Bear. Thus was born the oldest magician and the wisest and sweetest of singers.

All this Vainamoinen sang anew, playing the while on his birch-wood kantele with his ten fingers, so that the folk rejoiced to hear him. There was no song too strange and no music too wonderful for him. And the old men listened and nodded, and the young men heard and applauded. The women laughed for pleasure and the young girls were dancing. And all the little children marveled.

But lusty old Vainamoinen could not remain forever in one place. He could not sing always. He felt the need for journeying farther. So he boarded his ship, a splendid ship with a copper deck, and he took his birch-wood kantele on his arm, and bade the Land of Heroes farewell.

None knows where he sailed or whether he will return. None has heard since the pure strains of his kantele. But parts of his songs are remembered and sung even now, and most of them you have heard, and the few remaining, if you are eager for them, it may be that one day you shall yet hear.

From *Heroes of the Kalevala*, by Babette Deutsch (New York: Julian Messner, Inc., 1940).

THE PIG-HEADED WIFE

When Matti married Liisa, he thought she was the pleasantest woman in the world. But it wasn't long before Liisa began to show her real character. Headstrong as a goat she was, and as fair set on having her own way.

Matti had been brought up to know that a husband should be the head of his family, so he tried to make his wife obey. But this didn't work with Liisa. It just made her all the more stubborn and pig-headed. Every time that Matti asked her to do one thing, she was bound to do the opposite, and work as he would she generally got her own way in the end.

Matti was a patient sort of man, and he put up with her ways as best he could, though his friends were ready enough to make fun of him for being henpecked. And so they managed to jog along fairly well.

But one year as harvest time came round, Matti thought to himself, "Here am I, a jolly goodhearted fellow, that likes a bit of company. If only I had a pleasant sort of wife, now, it would be a fine thing to invite all our friends to the house and have a nice dinner and drink and a good time. But it's no good thinking of it, for as sure as I propose a feast, Liisa will declare a fast."

And then a happy thought struck him.

"I'll see if I can't get the better of Liisa, all the same. I'll let on I want to be quiet, and then she'll be all for having the house full of guests."

So a few days later he said, "The harvest holidays will be here soon, but don't you go making any sweet cakes this year. We're too poor for that sort of thing."

"Poor! What are you talking about?" Liisa snapped. "We've never had more than we have this year. I'm certainly going to bake a cake, and a good big one too."

"It works," thought Matti. "It works!" But all he said was, "Well, if you make a cake, we won't need a pudding too. We mustn't be wasteful."

"Wasteful, indeed!" Liisa grumbled. "We shall have a pudding, and a big pudding!"

Matti pretended to sigh, and rolled his eyes. "Pudding's bad enough, but if you take it in your head to serve stuffed pig again, we'll be ruined!"

"You'll kill our best pig," quoth Liisa, "and let's hear no more about it."

"But wine, Liisa," Matti went on. "Promise me you won't open a single bottle. We've barely enough to last us through the winter as it is."

Liisa stamped her foot. "Are you crazy, man? Who ever heard of stuffed pig without wine! We'll not only have wine, but I'll buy coffee too. I'll teach you to call me extravagant by the time I'm through with you!"

"Oh, dear, oh, dear," Matti sighed. "If you're going to invite a lot of guests, on top of everything else, that'll be the end of it. We can't possibly have guests."

"And have all the food spoil with no one to eat it, I suppose?" jeered Liisa. "Guests we'll have, and what's more, you'll sit at the head of the table, whether you like it or not."

"Well, at any rate I'll drink no wine myself," said Matti, growing bolder. "If I don't drink the others won't, and I tell you we'll need that wine to pull us through the winter."

Liisa turned on him, furious. "You'll drink with your guests as a host should, till every bottle is empty. There! Now will you be quiet?"

When the day arrived the guests came, and great was the feasting. They shouted and sang round the table, and Matti himself made more noise than any of his friends. So much so, that long before the feast was over Liisa began to suspect he had played a trick on her. It made her furious to see him so jolly and carefree.

As time went on she grew more and more contrary, until there was no living with her. Now it happened one day in the spring, when all the streams were high, that Matti and Liisa were crossing the wooden bridge over the little river which separated two of their meadows. Matti crossed first, and, noticing that the boards were badly rotted, he called out without thinking, "Look where you step, Liisa! The plank is rotten there. Go lightly or you'll break through."

"Step lightly!" shouted Liisa. "I'll do as—"

But for once Liisa didn't finish what she had to say. She jumped with all her weight on the rotted timbers and fell plop into the swollen stream.

Matti scratched his head for a moment; then he started running upstream as fast as he could go.

Two fishermen along the bank saw him and called, "What's the matter, my man? Why are you running upstream so fast?"

"My wife fell in the river," Matti panted, "and I'm afraid she's drowned."

"You're crazy," said the fishermen. "Anyone in his right mind would search downstream, not up!"

"Ah," said Matti, "but you don't know my Liisa! All her life she's been so pig-headed that even when she's dead she'd be bound to go against the current!"

From *Tales from a Finnish Tupa*, by James Cloyd Bowman and Margery Bianco (Chicago: Albert Whitman & Co., 1936).

LIPPO AND TAPIO

THERE was once a famous hunter named Lippo. All winter long he used to travel in search of game, and he was as much at home on his skis as a bird is in the air.

One day Lippo and two of his friends set out to the Northland to hunt moose. All day long they followed tracks in the snow, but without meeting any game. At dusk they came to a small hut where they slept the night. Next morning they started out bright and early, again on their skis. Lippo, who was setting the pace, kicked one ski against the other and said in fun, "Today we must get a moose for each ski, and one for the ski staff!"

New snow had fallen during the night, and presently, sure enough, they saw before them the fresh tracks of three large moose. They hastened their pace and soon caught up with two of the moose, who were fighting so hard that they paid no attention to the hunters. But the third moose saw them coming and galloped off through the forest.

"Here's a piece of luck," whispered Lippo to his friends. "You shoot these two, and I will track down the third."

His friends killed the two moose and dragged them homeward, while Lippo swept forward on his skis, lighthearted and alone. He flew swiftly over the snow, but however swiftly he traveled, the tracks still stretched ahead of him, farther than his eyes could reach. At last, as night was falling, they led him through a fence and into a garden.

There, in the doorway of his house, stood Tapio, God of the Forests. His long beard was the color of moss, and he wore a cap of leaves on his head. The moose, grunting with fright, stood beside him.

When Tapio saw Lippo he shouted angrily, "How dare you hunt my moose and drive him into a foaming sweat!"

"How could I tell he was your moose?" said Lippo. "He had strayed far into the forest."

When Tapio saw that Lippo was a plain, honest man, his anger left him. He said, "It is late, and you are far from home. Come into my *tupa* and stay the night."

Lippo shook the snow from his skis and set them up against the wall. When he followed the old man into the house, he was surprised to see the room crowded with wild animals. Elk, bear, moose, wolf and fox, rabbit and weasel, there they all sat round the fire, talking each in his own tongue.

Tapio called in a loud voice like the sound of wind in the fir trees, "Daughter! We have a guest!"

And there entered a lovely girl dressed in a robe of green leaves. She set a supper of honey, milk, and bread on the birch-log table, and Lippo ate hungrily.

When he had eaten he turned to the girl, who was sitting now beside the fire, holding a fox in her arms, and asked her, "Who are you, and what is the name of this far north country?"

She answered, "I am Tellervo, daughter of Tapio, God of the Forests. My father takes care of every living creature in the woods. And this country is Pohjola, far to the north of your native Finland."

As darkness drew on and the first star came into the skies, the wild creatures began to file out into the forest, each to his own home. When the last had disappeared through the doorway, Tapio gave Lippo a bed of fir boughs beside the fire.

In the morning Lippo was up early, all ready to start out again in search of game, but nowhere could he find his skis. They were gone as if by magic. When he asked Tapio what had happened to them, the old man said, "You will find them when you wish to go back to your own people. I have but one daughter, Tellervo. How would you like to stay here as my son-in-law?"

"I would gladly stay," said Lippo, "but I am only a poor man."

"Ho, don't let that worry you," Tapio said. "Lack of money is no crime. Here we need no gold."

So Lippo, the forest wanderer, married Tellervo, and together they lived in the hut in the woods with the old man, her father. Soon Lippo learned to speak the language of every creature living in the forest.

After three years a son was born to Lippo and Tellervo. Lippo was so proud that he wanted at once to go back to his family for a visit and tell them all the good news. He begged Tapio to go with him, but Tapio said, "First you must make me a pair of skis. If the skis are to my liking, then I will come with you."

Lippo went into the forest and began to hew out wood for the skis. A little titmouse sat on a branch over his head, singing:

> "*Tii, tii, tiiainen,*
> *Vati, kuti, varpunen.*
>
> Tit, tit, titmouse,
> Spicker, spacker, sparrow,
> Set the branch upon the shoulder,
> Form a head upon the foot rest."

The titmouse made Lippo so fidgety with its chirping that he did not even listen to what it said. He flung a stick at it and shouted, "Stop your noise, you chatterbox!"

Then he forgot all about the bird, so intent was he on fashioning his skis. He made them as beautifully as he knew how. And when at last they were finished, he brought them to his father-in-law. Tapio fastened the skis to his feet and took a turn round the garden on them, saying, "These skis are not for me. They don't fit me. You will have to make me a better pair."

Again Lippo went into the forest. And again the titmouse flew to a branch over his head and sang:

> "*Tii, tii, tiiainen,*
> *Vati, kuti, varpunen,*
>
> Tit, tit, titmouse,
> Spicker, spacker, sparrow,
> Set the branch upon the shoulder,
> Form a head upon the foot rest."

Again Lippo was very annoyed by this chattering. "Why must you be always chirping and chattering, you scamp!" he shouted, and this time he threw a chip of wood to frighten the bird away.

When the second pair of skis were finished, Tapio tried them out and said, "These skis are not for me, either. You'll have to keep on trying till you can do better."

Lippo went a third time into the forest, determined to please his father-in-law. And a third time the titmouse sang:

> "*Tii, tii, tiiainen,*
> *Vati, kuti, varpunen.*"

This time Lippo stood listening.

"What are you trying to tell me, you little fidget? I'll try your advice. You can't be singing the same thing over and over for no reason at all."

He worked fast, and did as the bird said. In the center of the ski he fashioned a shoulder for Tapio to stand upon. He bent the front end of the ski slightly upward into a head, so that it would glide more easily over the snow.

When Tapio tried this new pair of skis he was delighted. "*Ka*, these are the skis for me! They fit me perfectly. You must have learned at last to listen to the words of your little forest friends, my Lippo, or you would never have known how to please me. Now you may go home!"

So they started, Tapio first, Lippo with his child strapped to his back, and Tellervo his wife close behind him.

When they had gone far into the deep wild forest Tapio stopped and said, "From now on I shall travel ahead of you. Follow my tracks in the snow. Each time you see the hole of my pointed ski staff, there make your camp for the night. Weave the roof of your lodge carefully of fir boughs, and be sure that no light from the stars can shine through to work you harm."

And he set off ahead like a flash of light on his skis and was gone.

All day long Lippo followed the ski tracks, with Tellervo and his child. Night was falling when they saw the first hole made by Tapio's staff. Here they found a moose broiled and steaming for their supper.

Lippo built a lodge as Tapio had told him. He wove the fir branches carefully so that no starlight could shine through. He took the birch-bark pack from his shoulders and set his child in the lodge before the fire. Here they all three slept the night.

In the morning they ate again, took enough moose meat for a meal during the day, and set out to follow Tapio's ski tracks.

Again at nightfall they saw the second hole made by Tapio's staff. Beside it was a deer roasted and steaming. They ate, built a lodge of fir boughs as before, and slept the night.

The third day they pushed forward on their skis, and at nightfall found only a wood grouse fried and steaming. They were so hungry that no morsel remained for next day's meal.

Lippo was greatly disheartened. He said, "Tellervo, we cannot travel without food. My bow and arrows I left in the hut. Tapio and his magic have failed us, and my home is still far away."

That night he took no heed how he built their lodge. He wove the fir boughs carelessly, and through the bare chinks the starlight shone through on them.

In the morning when Lippo rose to stir the campfire, he found that his wife, Tellervo, was gone. Far and near Lippo searched, but he could not find her. He asked the birds in the trees where she had gone, but, when they answered him, he found he could no longer understand their language.

He went into the hut and took his child upon his knee. Sad and hopeless he sat there before the fire. He saw moose and deer outside in the forest, but he had no weapons to hunt them.

The next morning and the next and the next, every morning when he awoke, Lippo found a wood grouse cooked and steaming before the door. Many years passed, and still Lippo lived in his lodge of fir boughs before the open fire in the forest. He dreamed of home, but he no longer had courage to set out on the search for it.

Lippo's son grew into a tall boy, and from boyhood he grew to manhood. He asked Lippo to teach him about the stars, so that he could travel alone and learn more about the world.

One day when he came back from exploring the forest he said, "Father, we are not far from your home. To the south lie your home fields."

Then he took his father, who was now an old man, and together they set out on the journey. After a day's travel they found themselves at Lippo's old home. Tears came to Lippo's eyes at the sight of his old country after all these years, but the boy was not content to stay there. He left his father behind and traveled north once more to make a home for himself.

And to this very day the Laplanders proudly trace their descent from this wise and restless son of Lippo, the mighty hunter.

From *Tales from a Finnish Tupa.*

French

Devil-May-Care

ALTHOUGH French country folk tell their tales and fables in much the same unpretentious manner as country folk elsewhere, it is a curious fact that in the late eighteenth century the upper classes of France decided to make a fashion of the ways and amusements of the plain people. One spectacular effect was the miniature farm set up for Marie Antoinette in the park at Versailles. But the fashion had scarcely less influence on folk story. Under the title of *Contes de ma mère l'oie* (Mother Goose stories), Charles Perrault, literary critic and poet, published a handful of tales, including Cinderella, Bluebeard, Little Thumb, Puss in Boots, Sleeping Beauty, and Little Red Ridinghood, marked by literary finish and touches of elegance. It was an immediate success, and soon a flock of titled dilettantes, presumably inspired by M. Perrault's Mother Goose, were spinning intolerably long and ornate romances. By 1789 an anthology of forty volumes was required to contain their effusions. And although a century later the Grimms were to be hailed for introducing the idiom of the common people in folk tales, the French versions have never fallen out of favor in the nurseries of gentlefolk.

But French popular story has other aspects worth notice. Whether the cycle of Reynard, or Renard, the Fox is originally German, Flemish, or French, it appears at a very early time in France, and in its satiric aspects seems much closer to Gallic than Teutonic traditions. The beast fable is a very old form, and it has always had its very clever animals, but the Reynard of European stories is surely its most remarkable creation. Jackal of India and Africa, Brer Rabbit of the southern United States, Don Coyote of Mexico, Anansi the spider of Haiti and West Africa, are all shrewd and resourceful, but Reynard is peerless for cunning and quick wit, as fully realized a character as Volpone or Puck or Falstaff.

Still another pattern of European story is that inspired by Christianity. The deeds and visions of the pious gave rise early in the Middle Ages to many wondrous legends, and the clergy created a new lore, as in the immensely popular *Gesta Romanorum*, by adapting old tales to moral ends. A number of the legends, and chief among them "Our Lady's Tumbler," have become popular among members of every sect. It is possible, for example, that such a Jewish tale as "Alone with God" (page 575) belongs in this tradition.

Travelers in the more isolated sections of the Brittany peninsula, where prehistoric dolmens and menhirs cast their shadows on every side, have noted the strong grip that the old religious faith and ancient beliefs have on the peasant and fisher folk. Such characteristics are illustrated in "The Shroud of Mari-Yvonne" and many other legends in the Breton collections made by Anatole Le Braz, F. M. Luzel, Emile Souvestre, and others in the late nineteenth century.

THE ADVENTURES OF RENARD

I

How on one day of great hunger Master Renard tricked three fishermen and filled his empty stomach at their expense.

Over fields and hedges, along limpid streams with their clattering pebbles, trotted Master Renard.

His tail, once red as the slopes in autumn, now hung down pitifully, trailing in the dust of the roads. His pointed muzzle snarled angrily and showed the hungry gleam of his teeth.

For the last three days, in bitter winter weather, he had beaten the bushes, prowled around the enticing holes of the many burrows, watched the tracks of paws on the decayed leaves. For the last three days too, his meager flanks had been ready in vain for any tricks or conflicts. No one had come in his way; neither the fluffy backs of rabbits that had scampered over the third mount to celebrate the wedding of Couart, their cousin, the hare; nor even the pointed noses of the mice.

And the tomtits in blue bonnets lightly touched him with their wings and mockingly chirruped into the evening:

"A poor hunt for the fox, peace and joy to those who wear feathers.

"Renard, Renard, O great fox, have the bog-sprites clawed the hairs of thy tail that for the last three days with lolling tongue and glistening eye thou chasest over the hills and dales?

"Return, return quickly, O wonderful hunter, return with a rich booty, to taste of the family joys in thy castle of Maupertuis. Dame Hermeline, thy gentle wife, is listening to hunger singing in her lean flanks, and thy children yelp and growl and lick the stones of the hearth. What art thou waiting for, what art thou waiting for, O frivolous husband, O thoughtless father? Wouldst thou perchance like to come up on our branch and give us the kiss of

pardon and peace? We would offer thee as a seal of our pact a fat worm or a plump fly."

Thus sang the mocking tomtits, and Renard, mad with rage, ground his teeth and kept on running.

As he was passing close by a road, he scented the bitter smell of fresh fish in the air. He stopped so sharply that his hind paws doubled under him and his claws dug into the ground.

He stole up to the road and poked his head through a hedge. A cart appeared on the brow of the hill and clattered over the stones. It was laden with baskets of herrings, eels, and lampreys.

By the side of the horse walked three fishermen, who were lustily singing a jolly song and beating the ground with their heavy clogs. At sea, with the help of the breeze and the wind, their catch had been good, and the three men were now taking the fresh fish to a neighboring market.

The burning sun glowed red on the broken panes of the cottage windows, and already the shades of night were stealing over the bushes. Renard, with a greedy gleam in his eye, dilated his nostrils. He was thinking. Very quietly he smacked his chops. Gliding out of the thicket, he stretched himself on the road in the mud and the dust, his four paws rigid, his teeth clenched in a last appeal to the clear sky.

The rhythmic steps of men and a horse were nearing.

"Hey, there, my friends," cried out the first fisherman, "as true as the wind that blows from the north, there lies a dead beast on the road."

"A dead dog, and nothing else," replied the others. "Let us hurry, for the night is near and the town distant."

"Not a dog, but a fox, and a good-sized one too," called out the first fisherman, bending over the false corpse. "Friends, the day is good: full baskets, and a thick fur. Renard, old rogue, no more hens will you steal from farmyards. I shall soon tan your skin so well that your own mother will refuse to know you."

Seized roughly by his brush, Renard turned a somersault in the evening air as he was thrown into the cart onto a bed of scaly fish. The wheels creaked and the cart rattled.

The three men marched on.

"I will offer you thirty herrings," one proposed, "for the fur of that animal. His skin will be soft on my wife's shoulder. She who is as redhaired as he."

The bargain was joyfully struck. Night fell. Renard nimbly poked his nose into a basket, and the blue herrings and seawrack crunched under his greedy teeth. Thus three baskets were soon emptied. His hunger appeased, he wound about his neck a triple necklace of eels and noiselessly slipped to the ground. He fled along the road under the noses of the astonished fishermen.

As he passed them he shouted, "The fox and the fish, noble sirs, one carrying the other—come and catch them!"

Then he vanished into the bushes.

And that night there was a savory feast and juicy fare at the castle of Maupertuis.

II

How Master Renard persuaded Master Ysengrin to enter Holy Orders; how together they went fishing and a tail was lost.

Snow had fallen and had hardened in the sun. Frost had seized the flow of waters and had covered the branches with white coral. The beasts of the fields, meadows, and woods came into the light without fear of leaving their traces on the ice. The hares returned to their circles under the opal light of the moon, and the scampering mice gathered the scarlet holly berries. But it was hard for the toothed hunters, for the wolves and badgers, who snuffed in vain at the confused traces round by the trees and over the ground. At night the dogs howled louder than ever at furtive shadows that prowled round the farms.

Only Master Renard in his manor of Maupertuis was oblivious of the irritation of a fruitless hunt. Dame Hermeline, his prudent and thrifty spouse, had preserved and salted the eels stolen from the fishermen, and she had done this so well that, while other beasts hunted in vain, Master Renard, with his smooth and glossy coat, warmed his flanks at the hearth. His three sons, Pierce-Hedge, Malebranche, and Rovel, gamboled together with clumsy paws and bit one another's fur. Innocence and slyness already mingled in them. Short blue flames flickered on the bark of logs and rose in waves of sunshine. The wind whistled under the door. A smell of roast eels wafted outside. Renard was proudly telling his sons, whose three little muzzles gaped with admiration, how one day he duped Brother Bruin, the bear, by persuading him to thrust his head and paws into a piece of split oak smeared with golden honey. Bruin left there the skin of his head and paws.

Then, said Renard gleefully, "As I had pinched the corners together I was going to warn—" He stopped and sharpened his ears.

"Hermeline, my sweet, canst thou hear anything under the windows?"

"It's the plaintive wind as it lashes against the shutters, my dear," she replied.

"Well, then, my pets," continued Renard, "I was going to warn the peasant, the owner of this piece of wood, while dear Bruin howled piteously—yes, my dears, just as piteously as that being under the window who is not the wind."

A yellow light from the window lit up a black shadow that crouched on the ground.

"Well," cried Renard, "it is Master Ysengrin, the wolf, who is looking so wretched."

"Alack," wailed the voice, "it is really I. I have suffered great pain as I lay smelling the sweet odor of your food. Happy is he who does not feel the pangs of hunger gnawing at his flanks. Pray, give me a place at thy table. I shall pay thee back in curly lambs as soon as they open the doors of the sheepfold."

"O brother," replied Renard, chuckling to himself, "my heart is breaking, but I must refuse thee. Knowst thou not that for some time now I have belonged to a holy brotherhood, and thou wouldst need to become a monk and a holy man to partake of my meal?"

"A monk? And a holy man? Can I not become one?" begged Ysengrin. "Speak well of me to thy superiors. I feel growing within me an irresistible calling. I am ready to renounce the world, its pomp and vanity. I am ready to ring the bells and wash the flagstones of the monastery, if only they will give me tasty fried fish."

Renard thought for an instant, and his eyes lit up with a wicked idea. His sons hovered round Dame Hermeline and shivered with excitement.

"It is possible, quite possible," he declared gravely, "but art thou willing to submit to the test of admission into our brotherhood?"

"The test? What test?" sighed Ysengrin. "Wilt thou imprint a cross with a red-hot iron to my velvety coat?"

"None of that, old friend," replied Renard. "Only a tonsure must be made on thy head, and thou must wear sackcloth. Meantime, relish these snippets of eels, golden brown and fried to a nicety."

Three tasty bits flew through the window onto the snow.

"I will submit to all tests," clamored the foolish Ysengrin. "Speak, and I obey."

"Enter, brother," said Renard as he opened the door of his house. "Warm thy limbs by the fire and dry thy wet fur. Monk thou shalt be. I will imprint on thy head the seal of thy new dignity. Henceforth shaved and shorn thou shalt be, the respect and envy of all thy kin."

Water sang on the hob. Boiling water, poured solemnly by Dame

Hermeline, bit into the head of groaning Ysengrin and cut a large tonsure. Renard dressed him in sackcloth and soothed him gently.

"Be calm, be calm, Ysengrin, my friend. From now on a tonsured beggar, thou shalt have a fat paunch and sing psalms through the nose; but to fill thy pouch with white, juicy eels, thou must earn them."

"What!" cried the wretched victim, "thine eels are not common fare?"

"To be sure they are," replied Renard. "But there is only one head of a fish left in the larder of Hermeline, my spouse. Come then with

me to our monastery fish pond; let us fish for leaping fish with golden eyes and silver scales. Just think of thy joy when thou wilt hear a savory grilling on the oven of thy Dame Hersent."

"Let us go," sighed Ysengrin, resigned, "but let us go quickly."

And they sallied out into the cold air. Snow, blue under the moonbeams, crunched under their feet. Branches fell, snapped by the wind; now and then a snowball scattered in a shower of icy dust and settled in crystals on the furry coats of the animals.

Ysengrin, with a vision of future feasts before his eyes, followed his sly brother; his garment of sackcloth hindered his walk; his recent tonsure smarted cruelly. Thus they arrived at a pond that slept under a thin blanket of blue ice. A hole, with sharp edges, revealed the dark, still deep of the water. Close by lay a bucket, forgotten by peasants.

"Monk Ysengrin," began Renard, "it is here, in this rich pond, that destiny shall furnish thee with ample pasture. Seat thyself in a wise and mysterious pose, and dangle thy tail into the water. To thy tail I shall tie this bucket, which the foresight of our superiors has left for the use of the new members of our order. Believe me, the fish will rush into this bucket as a reward for the patience and stillness of which thou must now give proof."

Obedient and convinced, Brother Ysengrin squatted down on the ice and plunged his tail and the bucket into the freezing water.

"Wait for me," cried Renard to him, "while I run home to fetch some large baskets for thy catch."

And the treacherous one ran off, frisking with joy, for there was no better meal for him than to deceive foolish dupes, stuck fast in the honey of his flowery words.

Ysengrin remained alone.

The wind, enraged by this nonsense, beat its wings on the wolf's bristling hackle and then hid itself to laugh in the bushes. The wolf felt the darts of cold penetrate little by little and pierce his skin just as the quick needle of a tailor runs through his supple cloth. A hare appeared on the edge of the pond, raised his ears in exclamation marks, then, in a terrified leap, disappeared into the plain. Ysengrin saw the moon revolve and the trembling of timid stars.

The water was slowly freezing and setting into an opaque whiteness. His teeth chattered, and he saw and felt nothing of his body except his tail held fast by the ice. In the simplicity of his heart, Ysengrin rejoiced greatly, and visions of delicious feasts floated before his eyes. He was dozing, overpowered with sleep and cold, when a mocking voice roused him. "Halloo, brother," exclaimed Renard, carrying two large baskets, "thy patience is worthy of our order. Take out thy haul of fish, and may it be velvet to thine empty stomach."

Ysengrin strained his limbs, and with taut muscles tugged at his tail. "There are too many fish, dear brother," he pleaded with joy. "Help me, the bucket is so heavy that I cannot lift it."

"Really," giggled Renard, "hast thou perchance caught a couple of whales? Hasten, clumsy one, for day is near."

His paws slipping over the polished surface of the pond, Ysengrin pulled furiously at his tail.

Voices sounded close by and the yapping of dogs pierced the gray mists of morning. "Save me, Renard, my dear companion," wailed the wolf. "I will give up to thee this cursed haul that a thousand devils are holding. Dost thou not hear the noise of the chase and the voice of the dogs?"

Renard sniffed the air, capered around in the snow, and then, bowing to Ysengrin, said, "Excuse me, it is late, and my business calls. I must pull the bells and wake the superior of the monastery. My respects to Dame Hersent, thy gracious spouse, my love to the wolf cubs, thy darling children." Agile and nimble he vanished behind the bushes.

A yelping pack, black and white, rushed out of the forest. Constant de Granges, a zealous hunter and a noble baron, emerged into the light of the rising sun, holding his sword in one hand and staying his horse with the other. Dogs rushed to the pond, snapping and snarling at Ysengrin, who was howling with fright.

The Baron jumped off his horse and ran straight at the wolf, for with one blow of his sword he hoped to cleave off the wolf's head. But he slipped on the ice and, in falling, cut off the wolf's tail.

Freed from his icy prison, Ysengrin escaped into the bushes, chased by the Baron's mastiffs.

Back in his home, he lay abed for several weeks, and his life was saved only by the tender ministrations and brews of Dame Hersent. The wolf cubs, his sons, ran round his lopped tail in great scorn, and the birds whistled the tale of his glorious haul of fish to all the beasts of the forest.

III

How Master Renard enticed Ysengrin to eat the Moon, and how he was judged by the Court of the Lion.

The earth, heavy with the heat of summer, breathed out into the night. The sad, monotonous croaking of frogs rose over dank marshes, and the cloudy moon was set in the shell of the sky. Close to dark villages, huddled under the weight of sleep, Renard was softly prowling, his red tongue lolling over his chest, as he hunted the partridge or dozed in the shade. All day his throat had been parched. He saw near to a farm the shadow of a well, with its two buckets swaying in the breeze. Everyone was asleep; nowhere was there a trace of a dog or the shadow of a man. The strident song of grasshoppers rang out from the meadows.

Renard jumped onto the edge of the well, and he felt the welcome freshness of the water below. His parched throat now burning still more from impatience, he threw prudence to the wind. He jumped into an empty bucket; the chain unraveled and creaked on the pulley. In a whirling, rapid descent, he went to the bottom of the well. Greedily he lapped the silent waters, and an exquisite freshness stole over his body.

His thirst quenched, he lost his weariness and, terrified, he suddenly thought of his return. The second bucket high up on the pulley blocked his way, and only by a heavy weight in it could he be raised to the well-brim.

"How can I find a beast silly enough to take my place?" wondered Renard dejectedly.

Destiny's reply was swifter than the flight of swallows. Renard raised his muzzle and saw Ysengrin's head and sharp pointed ears over the edge of the well. He was calmly admiring his reflection in the water and grunting with pleasure.

"Seek a fool, and Ysengrin is sure to be there," chuckled Renard to himself and smacked his wet chops.

"Hi, there, my old friend Ysengrin," he shouted to the wolf, "have you not heard Dame Hermeline shouting to all the echoes for the last two hours?"

At the sound of this sepulchral voice from the depths of the well Ysengrin sprang back terrified, then timidly he ventured to push his muzzle over the edge of the well.

"Can it be you, Master Cheat and Rogue, who calls to me from hell?" he asked.

"Say rather from paradise, and what a delicious paradise too," replied sly Renard. "Do you not see by my side this marvelous cheese with which I delight my eye and regale my gullet?" And he pointed his paw at the moon's white reflection in the well.

"If your cheese is as tasty as the fish from the pond, then I do not envy you your meal," replied Ysengrin with distrust.

"Who has invited you, silly ninny?" retorted Renard, feigning impatience. "You can fast, my friend. What do I care? I would sooner pluck out my silky mustache than try to convince you. Only, on thy way home, tell Dame Hermeline, my spouse, to come to me. Tell her this cheese is cream and velvet, and I am sorry to have eaten a whole quarter without her."

The moon was in the third phase of her slow waxing, and her face seemed to have been cut by a sharp knife.

Ysengrin, enticed, believed Renard's words and his mistrust gave way to greed. "I will gladly fetch your wife and even your three sons," said Ysengrin, "but before that will you not offer me a bit of this cheese?"

Renard seemed to waver for a second. "You hardly deserve it, but I have a kind heart and do not nurse grudges. Jump into the bucket that hangs on the pulley and come and share my banquet."

Ysengrin jumped joyfully into the bucket and, knocking against the sides of the well, he reached the bottom. Lifted by Ysengrin's weight, Master Renard said to him, amiably, "I have had my fill of this cheese. It is really rather tasteless. Help yourself, old friend, but do not eat too much of it, or else your skin at dawn may deck the door of some peasant."

He climbed over the edge of the well and ran off into the night.

Ysengrin, deep down in the well, called plaintively for help. He howled so much and so well that peasants armed with forks came out from the farmsteads and hurled stones at him at the bottom of the well. At dawn, Brichemer, the stag, brayed over the whole forest the news of Ysengrin's death, and the lion gathered his subjects together for the solemn burial of the wolf and the judgment of Renard. It was a wonderful gathering, for there was no beast, feathered or furred, bold enough to ignore the king's call. All left their hunt or travels and came out of thickets, shrubs, lairs, and caves, and down from the branches. Ysengrin's body was buried in a grave dug by Beaucent, the boar, and a marble slab gave his name and martyrdom to posterity. Tardiff, the snail, Brichemer, the stag, and Tilbert, the cat, sang the burial service. The mourners were headed by Dame Hersent, the widow of the wolf. The lion presided under an oak tree.

Roonel, the dog, guarded Renard, whose feet were bound together. Bruin, the bear, a procurator's cap on his head, insisted on death to the prisoner in the name of the law of the forest, but Grimbert, the badger, Renard's cousin, cleverly pleaded for him, and the lion hesitated when the accused spoke thus:

"O most powerful of all sovereigns, and all ye proud barons, know ye that my heart is free from sin. Ysengrin died through his own folly. The law of the forest only punishes him who by violence delivers his friend into the hands of man. How, how could I have forced the wolf to come down into the well when I, myself, was sitting inside it in a bucket? If he came down it was of his own free will and because he was drawn by foolish greed. When I compared the moon to a cheese it was just poetry that inspired me. Ysengrin, the dense blockhead, did not understand my metaphor. Weary of life for some time now, I have long planned to go to Rome to see the Pope and then to retire as a humble hermit into the desert. Do not frustrate my pious projects by an unjust death."

Sire Noble, weary of all this talk, pardoned him.

Wrapped in a scarf and armed with a pilgrim's staff, Renard drew up his last will and testament on a parchment of donkey's skin.

To Hermeline, his spouse, he left his memories.

To his children, his wiles.

To the forest wind, his scent.

To the night, his sight.

This done, he set out on the road to Rome, his head covered with ashes.

History does not relate that he ever arrived.

From *Three and the Moon, Legendary Stories of Old Brittany, Normandy and Provence,* told by Jacques Dorey (New York: Alfred A. Knopf, Inc., 1929).

THE THEFT OF A SMELL

In Paris, near the Petit-Chatelet rotisserie, in front of the baker's shop, a street-porter was engaged in munching a slice of bread, holding it in the smoke from the roasts, finding it, thus flavored, a very tasty tidbit. The baker permitted him to do this. But when the porter's loaf was all guzzled, the baker grabbed the fellow by the neck and insisted that he be paid for the smoke from his roast. The porter protested that he had not damaged the baker's goods in the slightest, that he had not taken anything that belonged to the other, and that, as a consequence he owed nothing. The smoke in question was evaporated into the air and so was being wasted anyway. Moreover, it was an unheard-of thing in Paris for anyone to sell, in the street, the smoke that came from a roast. The baker replied that the smoke from his particular roast was not intended to keep street-porters from starving, and threatened, in case he wasn't paid, to knock the poor fellow's teeth out. The porter thereupon drew his cudgel and prepared to defend himself. The altercation grew, and the stupid Parisians came running up from all sides to see the fun.

It was then that old John the Fool, a citizen of Paris, happened along. When he saw the fool, the baker inquired of the porter, "Are you willing to have good old John here settle our dispute?"

"Holy Christ, yes," said the porter.

Old John, then, having heard their stories, directed the porter to take a piece of change from his belt. The porter put a Philip of Tours in the fool's hand. Old John took it and placed it upon his left shoulder, as though he were testing the coin's weight. Then he tapped it on the palm of his left hand, as though he were seeing whether or not it was counterfeit. Then he placed it over the ball of his right eye, as though to see if it were properly engraved.

While all this was going on, the silly mob stood silent, fully expecting a decision in favor of the baker, being certain that the porter did not have a chance. Finally the fool rang the coin on the counter a number of times; after which, with a presidential majesty, holding his wand in his hand as though it were a scepter, he proceeded to jam his pointed, ape-faced, marten-skin cap with its ruffled-paper ears down over his head, gave two or three good preliminary coughs, and announced in a loud voice, "This court rules that the porter, who has eaten his bread in the smoke from the roast, shall be condemned to pay the baker with the sound of his money. And the said court further directs that each now return to his eachery, without costs and for just cause."

From *The Works of François Rabelais,* translated by Samuel Putnam (New York: Covici Friede, 1929).

THE SHROUD OF MARI-YVONNE

Mari-Yvonne Helary had lived alone for many years in a little cottage by the seashore. All day long she sat at her threshold plying her distaff. Life had no greater joy for her than to watch the pile of linen growing in her press, its thread spun by her own hands and woven by the village weaver.

One evening an illness seized her, and from that day the industrious spinner plied her distaff no more.

Her only neighbors, the Rojous, dwelt in a farmstead a full half-mile inland: and so it happened that the poor old woman died, as she had lived, alone.

On the day after her death, Goneri Rojou, gathering seaweed on the shore, missed the familiar face at the cottage threshold; moreover, the door was closed. "Mayhap Mari-Yvonne has gone on some pilgrimage," he said to his wife that evening.

Two days passed. "I shall walk round by Mari-Yvonne's and see if she is home again," said Lenan Rojou on the third day.

Reaching the old woman's cottage, she found the door still closed. She looked through the window, and it was a pitiful sight that met her eyes. The body of Mari-Yvonne hung half out of the bed, her head resting on the wooden chest beside it.

Without pausing once to take breath, Lenan Rojou hurried to the farm. "Bring a lever," she panted, "and follow me."

By means of the tool they forced the cottage door, and found the poor woman quite dead. Rojou and his wife took the body from the bed and laid it on the table.

"We must wrap a shroud about her," said Goneri. "Look in the linen press; there you may find a piece of clean linen, for these sheets are in rags."

Lenan opened the cupboard door and stood spellbound. The press was full of beautiful new linen, white as snow, soft as silk, and fragrant with lavender.

"Oh, the linen, the fine white linen! By the Virgin, it is white!" she exclaimed. But the thought that came to her was black.

Every good housewife loves her linen. It makes her heart glad to see its folds flap in the wind, to smooth it out and range it white and soft along the shelves of the oaken press. It had been the dream of Lenan Rojou's life to spend her days as did old Mari-Yvonne, her friend, spinning fine thread to be woven into fine linen. But she had to labor for a husband and four children, and to tend the animals at the farm. Twelve years she had been married, for twelve years her spinning wheel had lain idle in the corner of the kitchen; and as for fine thread, it was the spider only who wove fine thread in the house of Lenan Rojou.

As she gazed at the white linen, her thought grew more black. Whence came that low voice which seemed to quench the sunlight and cover as a pall the white blossoms on the hill slope?

"Lenan," it said, "you and your man are alone here. No one knows that Mari-Yvonne is dead. No one knows of the white linen. No man can claim it, for she was the last of her race. The fruits of her spinning will pass to the state, which in her life cared naught for her. You have always shown her kindness; you will perform for her the last offices of the dead. Take your share of what is in the house. Mari-Yvonne needs it no more."

Thus whispered the voice.

Lenan Rojou was an honest woman, but she was the daughter of her mother, and her mother was a daughter of Eve: she listened.

"Look, Goneri," she said at last, "there is no lack of winding sheets. Here is linen enough to enshroud a hundred corpses. Look!"

Goneri, too, marveled at the wealth of the old woman.

"If we will, all this white linen, save the length of a shroud, can be ours," said his wife, albeit the first words were as if spoken by some other Lenan.

"And why should it not belong to us rather than to a stranger?" came from Goneri after a pause.

"There is enough to make six dozen sheets, as many cloths to wrap round the bread, and dozens of shirts for us and for our children. By the Virgin, it is true, Goneri!"

"Ay, indeed. Listen, then. You stay here and watch by the body. I will carry the linen to the farm. None will either see or hear. One piece only will I leave. With it, while I am absent, you can make the shroud."

Goneri set off, heavily laden, but the weight of his black sin was not yet added to the weight of the white linen.

Half an hour passed, and he returned.

The corpse of Mari-Yvonne still awaited its shroud. A piece of spotless white linen was spread on the floor, and Lenan Rojou knelt beside it, scissors in hand.

"By Sant-Paol!" cried Goneri as he stood on the threshold, "you have been idle!"

"Oh, the pity of it! Why cut this beautiful piece of new linen to wind about a dead body? Will not Mari-Yvonne sleep contentedly in the sheets which she always used?"

"Maybe you are right," rejoined Rojou, ready to acquiesce.

And thus it was decided.

The same evening a funeral knell rang from the village belfry, and Mari-Yvonne was buried. Goneri Rojou it was who paid for everything, and one and all praised him for his generosity. On the Sunday that followed the priest spoke from the pulpit of the Christ-like conduct of Lenan and Goneri. They were humble, and because of this the folk of the country revered them the more. But, for sure, a black cloud was over the hearts of each. True, the sight of the piles of white linen gladdened the heart of Lenan, but the man did not share in this pleasure. His spirit left him, he ate nothing, and his sleep was broken.

One night he started up in his bed: there was a knock at the door.

"Who is there?" he asked. But no answer came.

Could it be some drunken man who had lost his way? he thought. "Who knocks?" he asked a second and yet a third time. Still no voice replied. "You shall soon tell me your name, come you from God or devil!" With that he was about to rise, when, his head thrust out of bed, he was transfixed with terror.

The door of the house stood wide open, though he remembered to have fastened it securely before going to bed. But this was not all. The breadcloth on the kitchen table was slowly unfolding. On the cloth lay a rigid corpse, its head resting on the loaf of bread. Gradually the head raised itself. Horror-struck, Goneri closed his eyes, determined to see no more; but this was of little avail, for he heard a step cross the kitchen, he heard the opening of a creaking cupboard door, and a trembling voice mockingly repeat the words Lenan had uttered at sight of the linen of Mari-Yvonne.

"Oh, the linen, the fine white linen! By the Virgin, it is white!"

Goneri could keep his eyes closed no longer, so irresistibly was he compelled to see as well as hear what passed.

Through the open doorway the moonlight fell obliquely onto the clay floor, making it white as an outspread cloth. An old woman knelt there, holding in her right hand a pair of scissors. Goneri recognized the face of Mari-Yvonne.

"Oh, the pity of it! Why cut this beautiful piece of white linen to wind about a dead body?"

At that, a cold sweat was on the brow of Goneri.

After a long pause the voice continued, "No! No! No! I *will* lie in the linen which I have spun."

Three times the woman repeated insistently, "I seek my shroud! I seek my white shroud! I seek my white shroud!"

Thereupon she vanished.

Goneri had not aroused his wife, and it was not until a gray light filtered through the small window of the farmstead that she opened her eyes.

"Know you what you must do this morning, Lenan?"

"The animals are my first care, then I must wash the children," she answered.

"Try rather to reach the church before the priest leaves it. To him you must confess the sin that is upon us."

"You think I will be doing that, Goneri! How does it concern you, I should like to know?"

But fear was upon the man, and he said only, "I shall follow you with the linen. The priest will say what we must do with it."

"What we must do with it! What we must do with it!" burst from the angry woman. "I should know that, and not the priest, who has neither wife nor children. Don't you trouble about the linen."

"But I have good reason to trouble," said Goneri. "Our happiness, both in this world and the next, lies therein."

And then he told of the strange visitant in the moonlight, of the ghostly voice that still rang in his ears, of the face of the dead woman with the grin upon it.

When Lenan had heard all she demurred no longer but helped her husband to shoulder the heap of linen, and together they set off for the village. On reaching the church, the woman threw herself on her knees in the confessional, while Goneri, with his burden, awaited her near the font.

After Lenan had made her confession the priest said, "Return with your husband at nightfall, my daughter. The linen must be left in the vestry. If God hear the supplications of a devout man of Léon, of a priest who loves his flock, the demon, birthed at time of your wrongdoing, shall be driven forth."

Lenan and Goneri walked slowly back to the farm; the man with the firm step of a year before, the woman half relieved, half disconsolate.

The evening found them again in prayer with the servant of God. As midnight struck in the belfry at the western end of the little church the priest made a sign to Lenan.

"The time has come," he said. "Gather up the linen, and go lay it piece by piece on the green grave of Mari-Yvonne. Spread not a second piece until the first is gone. Goneri will watch with me in prayer. When all is over, return and tell us what has passed."

In the deep quiet of the midnight hour Lenan Rojou went humbly to the place of the dead, there to atone for her sin; humbly, too, did Goneri kneel in prayer, offering up petitions for her safe return.

When, after a brief time, he saw her re-enter the church, a sigh of thanksgiving escaped his lips.

"Speak, Lenan, daughter of Loiz," commanded the priest.

Then the woman, trembling as one who has seen strange things, spoke. "I spread one piece of linen over the green grave; a gust of wind came, and it was a sob I heard as it was borne into the darkness. I unfolded a second piece; again the wind rose, but this time no sound came as it was carried thence. I opened a third piece; through it passed a murmur sweet as the first breath of spring; the sheet swelled out like a lugger-sail and rose toward heaven. Then the green turf fell away, and I saw Mari-Yvonne lying naked in her grave. I unfolded the fourth piece of linen; it was dragged downward, and the dead woman wrapped it around her, shivering the while. As I prepared to spread the fifth and last piece on the ground, four angels took it from my hands and bore it away, while a soft voice whispered in my ear, 'Thou art forgiven.' "

Thereupon, making the sign of the Cross, the priest said, "A black deed it was to take the white linen of Mari-Yvonne, and black have been your days since that white blossom time, but the good God has heard our prayers. Go in peace."

From *The Shadow of Arvor: Legendary Romances and Folk-Tales of Brittany*, translated by Edith Wingate Rinder from the writings of Anatole Le Braz, F. M. Luzel, Emile Souvestre, etc. (Edinburgh: P. Geddes, n.d.).

DEVIL-MAY-CARE

On a day of the days in the time of our fathers, a Breton soldier fared homeward. Because of his gaiety and recklessness this good fellow had earned the sobriquet of Devil-may-care. Little suggestion of this, however, was in the aspect of the tired wayfarer who journeyed along the highway to his native village, Lourgat, the tall spire of which rises over against the slope of Menez-Bre.

At last, after a march of many hours, he found himself toward sunset beneath the walls of an old fortified castle. Here, hungry, weary, and penniless, he decided to seek shelter.

In response to his knock at the gate the man on guard demanded what brought him thither.

"I seek a resting place for this one night," Devil-may-care replied, "for I have been afoot since dawn, and I am weary."

"Wait a moment, and I will ask my master if he will grant you a night's rest under his roof."

The sentinel hastened to the lord of the castle and told him that a soldier, spent with fatigue and seeking hospitality, stood at the gate.

"Bring him to me," said Laouik of Kerdluz.

As Devil-may-care entered the large hall, where a blazing fire of pine logs lit up the shining surfaces of dark oak dressers and chests, the lord of the castle turned to greet him.

"What would you of me?"

"I ask a night's rest, for I am spent with fatigue, and am hungry and penniless."

"Gladly will I shelter and feed you, if you are brave, and dare to pass the night in a certain room of the castle, haunted by ghosts or devils or some strange visitants. Ere midnight strikes, there is such wild confusion, such unholy reveling, that none may sleep there in peace. No man has passed through the ordeal and lived. If haply you drive forth these evil spirits, it will not be a vain thing you do. Your reward shall be a fitting one."

"I will face the danger, happen what may," replied Devil-may-care. "I am no coward: indeed, it would be a joy to me to see the devil as he really is. I have heard so much of Guillou-goz, and yet I do not know him. Perhaps, too, he may not be so black as he is painted."

"Your words please me, my brave lad. You seem a man of valor. I myself will show you the room, where there is pine wood to make a blazing fire; you shall have bread, meat, and wine in plenty. You can be your own cook if you will."

Without more ado, Devil-may-care was duly installed in the haunted room. Serving-men brought him a quarter of raw mutton, a large loaf of white bread, and six bottles of old wine. Thus well provided, he was left alone. His first care was to make a big fire and put the mutton on the spit; thereafter he seated himself in an armchair, set light to his pipe, uncorked a bottle of wine, and quaffed a full flagon.

As he puffed contentedly at his pipe, with his gaze fixed on the meat slowly swinging before him, he reflected, "What do men mean by fear! They would have me believe that here are ghosts or devils! It is silent and peaceful as the grave! What care I? I should be quite satisfied to live in this room were I always treated as well as I am now."

Thereupon the doughty soldier poured out a second glass of wine. He was about to raise it to his lips when he heard a great noise in the chimney—a rattling and scratching, followed by the abrupt descent of a strange little being right into the fire. A devil no doubt he was, for he did not seem in any way disturbed by the heat. The next moment, jumping out of the flames, he seized Devil-may-care by the shoulders, flung the veteran to the other end of the room as if he had been a log of wood, and then calmly seated himself in the armchair.

"It would seem that the revel is about to begin," said the soldier to himself. "But we shall see how it will end."

He rose and, walking back to the hearth, seated himself in another armchair on the opposite side. No sooner had he done this than again he heard a noise in the chimney; and a second being, exactly like the first, fell into the fire, sprang out unsinged, threw Devil-may-care to the farther end of the room, and seated himself in the armchair facing his companion.

"Well! I have strange comrades, for sure," thought the soldier as he picked himself up. "But my meat must be cooked. I will go and take it off the spit, lest my visitors eat it."

Thereat he returned quietly to the fireplace and was about to unhook the meat when a third creature swooped down upon him, and flung him, his meat, and his spit, to the extreme corner of the room.

"I am beginning to get tired of this little game," he said, rubbing himself. "But since they seem to like the fire, let them warm themselves at their ease. I'll jump into bed and take my meat and wine with me. It may be they'll let me eat my supper in peace."

He climbed into a bed at the far end of the room. But no sooner was he there than the three devils, for devils they were in truth, came up to him, and said, "Ah! Devil-may-care, the fearless one! So you think that we will be letting you eat and drink and sleep quietly in our domain, just as if you were at home! You are mistaken if that thought is yours; and, by the same token, we mean to make away with you!"

"I would ask one thing of you, my lords. Just be bearing in mind I am an honest soldier, so don't kill me here in my bed, and three to one at that! Let me get up to defend myself! I hope it's gentlemen I'm fighting, not cowards."

"Rise, then," they replied, sullenly enough.

Devil-may-care sprang from his bed. The night before, not being able to find shelter, he had slept in a church, and in the morning, ere he set forth again, he had filled an empty cider bottle with holy water. Now he uncorked this bottle and promptly sprinkled its contents over the three demons. When the first drop touched them, they began to leap wildly to and fro: now springing up to the roof, now striking against the wall, seeking ever to escape, and uttering savage yells.

"Have pity! Have pity!" they cried. "Release us! Devil-may-care, have pity! Enough, enough!"

"I will let you go if you promise never to return to this castle."

"So be it. We will never be seen within its walls again," each made answer.

"Then sign this contract with your blood."

The three signed with their blood the piece of parchment which lay at hand, and then Devil-may-care allowed them to depart, as they had come, by the chimney. This done, he supped in peace, and afterward fell into a profound sleep. On the morrow the lord of the manor came to the room and marveled to find the soldier so happy.

"You are not dead!" he exclaimed.

"As you see, my lord, I am alive. No harm has come to me."

"And in very truth you have spent the whole night here?"

"Yes, that too."

"And you saw nothing strange?"

"Ah! as for that, if . . . I certainly had to do with some curious beings; but, be reassured, I have rid you of them forever."

"And how can I prove the truth of your words?"

"Take this parchment and see what is written there." Whereupon the soldier showed him the paper which the three devils had signed with their blood.

Laouik of Kerdluz took the parchment, examined it carefully, and cried, "Never can I repay this service. Ask what you will as your reward, and I will grant it to you, even to the hand of my daughter."

"My lord, I do not deserve so great an honor, nor do I aspire so high. I am a blacksmith by trade, as was my father, and my father's father before him; if you would make me happy, build me a forge on the highway and provide me with iron and coal. I will shoe your horses, your farmers' horses, and those of all the travelers who pass that way; thus I shall live by the work of my own hands, as an honest man should do."

Laouik of Kerdluz built the forge on the highway. Devil-may-care settled there, and from morning till night his hammer might be heard ringing on the anvil, for he loved work, and his customers were many.

On a day when he was in his forge, his shirtsleeves rolled up, his face blackened with smoke, two strangers passed by; one young, the other old. They paused to look at him.

"You work well, Devil-may-care," said the younger of the men.

"One needs must work, sirs, to earn one's bread," he replied.

With these words he put the iron into the fire and blew the bellows till the sparks flew; when red hot, he withdrew the metal to shape it upon the anvil, whereat the sweat poured from his brow. The two passers-by watched him admiringly.

"Hard workers like you please me," said the stranger. "Choose, therefore, three things to ask of me. They shall surely be granted you."

Devil-may-care, mistrustful of the promise, smiled and glanced slyly at the onlookers.

"Ask for a place in paradise," prompted the elder of the two.

"Paradise, wayfarer, is only for those who gain it, and can hardly be won so easily, methinks."

"You are right, Devil-may-care," replied the other traveler. "But ask me three things, and I promise to grant them, be they what they may."

"I am often thirsty with beating the hot iron in my forge, and the well is distant. Grant that the old pear tree which grows in my yard may bear fruit all the year, even in winter."

"Your wish is granted."

In a moment the pear tree was covered with fair white flowers, its branches borne down with the weight of beautiful golden pears, albeit the month was January.

"And your second request, toiler?"

"Make sure of a place in paradise this time," again suggested the old man.

"Enough of your paradise! I have told you that paradise is for those who deserve it, and I am thinking that after my death a place may be found for me there if the good God so wills."

"Maybe," assented the younger stranger. "Make known your second wish."

"I would have in the corner of my forge a good armchair; and when someone seats himself thereon, grant that he may not have power to rise until such time as it please me."

"You have your wish." And with these words the armchair stood in the corner of the forge.

"And your third wish?"

"Now, sure, is your last chance to win a place in paradise—your very last," urged the old man with eager accent.

"Leave me alone, I tell you, with your paradise. I have heard enough of that. I ask now for a pack of cards wherewith I shall always win, whoever be my adversary."

"And that is granted too. Here are the cards." A pack of new cards lay on the anvil.

The two travelers then bade farewell to the smith and continued their way. Jesus and Sant-Per it was who thus journeyed on foot through the land of Arvor.

Many years passed after Devil-may-care received the visit of Jesus and His saint: years in which he lived happily and worked well. One day, and this was a day when he was no longer young, he received another visit of a less welcome kind; from none other than the Ankou [death] himself. None could fail to recognize those white rattling bones, that fateful sickle. The blacksmith, however, went on striking his iron on the anvil as if an ordinary customer stood there. But the importunate visitor brandished his sickle, crying, "Now! Devil-may-care! Make ready to follow me. Your turn has come."

"My turn for what?" he asked, feigning not to understand.

"Aha! So you are not for knowing me then? I am Ann-Ankou, my friend!"

"So you are the Great Reaper, are you? Well, well! I have often heard tell of you. Forgive me for not knowing you straightway."

"Oh, there's no harm done. But come quickly now, for I've no time to lose."

"Yes, certainly, if as you say my hour is here. First, however, I must shoe the horses which stand at my door. Be seated for a moment in that armchair. I shall only be a few seconds; then I will follow you."

"Nay, time speeds. I must strike the fatal blow." Whereupon he raised his scythe.

"Be patient a little. What difference can it make, for you can easily regain lost time? Just let me finish shoeing the priest's mare. Three nails are already in; one only is wanting, and I could not leave in such a state the last horse which I shall ever shoe. What would the blessed Sant-Aler say when I stand before him up there? Sit down in that armchair, I beg you. I'll be ready in a moment."

The Ankou once seated, Devil-may-care was quite at his ease. He resumed his work, whistling and singing the while; leisurely he put the iron in the fire, blew the bellows, withdrew it, and shaped it on the anvil. Then, having finished with the priest's mare, he shod several other horses. Seeing this, Death grew impatient.

"Come, we must be off. I fare far today; I cannot wait."

"You weary me. Leave me in peace to do my work."

Thus the smith continued to work all day, and the day that followed, and the next day again, and so on for months and years, and the Ankou remained fixed to the chair. When he sought to escape Devil-may-care whistled.

A hundred years passed, and Death was still a prisoner in the forge. On all sides men sought him. Even those who in former days cursed his presence, now implored him to come to their aid. None died, and

all looked upon life as the greatest of evils. At last the good God had pity on His children and sent the Angel of Death to bid Devil-may-care liberate the Ankou.

When the angel reached the forge, he found Devil-may-care shoeing horses as was his wont. "How is it that you thus keep Death prisoner at your forge? A century has passed, and no man has died. Everywhere, in hell, in paradise, in purgatory, and, above all, on earth, is wailing. All men implore Death as a liberating angel, a healer of woes. God bids you set him free."

"It is true," replied Devil-may-care. "Ann-Ankou has sat in my armchair for long; so silently sleeps he that I had forgotten his presence. He shall have his liberty. But at this moment I am busy. You see what a number of horses there are at my door! Give me but time to put a few nails into the hind shoe of that white mare, and I am ready. Sit down a moment in the armchair beside Death. There is room for him and for you."

At that the angel seated himself by the Ankou's side, and the blacksmith closed the door of his forge, put the key in his pocket, and set out with the pack of cards, never yet used, which the good God had given him. He had not journeyed far when he met a strange-looking man, who, seeing the cards in his hand, accosted him.

"Will you have a game with me, comrade?" It was Lucifer himself, who, having nothing to do in those days, wandered about aimlessly.

"As you will," replied Devil-may-care.

They seated themselves on a large flat stone in the midst of a wide-stretching plain. The cards dealt, the blacksmith asked what the stakes should be.

"Let's play soul for soul, yours against mine," answered the devil.

Amazed at this reply, the smith eyed him from head to foot, but, seeing that his feet were cleft, he knew that it was the Evil One with whom he had to reckon. Nevertheless, as he trusted in his cards, he said to himself, "You know not what awaits you, my friend."

The play began, and Devil-may-care won the first game.

"We will go on," said his adversary. "Two other souls against the two which you now possess, yours and mine."

"Agreed. Deal the cards."

The cards were divided, and for the second time the blacksmith won.

"Four souls against your four souls," cried the now exasperated fiend.

"So be it," was the answer, and the luck was with Devil-may-care once more.

Thus they played for a hundred years; at each game the stake was doubled, and ever Devil-may-care won. So many souls fell to his lot that not one sinner was left in the Ankou's realm. As each was delivered, it passed into purgatory, and because of the vast number of them, the souls which were in purgatory when the game began were sent to paradise.

At last the luckless player uttered a piercing yell; he struck the rock with his cloven hoof, and the mark of it may be seen to this day. Thereafter the earth was rent: and he sank into the abyss.

Throughout this time Death and his angel were prisoners in the forge, and as no man died, great was the misery upon earth.

"To die! To die!" men cried as they raised their hands heavenward. "O Death, have mercy on us!" was the wail of all.

Devil-may-care was moved to pity, and he said, "I have lived too long. In this world it is ever the same: good or bad, rich or poor, none are content with their lot. I will journey to the other world."

He returned to his forge to find Death and his angel still sleeping profoundly in the armchair. "Awake, sluggards! Go work, for all murmur at your slothfulness. Ay, every creature in heaven and earth."

Rising, the Ankou waved his sickle, which cut down Devil-may-care where he stood. Then Death fared forth into the world and labored rapidly and unceasingly to repair the waste of forfeited years.

Blow followed blow, with the swiftness of lightning, with the insistence of wave upon wave, and men fell as fall the grass and wild flowers beneath the sickle in the month of the hay harvest.

Meantime the soul of the blacksmith had ascended heavenward. When high enough, he rapped at the gate of paradise.

"Who is there?" cried Sant-Per from behind the portal.

"Devil-may-care. Let me enter, I pray you."

"There is no room for you here."

"Wherefore, my lord Sant-Per?"

"Remember you not the day when Jesus Christ, traveling in Brittany, found you working at your forge? When the Lord Himself bade you make three demands, which He would grant, whatever they might be?"

"Well I remember that day."

"Thrice I counseled you to ask for a place in heaven; thrice you refused. Nay, more than that, you even spoke disrespectfully to me. Is it not true?"

"So indeed was it, my lord Per. But I implore you to forget the past, and open to me."

"No, no, Devil-may-care. There is no room for you here."

"Whither shall I go?"

"Wheresoever you will. To the devil if it please you!"

"To the devil! I know him well! But where does he live?"

"The second door to the left."

"I will go there, for I do not fear him."

Devil-may-care knocked at the gates of hell.

"Who is there?" cried a voice from within.

"Devil-may-care."

"Do not think to enter here. We have not forgotten how you drove us from the old castle. Moreover, by keeping Death a prisoner so long in your armchair, hell is deserted. Away with you!" And the door was closed against him.

"Now, that's odd! Neither in heaven nor in hell will they have me! I must knock at this other door, here between them. It may be they will receive me." And he knocked at the third door, which was the gate of purgatory.

"Who is there?" questioned a voice.

"It is I, Devil-may-care."

"Away, away, wretched one! You it was who sent the inmates of hell to us. Be off with you!"

"Of a truth no one will have me," said Devil-may-care, concerned now as to where he should go. "But I can't remain outside; I must find shelter somewhere, that is sure. I will go and knock again at Sant-Per's gate; there was a kind look about him after all, and I may find means to make him open his door."

Thereat he knocked at the gate of paradise a second time.

"Who troubles me?" cried the saint.

"Devil-may-care, holy Per."

"You again! Have I not already told you I will not open to you? Go elsewhere."

"But no one will take me in. I implore you to receive me."

"No, no! You shall not come here."

"I beseech you to open the gate, if ever so little, that I may see how fair is your paradise."

The good God, who walked toward the portal to speak with His servant, the Keeper of the Keys, was moved when He heard that none would receive Devil-may-care, and said, "Open the door a little, that he may catch a glimpse of our paradise."

As Sant-Per opened the door, Devil-may-care deftly flung in his cap, and it fell in the center of paradise.

"Let me enter, good Sant-Per, if only to pick up my cap."

"A wise man never parts with his cap. You shall not cross the threshold."

"Then," said Devil-may-care, "it must stay in paradise and keep a place for me until the day of judgment, when you must needs receive me among the blessed."

Sant-Per, struck by his words, opened the gate. "Enter, and pick it up, but then begone," he said.

Once in that place of rest, however, Devil-may-care began to run through paradise as a horse scampers over green turf.

"Sant-Per," he cried, "a wise man never parts from his cap. It is you who told me that thing. I shall never part from mine." And he seated himself, cross-legged, on his property.

Every saint in paradise laughed, and the holy Virgin said, "Let the man rest here."

Thus it is that Devil-may-care sits on his cap in the midst of paradise, awaiting the day of judgment.

From *The Shadow of Arvor: Legendary Romances and Folk-Tales of Brittany.*

THE MEN WHO WOULDN'T STAY DEAD

GENTLEMEN, if you choose to listen, I will recount to you an adventure which once happened in a castle that stood on the bank of a river, near a bridge, and at a short distance from a town, of which I forget the name, but which we may suppose to be Douai. The master of this castle was humpbacked. Nature had exhausted her ingenuity in the formation of his whimsical figure. In place of understanding, she had given him an immense head, which, nevertheless, was lost between his two shoulders; he had thick hair, a short neck, and a horrible visage. Spite of his deformity, this bugbear bethought himself of falling in love with a beautiful young woman, the daughter of a poor but respectable burgess of Douai. He sought her in marriage, and, as he was the richest person in the district, the poor girl was delivered up to him. After the nuptials he was as much to pity as she, for, being devoured by jealousy, he had not tranquillity night or day, but went prying and rambling everywhere, and suffered no stranger to enter his castle.

One day during the Christmas festival, while standing sentinel at his gate, he was accosted by three humpbacked minstrels. They saluted him as a brother and as such asked for refreshment. Contrary to expectation, he led them to his kitchen, gave them a capon with peas, and to each a piece of money. Before they departed, however, he warned them never to return, on pain of being thrown into the river. At this threat of the chatelain the minstrels laughed heartily, and took the road to the town, singing in full chorus, and dancing in grotesque derision. He, on his part, without paying any further attention to them, went to walk in the fields.

The lady, who saw her husband cross the bridge, and had heard the minstrels, called them back to amuse her. They had not been long returned to the castle when her husband knocked at the gate, by which she and the minstrels were equally alarmed. Fortunately the lady perceived, on a bedstead in a neighboring room, three empty coffers. Into each of them she stuffed a minstrel, shut the covers, and then opened the gate to her husband. He had only come back to spy the conduct of his wife, as usual, and after a short stay went out anew, at which you may believe his wife was not dissatisfied. She instantly ran to the coffers to release the minstrels, for night was approaching, and her husband would not probably be long absent. But what was her dismay when she found them all three suffocated! Lamentation, however, was useless. The main object now was to get rid of the dead bodies, and she had not a moment to lose. She ran then to the gate and, seeing a peasant go by, offered him a reward of thirty livres, and leading him into the castle, she took him to one of the coffers and, showing him its contents, told him he must throw the dead body into the river. He asked for

a sack, put the carcass into it, pitched it over the bridge into the stream, and then returned quite out of breath to claim the promised reward. "I certainly intended to satisfy you," said the lady, "but you ought first to fulfill the conditions of your bargain; you have agreed to rid me of the dead body, have you not? There, however, it is still"; saying this, she showed him the other coffer, in which the second hunchback had expired. At this sight the clown was perfectly confounded, saying, "How the devil! come back! a sorcerer!" He then stuffed the body into the sack, and threw it, like the other, over the bridge, taking care to put the head down and to observe that it sank.

Meanwhile the lady had again changed the position of the coffers, so that the third was now in the place which had been successively occupied by the two others. When the peasant returned she showed him the remaining body. "You are right, friend," said she, "he must be a magician, for there he is again." The rustic gnashed his teeth with rage. "What the devil! Am I to do nothing but carry about this accursed hunchback?" He then lifted him up, with dreadful imprecations, and, having tied a stone round the neck, threw him into the middle of the current, threatening, if he came out a third time, to dispatch him with a cudgel. The first object that presented itself to the clown on his way back for the reward was the hunchbacked master of the castle returning from his evening walk and making toward the gate. At this sight the peasant could no longer restrain his fury. "Dog of a hunchback, are you there again?" So saying, he sprang on the chatelain, stuffed him into a sack, and threw him headlong into the river after the minstrels. "I'll venture a wager you have not seen him this last time," said the peasant, entering the room where the lady was seated. She answered that she had not. "Yet you were not far from it," replied he. "The sorcerer was already at the gate, but I have taken care of him. Be at your ease, he will not come back now." The lady instantly understood what had happened and repaid the peasant to his satisfaction.

From *The Fabliaux* of Le Grand d'Aussy, translated in John Dunlop's *History of Fiction* (Philadelphia, 1842).

OUR LADY'S TUMBLER

A CERTAIN minstrel wandered to and fro, over so many a plot and place, that he grew weary of the world and gave himself up to a Holy Order. Horses, robes, money, and whatsoever he had he straight surrendered to it and clean dismissed himself from the world, entering that Holy Order—as folk say—in Clairvaux. But when this dancer had given himself to the monastery, although he was comely and well made, he found he knew no trade that he could ply therein. For all his life he had spent in tumbling and leaping and dancing. He understood how to trip and spring but naught beside, neither paternoster, nor chant, nor credo, nor ave, nor aught that might make for his salvation.

When he had entered the Order, he saw the monks therein converse by signs, no sound passing their lips; and he supposed that they could not speak. But presently he learned the truth—that for penance they were forbidden to speak and therefore were silent. He was all abashed amongst them, for he beheld each one serving God according to the office he held. One recited verses and another a lesson; the choristers were at the psalters, the converts at the misereres, and even the simplest at paternosters.

"O wretched me!" he cried. "What am I doing here? For there is none here so mean that he does not vie with all the rest in serving God after his trade, but I have no business here, for I know not what to do or say." Then he wept for woe and wished that he were dead. "Holy Mary, Mother!" he said, "do pray your Sovereign Father that He send me His good counsel, that I may have the power to serve Him and you and may earn the food that I eat, for I know that I do not yet earn it."

Thus filled with grief he crept off into a corner of the monastery. There, coming upon a crypt, he crouched down by an altar, above which was the form of our lady the Virgin Mary. When he heard them sound for Mass he looked up, all dismayed, crying, "Now each one will say his stave, and here am I like a tethered ox, doing naught but browse, and spoiling food to no purpose." A while longer he crouched there and then burst out, "Shall I do it? By the Mother of God I will! I shall never be blamed if I serve the Mother of God according to my trade." Immediately he removed his cloak and stripped himself, laying his clothes beside the altar.

"Lady," said he to the form above the altar, "to your protection I commend my body and my soul. Sweet Queen, despise not what I know, for I would fain serve you in good faith. I cannot chant or read to you, but I would do for you the choicest of all my feats. Now, may I be like the bull-calf that leaps and bounds before his mother." Then he began his leaps before her, first low and small, then great and high, first under and then over. He tumbled and leaped, doing the vault of Metz over his head. He saluted the image and then he did the French vault and the vault of Champagne, and then the Spanish vault and the vaults they do in Brittany, and then the vault of Lorraine, straining himself to do the best he could. And when he heard the others raise their voices in the chants he laid to in earnest, and as long as the Mass lasted he did not cease to dance and trip and leap, till he grew so faint he could no longer stand upon his feet and dropped from very weariness. And as blood drips from the spit, so the sweat started from him.

"Lady," he said then, "I can do no more now, but I shall do more another time."

Then he put on his vestments again, and when he was clothed he saluted the image and went his way. "Adieu, sweet friend," he said. "Be not cast down, for if I can I will come again."

This life he led a long time, thenceforth going at every hour to render his service and his homage before the image; and never did he desire other sport. Now the others knew, of course, that he went every day into the crypt, but no man on earth knew what it was that he did there; nor would the tumbler, for all the wealth the world possesses, have had any know what he did, save God alone.

So went it with the good man for a long space. I cannot tell you how many years it was, but at last the time came when he was made uneasy again, for a monk took note of him and blamed him in his heart for not coming to matins. Wondering what became of him when he went off by himself and how he earned his bread, the monk followed him and spied on him until he plainly saw him plying his trade, as I have told you.

This monk went to the abbot and told him, from end to end, relating it just as you have heard. Whereupon the abbot said to the monk, "Now hold your peace, and do not make a scandal of him. And we will go this day and find out what it may mean." Then they went and hid themselves hard by the altar in a nook where he could not see them. And the abbot and the monk witnessed all the vaults he made, and his leaping and dancing and saluting the image, and his tripping and bounding, until he became faint and, the sweat starting out all over him, he dropped down at last upon the floor of the crypt.

Then the abbot looked and saw descending from the vault a Dame more glorious than any other that ever man has seen. And as they watched, the sweet Queen knelt and with a white napkin fanned her minstrel before the altar. Sweetly and meekly she fanned his neck and body and face to cool him. And this the abbot and his monk saw happen a good four times, for at every hour it came to pass that the Mother of God came to succor her servant. Now the abbot had joy, for God had shown him that the service which the poor man had rendered pleased Him. The monk, all confounded, said to the abbot, "Have Mercy, sire! This is a holy man that we see here. If I have said aught amiss concerning him, lay on me my penance, for beyond all doubt this is a good man."

Said the abbot, "You speak truth, and I command you that you speak to no man of what you have seen, if it be not to God and to me."

"And I give you my promise," said the other.

And so the time came and went until a little afterward the abbot sent for the man. When he heard that the abbot was asking for him, the tumbler's heart was so full of sorrow that he knew not what he should say. "Ah, me!" he cried, "I am accused. Never again shall I be a day without misery and toil and shame, for my service comes to nought." Weeping, he came before the abbot and knelt, crying, "Sire, say what you command. I will do your will." The abbot said, "I will to know what is your worth, and how you earn your bread."

"Alas!" said he, "I knew it well that I should be sent on my way as soon as my doings should be known. How this command hurts me!" Then he told the abbot all his doings, from end to end, just as I have related them.

The abbot turned to him and, weeping, raised him up and kissed his eyes. "Brother," said he, "now hold thy peace, for I consent that you shall be of our convent. And God grant that we may be of yours. Sweet brother, pray for me, and I will pray for you. And I command you that you do your service frankly, even as you have done it—ay, and even better, if you have the skill."

Whereat the good man's bosom leapt with joy. And thereafter he did his service without rest, morning and evening, day and night, never missing an hour until he was smitten with an illness from which he could not rise.

Abridged from a translation by P. H. Wicksteed of *Le tombeur de Notre Dame* (London: privately printed, 1894).

CINDERILLA

ONCE there was a gentleman who married, for his second wife, the proudest and most haughty woman that was ever seen. She had, by a former husband, two daughters of her own humor and exactly like her in all things. He had likewise, by another wife, a young daughter, but of unparalleled goodness and sweetness of temper, which she took from her mother, who was the best creature in the world.

No sooner were the ceremonies of the wedding over but the mother-in-law began to show herself in her colors. She could not bear the good qualities of this pretty girl and the less because they made her own daughters appear the more odious. She employed her in the meanest work of the house; she made her scour the dishes and tables, and clean madam's chamber, and those of misses, her daughters. She lay up in a sorry garret, upon a wretched straw bed, while her sisters lay in fine rooms, with floors all inlaid, upon beds of the very newest fashion, and where they had looking-glasses so large that they might see themselves full length, from head to foot. The poor girl bore all patiently, and dare not tell her father, who would have rattled her off; for his wife governed him entirely. When she had done her work she used to go into the chimney corner and sit down among cinders and ashes, which made her commonly be called Cinder-breech; but the next youngest, who was not so rude and uncivil as the eldest, called her Cinderilla. However, Cinderilla, notwithstanding her mean apparel, was a hundred times handsomer than her sisters, though they were always dressed very richly.

It happened that the king's son gave a ball and invited all persons of fashion to it. Our young misses were also invited, for they cut a very grand figure among the quality. They were mightily delighted at this invitation, and wonderfully busy in choosing out such gowns, petticoats, and headclothes as might best become them. This was a new trouble to Cinderilla; for it was she who ironed her sisters' linen and plaited their ruffles. They talked all day long of nothing but how they should be dressed.

"For my part," said the eldest, "I will wear my red velvet suit, with French trimming."

"And I," said the youngest, "shall have only my usual petticoat; but then, to make amends for that, I will put on my gold-flowered manteau, and my diamond stomacher, which is far from being the most ordinary one in the world."

They sent for the best tire-woman they could get, to make up their headdresses and adjust their double-pinners, and they had their red brushes, and patches from Mademoiselle de la Poche. Cinderilla was likewise called up to them to be consulted in all these matters, for she had excellent notions and advised them always for the best—nay, and offered her service to dress their heads, which they were very willing she should do.

As she was doing this they said to her, "Cinderilla, would you not be glad to go to the ball?"

"Ah!" said she, "you only jeer at me. It is not for such as I am to go thither."

"Thou art in the right of it," replied they. "It would make the people laugh to see a Cinder-breech at a ball."

Anyone but Cinderilla would have dressed their heads awry, but she was very good, and dressed them perfectly well. They were almost two days without eating, so much were they transported with joy. They broke above a dozen laces in trying to be laced up close, that they might have fine slender shapes; and they were continually at their looking-glass. At last the happy day came; they went to court, and Cinderilla followed them with her eyes as long as she could, and when she had lost sight of them, fell a-crying.

Her godmother, who saw her all in tears, asked her what was the matter. "I wish I could— I wish I could—" She was not able to speak the rest, being interrupted by her tears and sobbing; so this godmother of hers, who was a Fairy, said to her, "Thou wishest thou couldst go to the ball—is it not so?"

"Y-es," cried Cinderilla with a great sigh.

"Well," said her godmother, "be a good girl, and I will contrive that thou shalt go."

Then she took her into her chamber and said to her, "Run into the garden and bring me a pompion."

Cinderilla went immediately to gather the finest she could get and brought it to her godmother, not being able to imagine how this pompion could make her go to the ball. Her godmother scooped out all the inside of it, leaving nothing but the rind; which done, she struck it with her wand, and the pompion was instantly turned into a fine coach, gilded all over with gold.

She then went to look into her mouse trap, where she found six mice alive, and ordered Cinderilla to lift up a little the trap-door. Thereupon she gave each mouse, as it went out, a little tap with her wand, and the mouse was at that moment turned into a fair horse, which altogether made a very fine set of six horses of a beautiful mouse-colored dapple-gray. Being at a loss for a coachman, "I will go and see," says Cinderilla, "if there be never a rat in the rat trap—we may make a coachman of him."

"Thou art in the right," replied her godmother. "Go and look." Cinderilla brought the trap to her, and in it there were three huge rats. The Fairy made choice of the one which had the largest beard, and, having touched him with her wand, she turned him into a fat, jolly coachman, who had the smartest whiskers eyes ever beheld.

After that she said to her, "Go again into the garden, and you will find six lizards behind the watering pot; bring them to me." She had no sooner done so, but her godmother turned them into six footmen, who skipped up immediately behind the coach, with their liveries all bedaubed with gold and silver, and clung as close behind each other as if they had done nothing else their whole lives.

The fairy then said to Cinderilla, "Well, you see here an equipage fit to go to the ball with. Are you not pleased with it?"

"Oh, yes," cried she, "but must I go thither as I am, in these poisonous nasty rags?"

Her godmother only just touched her with her wand, and, at the same instant, her clothes were turned into cloth of gold and silver, all beset with jewels. This done she gave her a pair of glass slippers, the prettiest in the whole world.

Being thus decked out, she got up into her coach; but her godmother commanded her, above all things, not to stay till after midnight, telling her that if she stayed at the ball one moment longer, her coach would be a pompion again, her horses mice, her coachman a rat, her footmen lizards, and her clothes just as they were before.

She promised her godmother she would not fail to leave the ball before midnight; and then away she drove off, scarce able to contain herself for joy. The king's son, who was told that a great princess, whom nobody knew, was come, ran out to receive her; he gave her his hand as she alighted from the coach, and led her into the hall, among all the company. There was immediately a profound quiet, so attentive was everyone to the singular beauties of the unknown newcomer. Nothing was then heard but a confused noise of "Ah! how handsome she is! How handsome she is!" The king himself, old as he was, could not help ogling her and telling the queen softly that it was a long time since he had seen so beautiful and lovely a creature. All the ladies were busy staring at her clothes and headdress, in order that they might have some made after the same pattern, provided they could meet with such fine materials, and as able hands to make them.

The king's son conducted her to the most honorable seat, and afterward took her out to dance with him; and she danced so very gracefully that they all admired her more and more. A fine collation was served up, whereof the young prince ate not a morsel, so very intent was he with gazing on her. She went and sat by her sisters, showing them a thousand civilities, giving them part of the oranges and citrons which the prince had presented her with; which very much surprised them, for they did not know her. While Cinderilla was thus amusing her sisters, she heard the clock strike eleven and three quarters, whereupon she immediately made a courtesy to the company and hastened away as fast as she could.

Once home, she ran to seek out her godmother, and after having thanked her, she said she could not but heartily wish she might go next day to the ball, because the king's son had desired her. As she was eagerly telling her godmother what had passed at the ball, her two sisters knocked at the door, which Cinderilla ran and opened.

"How long you have stayed," cried she, gaping, rubbing her eyes, and stretching herself as if she had just been awakened out of sleep.

"If thou hadst been at the ball," says one of her sisters, "thou wouldst not have been so tired with it; there came thither the finest princess, the most beautiful ever was seen with mortal eyes; she showed us a thousand civilities and gave us oranges and citrons." Cinderilla seemed very indifferent; indeed, she asked them the name of that princess, but they told her they did not know it and the king's son himself would give all the world to know who she was.

At this Cinderilla, smiling, replied, "She must then be very beautiful indeed. Lord! how happy you have been! Could I not see her?

Ah! dear Miss Charlotte, do lend me your yellow suit of clothes which you wear every day."

"Ay, to be sure!" cried Miss Charlotte. "Lend my clothes to such a dirty Cinder-breech as thou! Who would be the fool then?"

Cinderilla, indeed, expected some such answer, and was very glad of the refusal; for she would have been sadly put to it if her sister had lent her what she asked for.

The next day the two sisters were at the ball, and so was Cinderilla, but dressed even more magnificently than before. The king's son was always by her, never ceasing his compliments and amorous speeches, and all this was so far from being tiresome that she quite forgot what her godmother had recommended to her, so that at last she counted the clock striking twelve, when she took it to be no more than eleven. She then rose up and fled as nimble as a deer. The prince followed but could not overtake her. She left behind one of her glass slippers, which the prince took up most carefully. She got home, but quite out of breath, without coach or footmen, and in her nasty old clothes, having nothing left of all her finery but one of the slippers, fellow to the one she had dropped. The guards at the palace gate were asked if they had not seen a princess go out, and they answered that they had seen nobody go out but a young girl, very meanly dressed, who had more the air of a poor country wench than a gentlewoman.

When the two sisters returned from the ball Cinderilla asked them if they had been well diverted and if the fine lady had been there. They told her yes, but that she hurried away immediately when it struck twelve, and with so much haste that she had dropped one of her little glass slippers, the prettiest in the world, and that the king's son had taken it up; that he had done nothing but look at her all the time of the ball, and that most certainly he was very much in love with the beautiful person who owned the little slipper.

What they said was very true; for, a few days after, the king's son caused it to be proclaimed by sound of trumpet that he would marry her whose foot this slipper would just fit. They whom he employed began to try it on upon the princesses, then the duchesses, and all the court, but in vain. It was brought to the two sisters, who did all they possibly could to thrust a foot into the slipper, but they could not.

Cinderilla, who saw all this, and knew her slipper, said to them, laughing, "Let me see if it will not fit me." Her sisters burst out a-laughing and began to banter her. The gentleman who was sent to try the slipper looked earnestly at Cinderilla, and, finding her very handsome, said it was but just that she should try, and that he had orders to let everyone make trial. He made Cinderilla sit down, and, putting the slipper to her foot, he found it went in very easily and fitted her as if it had been made of wax. The astonishment of her two sisters was excessively great, but it was still abundantly greater when Cinderilla pulled out of her pocket the other slipper and put it on her foot. Thereupon, in came her godmother, who, touching Cinderilla's clothes with her wand, made them richer and more magnificent than any of those she had had before.

And now her two sisters found her to be that fine beautiful lady whom they had seen at the ball. They threw themselves at her feet and begged pardon for all the ill treatment they had made her undergo. Cinderilla took them up and, as she embraced them, cried that she forgave them with all her heart and desired them always to love her. She was conducted to the young prince, dressed as she was; he thought her more charming than ever, and, a few days after, married her. Cinderilla, who was no less good than beautiful, gave her two sisters lodging in the palace, and that very same day matched them with two great lords of the court.

From a translation by R. Samber, made in 1729, of *The Fairy Tales of Mother Goose*, collected by Charles Perrault.

German

Tyll Ulenspiegel

IN THIS handful of tales taken from the two-hundred-odd in the *Kinder- und Hausmärchen* collected by the brothers Grimm, almost the entire spectrum of folk-tale modes and moods is reflected: wishful wonder in "The Frog King"; absolute innocence versus grotesque evil in "Hansel and Grethel"; the crude comedy of fabliaux in "Old Hildebrand"; the note of morality in "Death's Messengers"; and sheer nonsense in "The Fox and the Geese" and "Knoist and His Three Sons." If today, after almost a century and a half, these tales seem no longer peculiarly German, less the property of one European nation than of the entire world, that is an accurate measure of their appeal.

It may seem curious that the brothers who assembled the best-known collections of children's and household tales were first of all earnest professors of philology. But it was surely their very interest in the traditions of language that accounts for the respect with which they approached the storytellers of their native Hesse and for the loving care with which they wrote down what they heard. It was they who first propagated the notion that the idiom in which a story is told is as much worth preserving as the content. The romantic admiration for simple folk and the nationalistic concern with local traditions that marked most of Europe in the opening years of the nineteenth century surely encouraged the interest of the brothers in the legends and hero tales of their countrymen. But it could only have been a combination of special gifts that enabled them to put together a collection so rich in homely charm, humor, and fantasy.

Stories of the folk clown and country-bred rascal known as Tyll Eulenspiegel (or Ulenspiegel) were circulated all over northern Europe during the Middle Ages, and under the name of Howleglas he turned up as far west as England. In the several score adventures generally credited to him, Tyll is usually a scamp who amuses himself by playing pranks on poor burghers, but sometimes he is the jester whose thrusts deflate the vain and tumble the haughty. Charles de Coster, nineteenth-century Belgian novelist, made him into a symbol of Flemish popular resistance against an oppressor, but in the folk literature of the Continent Tyll remains essentially a figure of picaresque comedy, the foremost practical joker of all.

Legends of men who fall asleep in the mountains and awaken decades or even centuries later are very old, but the immediate source of the best-known literary version, "Rip Van Winkle," is a tale of the Kyffhäusen mountain that is sometimes told of Peter Klaus the goatherd and sometimes of Frederick Barbarossa.

THE FROG-KING, OR IRON HENRY

IN OLDEN days when wishing still helped one, there lived a king whose daughters were all beautiful, but the youngest was so beautiful that the sun itself, which has seen so much, was astonished whenever it shone on her face. Close by the king's castle lay a great dark forest, and under an old lime tree in the forest was a well, and when the day was very warm, the king's child went out into the forest and sat down by the side of the cool fountain, and when she was bored she took a golden ball and threw it up on high and caught it, and this ball was her favorite plaything.

Now it so happened that on one occasion the princess's golden ball did not fall into the little hand which she was holding up for it, but onto the ground, and rolled straight into the water. The king's daughter followed it with her eyes, but it vanished, and the well was deep, so deep that the bottom could not be seen. Thereupon she began to cry, and cried louder and louder, and could not be comforted. And as she thus lamented, someone said to her, "What ails thee, king's daughter? Thou weepest so that even a stone would show pity." She looked round to the side from which the voice came, and saw a frog stretching forth its thick, ugly head from the water. "Ah! old water-splasher, is it thou?" said she. "I am weeping for my golden ball, which has fallen into the well."

"Be quiet, and do not weep," answered the frog. "I can help thee, but what wilt thou give me if I bring thy plaything up again?"

"Whatever thou wilt have, dear frog," said she. "My clothes, my pearls and jewels, and even the golden crown which I am wearing."

The frog answered, "I do not care for thy clothes, thy pearls and jewels, or thy golden crown, but if thou wilt love me and let me be thy companion and playfellow, and sit by thee at the little table, and eat off thy little golden plate, and drink out of thy little cup, and sleep in thy little bed–if thou wilt promise me this I will go down below and bring thee thy golden ball up again."

"Oh, yes," said she, "I promise thee all thou wishest, if thou wilt but bring my ball back again." She, however, thought, "How the silly frog does talk! He lives in the water with the other frogs and croaks, and can be no companion to any human being!"

But the frog, when he had received this promise, put his head into the water and sank down, and in a short time came swimming up

again with the ball in his mouth and threw it on the grass. The king's daughter was delighted to see her pretty plaything once more, and picked it up, and ran away with it. "Wait, wait!" said the frog. "Take me with thee. I can't run as thou canst." But what did it avail him to scream his croak, croak, after her, as loudly as he could? She did not listen to it, but ran home and soon forgot the poor frog, who was forced to go back into his well again.

The next day when she had seated herself at table with the king and all the courtiers, and was eating from her little golden plate, something came creeping splish splash, splish splash, up the marble staircase, and when it had got to the top, it knocked at the door and cried, "Princess, youngest princess, open the door for me."

She ran to see who was outside, but when she opened the door, there sat the frog in front of it. Then she slammed the door to, in great haste, sat down to dinner again, and was quite frightened. The king saw plainly that her heart was beating violently and said, "My child, what art thou so afraid of? Is there perchance a giant outside who wants to carry thee away?" "Ah, no," replied she, "it is no giant, but a disgusting frog."

"What does the frog want with thee?" "Ah, dear father, yesterday, when I was in the forest sitting by the well, playing, my golden ball fell into the water. And because I cried so, the frog brought it out again for me, and because he insisted so on it, I promised him he should be my companion, but I never thought he would be able to come out of his water! And now he is outside there and wants to come in to me."

In the meantime it knocked a second time and cried:

"Princess! youngest princess!
Open the door for me!
Dost thou not know what thou saidst to me
Yesterday by the cool waters of the fountain?
Princess, youngest princess!
Open the door for me!"

Then said the king, "That which thou hast promised must thou perform. Go and let him in." She went and opened the door, and the frog hopped in and followed her, step by step, to her chair. There he sat still and cried, "Lift me up beside thee." She delayed, until at last the king commanded her to do it. When the frog was once on the chair he wanted to be on the table, and when he was on the table he said, "Now, push thy little golden plate nearer to me that we may eat together." She did this, but it was easy to see that she did not do it willingly. The frog enjoyed what he ate, but almost every mouthful she took choked her. At length he said, "I have eaten and am satisfied; now I am tired; carry me into thy little room and make thy little silken bed ready, and we will both lie down and go to sleep."

The king's daughter began to cry, for she was afraid of the cold frog which she did not like to touch, and which was now to sleep in her pretty, clean little bed. But the king grew angry and said, "He who helped thee when thou wert in trouble ought not afterward to be despised by thee." So she took hold of the frog with two fingers, carried him upstairs, and put him in a corner. But when she was in bed he crept to her and said, "I am tired, I want to sleep as well as thou, lift me up or I will tell thy father."

Then she was terribly angry and took him up and threw him with all her might against the wall. "Now thou wilt be quiet, hateful frog," said she. But when he fell down he was no frog but a king's son with beautiful, kind eyes. He by her father's will was now her dear companion and husband. Then he told her how he had been transformed by a wicked witch, and how no one could have delivered him from the well but herself, and that tomorrow they would go together into his kingdom. Then they went to sleep, and next morning when the sun awoke them, a carriage came driving up with eight white horses that had white ostrich feathers on their heads and were harnessed with golden chains, and behind stood the young king's servant, faithful Henry. Faithful Henry had been so unhappy when his master was changed into a frog that he had caused three iron bands to be laid round his heart, lest it should burst with grief and sadness. The carriage was to conduct the young king into his kingdom. Faithful Henry helped them both in, and placed himself behind again, and was full of joy because of this deliverance. And when they had driven a part of the way, the king's son heard a cracking behind him as if something had broken. So he turned round and cried, "Henry, the carriage is breaking."

"No, master, it is not the carriage. It is a band from my heart, which was put there in my great pain when you were a frog and imprisoned in the well." Again and once again while they were on their way something cracked, and each time the king's son thought the carriage was breaking; but it was only the bands which were springing from the heart of the faithful Henry because his master was set free and was happy.

From *Grimm's Household Tales,* translated by Margaret Hunt (London: G. Bell and Sons, 1884).

THE VALIANT LITTLE TAILOR

One summer's morning a little tailor was sitting on his table by the window; he was in good spirits, and sewed with all his might. Then came a peasant woman down the street, crying, "Good jams, cheap! Good jams, cheap!" This rang pleasantly in the tailor's ears; he stretched his scrawny head out of the window and cried, "Come up here, dear woman; here you will get rid of your goods." The woman came up the three steps to the tailor with her heavy basket, and he made her unpack all of her pots for him. He inspected them, lifted them up, put his nose to them, and at length said, "The jam seems to me to be good, so weigh me out four ounces, dear woman, and if it is a quarter of a pound that is of no consequence." The woman, who had hoped to find a good sale, gave him what he desired, but went away quite angry and grumbling. "Now, God bless the jam to my use," cried the little tailor, "and give me health and strength"; so he brought the bread out of the cupboard, cut himself a piece right across the loaf, and spread the jam over it. "This won't taste bitter," said he, "but I will just finish the jacket before I take a bite." He laid the bread near him, sewed on, and in his joy made bigger and bigger stitches.

In the meantime the smell of the sweet jam ascended so to the wall, where the flies were sitting in great numbers, that they were attracted and descended on it in hosts. "Hola! who invited you?" said the little tailor, and drove the unbidden guests away. The flies, however, who understood no German, would not be turned away, but came back again in ever-increasing companies. Then the little tailor at last lost all patience, and got a bit of cloth from the hole under his work table, and saying, "Wait, and I will give it to you," struck them mercilessly with it. When he drew it away and counted, there lay before him no fewer than seven, dead and with legs stretched out. "Art thou a fellow of that sort?" said he, and could not help admiring his own bravery. "The whole town shall know of this!" And the little tailor hastened to cut himself a girdle, stitched it, and embroidered on it in large letters, "Seven at one stroke!" "What, only the town!" he continued. "The whole world shall hear of it!" And his heart wagged with joy like a lamb's tail.

The tailor put on the girdle and resolved to go forth into the world, because he thought his workshop was too small for his valor. Before he went away he sought about in the house to see if there was anything which he could take with him; however, he found nothing but an old cheese, and that he put in his pocket. In front of the door he observed a bird which had caught itself in the thicket. It had to go into his pocket with the cheese. Now he took to the road boldly, and as he was light and nimble, he felt no fatigue. The road led him up a mountain, and when he had reached the highest point of it, there sat a powerful giant, looking about him quite comfortably. The little tailor went bravely up, spoke to him, and said, "Good day, comrade, so thou art sitting there overlooking the widespread world! I am just on my way thither, and want to try my luck. Hast thou any inclination to go with me?" The giant looked contemptuously at the tailor and said, "Thou ragamuffin! Thou miserable creature!"

"Oh, indeed?" answered the little tailor, and unbuttoned his coat, and showed the giant the girdle. "There mayest thou read what kind of a man I am!" The giant read, "Seven at one stroke," and thought that they had been men whom the tailor had killed, and began to feel a little respect for the tiny fellow. Nevertheless, he wished to try him first, and took a stone in his hand and squeezed it together so that water dropped out of it. "Do thou likewise," said the giant, "if thou hast strength." "Is that all?" said the tailor. "That is child's play with us!" And he put his hand into his pocket, brought out the soft cheese, and pressed it until the liquid ran out of it. "Faith," said he, "that was a little better, wasn't it?" The giant did not know what to say, and could not believe it of the little man.

Then the giant picked up a stone and threw it so high that the eye could scarcely follow it. "Now, little mite of a man, do thou likewise." "Well thrown," said the tailor, "but after all the stone came down to earth again. I will throw you one which shall never come back at all." And he put his hand into his pocket, took out the bird, and threw it into the air. The bird, delighted with its liberty, rose, flew away, and did not come back. "How does that shot please you, comrade?" asked the tailor. "Thou canst certainly throw," said the giant, "but now we will see if thou art able to carry anything properly." He took the little tailor to a mighty oak tree, which lay there felled on the ground, and said, "If thou art strong enough, help me to carry the tree out of the forest." "Readily," answered the little man. "Take thou the trunk on thy shoulders, and I will raise up the branches and twigs; after all, they are the heaviest." The giant took the trunk on his shoulder, but the tailor seated himself on a branch, and the giant, who could not look round, had to carry away the whole tree, and the little tailor in the bargain: he, behind, was quite merry and happy, and whistled the song "Three tailors rode forth from the gate" as if carrying the

tree were child's play. The giant, after he had dragged the heavy burden part of the way, could go no farther and cried, "Hark you, I shall have to let the tree fall!" The tailor sprang nimbly down, seized the tree with both arms as if he had been carrying it, and said to the giant, "Thou art such a great fellow, and yet canst not even carry the tree!"

They went on together, and as they passed a cherry tree the giant laid hold of the top of the tree where the ripest fruit was hanging, bent it down, gave it into the tailor's hand, and bade him eat. But the little tailor was much too weak to hold the tree, and when the giant let it go, it sprang back again, and the tailor was hurled into the air by it. When he had fallen down again without injury, the giant said, "What is this? Hast thou not strength enough to hold the weak twig?" "There is no lack of strength," answered the little tailor. "Dost thou think that could be anything to a man who has struck down seven at one blow? I leaped over the tree because the huntsmen are shooting down there in the thicket. Jump as I did, if thou canst do it." The giant made the attempt, but could not get over the tree, and remained hanging in the branches, so that in this also the tailor kept the upper hand.

The giant said, "If thou art such a valiant fellow, come with me into our cavern and spend the night with us." The little tailor was willing, and followed him. When they went into the cave, other giants were sitting there by the fire, and each of them had a roasted sheep in his hand and was eating it. The little tailor looked round and thought, "It is much more spacious here than in my workshop." The giant showed him a bed and said he was to lie down in it and sleep. The bed was, however, too big for the little tailor; he did not lie down on it, but crept into a corner. When it was midnight, and the giant thought that the little tailor was lying in a sound sleep, he got up, took a great iron bar, cut through the bed with one blow, and thought he had given the grasshopper his finishing stroke. With the earliest dawn the giants went into the forest, and had quite forgotten the little tailor, when all at once he walked up to them quite merrily and boldly. The giants were in dread fear that he would strike them all dead and ran away in a great hurry.

The little tailor went onward, always following his own pointed nose. After he had walked for a long time he came to the courtyard of a royal palace, and as he felt weary, he lay down on the grass and fell asleep. While he lay there the people came and inspected him on all sides and read on his girdle, "Seven at one stroke." "Ah!" said they, "what does the great warrior here in the midst of peace? He must be a mighty lord." They went and announced him to the king, and gave it as their opinion that if war should break out, this would be a weighty and useful man who ought on no account to be allowed to depart. The counsel pleased the king, and he sent one of his courtiers to the little tailor to offer him military service when he awoke. The ambassador remained standing by the sleeper, waited until he stretched his limbs and opened his eyes, and then conveyed to him this proposal. "For this very reason have I come here," the tailor replied. "I am ready to enter the king's service." He was therefore honorably received, and a separate dwelling was assigned him.

The soldiers, however, were set against the little tailor and wished him a thousand miles away. "What is to be the end of this?" they said among themselves. "If we quarrel with him, and he strikes about him, seven of us will fall at every blow; not one of us can stand against him." They came therefore to a decision, betook themselves in a body to the king, and begged for their dismissal. "We are not prepared," said they, "to stay with a man who kills seven at one stroke." The king was sorry that for the sake of one he should lose all his faithful servants, wished that he never set eyes on the tailor, and would willingly have been rid of him again. But he did not venture to give him his dismissal, for he dreaded lest he should strike him and all his people dead and place himself on the royal throne. He thought about it for a long time, and at last found good counsel.

He sent to the little tailor and caused him to be informed that as he was such a great warrior he had one request to make to him. In a forest of his country lived two giants, who caused great mischief with their robbing, murdering, ravaging, and burning, and no one could approach them without putting himself in danger of death. If the tailor conquered and killed these two giants, he would give him his only daughter to wife, and half of his kingdom as a dowry, and one hundred horsemen should go with him to assist him.

"That would indeed be a fine thing for a man like me!" thought the little tailor. "One is not offered a beautiful princess and half a kingdom every day in one's life!" "Oh, yes," he replied, "I will soon subdue the giants, and do not require the help of the hundred horsemen to do it. He who can hit seven with one blow has no need to be afraid of two."

The little tailor went forth, and the hundred horsemen followed him. When he came to the outskirts of the forest he said to his followers, "Just stay waiting here, I alone will soon finish off the giants." Then he bounded into the forest and looked about right and left. After a while he perceived both giants. They lay sleeping under a tree, and snored so that the branches waved up and down. The little tailor, not idle, gathered two pocketfuls of stones, and with these climbed the tree. When he was halfway up he slipped down by a branch, until he sat just above the sleepers, and then let one stone after another fall on the breast of one of the giants. For a long time the giant felt nothing, but at last he awoke, pushed his comrade, and said, "Why art thou knocking me?" "Thou must be dreaming," said the other, "I am not knocking thee." They laid themselves down to sleep again, and then the tailor threw a stone done on the second. "What is the meaning of this?" cried the other. "Why art thou pelting me?" "I am not pelting thee," answered the first, growling. They disputed about it for a time, but as they were weary they let the matter rest, and their eyes closed once more. The little tailor began his game again, picked out the biggest stone and threw it with all his might on the breast of the first giant. "That is too much!" cried he, springing up like a madman and pushing his companion against the tree until it shook. The other paid him back in the same coin, and they got into such a rage that they tore up trees and belabored each other so long that at last they both fell dead at the same time.

Then the little tailor leaped down. "It is a lucky thing," said he, "that they did not tear up the tree on which I was sitting, or I should have had to spring onto another like a squirrel; but we tailors are nimble." He drew out his sword and gave each of them a couple of thrusts in the breast, and then went out to the horsemen and said, "The work is done; I have given both of them their finishing stroke, but it was hard work. They tore up trees in their sore need, and defended themselves with them, but all that is to no purpose against a man like myself, who can kill off seven at one blow." "But are you not wounded?" asked the horsemen. "You need not concern yourself about that," answered the tailor. "They have not bent one hair of mine." The horsemen would not believe him and rode into the forest; there they found the giants swimming in their blood, and all round about lay the torn-up trees.

The little tailor demanded of the king the promised reward; he, however, repented of his promise, and again bethought himself how he could get rid of the hero. "Before thou receivest my daughter, and the half of my kingdom," said he to him, "thou must perform one more heroic deed. In the forest roams a unicorn which does great harm, and thou must catch it first." "I fear one unicorn still less than two giants. Seven at one blow is my kind of affair." He took a rope and an ax with him, went forth into the forest, and again bade those who were sent with him to wait outside. He had not to seek long. The unicorn soon came toward him, and rushed directly on the tailor, as if it would spit him on its horn without more ceremony. "Softly, softly, it can't be done as quickly as that," said he, and stood still and waited until the animal was quite close, and then sprang nimbly behind a tree. The unicorn ran against the tree with all its strength, and struck its horn so fast in the trunk that it had not strength enough to draw it out again, and thus it was caught. "Now, I have got the bird," said the tailor, and came out from behind the tree and put the rope round its neck, and then with his ax he hewed the horn out of the tree, and when all was ready he led the beast away and took it to the king.

The king still would not give him the promised reward and made a third demand. Before the wedding the tailor was to catch him a

wild boar that made great havoc in the forest, and the huntsmen should give him their help. "Willingly," said the tailor. "That is child's play!" He did not take the huntsmen with him into the forest, and they were well pleased that he did not, for the wild boar had several times received them in such a manner that they had no inclination to lie in wait for him. When the boar perceived the tailor, it ran at him with foaming mouth and whetted tusks, and was about to throw him to the ground, but the agile hero sprang into a chapel which was near, and up to the window at once, and in one bound out again. The boar ran in after him, but the tailor ran round outside and shut the door behind it, and then the raging beast, which was much too heavy and awkward to leap out of the window, was caught. The little tailor called the huntsmen thither that they might see the prisoner with their own eyes. The hero, however, went to the king, who was now, whether he liked it or not, obliged to keep his promise to give him his daughter and the half of his kingdom. Had he known that it was no warlike hero, but a little tailor who was standing before him, it would have gone to his heart still more than it did. The wedding was held with great magnificence and small joy, and out of a tailor a king was made.

After some time the young queen heard her husband say in his dreams at night, "Boy, make me the doublet, and patch the pantaloons, or else I will rap the yardmeasure over thine ears." Then she discovered in what state of life the young lord had been born, and next morning complained of her shame to her father, and begged him to help her to get rid of this husband who was nothing but a tailor. The king comforted her and said, "Leave thy bedroom door open this night, and my servants shall stand outside, and when he has fallen asleep, shall go in, bind him, and take him on board a ship which shall carry him into the wide world." The woman was satisfied with this; but the king's armor-bearer, who had heard all, was friendly with the young lord and informed him of the whole plot. "I'll put a screw into that business," said the little tailor.

At night he went to bed with his wife at the usual time, and when she thought that he had fallen asleep she got up, opened the door, and then lay down again. The little tailor, who was only pretending to be asleep, began to cry out in a clear voice, "Boy, make me the doublet and patch the pantaloons, or I will rap the yardmeasure over thine ears. I smote seven at one blow. I killed two giants, I brought away one unicorn, and caught a wild boar, and am I to fear those who are standing outside the room!" When these men heard the tailor speaking thus, they were overcome by a great dread, and ran as if a wild huntsman were behind them. And none of them would venture anything further against him. So the little tailor was a king and remained one to the end of his life.

From *Grimm's Household Tales.*

THE FOX AND THE GEESE

THE FOX once came to a meadow in which was a flock of fine fat geese. He smiled at them and said, "I come in the nick of time; you are sitting together quite beautifully, so that I can eat you up one after the other." The geese cackled with terror, sprang up, and began to wail and beg piteously for their lives. But the fox would listen to nothing and said, "There is no mercy to be had! You must die." At length one of them took heart and said, "If we poor geese are to yield up our vigorous young lives, show us the only possible favor and allow us one more prayer, that we may not die in our sins, and then we shall place ourselves in a row, so that you can always pick yourself the fattest." "Yes," said the fox, "that is reasonable, and a pious request. Pray away, I will wait till you are done." Then the first began a good long prayer, forever saying, "Ga! Ga!" And as she would make no end, the second did not wait until her turn came but began also, "Ga! Ga!" The third and fourth followed her, and soon they were all cackling together.

When they have done praying, the story shall be continued further, but at present they are still praying without stopping.

From *Grimm's Household Tales.*

OLD HILDEBRAND

ONCE upon a time lived a peasant and his wife, and the parson of the village had a fancy for the wife, and had wished for a long while to spend a whole day happily with her, and the peasant woman, too, was quite willing. One day, therefore, he said to the woman, "Listen, my dear friend, I have now thought of a way in which we can for once spend a whole day happily together. I'll tell you what: on Wednesday you must take to your bed and tell your husband you are ill, and if you only complain and act as though you were ill and go on doing it until Sunday when I have to preach I will then say in my sermon that whosoever has at home a sick child, a sick husband, a sick wife, a sick father, a sick mother, a sick sister, brother, or whosoever else it may be, and makes a pilgrimage to the Gockerli hill in Italy, where you can get a peck of laurel leaves for a kreuzer, the child, the husband, the wife, the father or mother, the sister, or whosoever else it may be, will be restored to health immediately."

"I will manage it," said the woman directly. Now, therefore, on the Wednesday, the peasant woman took to her bed and complained and lamented as agreed on, and her husband did everything for her that he could think of, but nothing did her any good. And when Sunday came the woman said, "I feel as ill as if I were going to die at once, but there is one thing I should like to do before my end—I should like to hear the sermon the parson is going to preach today." Thereupon the peasant said, "Ah, my child, do not do it. Thou mightest make thyself worse if thou wert to get up. Look, I will go to the sermon, and will attend very carefully, and will tell thee everything the parson says."

"Well," said the woman, "go then, and pay great attention, and repeat to me all that thou hearest." So the peasant went to the sermon, and the parson began to preach and said that if anyone had at home a sick child, a sick husband, a sick wife, a sick father, a sick mother, a sick sister, brother, or anyone else, and would make a pilgrimage to the Gockerli hill in Italy, where a peck of laurel leaves costs a kreuzer, the child, husband, wife, father, mother, sister, brother, or whosoever else it might be would be restored to health instantly, and whosoever wished to undertake the journey was to go to him after the service was over, and he would give him the sack for the laurel leaves and the kreuzer. Then no one was more rejoiced than the peasant, and after the service was over he went at once to the parson, who gave him the bag for the laurel leaves and the kreuzer.

After that he went home, and even at the house door he cried, "Hurrah! dear wife, it is now almost the same thing as if thou wert well! The parson has preached today that whosoever had at home a sick child, a sick husband, a sick wife, a sick father, a sick mother, a sick sister, brother, or whoever it might be, and would make a pilgrimage to the Gockerli hill in Italy, where a peck of laurel leaves costs a kreuzer, the child, husband, wife, father, mother, sister, brother, or whosoever else it was would be cured immediately, and now I have already got the bag and the kreuzer from the parson, and will at once begin my journey so that thou mayst get well the faster." And thereupon he went away. He was, however, hardly gone before the woman got up, and the parson was there directly.

But now we will leave these two for a while and follow the peasant, who walked on quickly without stopping, in order to get the sooner to the Gockerli hill, and on his way he met his gossip. His

gossip was an egg merchant and was just coming from the market where he had sold his eggs. "May you be blessed," said the gossip. "Where are you off to so fast?"

"To all eternity, my friend," said the peasant. "My wife is ill, and I have been today to hear the parson's sermon, and he preached that if anyone had in his house a sick child, a sick husband, a sick wife, a sick father, a sick mother, a sick sister, brother, or anyone else, and made a pilgrimage to the Gockerli hill in Italy, where a peck of laurel leaves costs a kreuzer, the child, the husband, the wife, the father, the mother, the sister, brother, or whosoever else it was would be cured immediately."

"But listen, gossip," said the egg merchant to the peasant, "are you then stupid enough to believe such a thing as that? Don't you know what it means? The parson wants to spend a whole day with your wife in peace, so he has given you this job to get you out of the way."

"My word!" said the peasant. "How I'd like to know if that's true!"

"Come then," said the gossip, "I'll tell you what to do. Get into my egg basket and I will carry you home, and then you will see for yourself." So that was settled, and the gossip put the peasant into his egg basket and carried him home.

When they got to the house, hurrah! but all was going merrily there! The woman had already had nearly everything killed that was in the farmyard, and had made pancakes, and the parson was there, and had brought his fiddle with him. The gossip knocked at the door, and the woman asked who was there. "It is I, gossip," said the egg merchant. "Give me shelter this night; I have not sold any eggs at the market, so now I have to carry them home again, and they are so heavy that I shall never be able to do it, for it is dark already."

"Indeed, my friend," said the woman, "thou comest at a very inconvenient time for me, but as thou art here it can't be helped, come in, and take a seat there on the bench by the stove." Then she placed the gossip and the basket which he carried on his back on the bench by the stove. The parson, however, and the woman were as merry as possible. At length the parson said, "Listen, my dear friend, thou canst sing beautifully, sing something to me." "Oh," said the woman, "I cannot sing now; in my young days indeed I could sing well enough, but that's all over now."

"Come," said the parson once more, "do sing some little song." At that the woman began and sang:

> "I've sent my husband away from me
> To the Gockerli hill in Italy."

Thereupon the parson sang:

> "I wish 'twas a year before he came back;
> I'd never ask him for the laurel-leaf sack.
> Hallelujah."

Then the gossip who was in the background began to sing (but I ought to tell you the peasant was called Hildebrand); and the gossip sang:

"What art thou doing, my Hildebrand dear,
There on the bench by the stove so near?
Hallelujah."

And then the peasant sang from his basket:

"All singing I ever shall hate from this day,
And here in this basket no longer I'll stay.
Hallelujah."

And he got out of the basket and cudgeled the parson out of the house.

From *Grimm's Household Tales.*

KNOIST AND HIS THREE SONS

BETWEEN Werrel and Soist there lived a man whose name was Knoist, and he had three sons. One was blind, the other lame, and the third naked. Once on a time they went into a field, and there they saw a hare. The blind one shot it, the lame one caught it, the naked one put it in his pocket. Then they came to a mighty big lake, on which there were three boats, one sailed, one sank, the third had no bottom to it. They all three got into the one with no bottom to it. Then they came to a mighty big forest in which there was a mighty big tree; in the tree was a mighty big chapel; in the chapel was a sexton made of beech wood and a boxwood parson, who dealt out holy water with cudgels.

How truly happy is that one
Who can from holy water run!

From *Grimm's Household Tales.*

DEATH'S MESSENGERS

In ancient times a giant was once traveling on a great highway when suddenly an unknown man sprang up before him and cried, "Halt, not one step farther!" "What!" cried the giant, "a creature whom I can crush between my fingers wants to block my way? Who art thou that dare speak so boldly?" "I am Death," answered the other. "No one resists me, and thou also must obey my commands." But the giant refused, and began to struggle with Death. It was a long, violent battle, but at last the giant got the upper hand and struck Death down with his fist, so that he dropped by a stone. The giant went his way, and Death lay there conquered, and so weak that he could not get up again. "What will be done now," said he, "if I stay lying here in the corner? No one will die now in the world, and it will get so full of people that they won't have room to stand beside each other."

In the meantime along the road came a young man who was strong and healthy, singing a song, and glancing around on every side. When he saw the half-fainting one, he went compassionately to him, raised him up, poured a strengthening draught out of his flask for him, and waited till he came round. "Dost thou know," said the stranger whilst he was getting up, "who I am, and who it is whom thou hast helped on his legs again?" "No," answered the youth, "I do not know thee." "I am Death," said he. "I spare no one, and can make no exception with thee; but that thou mayst see that I am grateful, I promise thee that I will not fall on thee unexpectedly, but will send my messengers to thee before I come and take thee away." "Well," said the youth, "it is something gained that I shall know when thou comest, and at any rate be safe from thee for so long."

Then he went on his way, and was lighthearted, and enjoyed himself, and lived without thought. But youth and health did not last long; soon came sickness and sorrows, which tormented him by day, and took away his rest by night. "Die I shall not," said he to himself, "for Death will send his messengers before that, but I do wish these wretched days of sickness were over." As soon as he felt himself well again he began once more to live merrily. Then one day someone tapped him on the shoulder. He looked round, and Death stood behind him, and said, "Follow me, the hour of thy departure from this world has come." "What," replied the man, "wilt thou break thy word? Didst thou not promise me that thou wouldst send thy messengers to me before coming thyself? I have seen none!" "Silence!" answered Death. "Have I not sent one messenger to thee after another? Did not fever come and smite thee, and shake thee, and cast thee down? Has dizziness not bewildered thy head? Has not gout twitched thee in all thy limbs? Did not thine ears sing? Did not toothache bite into thy cheeks? Was it not dark before thine eyes? And besides all that, has not my own brother Sleep reminded thee every night of me? Didst thou not lie by night as if thou wert already dead?"

The man could make no answer. He yielded his fate and went away with Death.

From *Grimm's Household Tales.*

HANSEL AND GRETHEL

HARD by a great forest dwelt a poor woodcutter with his wife and his two children. The boy was called Hansel and the girl Grethel. He had little to bite or to break fast with, and when a scarcity fell on the land he could no longer procure daily bread. Now when he thought this over at night in his bed, and tossed about in his anxiety, he groaned and said to his wife, "What is to become of us? How are we to feed our poor children when we no longer have anything even for ourselves?" "I'll tell you what, husband," answered the woman. "Early tomorrow morning we will take the children out into the forest to where it is the thickest. There we will light a fire for them, and give each of them one piece of bread more, and then we will go to our work and leave them alone. They will not find the way home again, and we shall be rid of them."

"No, wife," said the man, "I will not do that. How can I bear to leave my children alone in the forest? The wild animals would soon come and tear them to pieces." "Oh, thou fool!" said she, "then we must all four die of hunger! Thou mayest as well plane the planks for our coffins," and she left him no peace until he consented. "But I feel very sorry for the poor children, all the same," said the man.

The two children had also not been able to sleep for hunger, and had heard what their stepmother had said to their father. Grethel wept bitter tears and said to Hansel, "Now all is over with us." "Be quiet, sister Grethel," said Hansel, "do not be afraid; I will soon find a way to help us." And when the old folks had fallen asleep, he got up, put on his little coat, opened the door below, and crept outside. The moon shone brightly, and the little white pebbles which lay in front of the house glittered like real silver pennies. Hansel stooped and put as many of them in the little pocket of his coat as it could possibly hold. Then he went back and said to Grethel, "Do not worry, dear little sister, and sleep in peace. God will not forsake us." And he lay down again in his bed.

When day dawned, but before the sun had risen, the woman came and awoke the two children, saying, "Get up, you sluggards! we are going into the forest to fetch wood." She gave each a little piece of bread and said, "There is something for your dinner, but do not eat it up before then, for you will get nothing else." Grethel took the bread under her apron, as Hansel had the stones in his pocket. Then they all set out together on the way to the forest. When they had walked a short time Hansel stood still and looked back at the house, and did so again and again. His father said, "Hansel, what art thou looking at and why art thou lagging so?" "Ah, father," said Hansel, "I am looking at my little white cat, which is sitting up on the roof and wants to say good-by to me." The wife said, "Fool, that is not thy little cat, that is the morning sun which is shining on the chimney." Hansel, however, had not been looking back at the cat, but had been dropping the white pebbles out of his pocket onto the road.

When they had reached the middle of the forest the father said, "Now, children, pile up some wood, and I will light a fire that you may not be cold." Hansel and Grethel gathered brushwood together, as high as a little hill. The brushwood was lighted, and when the flames were burning very high the woman said, "Now, children, lay yourselves down by the fire and rest, we will go into the forest and cut some wood. When we have done, we will come back and fetch you away."

Hansel and Grethel sat by the fire, and when noon came each ate a little piece of bread, and as they heard the strokes of the wood ax they believed that their father was near. It was, however, not the ax; it was a branch which he had fastened to a withered tree which the wind was blowing backward and forward. And as they had been sitting such a long time, their eyes shut with fatigue and they fell fast asleep. When at last they awoke it was already dark night. Grethel began to cry and said, "How are we to get out of the forest now?" But Hansel comforted her and said, "Just wait a little, until the moon has risen, and then we will soon find the way." And when the full moon had risen Hansel took his little sister by the hand and followed the pebbles which shone like newly coined silver pieces and showed them the way.

They walked the whole night long and by break of day came once more to their father's house. They knocked at the door, and when the woman opened it and saw that it was Hansel and Grethel, she said, "You naughty children, why have you slept so long in the forest? We thought you were never coming back at all!" The father, however, rejoiced, for it had cut him to the heart to leave them behind alone.

Not long afterward there was once more great scarcity everywhere, and the children heard their mother saying at night to their father, "Everything is eaten again, we have one-half loaf left, and after that there is an end. The children must go; we will take them farther into the wood so that they will not find their way out again; there is no other means of saving ourselves!" The man's heart was heavy, and he thought, "It would be better for thee to share the last mouthful with thy children." The woman, however, would listen to nothing he had to say, but scolded and reproached him. He who says A must say B, and as he had yielded the first time he had to do so a second time.

The children were, however, still awake and had heard the conversation. When the old folks were asleep, Hansel again got up and wanted to go out and pick up pebbles, but the woman had locked the door, and Hansel could not get out. Nevertheless he comforted his little sister and said, "Do not cry, Grethel, go to sleep quietly. The good God will help us."

Early in the morning the woman came and took the children out of their beds. Their bit of bread was given to them, but it was still smaller than the time before. On the way into the forest Hansel crumbled his in his pocket, and often stood still and threw a morsel on the ground. "Hansel, why dost thou stop and look around?" said the father. "Go on." "I am looking back at my little pigeon which is sitting on the roof and wants to say good-by to me," answered Hansel. "Simpleton!" said the woman, "that is not the little pigeon, that is the morning sun that is shining on the chimney." Hansel, however, little by little, threw all the crumbs on the path.

The woman led the children still deeper into the forest, where they had never in their lives been before. Then a great fire was made again, and the mother said, "Just sit there, you children, and when you are tired you may sleep a little; we are going into the forest to cut wood, and in the evening when we are done, we will come and fetch you away." When it was noon Grethel shared her piece of bread with Hansel, who had scattered his by the way. Then they fell asleep, and evening came and went, but no one came to the poor children. They did not awake until it was dark night, and Hansel comforted his little sister and said, "Just wait, Grethel, until the moon rises, and then we shall see the crumbs of bread which I have strewn about. They will show us our way home again." When the moon came they set out, but they found no crumbs, for the many thousands of birds which fly about in the woods and fields had picked them all up. Hansel said to Grethel, "We shall soon find the way," but they did not find it. They walked the whole night and all the next day too, from morning till evening, but they did not get out of the forest, and were very hungry, for they had nothing to eat but two or three berries that grew on the ground. And as they were so weary that their legs would carry them no longer, they lay down beneath a tree and fell asleep.

It was now three mornings since they had left their father's house. They began to walk again, but they always got deeper into the forest, and if help did not come soon they would die of hunger and weariness. When it was midday they saw a beautiful snow-white bird sitting on a bough, and it sang so delightfully that they stood still and listened to it. And when it had finished its song it spread its wings and flew away before them, and they followed it until they reached a little house on the roof of which it alighted; and when they came quite up to the little house they saw that it was built of bread and covered with cakes, but that the windows were of clear sugar. "We will set to work on that," said Hansel, "and have a good meal. I will eat a bit of the roof, and thou, Grethel, canst eat some of the window; it will taste sweet." Hansel reached up above and broke off a little of the roof to try how it tasted, and Grethel leaned against the window and nibbled at the panes. Then a soft voice cried from the room:

"Nibble, nibble, gnaw,
Who is nibbling at my little house?"

The children answered:

"The wind, the wind,
The heaven-born wind,"

and went on eating without disturbing themselves. Hansel, who thought the roof tasted very nice, tore down a great piece of it, and Grethel pushed out the whole of one round window pane, sat down, and enjoyed herself with it. Suddenly the door opened, and a very, very old woman, who supported herself on crutches, came creeping out. Hansel and Grethel were so terribly frightened that they let fall what they had in their hands. The old woman, however, nodded her head and said, "Oh, you dear children, who has brought you here? Do come in and stay with me. No harm shall happen to you." She took them both by the hand and led them into her little house. Then good food was set before them, milk and pancakes, with sugar, apples, and nuts. Afterward two pretty little beds were covered with clean white linen, and Hansel and Grethel lay down in them and thought they were in heaven.

The old woman had only pretended to be so kind; she was in reality a wicked witch, who lay in wait for children, and had only built the little bread house in order to entice them there. When a child fell into her power, she killed it, cooked and ate it, and that was a feast day with her. Witches have red eyes and cannot see far, but they have a keen scent, like the beasts, and are aware when human beings draw near. When Hansel and Grethel came into her neighborhood she laughed maliciously and said mockingly, "I have them, they shall not escape me again!" Early in the morning before the children were awake, she was already up, and when she saw both of them sleeping and looking so pretty, with their plump red cheeks, she muttered to herself, "That will be a dainty mouthful!" Then she seized Hansel with her shriveled hand, carried him into a little stable, and shut him in behind a grated door. He might scream as he liked, it was of no use. Then she went to Grethel, shook her till she awoke, and cried, "Get up, lazy thing, fetch some water, and cook something good for thy brother, he is in the stable outside, and is to be made fat. When he is fat, I will eat him." Grethel began to weep bitterly, but it was all in vain, and she was forced to do what the wicked witch ordered.

And now the best food was cooked for poor Hansel, but Grethel got nothing but crab shells. Every morning the woman crept to the little stable and cried, "Hansel, stretch out thy finger that I may feel if thou wilt soon be fat." Hansel, however, stretched out a little bone to her, and the old woman, who had dim eyes, could not see it, and thought it was Hansel's finger, and was astonished that there was no way of fattening him. When four weeks had gone by, and Hansel still seemed to continue thin, she was seized with impatience and would not wait any longer. "Hola, Grethel," she cried to the girl, "be active and bring some water. Let Hansel be fat or lean, tomorrow I will kill him and cook him." Ah, how the poor little sister did lament when she had to fetch the water, and how her tears did flow down her cheeks! "Dear God, do help us," she cried. "If the wild beasts in the forest had but devoured us, we should at any rate have died together." "Just keep thy noise to thyself," said the old woman. "All that won't help thee at all."

Early in the morning Grethel had to go out and hang up the caldron with the water and light the fire. "We will bake first," said the woman. "I have already heated the oven and kneaded the dough." She pushed poor Grethel out to the oven, from which flames of fire were already darting. "Creep in," said the witch, "and see if it is properly heated, so that we can shut the bread in." Once Grethel was inside the witch intended to shut the oven and let her bake in it, and then eat her too. But Grethel saw what she had in mind and said, "I do not know how to do it. How do you get in?" "Silly goose," said the old woman. "The door is big enough. Just look, I can get in myself!" And she crept up and thrust her head into the oven. Then Grethel gave her a push that drove her far into it, and shut the iron door, and fastened the bolt. Oh! then she began to howl quite horribly, but Grethel ran away, and the godless witch was miserably burned to death.

Grethel, however, ran as quick as lightning to Hansel, opened his little stable, and cried, "Hansel, we are saved! The old witch is dead!" Then Hansel sprang out like a bird from its cage when the door is opened for it. How they did rejoice and embrace each other, and dance about and kiss each other! And as they had no longer any need to fear her, they went into the witch's house, and in every corner there stood chests full of pearls and jewels. "These are far better than pebbles!" said Hansel and thrust into his pockets whatever could be got in, and Grethel said, "I too will take something home with me," and filled her pinafore full. "But now we will go away," said Hansel, "that we may get out of the witch's forest."

When they had walked for two hours they came to a great body of water. "We cannot get over," said Hansel. "I see no foot plank and no bridge." "And no boat crosses either," answered Grethel,

"but a white duck is swimming there. If I ask her she will help us over." Then she cried:

> "Little duck, little duck, dost thou see
> Hansel and Grethel are waiting for thee?
> There's never a plank or bridge in sight,
> Take us across on thy back so white."

The duck came to them, and Hansel seated himself on its back and told his sister to sit by him. "No," replied Grethel, "that will be too heavy for the little duck; she shall take us across one after the other." The good little duck did so, and when they were once safely across and had walked for a short time the forest seemed to be more and more familiar to them, and at length they saw from afar their father's house. Then they began to run, rushed into the parlor, and threw themselves into their father's arms. The man had not known one happy hour since he had left the children in the forest; the woman, however, was dead. Grethel emptied her pinafore until pearls and precious stones rolled around the room, and Hansel threw one handful after another out of his pocket to add to them. Then all anxiety was at an end, and they lived together in perfect happiness.

From *Grimm's Household Tales.*

PETER KLAUS

IN THE village of Sittendorf, at the foot of a mountain, lived Peter Klaus, a goatherd who was in the habit of pasturing his flock upon the near-by Kyffhäusen Hills. Toward evening he generally let them browse upon a green plot surrounded by an old ruined wall, from which he could take a muster of his whole flock.

During one period he observed that one of his prettiest goats usually disappeared soon after its arrival at this spot and did not join the fold again until late in the evening. He watched her again and again, and at last found that she slipped through a gap in the old wall. He followed her and discovered that the gap led into a passage which widened into a cavern. When he entered the cavern he found the goat busy picking up oats that fell through some crevices above. He looked up, shook his head at this odd shower, and at first could find no explanation for it.

At length he heard over his head the neighing and stamping of horses; he listened, and concluded that the oats must have fallen through a manger where horses were being fed. The poor goatherd was sadly at a loss to know what horses were doing in that uninhabited part of the mountain, but so it was, for a groom soon made his appearance, and, without saying a word, beckoned him to follow. Peter obeyed and followed him up some steps which led into an open courtyard surrounded by old walls. Next to this was a still more spacious ravine, surrounded by rocky heights and overhung with trees and shrubs which admitted only a kind of twilight. Peter continued on and came at last to a smoothshaven green, where twelve ancient knights, none of whom spoke a word, were engaged in playing ninepins. His guide now beckoned to Peter to pick up the ninepins and then went his way. At first, trembling in every limb, Peter did not venture to disobey, but after a time he began to cast stolen glances at the players, and saw at once that their long beards and slashed doublets belonged to a fashion long past. By degrees his looks grew bolder, and, noting among other things a tankard near him filled with wine whose aroma was excellent, he took a draught. It seemed to give him renewed life; and whenever he began to feel tired, he applied with fresh ardor to the tankard. Finally it overpowered him, and he fell asleep.

When he opened his eyes again he found himself on the grassy plot once more, in the same old spot where he was in the habit of feeding his goats. He rubbed his eyes and looked round but could see neither dog nor flock. This surprised him, but he was even more surprised at the long rank grass that grew about him, and at trees and bushes which he had never before seen. He shook his head and walked a little farther, looking for the old sheep path and the hillocks and road where he used daily to drive his flock; but he could find no trace of them. Yet he saw the village just before him: and it was undoubtedly the same Sittendorf. Scratching his head, he hastened down the hill to inquire after his flock.

All the people whom he met going into the village were strangers to him, and all were strangely dressed and spoke in a way different from that of his old neighbors. When he asked about his goats, these people only stared at him and fixed their eyes upon his chin. He put his hand unconsciously to his mouth, and to his great surprise found that he had grown a beard at least a foot long. He now began to think that both he and all the world around him were in a dream; and yet he knew the mountain he had just come down was the Kyffhäusen. And there were the cottages with their gardens and grassy plots, much as he had left them. Besides, when he asked the lads who had collected round him what place it was, they answered that it was Sittendorf.

Still shaking his head, he went farther into the village to look for his own house. He found it, but greatly altered, and for the worse: a strange goatherd in an old tattered frock lay before the door, and near him lay Peter's old dog, which only growled and showed its teeth when Peter tried to call him. He went through the entrance which had once had a door, but all within was empty and deserted.

He staggered out of the house like a drunken man, and called for his wife and children by name; but no one listened and no one gave answer.

Soon, however, a crowd of women and children gathered round the stranger with the long hoary beard and asked him what it was he wanted. Peter thought it was such a strange kind of thing to stand before his own house and inquire for his own wife and children, as well as about himself, that, evading these questions he asked for an old neighbor, Kurt Steffen, the blacksmith. Most of the spectators only stared at him blankly, till an old woman at last said, "Why he has been in Sachsenburg these twelve years."

"Where then is Valentine Meier, the tailor?" Peter asked.

"The Lord rest his soul!" cried another old woman leaning upon her crutch. "He has been lying more than these fifteen years in a house he will never leave."

Then Peter recognized in these women two who had been young neighbors of his. They seemed to have grown old with incredible suddenness, but he had little inclination to inquire further.

At this moment there appeared, making her way through the crowd of spectators, a sprightly young woman with a year-old baby in her arms and with a girl of about four holding her hand. All three bore a striking resemblance to the wife he was seeking.

"What are your names?" he cried out in surprise.

"Mine is Maria," the woman said.

"And your father's?" continued Peter.

"God rest his soul! Peter Klaus, to be sure. It is now twenty years since we were all looking for him day and night upon the Kyffhäusen—after his flock came home without him. I was then," continued the woman, "only seven years old."

The goatherd could no longer contain himself. "I am Peter Klaus," he cried, "Peter and no other." And he took his daughter's child and kissed it. The spectators were struck dumb with astonishment, until first one and then another began to say, "Yes, indeed, that is Peter Klaus! Welcome, good neighbor, after twenty years' absence, welcome home."

From a tale by Otmar, translated by Thomas Roscoe in *The German Novelists* (London, 1826).

THE SCHILDBÜRGER BUILD A COUNCIL HOUSE

THE FIRST folly of the boors of Schilda was to build a council house without windows. When they entered it, and, to use the words of the nursery ballad, "saw they could not see," they were greatly puzzled to account for such a state of things; and having in vain gone outside and examined the building to find why the inside was dark, they determined to hold a council upon the subject on the following day.

At the time appointed they assembled, each bringing with him a torch, which, when he seated himself, he stuck in his hat. After

much discussion, one genius, brighter than the rest, decided that they could not see for lack of daylight and that they ought on the morrow to carry in as much of it as possible. Accordingly, the next day, when the sun shone, all the sacks, bags, boxes, baskets, tubs, and pans of the village were filled with beams of light and carefully carried into the council house and emptied there, but without noticeable effect. After this they removed the roof, following the advice of a traveler, whom they rewarded amply for the suggestion. This plan served their purposes famously during the summer, but when the rains of winter fell and they were forced to replace the roof, they found the house just as dark as ever.

Again they met, again they stuck their torches in their hats, but to no purpose, until one of them, about to leave the building, was groping his way along the wall when a ray of light fell through a crevice and upon his beard. He stared at it for a time and finally suggested that it was possible they might get daylight in by making a window.

After much deliberation and much stroking of beards the others agreed that this might be worth trying.

From *Book of Noodles*, by W. A. Clouston (London: Elliot Stock, 1888).

TYLL ULENSPIEGEL

The Tale of a Merry Dance

As the summers and winters passed, Tyll's mind grew in wit and mischievousness. One day, when still very young, he taught his playmates and the mean fellows of the town a lesson they remembered for a long time.

It happened this way.

At the end of the street of the bright yellow-and-blue-painted houses where Tyll lived, there was a river that had an old willow tree on each bank. Many an afternoon Tyll passed the hot hours in their shade, wondering why they had been planted there, and one day he guessed the reason.

Why, for me to string a stout rope from one tree to the other and learn to be a rope-dancer like those I've seen at the market fairs! That is a fine profession for a fellow like me. It's little work and brings good money, with which I could buy many things.

He found a rope, and in the early morning hours, when all good children were still asleep and the birds were telling one another the dreams of the night, he strung it tight across from the willow on one bank to the willow on the other and practiced hard at the game. After a time he could walk across the river, high in the air, as well as anyone who walked a rope for gain or fame.

Sunday that week, soon after vespers, when all the townspeople were out along the river to breathe the fresh air, he too came, with his rope. He tied it across the trees, hallooing and shouting to gain the eyes of the passers-by, and then he danced, skipped, leaped, and capered on it, much to the amusement of the good folk and their wives and children.

When he had finished he passed his little cap among the good citizens, and many a one dropped in a coin or three for the pleasure Tyll had given them. He was so happy with this that he announced he would treat them to a finer spectacle next Sunday.

Now many of Tyll's playfellows looked on with green envy. They were jealous because he had gained money and fame, while they had neither. So they decided to clip his wings a little by spoiling his trick the next time.

Sunday after vespers came, and so did Tyll, true to his promise. But while he was tying the knots tightly, one fellow cut the rope, but only half through.

Tyll mounted and began dancing. No sooner had he taken the first leap than the rope broke and he fell into the water.

Tyll came ashore all wet, and everyone laughed and jeered, especially those who had caused his fall.

They shouted, "Ho, there, trickster! Where to? To teach the fish in the river to dance? Ho, ho, ho! Look at him now, he who would be more clever than the rest of us!"

Tyll shook himself like a dog and said to the jeering cowards who were running away in fear of a beating from him, "Don't run so fast! Don't be afraid! Come next Sunday. I'll dance again and share with you the money I earn."

That Sunday after vespers all the scamps of the town who knew Tyll, and many who did not, came to share his profits. They strung the rope for him and guarded it like a treasure so that no mishap would come to it. All the townspeople were there too.

Tyll, dressed this time with cap and bells and wearing a leather apron, was all ready. But before climbing on the rope he spoke, "Give me your shoes and I promise to dance with them no matter how large or small they are. If I don't, you may have all the money I earn; if I do, you get none."

"How can he dance on a rope with shoes that do not fit him?" they said among themselves. "We'll give him our shoes and take all his money. You can have our shoes," they shouted, and each and every one already heard the jingling of the coins in his leather bag.

Off went the shoes, and Tyll took them and put them in his leather apron. Then he climbed up on the rope.

"Let us see your trick," they said.

"You'll see it soon enough," he replied.

So they did, but not the kind they had expected. For with the shoes in his apron, not on his feet, Tyll began hopping and leaping and dancing. The shoes tumbled and tossed up and down until they were all mixed up, helter-skelter.

"Ho, there," shouted the boys, "you have lost your bet. We knew you were boasting and couldn't dance with our shoes. We get all the money."

"And what am I doing with your shoes, if not dancing with them? Blind moles! I said I would dance *with* them; I did not say I would dance *in* them. Am I not dancing with them right now?" He leaped high up, tossing the shoes even higher and catching them back in his apron.

"What do I see now?" he cried. "Eyes popping like frogs? If you don't like your wager, it's not too late to call it off. Here, take your shoes!" and he flung the apron full of shoes onto the green grass.

Each one rushed to find his own, but since the shoes were all mixed up there were soon strong arguments with words and stronger arguments with fists.

Meanwhile Tyll leaped down and ran off before anyone could see him. For a whole week he kept to his house, because those on whom he had played this trick were waiting to catch him and pay him back in kind. But they never did.

Tyll Proves to Fools How Great Is Their Folly

Tyll wandered this way and that way at his whim and fancy until one day he came to the well-known city of Magdeburg. He stayed there a long time and many of the people became his friends, for he was always supplying them with good laughter by quick talk and clever pranks; in return for this pleasure they gave him plenty of food. Finally the rich citizens, hearing of him, and not wanting to be left out, asked him to come to the council. When they saw that he was only a young fellow they told him they would not think he was a jester until he would prove it by some rare marvel or new trick.

"And so you don't believe, good fat citizens!" he thought to himself, "and I must do your bidding as if I were your slave. You would never even have noticed me if all the people had not spoken of me—now you doubt their word. Do you believe in anything but your money bags? Well, since you value them so much, you will have to pay me for giving you proof, and I will teach you a little lesson besides!"

He stood silent for a long time, thinking, and then he said, "I will show you a rare trick which you will remember for a long time. Only you must pay me, for it will be a valuable entertainment and it will teach you a lesson no university could teach.

"Masters, if you pay me twenty gold pieces," he continued, "I will fly without wings from the steeple of the town hall to the market place. I want the money in advance, for you can see I risk breaking my neck to entertain you."

Twenty gold pieces made a big sum, but the rich citizens figured that they would get it back quickly—if not from Tyll, then from a new kind of tax. They paid him the money and fed him for three days to boot, for he said he needed that much time to get ready for the undertaking.

The whole city had heard about it, and so at the time set the townsfolk were packed in the market place like herrings. The commanders came with their *Landsknechte*, which was the name then given to the soldiers, who pushed many of the onlookers back to make room for the rich. Soon Tyll was high up on the steeple, looking down on young and old, tall and short, their eyes and mouths wide open to see a man flying through the air.

Tyll looked at them a long time, shook his head solemnly, wiggled his ears, made a face like a baboon, and moved his arms up and down a few times. Then he stuck his thumbs in his ears, waved his hands, danced a little turn or three, began roaring with laughter, and shouted, "Noble citizens of Magdeburg, I thought I was the only fool in your benighted city, but now I see a city full of them before me. If all of you together who run the affairs of this place and all those who are rich had told me that you would fly through the air without wings or feathers, I would not have believed you, yet all of you wise men believed me, who am supposed to be only a clown. How could I fly, having no wings like a bird or a goose?"

He bid them a merry good day and was out of sight. The people went home laughing, but the councilmen and the rich men who had given the money were very angry. Yet they were ashamed to open their mouths, to show openly that a jester had made a jest of them before all.

Word, Wit, and Merry Game Bring Money, Joy, and Pleasant Fame

When Tyll was in Poland, King Casimir ruled, and a merry monarch he was. Instead of having one court jester, he had two, and when he heard Tyll was in the land he invited him also to his palace.

Now, the king was proud of his jesters and knew a trick or three himself. Often they argued, and Tyll was always ready with a quick answer, particularly when it came to answering the jesters. So one day the king decided to test which was the cleverest of the three.

There was a great gathering of nobles in the court when the king offered twenty gold pieces and a fine new coat to the one of the three who could make the greatest wish. All the court applauded the generosity of their ruler.

"And," added he, "the wish must be made right now before me and all the court."

Said the first jester, "I wish the heaven above us were nothing but paper and the sea nothing but ink so that I could write the figures of how much money should be mine."

Spoke the second, "I want as many towers and castles as there are stars in heaven so that I might keep all the money that my fellow court jesters here would have."

It was now Tyll's turn. He opened his mouth and spoke. "I would want the two here to make out their wills, leaving their money to me, and that you, Your Majesty, would order them to the gallows right after."

The king and all his court laughed merrily at this, and Tyll won the coat and the money.

Now you know how a quick and merry answer can bring one fame and fortune.

Tyll's Last Prank

There has always been a great dispute as to which is more glorious: to live merrily or to die merrily. But what is most glorious of all is to live and die merrily. This was Tyll's great fortune, and it is not given to many. And so, since I have told you of Tyll's wonderful birth, I will now tell you of his wonderful death. I know you will agree with me that nothing like it ever happened before.

When Tyll became ill and felt his end approaching, he went to an apothecary for some herbs. The man said that he loved Tyll and asked him to stay in his house. But the real reason he asked Tyll to stay in his house was that he thought Tyll was rich and he would inherit Tyll's money. So he treated him well, even though Tyll played the apothecary many a trick, for always the man hoped to be repaid with the jester's good gold.

One day Tyll felt that the end was at hand. He asked the apothecary to call his confessor first, and he made his confession. Then he called the town clerk and spoke to him. Finally he called for parchment to make out his will. In it he left one-third of his possessions to the apothecary, his friend; one-third to the town; and one-third to the confessor. For this he was to be buried on holy ground and masses were to be read for his soul.

He wrote that his possessions were buried in an iron chest, told them where it was, and gave each one a key. He also ordered them not to open the chest until four weeks after his death. Then he signed the parchment and put on it an owl and a mirror. And he died with a smile on his face.

People came from far and from near to see for the last time this jester who had become famous for his clever wit and merry pranks; and when they saw the waxen-colored face they wept at the folly of man.

Masses were read, there was music and preaching, and altogether there was a great to-do, which must have given Tyll much joy in the other world.

II

After three days Tyll was put in a coffin and brought to the cemetery, followed by a great crowd of mourning people. Prayers were read and words were spoken by many. Then the coffin was placed on two ropes, to be lowered into the grave. But no sooner were the ropes down a little than the one at the feet broke and the coffin slid down upright, so that the dead Tyll was standing on his feet instead of lying on his back as buried persons usually do.

The crowd marveled at that, and many said, "Let him stand this way; he was a queer fellow when he was alive on this earth and no doubt he wishes to remain the same under the earth."

So they covered him with the earth and put on it a stone that bore the sign of the owl and the mirror, which means that he was wise and always ready to show to all men their true selves.

III

Four weeks after Tyll was buried the apothecary, the priest, and the town clerk dug up the chest and opened it. Picture their faces when they found three compartments each filled with earth and stones. On the top there was a bit of parchment, and it read: "One-third: for my friend who kept me only because he thought I would pay him for it. I am rewarding him with earth and stones, which contain all the riches of the world. For my confessor the stones to help him repair the church, which is badly in need of it, and earth to plant food for the poor according to the word of God. The stones for the town as a remembrance for the judges and bailiffs who are often hard as stones. And the bit of earth so that they may remember that people need earth to live decently." At the end he had signed himself as usual.

The three could not say a word, for there were many people around and every word in the parchment was true as heaven and could not be argued. Whereupon they went home quietly.

In this way Tyll tried, even after his death, to help people to see their follies, to act more wisely and more justly, and so live according to the word of God.

From *Tyll Ulenspiegel's Merry Pranks,* retold by M. A. Jagendorf (New York: Vanguard Press, 1938).

Greek

Cupid and Psyche

THE ANCIENT Greek and Roman heroes, gods, and goddesses—the jealous Juno, for instance—are much more human than their Norse counterparts, but they move about in an airy sphere, far off in the empyrean. It is not surprising, therefore, that it was once thought that they were primitive interpretations of solar phenomena. Later, when this theory had been reduced, or extended, to absurdity, it was argued that they were vestiges of primitive religions, the shapely shells of discarded beliefs. Today it is said that in the form in which we know them they are the work of conscious artists—a far cry from anything primitive.

But whatever their origin, it is doubtful whether any collection of stories has produced a group of figures as enduringly significant as these of the Greco-Roman pantheon. Odysseus journeying among dangers and temptations, Icarus aspiring nobly and tragically, Narcissus, the victim of obsession with self, Prometheus, Hercules, Philomela, Pygmalion—each is a symbol at once Attic and timeless. The Grecian tales alone have endowed myth with the meaning of an imaginative creation embodying sublimely the dreams and visions of the race. They have given to language many of its richest images and to artists the molds of some of the greatest works of imagination.

The Greeks were masters of fable as well as myth. Traditionally their oldest fables have been attributed to Aesop, who is supposed to have been an Athenian slave of the fifth century B.C. But even if we concede that there ever was an Aesop, some of his fables undoubtedly go back well before his time and some were first attributed to him centuries after his death and after they had been made current by such other fabulists as Babrius (in Greek verse) and Phaedrus (in Latin). The great popularity of fables is easy to explain: they fuse story, wit, and wisdom in the simplest of narrative forms. And such is their nature that a Hottentot storyteller takes to them as readily, and sometimes as successfully, as a La Fontaine.

NOBODY AND POLYPHEMUS

When the blue hills of the Lotus-land had faded away in the far distance, the ships of Odysseus went on merrily with a fresh breeze; and the men thought that they would soon come to rocky Ithaca, where their homes were. But Athena was angry with Odysseus, and she asked Poseidon, the lord of the sea, to send a great storm and scatter his ships. So the wind arose, and the waters of the sea began to heave and swell, and the sky was black with clouds and rain. Many days and nights the storm raged fiercely; and when it was over, Odysseus could see only four or five of all the ships which had sailed with him from Troy. The ships were drenched with the waves which had broken over them, and the men were wet and cold and tired; and they were glad indeed when they saw an island far away. So they sat down on the benches and took the great oars and rowed the ships toward the shore; and as they came near they saw that the island was very beautiful with cliffs and rocks, and bays for ships to take shelter from the sea. Then they rowed into one of these quiet bays, where the water was always calm and where there was no need to let down an anchor or to tie the ship by ropes to the seashore, for the ship lay there quite still of itself. At the head of the bay a stream of fresh water trickled down from the cliffs and ran close to the opening of a large cave, and near the cave some willow trees drooped their branches over the stream which ran down toward the sea.

So they made haste to go on shore; and when they had landed they saw fine large plains on which the corn might grow, but no one had taken the trouble to sow the seed; and sloping hills for the grapes to ripen on the vines, but none were planted on them. And Odysseus marveled at the people who lived there, because they had no corn and no vines, and he could see no houses, but only sheep and goats feeding on the hillsides. So he took his bow and arrows and shot many of the goats, and he and his men lay down on the ground and had a merry meal, and drank the rich red wine which they had brought with them from the ship. And when they had finished eating and drinking they fell asleep and did not wake up till the morning showed its rosy light in the eastern sky.

Then Odysseus said that he would take some of his men and go to see who lived on the island, while the others remained in the ship close to the seashore. So they set out, and at last they came to the mouth of a great cave, where many sheep and goats were penned up in large folds; but they could see no one in the cave or anywhere near it; and they waited a long while, but no one came. So they lit a fire and made themselves merry as they ate the cheese and drank the milk which was stored up round the sides of the cave.

Presently they heard a great noise of heavy feet stamping on the ground, and they were so frightened that they ran inside the cave and crouched down at the end of it. Nearer and nearer came the Cyclops, and his tread almost made the earth shake. At last in he came, with many dry logs of wood on his back; and in came all the sheep, which he milked every evening; but the rams and the goats stayed outside. But if Odysseus and his men were afraid when they saw Polyphemus the Cyclops come in, they were much more afraid when he took up a great stone, which was almost as big as the mouth of the cave, and set it up against it for a door. Then the men whispered to Odysseus and said, "Did we not beg and pray you not to come into the cave? But you would not listen to us. And now how are we to get out again? Why, two-and-twenty wagons would not be able to take away that huge stone from the mouth of the cave." But they were shut in now, and there was no use in thinking of their folly for coming in.

So there they lay, crouching in the corner of the cave, and trembling with fear lest Polyphemus should see them. But the Cyclops went on milking all the sheep, and then he put the milk into the bowls round the sides of the cave, and lit the fire to cook his meal. As the flames shot up from the burning wood to the roof of the cave, it showed him the forms of Odysseus and his companions where they lay huddled together in the corner; and he cried out to them with a loud voice, "Who are you that dare to come into the cave of Polyphemus? Are you come to rob me of my sheep, or my cheese and milk that I keep here?"

Then Odysseus said, "No, we are not come to do you harm: we are Achaeans who have been fighting at Troy to bring back Helen, whom Paris stole away from Sparta, and we went there with the great king Agamemnon, whom everybody knows. We are on our way home to Ithaca; but Poseidon sent a great storm, because Athena was angry with me; and almost all our ships have been sunk in the sea or broken to pieces on the rocks."

When he had finished speaking, Polyphemus frowned savagely and said, "I know nothing of Agamemnon, or Paris, or Helen"; and he seized two of the men, and broke their heads against the stones, and cooked them for his dinner. That day Polyphemus ate a huge meal and drank several bowls full of milk; and after that he fell fast asleep. Then, as he lay there snoring in his heavy sleep, Odysseus thought how easy it would be to plunge the sword into his breast and kill him; and he was just going to do it when he thought of the great stone which Polyphemus had placed at the mouth of the cave; and he knew that if Polyphemus were killed no one else could move away the stone, and so they would all die shut up in that dismal place.

So the hours of the night went wearily on, but neither Odysseus nor his friends could sleep, for they thought of the men whom Polyphemus had eaten, and how they would very likely be eaten up themselves. At last they could tell, from the dim light which came in between the top of the stone and the roof of the cave, that the morning was come; and soon Polyphemus awoke and milked all the sheep again; and when he had done this he went to the end of the cave and took up two more men and killed and ate them. Then he took down the great stone from the mouth of the cave and drove all the cattle out to graze on the soft grass on the hills; and Odysseus began to hope that they might be able to get away before Polyphemus came back. But the Cyclops was not so silly as to let them go, for, as soon as the cattle were gone out, he took up the huge stone again as easily as if it had been a little pebble and put it up against the mouth of the cave; and there were Odysseus and his friends shut up again as fast as ever.

Then Odysseus began to think more and more how they were to get away, for if they stayed there they would all soon be killed if Polyphemus went on eating four of them every day. At last, near the sheepfold, he saw a club which Polyphemus was going to use as a walking stick. It was the whole trunk of an olive tree, fresh and green, for he had only just cut it and left it to dry, that he might carry it about when it was fit for use. There it lay like the mast of a ship, which twenty men could hardly have lifted; and Odysseus cut off a bit from the end, as much as a man could carry, and told the men to bring it to a very sharp point; and when they had done this he hardened it in the fire, and then hid it away till Polyphemus should come home. By and by, when the sun was sinking down, they heard the terrible tramp of his feet and felt the earth shake beneath his tread. Then the great stone was taken down from the mouth of the cave, and in he came, driving the sheep and goats and the rams also before him, for this time he let nothing stay outside. So he milked the sheep and the goats, as he had done the day before; and then he killed two more men and began to eat them for his supper. Then Odysseus went toward him with a bottle full of wine and said, "Drink this wine, Polyphemus; it will make your supper taste much nicer; I have brought it to you because I want you to do me some kindness in return." So the Cyclops stretched out his hand to take the wine, and he drank it off greedily and asked for more. "Give me more of this honey-sweet wine," he said; "surely no grapes on this earth could ever give such wine as this: tell me your name, for I should like to do you a kindness for giving me such wine as this." Then Odysseus said, "O Cyclops, I hope you will not forget to give me what you have promised: my name is Nobody." And Polyphemus said, "Very well, I shall eat up Nobody last of all, when I have eaten up all his companions; and this is the kindness which I mean to do for him." But by this time he was so stupid with all that he had been eating and drinking that he could say no more, but fell on his back fast asleep; and his heavy snoring sounded through the whole of the cave.

Then Odysseus cried to his friends, "Now is the time; come and help me, and we will punish this Cyclops for all that he has done." So he took the piece of the olive tree, which had been made sharp, and put it into the fire, till it almost burst into a flame; and then he and two of his men went and stood over Polyphemus and pushed the burning wood into his great eye as hard and as far down as they could. It was a terrible sight to see; but the Cyclops was so stupid and heavy in sleep that at first he could scarcely stir; but presently he gave a great groan, so that Odysseus and his people started back in a fright and crouched down at the end of the cave. And then the Cyclops put out his hand and drew the burning wood from his eye, and threw it from him in a rage, and roared out for help to his friends who lived on the hills round about. His roar was as deep and loud as the roar of twenty lions; and the other Cyclops wondered when they heard him shouting out so loud, and they said, "What can be the matter with Polyphemus? We never heard him make such a noise before. Let us go and see if he wants any help." So they went to the cave and stood outside the great stone which shut it in, listening to his terrible bellowings; and when they did not stop, they shouted to him and asked him what was the matter. "Why have you waked us up in the middle of the night with all this noise when we were sleeping comfortably? Is anyone taking away your sheep and goats, or killing you by craft and force?" And Polyphemus said, "Nobody, my friends, is killing me by craft and force." When the others heard this they were angry and said, "Well, then, if nobody is killing you, why do you roar so? If you are ill, you must bear it as best you can and ask our father Poseidon to make you well again"; and then they walked off to their beds and left Polyphemus to make as much noise as he pleased.

It was of no use that he went on shouting: no one came to him any more; and Odysseus laughed because he had tricked him so cunningly by calling himself Nobody. So Polyphemus got up at last, moaning and groaning with the dreadful pain, and groped his way with his hands against the sides of the cave until he came to the door. Then he took down the great stone and sat with his arms stretched out wide; and he said to himself, "Now I shall be sure to catch them, for no one can get out without passing me."

But Odysseus was too clever for him yet; for he went quietly and fastened the great rams of Polyphemus together with long bands of willow. He tied them together by threes, and under the stomach of the middle one he tied one of his men, until he had fastened them all up safely. Then he went and caught hold of the largest ram of all, and clung on with his hands to the thick wool underneath his stomach; and so they waited in a great fright, lest after all the giant might catch and kill them. At last the pale light of the morning came into the eastern sky, and very soon the sheep and the goats began to go out of the cave. Then Polyphemus passed his hands over the backs of all the sheep as they passed by, but he did not feel the willow bands, because their wool was long and thick, and he never thought that anyone would be tied up underneath their stomachs. Last of all came the great ram to which Odysseus was clinging; and when Polyphemus passed his hand over his back, he stroked him gently and said, "Is there something the matter with you too, as there is with your master? You were always the first to go out of the cave, and now today for the first time you are the last. I am sure that that horrible Nobody is at the bottom of all this. Ah, old ram, perhaps it is that you are sorry for your master, whose eye Nobody has put out! I wish you could speak like a man and tell me where he is. If I could but catch him I would take care that he never got away again, and then I should have some comfort for all the evil which Nobody has done to me."

So he sent the ram on. And when he had gone a little way from the cave, Odysseus got up from under the ram and went and untied all his friends, and very glad they were to be free once more; but they could not help grieving when they thought of the men whom Polyphemus had killed. But Odysseus told them to make haste and drive as many of the sheep and goats as they could to the ships. So they drove them down to the shore and hurried them into the ships and began to row away; and soon they would have been out of the reach of the Cyclops if Odysseus could only have held his tongue. But he was so angry himself that he thought he would like to make Polyphemus also still more angry; so he shouted to him and said, "Cruel Cyclops, did you think that you would not be punished for

eating up my friends? Is this the way in which you receive strangers who have been tossed about by many storms upon the sea?"

Then Polyphemus was more furious than ever, and he broke off a great rock from the mountain and hurled it at Odysseus. On it came, whizzing through the air, and fell just in front of his ship, and the water was dashed up all over it; and there was a great heaving of the sea, which almost carried them back to the land. Then they began to row again with all their might; but still, when they had got about twice as far as they were before, Odysseus could not help shouting out a few more words to Polyphemus. So he said, "If anyone asks you how you lost your eye, remember, O Cyclops, to say that you were made blind by Odysseus, the plunderer of cities, the son of Laertes, who lives in Ithaca."

Terrible indeed was the fury of Polyphemus when he heard this, and he said, "Now I remember how the wise Telemus used to tell me that a man would come here named Odysseus, who would put my eye out. But I thought he would have been some great strong man, almost as big as myself; and this is a miserable little wretch whom I could almost hold in my hand if I caught him. But stay, Odysseus, and I will show you how I thank you for your kindness, and I will ask my father Poseidon to send you a pleasant storm to toss you about upon the dark sea."

Then Polyphemus took up a bigger rock than ever and hurled it high into the air with all his might. But this time it fell just behind the ship of Odysseus: up rose the water and drenched Odysseus and all his people and almost sunk the ship under the sea. But it only sent them farther out of the reach of the Cyclops. And though he hurled more rocks after them, they now fell far behind in the sea and did them no harm. But even when they had rowed a long way they could still see Polyphemus standing on the high cliffs and shaking his hands at them in rage and pain. But no one came to help him for all his shouting, because he had told his friends that Nobody was doing him harm.

From *Tales of Ancient Greece* by Sir George W. Cox (London: Longmans, Green and Company, 1868).

TANTALUS

BENEATH the mighty rocks of Sipylos stood the palace of Tantalus, the Phrygian king, gleaming with the blaze of gold and jewels. Its burnished roofs glistened from afar like the rays which dance on ruffled waters. Far and wide was known the name of the mighty chieftain, who was wiser than all the sons of mortal men; for his wife Euryanassa, they said, came of the race of the undying gods, and to Tantalus Zeus had given the power of Helios, that he might know his secret counsels and see into the hidden things of the earth and air and sea. Many a time, so the people said, he held converse with Zeus himself in his home on high Olympus; and day by day his wealth increased, his flocks and herds multiplied exceedingly, and in his fields the golden corn waved like a sunlit sea.

But, as the years rolled round, there were dark sayings spread abroad that the wisdom of Tantalus was turned to craft, and that his wealth and power were used for evil ends. Men said that he had sinned like Prometheus the Titan, and had stolen from the banquet hall of Zeus the food and drink of the gods and given them to mortal men. And tales yet more strange were told, how that Pandareos brought to him the hound which Rhea placed in the cave of Dicte to guard the child Zeus, and how, when Hermes bade him yield up the dog, Tantalus laughed him to scorn and said, "Dost thou ask me for the hound which guarded Zeus in the days of his childhood? It were as well to ask me for the unseen breeze which sighs through the groves of Sipylos."

Then, last of all, men spake in whispers of a sin yet more fearful which Tantalus had sinned, and the tale was told that Zeus and all the gods came down from Olympus to feast in his banquet hall, and how, when the red wine sparkled in the golden goblets, Tantalus placed savory meat before Zeus and bade him eat of a costly food, and, when the feast was ended, told him that in the dish had lain the limbs of the child Pelops, whose sunny smile had gladdened the hearts of mortal men. Then came the day of vengeance, for Zeus bade Hermes bring back Pelops again from the kingdom of Hades to the land of living men, and on Tantalus was passed a doom which should torment him forever and ever. In the shadowy region where wander the ghosts of men, Tantalus, they said, lay prisoned in a beautiful garden, gazing on bright flowers and glistening fruits and laughing waters; but for all that his tongue was parched, and his limbs were faint with hunger. No drop of water might cool his lips, no luscious fruit might soothe his agony. If he bowed his head to drink, the water fled away; if he stretched forth his hand to pluck the golden apples, the branches vanished like mists before the face of the rising sun; and in place of ripe fruits glistening among green leaves, a mighty rock beetled above his head as though it must fall and grind him to powder. Wherefore men say, when the cup of pleasure is dashed from the lips of those who would drink of it, that on them has fallen the doom of the Phrygian Tantalus.

From *Tales of Ancient Greece.*

MEDEA

FAR AWAY in the Colchian land, where her father Aeëtes was king, the wise maiden Medea saw and loved Jason, who had come in the ship *Argo* to search for the golden fleece. To her Zeus had given a wise and cunning heart, and she had power over the hidden things of the earth, and nothing in the broad sea could withstand her might. She had spells to tame the monsters which vex the children of men, and to bring back youth to the wrinkled face and the tottering limbs of the old. But the spells of Eros were mightier still, and the wise maiden forgot her cunning as she looked on the fair countenance of Jason; and she said within herself that she would make him conqueror in his struggle for the golden fleece, and go with him to be his wife in the far-off western land. So King Aeëtes brought up in vain the fire-breathing bulls that they might scorch Jason as he plowed the land with the dragon's teeth; and in vain from these teeth sprang up the harvest of armed men ready for strife and bloodshed. For Medea had anointed the body of Jason with ointment, so that the fiery breath of the bulls hurt him not; and by her bidding he cast a stone among the armed men, and they fought with one another for the stone till all lay dead upon the ground. Still King Aeëtes would not give to him the golden fleece; and the heart of Jason was cast down till Medea came to him and bade him follow her. Then she led him to a hidden dell where the dragon guarded the fleece, and she laid her spells on the monster and brought a heavy sleep upon his eyes, while Jason took the fleece and hastened to carry it on board the ship *Argo*.

So Medea left her father's house and wandered with Jason into many lands—to Iolcus, to Athens, and to Argos. And wherever she went, men marveled at her for her wisdom and her beauty; but as they looked on her fair face and listened to her gentle voice, they knew not the power of the maiden's wrath if anyone should do her wrong. So she dwelt at Iolcus in the house of Pelias, who had sent forth Jason to look for the golden fleece that he might not be king in his stead; and the daughters of Pelias loved the beautiful Medea, for they dreamed not that she had sworn to avenge on Pelias the wrong which he had done to Jason. Craftily she told the daughters of Pelias of the power of her spells, which could tame the fire-breathing bulls, and lull the dragon to sleep, and bring back the brightness of youth to the withered cheeks of the old. And the daughters of Pelias said to her, "Our father is old, and his limbs are weak and tottering; show us how once more he can be made young." Then Medea took a ram and cut it up and put its limbs into a caldron, and when she had boiled them on the hearth there came forth a lamb; and she said, "So shall your father be brought back again to youth and strength if ye will do to him as I have done to the ram;

and when the time is come I will speak the words of my spell and the change shall be accomplished." So the daughters of Pelias followed her counsel and put the body of their father into the caldron; and, as it boiled on the hearth, Medea said, "I must go up to the housetop and look forth on the broad heaven that I may know the time to speak the words of my charm." And the fire waxed fiercer and fiercer, but Medea gazed on at the bright stars and came not down from the housetop till the limbs of Pelias were consumed.

Then a look of fierce hatred passed over her face, and she said, "Daughters of Pelias, ye have slain your father, and I go with Jason to the land of Argos." So thither she sped with him in her dragon chariot which bore them to the house of King Creon.

Long time she abode in Argos, rejoicing in the love of Jason and at the sight of her children who were growing up in strength and beauty. But Jason cared less and less for the wise and cunning Medea, for she seemed not to him as one of the daughters of men; and he loved more to look on Glauce, the daughter of the king, till at last he longed to be free from the love and the power of Medea.

Then men talked in Argos of the love of Jason for the beautiful Glauce; and Medea heard how he was going to wed another wife. Once more her face grew dark with anger, as when she left the daughters of Pelias mourning for their father; and she vowed a vow that Jason should repent of his great treachery. But she hid her anger within her heart, and her eye was bright and her voice was soft and gentle as she spake to Jason and said, "They tell me that thou art to wed the daughter of Creon; I had not thought thus to lose the love for which I left my father's house and came with thee to the land of strangers. Yet do I chide thee not, for it may be thou canst not love the wise Colchian maiden like the soft daughters of the Argive land; and yet thou knowest not altogether how I have loved thee. Go then and dwell with Glauce, and I will send her a bright gift, so that thou mayest not forget the days that are past."

So Jason went away, well pleased that Medea had spoken to him gently and upbraided him not; and presently his children came after him to the house of Creon and said, "Father, we have brought a wreath for Glauce, and a robe which Helios gave to our mother Medea before she came away with thee from the house of her father." Then Glauce came forth eagerly to take the gifts; and she placed the glittering wreath on her head and wrapped the robe round her slender form. Like a happy child, she looked into a mirror to watch the sparkling of the jewels on her fair forehead, and sat down on the couch, playing with the folds of the robe of Helios. But soon a look of pain passed over her face, and her eyes shone with a fiery light as she lifted her hand to take the wreath away; but the will of Medea was accomplished, for the poison had eaten into her veins, and the robe clung with a deadly grasp to her scorched and wasted limbs. Through the wide halls ran the scream of her agony, as Creon clasped his child in his arms. Then sped the poison through his veins also, and Creon died with Glauce.

Then Medea went with her children to the housetop and looked up to the blue heaven; and, stretching forth her arms, she said, "O

Helios who didst give to me the wise and cunning heart, I have avenged me on Jason, even as once I avenged him on Pelias. Thou hast given me thy power; yet, it may be, I would rather have the lifelong love of the helpless daughters of men."

Presently her dragon chariot rose into the sky, and the people of Argos saw the mighty Medea no more.

From *Tales of Ancient Greece.*

NARCISSUS

On the banks of Cephisus, Echo saw and loved the beautiful Narcissus; but the youth cared not for the maiden of the hills, and his heart was cold to the words of her love, for he mourned for his sister whom Hermes had taken away beyond the Stygian river. Day by day he sat alone by the stream side, sorrowing for the bright maiden whose life was bound up with his own, because they had seen the light of the sun on the selfsame day; and thither came Echo and sat down by his side and sought in vain to win his love. "Look on me and see," she said. "I am fairer than the sister for whom thou dost mourn." But Narcissus answered her not, for he knew that the maiden would ever have something to say against his words. So he sat silent and looked down into the stream, and there he saw his own face in the clear water, and it was to him as the face of his sister for whom he pined away in sorrow; and his grief became less bitter as he seemed to see again her soft blue eye and almost to hear the words which came from her lips. But the grief of Narcissus was too deep for tears, and it dried up slowly the fountain of his life. In vain the words of Echo fell upon his ears as she prayed him to hearken to her prayer. "Ah, Narcissus, thou mournest for one who cannot heed thy sorrow, and thou carest not for her who longs to see thy face and hear thy voice forever." But Narcissus saw still in the waters of Cephisus the face of his twin sister, and still gazing at it he fell asleep and died. Then the voice of Echo was heard no more, for she sat in silence by his grave; and a beautiful flower came up close to it. Its white blossoms drooped over the banks of Cephisus where Narcissus had sat and looked down into its clear water, and the people of the land called the plant after his name.

From *Tales of Ancient Greece.*

ORPHEUS AND EURYDICE

IN THE pleasant valleys of a country which was called Thessaly there lived a man whose name was Orpheus. Every day he made soft music with his golden harp and sang beautiful songs such as no one had ever heard before. And whenever Orpheus sang, then everything came to listen to him, and the trees bowed down their heads to hear; and even the clouds sailed along more gently and brightly in the sky when he sang, and the stream which ran close to his feet made a softer noise, to show how glad his music made it.

Now Orpheus had a wife who was called Eurydice, whom he loved very dearly. All through the winter when the snow was on the hills, and all through the summer when the sunshine made everything beautiful, Orpheus used to sing to her; and Eurydice sat on the grass by his side while the beasts came round to listen and the trees bowed down their heads to hear him.

But one day when Eurydice was playing with some children on the bank of the river she trod upon a snake in the long grass, and the snake bit her. And by and by she began to be very sick, and Eurydice knew that she must die. So she told the children to go to Orpheus (for he was far away) and say how sorry she was to leave him, and that she loved him always very dearly; and then she put her head down upon the soft grass and fell asleep and died. Sad indeed was Orpheus when the children came to tell him that Eurydice was dead. He felt so wretched that he never played upon his golden harp, and he never opened his lips to sing; and the beasts that used to listen to him wondered why Orpheus sat all alone on the green bank where Eurydice used to sit with him, and why it was that he never made any more of his beautiful music. All day long he sat there, and his cheeks were then wet with his tears. At last he said, "I cannot stay here any more; I must go and look for

Eurydice. I cannot bear to be without her, and perhaps the king of the land where people go after they are dead will let her come back and live with me again."

So he took his harp in his hand and went to look for Eurydice in the land which is far away, where the sun goes down into his golden cup before the night comes on. And he went on and on a very long way, till at last he came to a high and dark gateway. It was barred across with iron bars, and it was bolted and locked so that nobody could open it. It was a wretched and gloomy place, because the sunshine never came there, and it was covered with clouds and mist. In front of this great gateway there sat a monstrous dog with three heads and six eyes and three tongues; and everything was dark around, except his eyes, which shone like fire and which saw everyone that dared to come near. Now when Orpheus came looking for Eurydice the dog raised his three heads, and opened his three mouths, and gnashed his teeth at him, and roared terribly; but when Orpheus came nearer the dog jumped up upon his feet and got himself ready to fly at him and tear him to pieces. Then Orpheus took down his harp and began to play upon its golden strings. And the dog Cerberus (for that was his name) growled and snarled and showed the great white teeth which were in his three mouths; but he could not help hearing the sweet music, and he wondered why it was that he did not wish any more to tear Orpheus in pieces. Very soon the music made him quiet and still, and at last lulled him to sleep; and only his heavy breathing told that there was any dog there. So when Cerberus had gone to sleep Orpheus passed by him and came up to the gate, and he found it wide open, for it had come open of its own accord while he was singing. And he was glad when he saw this, for he thought that now he should see Eurydice.

So he went on and on a long way, until he came to the palace of the king; and there were guards placed before the door who tried to keep him from going in; but Orpheus played upon his harp, and then they could not help letting him go.

So he went into the great hall, where he saw the king and queen sitting on a throne; and as Orpheus came near the king called out to him with a loud and terrible voice, "Who are you, and how dare you to come here? Do you not know that no one is allowed to come here till after they are dead? I will have you chained and placed in a dungeon, from which you will never be able to get out."

Then Orpheus said nothing; but he took his golden harp in his hand and began to sing more sweetly and gently than ever, because he knew that, if he liked to do so, the king could let him see Eurydice again. And as he sang the face of the king began to look almost glad, and his anger passed away, and he began to feel how much happier it must be to be gentle and loving than to be angry and cruel. Then the king said, "You have made me feel happy with your sweet music, although I have never felt happy before; and now tell me why you have come, because you must want something or other, for, otherwise, no one would come, before he was dead, to this sad and gloomy land of which I am the king." Then Orpheus said, "O king, give me back my dear Eurydice, and let her go from this gloomy place and live with me on the bright earth again." So the king said that she should go. And the king said to Orpheus, "I have given you what you wanted, because you sang so sweetly; and when you go back to the earth from this place your wife whom you love shall go up after you: but remember that you must never look back until she has reached the earth, for, if you do, Eurydice will be brought back here, and I shall not be able to give her to you again, even if you should sing more sweetly and gently than ever."

Now Orpheus was longing to see Eurydice, and he hoped that the king would let him see her once; but when the king said that he must not try to see her till she had reached the earth, he was quite content, for he said, "Shall I not wait patiently a little while, that Eurydice may come and live with me again?" So he promised the king that he would go up to the earth without stopping to look behind to see whether Eurydice was coming after him.

Then Orpheus went away from the palace of the king, and he passed through the dark gateway, and the dog Cerberus did not bark or growl, for he knew that Orpheus would not have been allowed to come back if the king had not wished it. So he went on and on a long way; and he became impatient and longed more and more to see Eurydice. At last he came near to the land of living men, and he saw just a little streak of light, where the sun was going to rise from the sea; and presently the sky became brighter, and he saw everything before him so clearly that he could not help turning round to look at Eurydice. But, ah! she had not yet quite reached the earth, and so now he lost her again. He just saw something pale and white, which looked like his own dear wife; and he just heard a soft and gentle voice, which sounded like the voice of Eurydice, and then it all melted away. And still he thought that he saw that pale white face and heard that soft and gentle voice, which said, "O Orpheus, Orpheus, why did you look back? How dearly I love you, and how glad I should have been to live with you again; but now I must go back, because you have broken your promise to the king, and I must not even kiss you and say how much I love you."

And Orpheus sat down at the place where Eurydice was taken away from him; and he could not go on any farther, because he felt so miserable. There he stayed day after day, and his cheek became more pale, and his body weaker and weaker, till at last he knew that he must die. And Orpheus was not sorry; for although he loved the bright earth, with all its flowers and soft grass and sunny streams, he knew that he could not be with Eurydice again until he had left it. So at last he laid his head upon the earth and fell asleep and died: and then he and Eurydice saw each other in the land which is far away, where the sun goes down at night into his golden cup, and were never parted again.

From *Tales of Ancient Greece.*

DIANA AND ACTAEON

IT WAS midday, and the sun stood equally distant from either goal, when young Actaeon, son of King Cadmus, thus addressed the youths who with him were hunting the stag in the mountains, "Friends, our nets and our weapons are wet with the blood of our victims; we have had sport enough for one day, and tomorrow we can resume the pursuit. Now let us put by our weapons and rest."

In this region there was a valley thick with cypresses and pines, sacred to the huntress queen, Diana. A fountain poured from one side, whose open basin was bounded by a grassy rim. Here the virgin goddess of the woods used to come, when weary with hunting to cool her limbs in the sparkling water.

One day, having repaired there with her nymphs, she handed her javelin, her quiver, and her bow to one, her robe to another, while a third unbound the sandals from her feet. Then one of them arranged her hair and the rest drew water in urns. At that moment, Actaeon, having quit his companions, and rambling without any especial object, came to the place, led by his destiny. As he presented himself at the entrance of the cave, the nymphs, seeing a man, screamed and rushed toward the goddess to hide her with their bodies. But she was taller than the rest and overtopped them all by a head. Such a color as tinges the clouds at sunset or at dawn came over the countenance of Diana thus taken by surprise. Surrounded as she was by her nymphs, she yet turned half away and sought with a sudden impulse for her arrows. As they were not at hand, she dashed the water into the face of the intruder, adding these words, "Now go and tell, if you can, that you have seen Diana unclothed."

Immediately a pair of branching stag's horns grew out of his head, his neck gained in length, his ears grew sharp-pointed, his hands became feet, his arms long legs, and his body covered with a hairy, spotted hide. Fear took the place of his former boldness, and the hero fled. He could not but admire his own speed; but when he saw his horns in the water, "Ah, wretched me!" he would have said, but no sound followed the effort. He groaned, and tears flowed down the face which had taken the place of his own. Yet his consciousness remained. What should he do? go home to seek the palace, or lie hidden in the woods? The latter he was afraid, the former he was ashamed, to do.

As he hesitated the dogs saw him. First Melampus, a Spartan dog, gave the signal with a bark, then all the rest rushed after him swifter than the wind. Over rocks and cliffs, through mountain gorges that seemed impassable, he fled, and they followed. Where he had often chased the stag and cheered on his pack, his pack now chased him, cheered on by the huntsmen. He longed to cry out, "I am Actaeon; recognize your master!" but the words came not at his will. The air resounded with the bark of the dogs. Presently one fastened on his back, another seized his shoulder. While they held their master, the rest of the pack came up and buried their teeth in his flesh. He groaned—not in a human voice, yet certainly not in a stag's—and, falling on his knees, raised his eyes, and would have raised his arms in supplication, if he had had them. His friends and fellow huntsmen cheered on the dogs and looked everywhere for Actaeon, calling on him to join the sport. At the sound of his name he turned his head and heard them regret that he should be away. He would have been well pleased to see the exploits of his dogs, but to feel them was too much. They were all around him, rending and tearing; and it was not till they had torn his life out that the anger of Diana was satisfied.

Adapted from *The Age of Fable* of Thomas Bulfinch.

DAEDALUS, ICARUS, AND THE WINGS

THE LABYRINTH from which Theseus escaped by means of the clue of Ariadne was built by Daedalus, a most skillful artificer. It was a structure with numberless winding passages and turnings opening into one another, and seemed to have neither beginning nor end. Daedalus built the labyrinth for King Minos, but afterward lost the favor of the king and was shut up in a tower. He contrived to make his escape from his prison, but could not leave the island by sea, as the king kept strict watch on all the vessels and permitted none to sail without being carefully searched.

"Minos may control the land and sea," said Daedalus, "but not the regions of the air. I will try that way."

So he set to work to fabricate wings for himself and his young son Icarus. He wrought feathers together, beginning with the smallest and adding larger, so as to form an increasing surface. The larger ones he secured with thread and the smaller with wax, and gave the whole a gentle curvature like the wings of a bird. Icarus, the boy, stood and looked on, sometimes running to gather up the feathers which the wind had blown away, and then handling the wax and working it over with his fingers. When at last the work was done, the artist, waving his wings, found himself buoyed upward, and hung suspended, poising himself on the air. He next equipped his son in the same manner and taught him how to fly. When all was prepared for flight he said, "Icarus, my son, I charge you to keep at a moderate height, for if you fly too low the damp will clog your wings, and if too high the heat will melt them. Keep near me and you will be safe." While he gave him these instructions and fitted the wings to his shoulders, the father's hands trembled. He kissed the boy, not knowing that it was for the last time. Then, rising on his wings, he flew off, encouraging him to follow, and looked back from his own flight to see how his son managed his wings. As they flew the plowman stopped his work to gaze, and the shepherd leaned on his staff and watched them, astonished at the sight and thinking they were gods who could thus cleave the air.

They passed Samos and Delos on the left and Lebynthos on the right, when the boy, exulting in his career, began to leave the guidance of his companion and soar upward as if to reach heaven. The nearness of the blazing sun softened the wax which held the feathers together, and they came off. He fluttered with his arms but no feathers remained to hold the air. He tried desperately to call out but soon he was submerged in the blue waters of the sea—which thenceforth was called by his name. His father cried, "Icarus, Icarus, where are you?" At last he saw the feathers floating on the water, and bitterly lamenting his own arts, he buried the body and called the land Icaria in memory of his child.

Adapted from *The Age of Fable.*

CUPID AND PSYCHE

A CERTAIN king and queen had three daughters. The charms of the two elder were more than common, but the beauty of the youngest was so great that strangers from neighboring countries came to enjoy the sight and looked on her with amazement, paying her that homage which is due only to Venus herself.

This homage gave great offense to the real Venus. Shaking her locks with indignation, she exclaimed, "Am I to be eclipsed by a mortal girl? I will give her cause to repent."

Thereupon she called her son Cupid and roused him by her complaints. She pointed Psyche out to him and said, "My dear son, punish that beauty. Give your mother a revenge as sweet as her injuries are great; fill that girl with a passion for some mean and unworthy being, so that she may reap a shame as great as her present triumph."

Cupid prepared to obey the commands of his mother. There are two fountains in Venus's garden, one of sweet waters, the other of bitter. Cupid filled two vases, one from each, and hastened to the chamber of Psyche, whom he found asleep. He shed a few drops from the bitter fountain over her lips, though the sight of her almost moved him to pity; then touched her side with the point of his arrow. At the touch she awoke, and opened eyes upon Cupid (himself invisible), which so startled him that in his confusion he wounded himself with his own arrow. Heedless of his wound, his whole thought now was to repair the mischief he had done, and he poured the drops of joy over all her curls.

Psyche, henceforth frowned upon by Venus, derived no benefit from all her charms. True, all eyes were cast eagerly upon her and every mouth spoke her praises; but neither king, royal youth, nor plebeian presented himself to demand her in marriage. Her two elder sisters had now long been married to two royal princes; but Psyche, left alone, grew sick of that beauty which had failed to awaken love.

Her parents, afraid that they had unwittingly incurred the anger of the gods, consulted the oracle of Apollo and received this answer: "The virgin is destined to be the bride of no mortal lover. Her future husband awaits her on the top of the mountain. He is a monster whom neither gods nor men can resist."

This dreadful decree filled everyone with dismay, and her parents abandoned themselves to grief. But Psyche said, "Why, my dear parents, do you now lament me? You should rather have grieved when the people showered upon me undeserved honors and called me a Venus. I see now that I am a victim to that name. I submit. Lead me to that rock to which my unhappy fate has destined me." Accordingly, all things being prepared, the royal maid took her place in the procession and with her parents ascended the mountain, where they left her alone and with sorrowful hearts returned home.

By degrees Psyche's mind became composed, and she laid herself down on a grassy bank to sleep. When she awoke she looked round and beheld near by a pleasant grove of stately trees. She entered it, and in the midst discovered a fountain, sending forth crystal clear waters, and near by a magnificent palace that impressed her as the happy retreat of some god. Drawn by admiration and wonder, she approached the building and entered. Every object she saw filled her with amazement. Golden pillars supported the vaulted roof, and the walls were enriched with carvings and paintings representing beasts of the chase and rural scenes. Continuing, she came upon other chambers filled with all manner of treasures and precious works of nature and art.

While her eyes were thus occupied, a voice addressed her, uttering these words: "Sovereign lady, all that you see is yours. We whose voices you hear are your servants and shall obey all your commands with utmost care and diligence. Retire, therefore, to your chamber and rest on your bed of down. Supper awaits you in the alcove when it pleases you to eat."

Psyche gave ear to the voices and, after resting, seated herself in the alcove, where a table immediately appeared and, without any visible aid from waiters or servants, was covered with the greatest delicacies and the finest wines. At the same time she was entertained by music from invisible performers.

She had not yet seen her destined husband. He came only in the hours of darkness and fled before dawn. But when he came, his words were full of love, and they inspired a like passion in her. She often begged him to stay and give her a glimpse of him, but he would not consent. On the contrary, he charged her to make no attempt to see him, for it was his pleasure, for the best of reasons, to keep concealed. "Why should you wish to behold me?" he said. "Have you any doubt of my love? Have you any wish ungratified? If you saw me, perhaps you would fear me, perhaps adore me, but all I ask of you is to love me. I would rather you would love me as an equal than adore me as a god."

This reasoning quieted Psyche for a time, and while the novelty lasted she felt quite happy. But at length the thought of her parents, left in ignorance of her fate, and of her sisters, denied a share in her pleasures, preyed on her mind and made her begin to feel her palace as only a splendid prison. One night she told her husband her distress and at last drew from him an unwilling consent that her sisters should be brought to see her.

So, calling Zephyr, she gave him her husband's commands, and he soon brought them across the mountain down to their sister's valley. They embraced her, and she returned their caresses. "Come," said Psyche, "enter my house and enjoy whatever is in it." Then she committed them to the care of her invisible attendants to refresh them in her baths and at her table, and to show them all her treasures. The view of these delights caused envy in their hearts.

They asked her numberless questions, among others what sort of a person her husband was. Psyche replied that he was a beautiful youth, who generally spent the daytime in hunting. The sisters, not satisfied with this reply, soon made her confess that she had never seen him. Then they began to fill her mind with dark suspicions. "Remember," they said, "the Pythian oracle said that you were destined to marry a monster. The inhabitants of this valley say that your husband is a terrible serpent, who nourishes you for a while that he may by and by devour you. Take our advice. Provide yourself with a lamp and a sharp knife; conceal them, and when your husband is sound asleep, slip out of bed, bring out the lamp, and see for yourself whether what they say is true or not. If it is, don't hesitate to cut off his head and thereby recover your liberty."

Psyche resisted these suggestions as well as she could, but they had their effect on her, and when her sisters were gone her curiosity became too strong for her. So she prepared her lamp and a sharp knife and hid them out of sight of her husband. When he had fallen asleep she rose and, uncovering her lamp, beheld not a hideous monster, but the most beautiful of gods, with golden curls, wings whiter than snow, and shining feathers. As she tipped the lamp in order to get a better view of his face, a drop of burning oil fell on the shoulder of the god, whereupon he opened his eyes and fixed them upon her; then, without saying one word, he spread his wings and flew out of the window. Psyche, in vain endeavoring to follow him, fell from the window to the ground. Cupid, beholding her as she lay in the dust, stopped his flight for an instant and said, "O foolish Psyche, is it thus you repay my love? Go; return to your sisters. I inflict no other punishment on you than to leave you forever." So saying, he fled, leaving poor Psyche stretched on the ground, filling the place with lamentations.

When she had recovered sufficiently to look around her, the palace and gardens had vanished, and she found herself in the open field not far from the city where her sisters dwelt. She went to them and told them the whole story of her misfortunes, at which, while outwardly pretending to grieve, those spiteful creatures inwardly rejoiced. "For now," said they, "he will perhaps choose one of us." With this idea in mind, each of them rose early the next morning and climbed the mountain, and having reached the top, called upon Zephyr to receive her and bear her to his lord; then leaping up, and not being sustained by Zephyr, fell from the cliff and was dashed to pieces.

Psyche meanwhile wandered day and night, without food or rest, in search of her husband. Coming to a lofty mountain with a magnificent temple at its crest, she sighed and said to herself, "Perhaps my love lives there," and made her way toward it.

When she entered the temple she saw heaps of corn, some in loose ears and some in sheaves, mingled with ears of barley. Scattered about lay sickles and rakes and all the instruments of harvest, as if thrown carelessly aside by weary reapers.

Psyche began separating and sorting everything, believing that she ought to neglect none of the gods and hoping by her piety to engage them in her behalf. The holy Ceres, whose temple it was, finding her so religiously employed, thus spoke to her, "O Psyche, though I cannot shield you from the frowns of Venus, yet I can teach you how best to offset her displeasure. Go, then, and surrender yourself to her and try by modesty and submission to win her forgiveness, and perhaps her favor will restore to you the husband you have lost."

Psyche obeyed and made her way to the temple of Venus. Venus received her with angry words. "Most faithless of servants," said she, "do you at last remember that you really have a mistress? Or have you rather come to see your sick husband, laid up by the wound given him by his loving wife? The only way you can merit your lover must be by diligence. I will test you." Then she ordered Psyche to be led to the storehouse of her temple, filled to overflowing with wheat, barley, millet, vetches, beans, and lentils, and said, "Separate all these grains, putting all of the same kind in a parcel by themselves, and see that you get it done before evening." Then Venus left her to her task. But Psyche, baffled by the size of the task, sat stupid and silent, without moving a finger.

While she sat despairing, Cupid stirred up an ant to take compassion on her. The leader of the anthill, followed by his subjects, approached the heap and, grain by grain, they separated the pile, sorting each kind to its parcel; and when it was all done they vanished.

Venus, returning at twilight and seeing the task done, exclaimed, "This is no work of yours, wicked one, but his, whom to your own and his misfortune you have enticed." Then she threw her a piece of black bread for her supper and went away.

Next morning Venus ordered Psyche to be called and said to her, "In a grove which stretches along the riverside you will find sheep feeding without a shepherd, with golden fleece on their backs. Go fetch me a sample of that precious wool from every one of them."

Psyche obediently went to the riverside, prepared to do her best to execute the command. But the river god inspired the reeds to murmur, "O maiden, tempt not the flood, nor venture among the rams on the other side, for as long as they are under the influence of the rising sun they burn to destroy mortals with their sharp horns. But when the sun has driven the cattle to the shade, you may cross in safety, and you will find the woolly gold sticking to the bushes and the trunks of trees."

Thus the compassionate river god instructed Psyche, and she soon returned to Venus with her arms full of the golden fleece; but her implacable mistress said, "I know very well that you have had help in accomplishing this task, and I am not yet satisfied that you have any capacity to make yourself useful. Therefore I have another task for you. Take this box and go your way to the infernal regions and give it to Proserpine and say, 'My mistress Venus desires you to send her a little of your beauty, for in tending her sick son she has lost some of her own.' Be not too long, for I must paint myself with it before I join the circle of the gods and goddesses this evening."

Psyche was now sure that her end was at hand. So, to hasten what appeared inevitable, she climbed a tower intending to throw herself from it, thus to descend the shortest way to the shades below. But a voice from the tower said to her, "What cowardice, poor girl, makes you sink under this last danger when you have been so miraculously supported in all your previous trials?" Then the voice told her how by a certain cave she might reach the realms of Pluto, and how to pass by Cerberus, the three-headed dog, and prevail on Charon, the ferryman, to take her across the black river and bring her back again. But the voice added, "When Proserpine has given you the box filled with her beauty, you must remember above all never to open or look into the box."

Psyche, encouraged by this advice, obeyed it and traveled safely to the kingdom of Pluto. She was admitted to the palace of Proserpine, but did not accept the delicious banquet that was offered her, contenting herself with coarse bread, and delivered her message from Venus. Presently the box was returned to her, and she returned the way she came.

But having got so far successfully through her dangerous task, she was seized by a great desire to examine the contents of the box. "Shall I," said she, "the carrier of this divine beauty, not take the least bit to put on my cheeks to appear more attractive in the eyes of my beloved husband!" So she carefully opened the box, but found nothing there of any beauty at all, but only an infernal and Stygian sleep, which took possession of her, and she fell down in the middle of the road and sank into a deathlike sleep.

But Cupid, now recovered from his wound, and not able any longer to bear the absence of his Psyche, flew to the spot where Psyche lay, and, gathering up the sleep from her body, closed it again in the box, and awakened Psyche with a touch of one of his arrows. "Again," said he, "you have almost perished because of curiosity. But now perform exactly the task imposed on you by my mother, and I will take care of the rest."

Then Cupid presented himself before Jupiter with his supplication. Jupiter lent a favoring ear and pleaded the cause of the lovers so earnestly with Venus that he won her consent. Thereupon he sent Mercury to bring Psyche up to the heavenly assembly, and when she arrived, handing her a cup of ambrosia, he said, "Drink this, Psyche, and be immortal; nor shall Cupid ever break away from the knot in which he is tied, but this marriage shall be perpetual."

Adapted from *The Age of Fable.*

HERCULES: THE ELEVENTH TASK

NOW WHEN Zeus and Hera had been married, to their wedding feast had come all the gods and goddesses, bringing with them gifts. Demeter brought a tree that bore most wondrous golden apples, and the immortal pair were greatly pleased with this. Zeus made a garden in the farthest west, and called it the Garden of the Hesperides, and he set the tree in the midst of it. A sleepless dragon coiled about its trunk to guard it, and four fair nymphs called the Daughters of the West were set to watch both tree and dragon.

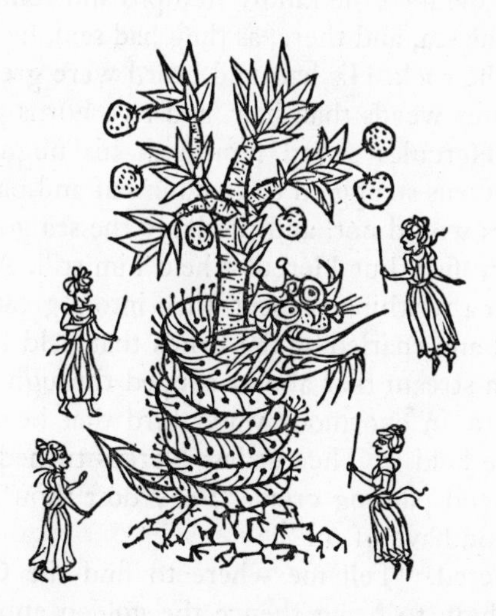

And now Eurystheus commanded Hercules to bring him these golden apples of the Hesperides.

Hercules set forth as he was commanded, but now he wandered aimlessly; for he knew not in which direction the garden lay, nor could he find any who could tell him though he asked all whom he met. At last in his wanderings he came to the river Rhône and sat to rest beside its brink, and as he sat there he saw the naiads at play in its waters, and he called to them, "Fair nymphs, out of your kindness, tell me if you can, where I may find the Garden of the Hesperides."

Then the nymphs ceased from play and raised themselves waist-high above the waters; and, seeing how great and tall the stranger was, they called to him, "Art thou Hercules?" for even in their river they had heard of him.

Hercules answered, "I am he."

Then the nymphs said, "Most gladly would we tell thee, if we could, where to find that garden, but few know save only the gods themselves. Nereus, the son-in-law of Oceanus, knows, and only a while ago we saw him by the sea asleep upon a rock. Hasten and thou still mayest find him there. Then catch and hold him fast until he tells thee. This he will be loath to do, and he will turn himself in thy grasp into many shapes, but do not let him go, and in the end he will be forced to tell thee."

Then Hercules thanked the kindly nymphs and followed the river on and down to the sea, and there, as they had said, he found Nereus still asleep upon the rock. His hair and beard were green and rough, and more like water weeds than hair, and two horns grew from his forehead. Then Hercules seized him with his mighty hands and woke him, and Nereus struggled to free himself and panted, "Let me go!" but Hercules would not; and suddenly the sea god turned himself into a slippery fish, but Hercules held him still. Afterward Nereus changed into a writhing serpent, then into a great three-headed dog that snapped and snarled at the hands that held him; after that he changed into a stream that almost slipped through Hercules' fingers, and then into an enormous water bird that beat him with its wings, but still he held it. Then at last Nereus turned back into his own shape again and panting cried, "Why dost thou hold me thus? What wouldst thou have of me?"

Hercules answered, "Tell me where to find the Garden of the Hesperides, and how to bring thence the golden apples, and I will let thee go."

Nereus replied, "The garden lies far to the west in Libya, but no mortal hand may pluck those apples. Only Atlas, the mighty Titan who upholds the sky upon his shoulders, may pluck them. Seek him first. If he will aid thee it is well, but if not thou needst not hope ever to gain those apples."

Then Hercules asked where he might find Atlas, and Nereus said, "Seek him too in Libya. And now let me go."

So Hercules loosed his hold, and Nereus slipped from his hands and plunged down into the sea.

But Hercules journeyed on to Libya, and he came to where a giant stood guarding the way, and the giant called to him, "I am Antaeus, the wrestler; none may pass this way unless they first have wrestled with me."

Hercules answered, "That will I gladly do," and he cast aside his lion skin and club and sprang at Antaeus, and they wrestled together up and down, and despite the giant's size, again and still again Hercules threw him, but always Antaeus started up again from the earth stronger than before, and Hercules could not understand the reason for it. But this giant was the son of Terra, as the earth is called, and all his strength flowed into him from her. The closer his body came to her, the stronger he grew. Then at last, after having thrown him many times, Hercules guessed his secret, and he caught the giant with his mighty hands, and instead of casting him down he heaved him up and held him high so that he could not touch the ground; and Antaeus struggled, and cried out, and strove to slip from his hands and fall to earth, and could not; slowly all the strength went out of him, till at last he hung, a helpless thing, in the hands of Hercules.

Then Hercules killed him and cast his body to the ground, for he knew that now not even his mother Earth could again put life into him.

But after this Hercules lost his way and wandered from Libya on into other countries; so he came to India, where Phoebus had his palace, and to the Caucasus where Prometheus lay bound; and Prometheus saw him even from afar and called him, "Hasten thy steps, O Hercules! For ages long I have awaited thee, and now thou hast come at last!"

Then Hercules drew near, and looked with wonder on Prometheus, and on the eagles that hovered over him, for though from childhood he had heard the story of Prometheus, he scarcely had believed that it was true. But now Prometheus told him with his own mouth of all his sufferings, and Hercules, filled with wrath and pity, drove away the eagles, and broke the fetters that held Prometheus, and set him free. So it was that the favored son of Zeus freed the one whom Zeus himself had bound.

And now Prometheus told Hercules that he wandered from his

way, and bade him retrace his steps to Libya, and he told him where to find Atlas.

So Hercules went back the way that he had come, and after long journeying he came again to Libya and to the place of which Prometheus had told him, and there he saw Atlas towering high above him, with his head among the clouds and the sky resting on his shoulders. Then Hercules called to him, "Ho, Atlas! with thy head among the clouds, canst thou hear me?"

And Atlas answered, "I can hear. Who art thou, calling there below in such a mighty voice? What seekest thou here?"

Hercules answered, "I am Hercules, the son of Zeus." And he told the Titan how he had been made subject to Eurystheus, and of how it was the will of the gods that he should carry out the king's commands until he had performed twelve labors. "So far," he said, "I have accomplished all the tasks that he has set for me; but now he has commanded me to bring to him the golden apples of the Hesperides, and this I cannot do without thy aid."

Atlas asked, "How can I aid thee? If I ceased from holding up the skies, even for a moment, they would fall upon the earth and both would be destroyed together."

Hercules replied, "I will myself support the sky in thy place, if thou wilt fetch the apples," and to this Atlas agreed. But Hercules lacked in height, so he climbed up a mountain and stood upon its top, and he cast off his lion skin and bared his back, and Atlas shifted the weight of the sky to his shoulders; slowly and carefully he shifted it, but even so, the sky was shaken so that many of the stars fell from their places, and people were terrified, fearing the whole of the heavens was about to fall.

Then Atlas strode away toward the west, and Hercules stood there with his shoulders bowed under the weight, and always the weight seemed heavier, and he was glad when, after a time, he heard Atlas returning, and he called, "Make haste, O Atlas, and take back the sky, for even already I am wearied of it."

Atlas said, "I was wearied long ago, and now I will myself carry the apples to King Eurystheus, and thou shalt stay here in my place."

Then Hercules was afraid, thinking that he might never be released, but he hid his fear and he said, "If I am to take thy place, let me at least spread my lion's skin on the rocks, for they are hard and rough beneath my feet."

Then Atlas agreed, and he put down the apples and took back the sky, thinking that presently he would again give it over to Hercules. But Hercules said, "It is thy task to support the sky, as it is mine to carry out the orders of Eurystheus. Thou wouldst have tricked me in this thing, but instead thou hast thyself been tricked. Farewell, O Atlas!"

And he took up the apples and returned with them to Eurystheus, leaving Atlas there with the weight of the heavens resting still upon his shoulders.

From *Heroic Tales from Greek Mythology*, retold by Katharine Pyle (Philadelphia: J. B. Lippincott Company, 1928).

FABLES

The Wolf and the Crane

A wolf had got a bone in his throat, and in the greatest agony ran up and down, beseeching every animal he met to relieve him, at the same time hinting at a very handsome reward to the successful operator. A crane, moved by his entreaties and promises, ventured her long neck down the wolf's throat and drew out the bone. She then modestly asked for the promised reward. To which the wolf, grinning and showing his teeth, replied with seeming indignation, "Ungrateful creature! to ask for any other reward than that you have put your head into a wolf's jaws and brought it safe out again!"

The Man and the Satyr

A man and a satyr, having struck up an acquaintance, sat down together to eat. The day being wintry and cold, the man put his fingers to his mouth and blew upon them. "What's that for, my friend?" asked the satyr. "My hands are so cold," said the man. "I do it to warm them." In a little while some hot food was placed before them, and the man, raising the dish to his mouth, again blew upon it. "And what's the meaning of that, now?" said the satyr. "Oh," replied the man, "my porridge is so hot, I do it to cool it." "Nay, then," said the satyr, "from this moment I renounce your friendship, for I will have nothing to do with one who blows hot and cold with the same mouth."

The House Dog and the Wolf

A lean, hungry wolf chanced one moonshiny night to fall in with a plump, well-fed house dog. After the first compliments were passed between them, "How is it, my friend," said the wolf, "that you look so sleek? How well your food agrees with you! And here am I striving for my living night and day and can hardly save myself from starving." "Well," says the dog, "if you would fare like me, you have only to do as I do." "Indeed!" says he, "and what is that?" "Why," replies the dog, "just to guard the master's house and keep off the thieves at night." "With all my heart; for at present I have but a sorry time of it. This woodland life, with its frosts and rains, is sharp work for me. To have a warm roof over my head and a bellyful of victuals always at hand will, methinks, be no bad exchange." "True," says the dog; "therefore you have nothing to do but to follow me."

Now as they were jogging on together the wolf spied a mark on the dog's neck and, having a strange curiosity, could not forbear ask-

ing what it meant. "Pooh! nothing at all," says the dog. "Nay, but pray—" says the wolf. "Oh! a mere trifle, perhaps the collar to which my chain is fastened." "Chain!" cries the wolf in surprise. "You don't mean to say that you cannot rove when and where you please?" "Why, not exactly perhaps; you see I am looked upon as rather fierce, so they sometimes tie me up in the daytime, but I assure you I have perfect liberty at night, and the master feeds me off his own plate, and the servants give me their tidbits, and I am such a favorite, and—but what is the matter? Where are you going?" "Oh, good night to you," says the wolf. "You are welcome to your dainties; but, for me, a dry crust with liberty against a king's luxury with a chain."

The Old Woman and the Wine Jar

An old woman saw an empty wine jar lying on the ground. Though not a drop of the noble Falernian wine with which it had been filled remained, it still yielded a grateful fragrance to the passers-by. The old woman, applying her nose as close as she could and snuffing with all her might and main, exclaimed, "Sweet creature! how charming must your contents once have been when the very dregs are so delicious!"

The Farthing Rushlight

A rushlight that had grown fat and saucy with too much grease boasted one evening before a large company that it shone brighter than the sun, the moon, and all the stars. At that moment a puff of wind came and blew it out. One who lighted it again said, "Shine on, friend rushlight, and hold your tongue; the lights of heaven are never blown out."

The Travelers and the Bear

Two friends were traveling on the same road together when they met with a bear. The one in great fear, without a thought of his companion, climbed up into a tree and hid himself. The other, seeing that he had no chance singlehanded against the bear, had nothing left but to throw himself on the ground and feign to be dead;

for he had heard that a bear will never touch a dead body. As he thus lay, the bear came up to his head, muzzling and snuffing at his nose, and ears, and heart, but the man immovably held his breath, and the beast, supposing him to be dead, walked away. When the bear was fairly out of sight his companion came down out of the tree and asked what it was that the bear whispered to him, "For," says he, "I observed he put his mouth very close to your ear." "Why," replies the other, "it was no great secret; he only bade me have a care how I kept company with those who, when they get into a difficulty, leave their friends in the lurch."

The Old Woman and the Physician

An old woman, who had become blind, called in a physician and promised him, before witnesses, that if he would restore her eyesight she would give him a most handsome reward, but that if he did not cure her, and her malady remained, he should receive nothing. The agreement being concluded, the physician tampered from time to time with the old lady's eyes, and meanwhile, bit by bit, carried off her goods. At length after a time he set about the task in earnest and cured her, and thereupon asked for the stipulated fee. But the old woman, on recovering her sight, saw none of her goods left in the house. When, therefore, the physician importuned her in vain for payment, and she continually put him off with excuses, he summoned her at last before the judges. Being now called upon for her defense, she said, "What this man says is true enough; I promised to give him his fee if my sight were restored, and nothing if my eyes continued bad. Now, then, he says that I am cured, but I say just the contrary; for when my malady first came on, I could see all sorts of furniture and goods in my house; but now, when he says he has restored my sight, I cannot see one jot of either."

The Ass Carrying Salt

A certain huckster who kept an ass, hearing that salt was to be had cheap at the seaside, drove down his ass thither to buy some. Having loaded the beast as much as he could bear, he was driving him home, when, as they were passing a slippery ledge of rock, the ass fell into the stream below, and the salt being melted, the ass was relieved of his burden, and having gained the bank with ease, pursued his journey onward, light in body and in spirit. The huckster soon afterward set off for the seashore for some more salt, and loaded the ass, if possible, yet more heavily than before. On their return, as they crossed the stream into which he had formerly fallen, the ass fell down on purpose, and by the dissolving of the salt was again released from his load. The master, provoked at the loss and thinking how he might cure him of this trick, on his next journey to the coast freighted the beast with a load of sponges. When they arrived at the same stream as before, the ass was at his old tricks again and rolled himself into the water; but the sponges becoming thoroughly wet, he found to his cost, as he proceeded homeward, that instead of lightening his burden he had more than doubled its weight.

The same measures will not suit all circumstances; and we may play the same trick once too often.

The Old Man and Death

An old man that had traveled a long way with a huge bundle of sticks found himself so weary that he cast it down and called upon Death to deliver him from his most miserable existence. Death came straightway at his call and asked him what he wanted. "Pray, good sir," says he, "do me but the favor to help me up with my burden again."

It is one thing to call for Death, and another to see him coming.

The Lion and Ass Go Hunting

A lion and an ass made an agreement to go out hunting together. By and by they came to a cave where many wild goats abode. The lion took up his station at the mouth of the cave, and the ass, going within, kicked and brayed and made a mighty fuss to frighten them out. When the lion had caught very many of them, the ass came out and asked him if he had not made a noble fight and routed the goats properly. "Yes, indeed," said the lion; "and I assure you, you would have frightened me too if I had not known you to be an ass."

The Bald Knight

A certain knight growing old, his hair fell off, and he became bald; to hide which imperfection, he wore a periwig. But as he was riding out with some others a-hunting, a sudden gust of wind blew off the periwig and exposed his bald pate. The company could not forbear laughing at the accident; and he himself laughed as loud as anybody, saying, "How was it to be expected that I should keep strange hair upon my head when my own would not stay there?"

The Fox and the Crow

A crow had snatched a goodly piece of cheese out of a window and flew with it into a high tree, intent on enjoying her prize. A fox spied the dainty morsel, and thus he planned his approaches. "O Crow," said he, "how beautiful are thy wings! how bright thine eye! how graceful thy neck! thy breast is the breast of an eagle! thy claws—I beg pardon—thy talons, are a match for all the beasts of the field. O that such a bird should be dumb and want only a voice!" The crow, pleased with the flattery, and chuckling to think how she would surprise the fox with her caw, opened her mouth. Down dropped the cheese! which the fox snapping up, observed, as he walked away, that whatever he had remarked of her beauty, he had said nothing yet of her brains.

The Ass's Shadow

A youth, one hot summer's day, hired an ass to carry him from Athens to Megara. At midday the heat of the sun was so scorching that he dismounted and would have sat down to repose himself under the shadow of the ass. But the driver of the ass disputed the place with him, declaring that he had an equal right to it with the other. "What!" said the youth, "did I not hire the ass for the whole journey?" "Yes," said the other, "you hired the ass, but not the ass's shadow." While they were thus wrangling and fighting for the place, the ass took to his heels and ran away.

From *Aesop's Fables*, translated by Thomas James.

Indian

The King Who Was Fried

INDIA may not have been, as certain scholars once thought, the original fountain of fable, but certainly no civilization of antiquity can boast richer collections of story. Among the richest and oldest collections—scenes from it appear on a monument in Central India that dates back to the third century B.C.—is the *Jataka*, a gathering of more than five hundred tales reputed to have been drawn by Buddha from his experiences in previous incarnations, when he was preparing to become Buddha. The tales are intended, as the concluding comment of each insists, to be instructive. Even though the moral sometimes seems farfetched or forced, the stories themselves are usually well and interestingly told, and many of them have become in one form or another among the most popular the world over. Readers will recognize in "The Golden Goose" the germ of the proverbial tale of the goose that laid the golden eggs, and in "The Robbers and the Treasure" the ancestor of a host of stories, from Chaucer's "Pardoner's Tale" to a modern novel and motion picture.

Hardly less influential than the *Jataka*, and perhaps even more of a germinal source of story, is the *Panchatantra*, or *Five Books*, which also brings together fables and stories, and also turns them to moral advantage. But the *Panchatantra* is definitely non-Buddhist, and its advice is shrewd and urbane—aimed at the best possible life in the actual world of men. After it was put down in Sanskrit in about 550 A.D., the *Panchatantra* was plundered to make popular volumes of moralized fables (including the *Hitopadesa* and the *Fables of Bidpai*) in a dozen languages. From "The Loyal Mungoose," for example, descend many similar stories, of which the Welsh "Llewelyn and Gelert," wherein the mungoose has become a dog, is probably the best known.

As an illustration of the successive embodiments that many of the best known of its fables have undergone, we might trace—as did Max Müller in his essay "On the Migration of Fable"—such a tale as "The

Brahman and the Pot of Rice" from its earliest form in the Sanskrit of the *Panchatantra* and the *Hitopadesa* through its translation into Pehlevi (ancient Persian) in the sixth century; thence into the fantastically ornate Arabian *Kalila and Dimna* in the eighth century; into a Greek version made by a Jew, Symeon Seth; into a widely circulated thirteenth-century Latin tale; into the Spanish vernacular of the *Conde Lucanor* of Don Juan Manuel, who died in 1347, and the sixteenth-century French *Contes et Nouvelles* of Bonaventure des Periers; and finally into the version best known today, the witty, highly civilized verses of La Fontaine. In that telescoped biography of an inconsequential folk tale lurks the whole history of a great tributary of Western culture during a period of almost two thousand years.

Like a huge reservoir draining the watershed of India's stories is the *Katha Sarit Sagara* (*Ocean of the Streams of Story*), which Somadeva assembled in about the year 1250. This huge collection is a Hindu *Arabian Nights*, a vast catch-all of fables, exempla, jests, and romances, theoretically held together by a framework narrative and theoretically dedicated to lofty moral ends. Hans Andersen, whose "The Princess on the Pea" (page 696) is a direct descendant of "The Three Fastidious Men" and of a companion story of sensitive young ladies, is only one of the many writers who have, directly or indirectly, tapped the *Katha Sarit Sagara*.

India today is as rich as ever in folk tales, and our last example comes from *Wide-awake Stories*, one of the earliest of many latter-day compilations.

HOLDING THE TRUTH

ONCE on a time in the city of Benares in the Kasi country there was a king named Brahmadatta. In those days the Bodhisatta was born into a merchant's family and, growing up in due course, used to journey about trading with five hundred carts, traveling now from east to west and now from west to east. There was also at Benares another young merchant, a stupid blockhead, lacking resource.

Now at the time of our story the Bodhisatta had loaded five hundred carts with costly wares of Benares and had got them all ready to start. And so had the foolish young merchant too. Thought the Bodhisatta, "If this foolish young merchant keeps me company all along, and the thousand carts travel along together, it will be too much for the road; it will be a hard matter to get wood, water, and so forth for the men, or grass for the oxen. Either he or I must go on first." So he sent for the other and laid his view before him, saying, "The two of us can't travel together; would you rather go first or last?" Thought the other, "There will be many advantages if I go on first. I shall have a road which is not yet cut up; my oxen will have the pick of the grass; my men will have the pick of the herbs for curry; the water will be undisturbed; and; lastly, I shall fix my own price for the barter of my goods." Accordingly he replied, "I will go first, my dear sir."

The Bodhisatta, on the other hand, saw many advantages in going last, for he argued thus to himself, "Those who go first will level the road where it is rough, whilst I shall travel along the road they have already traveled; their oxen will have grazed off the coarse old grass, whilst mine will pasture on the sweet young growth which will spring up in its place; my men will find a fresh growth of sweet herbs for curry where the old ones have been picked; where there is no water, the first caravan will have to dig to supply themselves, and we shall drink at the wells they dug. Haggling over prices is killing work; whereas I, following later, shall barter my wares at the prices they have already fixed." Accordingly, seeing all these advantages, he said to the other, "Then go you first, my dear sir."

"Very well, I will," said the foolish merchant. And he yoked his carts and set out. Journeying along, he left human habitations behind him and came to the outskirts of the wilderness. (Now wildernesses are of the five following kinds: robber wildernesses, wild-beast wildernesses, drought wildernesses, demon wildernesses, and famine wildernesses. The first is when the way is beset by robbers; the second is when the way is beset by lions and other wild beasts; the third is when there is no bathing or water to be got; the fourth is when the road is beset by demons; and the fifth is when no roots or other food are to be found. And in this fivefold category the wilderness in question was both a drought, and a demon, wilderness.)

Accordingly this young merchant took great big water jars on his carts and, filling them with water, set out to cross the sixty leagues of desert which lay before him. Now when he had reached the middle of the wilderness the goblin who haunted it said to himself, "I will make these men throw away their stock of water, and devour them all when they are faint." So he framed by his magic power a delightful carriage drawn by pure white young bulls. With a retinue of some ten or twelve goblins bearing bows and quivers, swords and shields, he rode along to meet them like a mighty lord in his carriage, with blue lotuses and white water-lilies wreathed round his head, with wet hair and wet clothes, and with muddy carriage wheels. His attendants too, in front and rear of him, went along with their hair and clothes wet, with garlands of blue lotuses and white water-lilies on their heads, and with bunches of white lotuses in their hands, chewing the esculent stalks, and dripping with water and mire.

Now the leaders of caravans have the following custom: whenever the wind blows in their teeth, they ride on in front in their

carriage with their attendants round them, in order to escape the dust; but when the wind blows from behind them, then they ride in like fashion in the rear of the column. And as on this occasion the wind was blowing against them, the young merchant was riding in front. When the goblin became aware of the merchant's approach he drew his carriage aside from the track and greeted him kindly, asking him whither he was going. The leader of the caravan too caused his carriage to be drawn aside from the track so as to let the carts pass by, whilst he stayed by the way and thus addressed the goblin: "We are just on our way from Benares, sir. But I observe that you have lotuses and water-lilies on your heads and in your hands, and that your people are chewing the esculent stalks, and that you are all muddy and dripping with wet. Pray did it rain while you were on the road, and did you come on pools covered with lotuses and water-lilies?"

Hereon the goblin exclaimed, "What did you say? Why, yonder appears the dark green streak of the forest, and thence onward there is nothing but water all through the forest. It is always raining there; the pools are full; and on every side are lakes covered with lotuses and water-lilies." Then, as the line of carts passed by, he asked where they were bound for. "To such and such a place," was the reply. "And what wares have you got in this cart and in this?" "So and so." "And what might you have in this last cart which seems to move as if it were heavily laden?" "Oh, there's water in that." "You did well to carry water with you from the other side. But there is no need for it now, as water is abundant on ahead. So break the jars and throw the water away, that you may travel easier." And he added, "Now continue on your way, as we have stopped too long already." Then he went a little way farther on, till he was out of sight, when he made his way back to the goblin city where he dwelt.

Such was the folly of that foolish merchant that he did the goblin's bidding and had his jars broken and the water all thrown away —without saving so much even as would go on the palm of a man's hand. Then he ordered the carts to drive on. Not a drop of water did they find on ahead, and thirst exhausted the men. All day long till the sun went down they kept on the march; but at sunset they unyoked their carts and made a laager, tethering the oxen to the wheels. The oxen had no water to drink, and the men none to cook their rice with and the tired-out band sank to the ground to slumber. But as soon as night fell the goblins came out from their city and slew every single one of those men and oxen; and when they had devoured their flesh, leaving only the bare bones, the goblins departed. Thus was the foolish young merchant the sole cause of the destruction of that whole band, whose skeletons were strewn in every conceivable direction, whilst the five hundred carts stood there with their loads untouched.

Now the Bodhisatta allowed some six weeks to pass by after the starting of the foolish young merchant before he set out. Then he proceeded from the city with his five hundred carts, and in due course came to the outskirts of the wilderness. Here he had his water jars filled and laid in an ample stock of water; and by beat of drum he had his men assembled in camp and thus addressed them: "Let not so much as a palmful of water be used without my sanction. There are poison trees in this wilderness; so let no man among you eat any leaf, flower, or fruit which he has not eaten before, without first asking me." With this exhortation to his men, he pushed on into the wilderness with his five hundred carts. When he had reached the middle of the wilderness the goblin made his appearance on the Bodhisatta's path as in the former case. But as soon as he became aware of the goblin the Bodhisatta saw through him; for he thought to himself, "There's no water here, in this Waterless Desert. This person with his red eyes and aggressive bearing casts no shadow. Very likely he has induced the foolish young merchant who preceded me to throw away all his water, and then, waiting till they were worn out, has eaten up the merchant with all his men. But he doesn't know my cleverness and ready wit."

Then he shouted to the goblin, "Begone! We're men of business, and do not throw away what water we have got before we see where more is to come from. But when we do see more, we may be trusted to throw this water away and lighten our carts."

The goblin rode on a bit farther till he was out of sight and then betook himself back to his home in the demon city. But when the goblin had gone the Bodhisatta's men said to him, "Sir, we heard from those men that yonder is the dark green streak of the forest appearing, where they said it was always raining. They had got lotuses on their heads and water-lilies in their hands and were eating the stalks, whilst their clothes and hair were wringing wet, with water streaming off them. Let us throw away our water and get on a bit quicker with lightened carts." On hearing these words the Bodhisatta ordered a halt and had the men all mustered. "Tell me," said he, "did any man among you ever hear before today that there was a lake, or a pool, in this wilderness?" "No, sir," was the answer, "Why, it's known as the Waterless Desert."

"We have just been told by some people that it is raining just on ahead, in the belt of forest; now how far does a rain-wind carry?" "A league, sir." "And has this rain-wind reached any one man here?" "No, sir." "How far off can you see the crest of a storm cloud?" "A league, sir." "And has any one man here seen the top of even a single storm cloud?" "No, sir." "How far off can you see a flash of lightning?" "Four or five leagues, sir." "And has any one man here seen a flash of lightning?" "No, sir." "How far off can a man hear a peal of thunder?" "Two or three leagues, sir." "And has any one man here heard a peal of thunder?" "No, sir." "These are not men but goblins. They will return in the hope of devouring us when we are weak and faint after throwing away our water at their bidding. As the young merchant who went on before us was not a man of resource, most likely he has been fooled into throwing his water away and has been devoured when exhaustion ensued. We may expect to find his five hundred carts standing just as they were loaded for the start; we shall come on them today. Press on with all possible speed, without throwing away a drop of water."

Urging his men forward with these words, he proceeded on his way till he came upon the five hundred carts standing just as they had been loaded and the skeletons of the men and oxen lying strewn in every direction. He had his carts unyoked and ranged in a circle so as to form a strong laager; he saw that his men and oxen had their supper early, and that the oxen were made to lie down in the middle with the men round them; and he himself with the leading men of his band stood on guard, sword in hand, through the three watches of the night, waiting for the day to dawn. On the morrow at daybreak, when he had had his oxen fed and everything needful done, he discarded his own weak carts for stronger ones, and his own common goods for the most costly of the derelict goods. Then he went on to his destination, where he bartered his stock for wares of twice or three times their value, and came back to his own city without losing a single man out of all his company.

From *Jataka Tales*, edited by E. B. Cowell and translated by various hands (London: Cambridge University Press, 1895-1913).

THE ROBBERS AND THE TREASURE

ONCE on a time when Brahmadatta was reigning in Benares, there was a Brahman in the village who knew the charm called Vedabbha. Now this charm, so they say, was precious beyond all price. For, if at a certain conjunction of the planets the charm was repeated and the gaze bent upward to the skies, straightway from the heavens there rained the Seven Things of Price: gold, silver, pearl, coral, cats-eye, ruby, and diamond.

In those days the Bodhisatta was a pupil of this Brahman; and one day his master left the village on some business or other and came with the Bodhisatta to the country of Ceti.

In a forest by the way dwelt five hundred robbers—known as the Dispatchers—who made the way impassable. And these caught the Bodhisatta and the Vedabbha-Brahman. (Why, you ask, were they called the Dispatchers? Well, the story goes that of every two prisoners they made they used to *dispatch* one to fetch the ransom; and that's why they were called the Dispatchers. If they captured a father and a son, they told the father to go for the ransom to free his son; if they caught a mother and a daughter, they sent the mother for the money; if they caught two brothers, they let the elder go; and so too, if they caught a teacher and a pupil, it was the pupil they set free. In this case, therefore, they kept the Vedabbha-Brahman and sent the Bodhisatta for the ransom.) And the Bodhisatta said with a bow to his master, "In a day or two I shall surely come back; have no fear; only fail not to do as I shall say. Today will come to pass the conjunction of the planets which brings about the rain of the Things of Price. Take heed lest, yielding to this mishap, you repeat the charm and call down the precious shower. For, if you do, calamity will certainly befall both you and this band of robbers." With this warning to his master the Bodhisatta went his way in quest of the ransom.

At sunset the robbers bound the Brahman and laid him by the heels. Just at this moment the full moon rose over the eastern horizon, and the Brahman, studying the heavens, knew that the great conjunction was taking place. "Why," thought he, "should I suffer this misery? By repeating the charm I will call down the precious rain, pay the robbers the ransom, and go free." So he called out to the robbers, "Friends, why do you take me a prisoner?" "To get a ransom, reverend sir," said they. "Well, if that is all you want," said the Brahman, "make haste and untie me. Have my head bathed, and new clothes put on me; and let me be perfumed and decked with flowers. Then leave me to myself." The robbers did as he bade them. And the Brahman, marking the conjunction of the planets, repeated his charm with eyes uplifted to the heavens. Forthwith the Things of Price poured down from the skies! The robbers picked them all up, wrapping their booty into bundles with their cloaks.

Then with their brethren they marched away, and the Brahman followed in the rear. But, as luck would have it, the party was captured by a second band of five hundred robbers! "Why do you seize us?" said the first to the second band. "For booty," was the answer. "If booty is what you want, seize on that Brahman, who by simply gazing up at the skies brought down riches as rain. It was he who gave us all that we have got." So the second band of robbers let the first band go and seized on the Brahman, crying, "Give us riches too!" "It would give me great pleasure," said the Brahman; "but it will be a year before the requisite conjunction of the planets takes place again. If you will only be so good as to wait till then, I will invoke the precious shower for you."

"Rascally Brahman!" cried the angry robbers, "you made the other band rich offhand but want us to wait a whole year!" And they cut him in two with a sharp sword and flung his body in the middle of the road. Then, hurrying after the first band of robbers, they killed every man of them too in hand-to-hand fight and seized the booty. Next they divided into two companies and fought among themselves, company against company, till two hundred and fifty men were slain. And so they went on killing one another till only two were left alive. Thus did those thousand men come to destruction.

Now when the two survivors had managed to carry off the treasure they hid it in the jungle near a village; and one of them sat there, sword in hand, to guard it, whilst the other went into the village to get rice and have it cooked for supper.

"Covetousness is the root of ruin!" mused he that stopped by the treasure. "When my mate comes back he'll want half of this. Suppose I kill him the moment he gets back." So he drew his sword and sat waiting for his comrade's return.

Meanwhile the other had equally reflected that the booty had to be halved and thought to himself, "Suppose I poison the rice, and give it him to eat and so kill him, and have the whole of the treasure to myself." Accordingly, when the rice was boiled, he first ate his own share, and then put poison in the rest, which he carried back with him to the jungle. But scarce had he set it down when the other robber cut him in two with his sword and hid the body away in a secluded spot. Then he ate the poisoned rice and died then and there. Thus, by reason of the treasure, not only the Brahman but all the robbers came to destruction.

Howbeit, after a day or two the Bodhisatta came back with the ransom. Not finding his master where he had left him, but seeing treasure strewn all round about, his heart misgave him that, in spite of his advice, his master must have called down a shower of treasure from the skies and that all must have perished in consequence; and he proceeded along the road. On his way he came to where his master's body lay cloven in twain upon the way. "Alas!" he cried, "he is dead through not heeding my warning." Then with gathered sticks he made a pyre and burned his master's body, making an offering of wild flowers. Farther along the road he came upon the five hundred Dispatchers, and farther still upon the two hundred and fifty, and so on by degrees until at last he came to where lay only two corpses. Marking

how of the thousand all but two had perished, and feeling sure that there must be two survivors, and that these could not refrain from strife, he pressed on to see where they had gone. So on he went till he found the path by which with the treasure they had turned into the jungle; and there he found the heap of bundles of treasure, and one robber lying dead with his rice bowl overturned at his side. Realizing the whole story at a glance, the Bodhisatta set himself to search for the missing man, and at last found his body in the secret spot where it had been flung. "And thus," mused the Bodhisatta, "through not following my counsel my master in his self-will has been the means of destroying not himself only but a thousand others also. Truly, they that seek their own gain by mistaken and misguided means shall reap ruin, even as my master." And he repeated this stanza:

"Misguided effort leads to loss, not gain;
Thieves killed Vedabbha and themselves were slain."

From *Jataka Tales,* selected by H. T. Francis and E. J. Thomas (London: Cambridge University Press, 1916) from the complete edition of E. B. Cowell.

THE GOLDEN GOOSE

ONCE upon a time when Brahmadatta was reigning in Benares, the Bodhisatta was born a Brahman, and, growing up, was married to a bride of his own rank, who bore him three daughters named Nanda, Nanda-vati, and Sundari-nanda. The Bodhisatta dying, they were taken in by neighbors and friends, whilst he was born again into the world as a golden mallard endowed with consciousness of its for-

mer existences. Growing up, the bird viewed its own magnificent size and golden plumage, and remembered that previously it had been a human being. Discovering that his wife and daughters were living on the charity of others, the mallard bethought him of his plumage like hammered and beaten gold and how by giving them a golden feather at a time he could enable his wife and daughters to live in comfort. So away he flew to where they dwelt and alighted on the top of the central beam of the roof. Seeing the Bodhisatta, the wife and girls asked where he had come from; and he told them that he was their father who had died and been born a golden mallard, and that he had come to visit them and put an end to their miserable necessity of working for hire. "You shall have my feathers," said he, "one by one, and they will sell for enough to keep you all in ease and comfort." So saying, he gave them one of his feathers and departed. And from time to time he returned to give them another feather, and with the proceeds of their sale these Brahman-women grew prosperous and quite well-to-do. But one day the mother said to her daughters, "There's no trusting animals, my children. Who's to say your father might not go away one of these days and never come back again? Let us use our time and pluck him clean next time he comes, so as to make sure of all his feathers." Thinking this would pain him, the daughters refused. The mother in her greed called the golden mallard to her one day when he came, and then took him with both hands and plucked him. Now the Bodhisatta's feathers had this property, that if they were plucked out against his wish they ceased to be golden and became like a crane's feathers. And now the poor bird, though he stretched his wings, could not fly, and the woman flung him into a barrel and gave him food there. As time went on his feathers grew again (though they were plain white ones now), and he flew away to his own abode and never came back again.

From *Jataka Tales.*

THE GREEDY JACKAL CAUGHT

ONCE on a time when Brahmadatta was reigning in Benares, the Bodhisatta was reborn into life as a jackal and dwelt in the forest by the riverside. Now an old elephant died by the banks of the Ganges, and the jackal, finding the carcass, congratulated himself on lighting upon such a store of meat. First he bit the trunk, but that was like biting a plow handle. "There's no eating here," said the jackal and took a bite at a tusk. But that was like biting bones. Then he tried an ear, but that was like chewing the rim of a winnowing basket. So he fell to on the stomach, but found it as tough as a grain basket. The feet were no better, for they were like a mortar. Next he tried the tail, but that was like the pestle. "That won't do either," said the jackal; and, having failed elsewhere to find a toothsome part, he tried the rear and found that like eating a soft cake. "At last," said he, "I've found the right place," and ate his way right into the belly, where he made a plenteous meal off the kidneys, heart, and the rest, quenching his thirst with the blood. And when night came he lay down inside. As he lay there the thought came into the jackal's mind, "This carcass is both meat and house to me, and wherefore should I leave it?" So there he stopped and dwelt in the elephant's inwards, eating away. Time wore on till the summer sun and the summer winds dried and shrank the elephant's hide, until the entrance by which the jackal had got in was closed and the interior was in utter darkness. Thus the jackal was, as it were, cut off from the world and confined in the interspace between the worlds. After the hide, the flesh dried up and the blood was exhausted. In a frenzy of despair he rushed to and fro, beating against his prison walls in the fruitless endeavor to escape. But as he bobbed up and down inside like a ball of rice in a boiling saucepan, soon a tempest broke and the downpour moistened the shell of the carcass and restored it to its former state, till light shone like a star through the way by which the jackal had got in. "Saved! saved!" cried the jackal, and, backing into the elephant's head, made a rush headfirst at the outlet. He managed to get through, it is true, but only by leaving all his hair on the way. And first he ran, then he halted, and then sat down and surveyed his hairless body, now smooth as a palm stem. "Ah!" he exclaimed, "this misfortune has befallen me because of my greed and my greed alone. Henceforth I will not be greedy nor ever again get into the carcass of an elephant." And his terror found expression in this stanza:

"Once bitten, twice shy. Ah, great was my fear!
Of elephants' inwards henceforth I'll steer clear."

And with these words the jackal made off, nor did he ever again so much as look either at that or any other elephant's carcass. And thenceforth he was never greedy again.

From *Jataka Tales.*

THE JUDAS TREE

ONCE on a time Brahmadatta, the king of Benares, had four sons. One day they sent for the charioteer, and said to him, "We want to see a Judas tree. Show us one!"

"Very well, I will," the charioteer replied. But he did not show it to them all together. He took the eldest at once to the forest in the chariot and showed him the tree at the time when the buds were just sprouting from the stem. To the second he showed it when the leaves were green, to the third at the time of blossoming, and to the fourth when it was bearing fruit.

After this it happened that the four brothers were sitting together, and someone asked, "What sort of a tree is the Judas tree?"

Then the first brother answered, "Like a burned stump!"

And the second cried, "Like a banyan tree!"

And the third, "Like a piece of meat!"

And the fourth said, "Like the acacia!"

They were vexed at each other's answers and ran to find their father. "My lord," they asked, "what sort of a tree is the Judas tree?"

"What did you say to that?" he asked. They told him the manner of their answers. Said the king, "All four of you have seen the tree. Only when the charioteer showed you the tree, you did not ask him 'What is the tree like at such a time?' or 'at such another time?' You made no distinctions, and that is the reason of your mistake." And he repeated the first stanza:

"All have seen the Judas tree,
What is your perplexity?
No one asked the charioteer
What its form the livelong year!"

From *Jataka Tales.*

RAMA AND SITA

ONCE upon a time, at Benares, a great king named Dasaratha renounced the ways of evil and reigned in righteousness. Of his sixteen thousand wives, the eldest and queen-consort bore him two sons and a daughter; the elder son was named Rāma-pandita, or Rāma the Wise, the second was named Prince Lakkhana, or Lucky, and the daughter's name was the Lady Sitā.

In course of time the queen-consort died. At her death the king was for a long time crushed by sorrow, but, urged by his courtiers, he performed her obsequies and set another in her place as queen-consort. She was dear to the king and beloved. In time she also conceived, and all due attention having been given her, she brought forth a son, and they named him Prince Bharata.

The king loved his son much and said to the queen, "Lady, I offer you a boon: choose." She accepted the offer, but put it off for the time. When the lad was seven years old she went to the king and said to him, "My lord, you promised a boon for my son. Will you give it me now?" "Choose, lady," said he. "My lord," quoth she, "give my son the kingdom." The king snapped his fingers at her. "Out, vile jade!" said he angrily. "My other two sons shine like blazing fires. Would you kill them and ask the kingdom for a son of yours?" She fled in terror to her magnificent chamber, and on other days again and again asked the king the same. The king would not give her this gift. He thought within himself, "Women are ungrateful and treacherous. This woman might use a forged letter or a treacherous bribe to get my sons murdered." So he sent for his sons and told them all about it, saying, "My sons, if you live here some mischief may befall you. Go to some neighboring kingdom, or to the woodland, and when my body is burned, then return and inherit the kingdom which belongs to your family." Then he summoned soothsayers and asked them the limits of his own life. They told him he would live yet twelve years longer. Then he said, "Now, my sons, after twelve years you must return and uplift the umbrella of royalty." They promised, and after taking leave of their father went forth from the palace weeping. The Lady Sitā said, "I too will go with my brothers"; she bade her father farewell and went forth weeping.

These three departed amidst a great company of people. They sent the people back and proceeded until at last they came to Himalaya. There in a spot well watered and convenient for the getting of wild fruits, they built a hermitage, and there lived, feeding upon the wild fruits.

Lakkhana-pandita and Sītā said to Rāma-pandita, "You are in place of a father to us; remain then in the hermitage, and we will bring fruits and feed you." He agreed: thenceforward Rāma-pandita stayed where he was, the others brought the fruits and fed him.

Thus they lived there, feeding upon the wild fruit; but King Dasaratha pined after his sons, and died in the ninth year. When his obsequies were performed, the queen gave orders that the umbrella should be raised over her son, Prince Bharata. But the courtiers said, "The lords of the umbrella are dwelling in the forest, and they would not allow it." Said Prince Bharata, "I will fetch back my brother Rāma-pandita from the forest and raise the royal umbrella over him." Taking the five emblems of royalty, he proceeded with a complete host of the four arms to their dwelling place. Not far away he caused camp to be pitched, and then with a few courtiers he visited the hermitage, at the time when Lakkhana-pandita and Sītā were away in the woods. At the door of the hermitage sat Rāma-pandita, undismayed and at ease, like a figure of fine gold firmly set. The prince approached him with a greeting and, standing on one side, told him of all that had happened in the kingdom, and, falling at his feet along with the courtiers, burst into weeping. Rāma-pandita neither sorrowed nor wept; he showed no change of feeling. When Bharata had finished weeping and sat down, toward evening the other two returned with wild fruits. Rāma-pandita thought, "These two are young: all-comprehensive wisdom like mine is not theirs. If they are told on a sudden that our father is dead, the pain will be greater than they can bear, and who knows but their hearts may break. I will find a device to persuade them to go down into the water, and then tell them the news." Then, pointing out to them a place in front where there was water, he said, "You have been out too long. Let this be your penance: go into that water and stand there." Then he repeated a half-stanza:

"Let Lakkhana and Sītā both into that pond descend."

One word sufficed, into the water they went and stood there. Then he told them the news by repeating the other half-stanza:

"Bharata says, King Dasaratha's life is at an end."

When they heard the news of their father's death they fainted. Again he repeated it, again they fainted, and when even a third time they fainted away, the courtiers raised them and brought them out of the water and set them upon dry ground. When they had been comforted, they all sat weeping and wailing together. Then Prince Bharata thought, "My brother Prince Lakkhana, and my sister the Lady Sītā, cannot restrain their grief to hear of our father's death; but Rāma-pandita neither wails nor weeps. I wonder what can the reason be that he grieves not? I will ask." Then he repeated the second stanza, asking the questions:

"Say by what power thou grievest not, Rāma, when grief should be?
Though it is said thy sire is dead grief overwhelms not thee!"

Then Rāma-pandita explained the reason of his not grieving by saying:

"When man can never keep a thing, though loudly he may cry,
Why should a wise intelligence torment itself thereby?

The young in years, the older grown, the fool, and eke the wise,
For rich, for poor, one end is sure: each man among them dies.

As sure as for the ripened fruit there comes the fear of fall,
So surely comes the fear of death to mortals one and all.

Who in the morning light are seen, by evening oft are gone,
And seen at evening time, is gone by morning many a one.

If to a fool infatuate a blessing could accrue
When he torments himself with tears, the wise this same would do.

By this tormenting of himself he waxes thin and pale;
This cannot bring the dead to life, and nothing tears avail.

Even as a blazing house may be put out with water, so
The strong, the wise, the intelligent, who well the scriptures know,
Scatter their grief like cotton when the stormy winds do blow.

One mortal dies—to kindred ties born is another straight:
Each creature's bliss dependent is on ties associate.

The strong man therefore, skilled in sacred text,
Keen-contemplating this world and the next,
Knowing their nature, not by any grief,
However great, in mind and heart is vext.

So to my kindred I will give, them will I keep and feed,
All that remain I will maintain: such is the wise man's deed."

In these stanzas he explained the impermanence of things.

When the company heard this discourse of Rāma-pandita, illustrating the doctrine of impermanence, they lost all their grief. Then Prince Bharata saluted Rāma-pandita, begging him to receive the kingdom of Benares. "Brother," said Rāma, "take Lakkhana and Sītā with you, and administer the kingdom yourselves." "No my Lord, you take it." "Brother, my father commanded me to receive the kingdom at the end of twelve years. If I go now, I shall not carry out his bidding. After three more years I will come." "Who will carry on the government all that time?" "You do it." "I will not." "Then until I come, these slippers shall do it," said Rāma, and doffing his slippers of straw, he gave them to his brother. So these three persons took the slippers and, bidding the wise man farewell, went to Benares with their great crowd of followers.

For three years the slippers ruled the kingdom. The courtiers placed these straw slippers upon the royal throne when they judged a cause. If the cause were decided wrongly, the slippers beat upon each other, and at that sign it was examined again; when the decision was right, the slippers lay quiet.

When the three years were over the wise man came out of the forest, and came to Benares, and entered the park. The princes, hearing of his arrival, proceeded with a great company to the park, and making Sītā the queen-consort, gave to them both the ceremonial sprinkling. The sprinkling thus performed, the Great Being, standing in a magnificent chariot, and surrounded by a vast company, entered the city, making a solemn circuit right-wise; then, mounting to the great terrace of his splendid palace Sucandaka, he reigned there in righteousness for sixteen thousand years, and then went to swell the hosts of heaven.

From *Jataka Tales.*

MOUSE-MAID MADE MOUSE

Though mountain, sun, and cloud, and wind
Were suitors at her feet,
The mouse-maid turned a mouse again–
Nature is hard to beat.

THE BILLOWS of the Ganges were dotted with pearly foam born of the leaping of fishes frightened at hearing the roar of the waters that broke on the rugged, rocky shore. On the bank was a hermitage crowded with holy men devoting their time to the performance of sacred rites–chanting, self-denial, self-torture, study, fasting, and sacrifice. They would take purified water only, and that in measured sips. Their bodies wasted under a diet of bulbs, roots,

fruits, and moss. A loin cloth made of bark formed their scanty raiment.

The father of the hermitage was named Yajnavalkya. After he had bathed in the sacred stream and had begun to rinse his mouth, a little female mouse dropped from a hawk's beak and fell into his hand. When he saw what she was, he laid her on a banyan leaf, repeated his bath and mouth rinsing, and performed a ceremony of purification. Then through the magic power of his holiness, he changed her into a girl and took her with him to his hermitage.

As his wife was childless he said to her: "Take her, my dear wife. She has come into life as your daughter, and you must rear her carefully." So the wife reared her and spoiled her with petting. As soon as the girl reached the age of twelve, the mother saw that she was ready for marriage and said to her husband, "My dear husband, how can you fail to see that the time is passing when your daughter should marry?"

And he replied, "You are quite right, my dear. The saying goes:

Before a man is gratified,
These gods must treat her as a bride—
The fire, the moon, the choir of heaven;
In this way, no offense is given.

Holiness is the gift of fire;
A sweet voice, of the heavenly choir;
The moon gives purity within:
So is a woman free from sin.

Before nubility, 'tis said
That she is white; but after, red;
Before her womanhood is plain,
She is, though naked, free from stain.

The moon, in mystic fashion, weds
A maiden when her beauty spreads;
The heavenly choir, when bosoms grow;
The fire upon the monthly flow.

To wed a maid is therefore good
Before developed womanhood;
Nor need the loving parents wait
Beyond the early age of eight.

The early signs one kinsman slay;
The bosom takes the next away;
Friends die for passion gratified;
The father, if she ne'er be bride.

For if she bides a maiden still,
She gives herself to whom she will;
Then marry her in tender age:
So warns the heaven-begotten sage.

If she, unwed, unpurified,
Too long within the home abide,
She may no longer married be:
A miserable spinster, she.

A father then, avoiding sin,
Weds her, the appointed time within
(Where'er a husband may be had)
To good, indifferent, or bad.

"Now I will try to give her to one of her own station. You know the saying:

Where wealth is very much the same,
And similar the family fame,
Marriage (or friendship) is secure;
But not between the rich and poor.

"And finally:

Aim at seven things in marriage;
All the rest you may disparage:

"But

Get money, good looks,
And knowledge of books,
Good family, youth,
Position, and truth.

"So, if she is willing, I will summon the blessed sun and give her to him."

"I see no harm in that," said his wife. "Let it be done."

The holy man therefore summoned the sun, who appeared without delay and said, "Holy sir, why am I summoned?" The father said, "Here is a daughter of mine. Be kind enough to marry her." Then, turning to his daughter, he said, "Little girl, how do you like him, this blessed lamp of the three worlds?" "No, father," said the girl. "He is too burning hot. I could not like him. Please summon another one, more excellent than he is."

Upon hearing this, the holy man said to the sun, "Blessed one, is there any superior to you?" And the sun replied, "Yes, the cloud is superior even to me. When he covers me, I disappear."

So the holy man summoned the cloud next and said to the maiden, "Little girl, I will give you to him." "No," said she. "This one is black and frigid. Give me to someone finer than he."

Then the holy man asked, "O cloud, is there anyone superior to you?" And the cloud replied, "The wind is superior even to me."

So he summoned the wind and said, "Little girl, I give you to him." "Father," said she, "this one is too fidgety. Please invite somebody superior even to him." So the holy man said, "O wind, is there anyone superior even to you?" "Yes," said the wind. "The mountain is superior to me."

So he summoned the mountain and said to the maiden, "Little girl, I give you to him." "O father," said she, "He is rough all over, and stiff. Please give me to somebody else."

"So the holy man asked, "O kingly mountain, is there anyone superior even to you?" "Yes," said the mountain. "Mice are superior to me."

Then the holy man summoned a mouse and presented him to the girl, saying, "Little girl, do you like this mouse?"

The moment she saw him she felt, "My own kind, my own kind," and her body thrilled and quivered, and she said, "Father dear, turn me into a mouse, and give me to him. Then I can keep house as my kind of people ought to do."

And her father, through the magic power of his holiness, turned her into a mouse, and gave her to him.

And that is why I say:

"Though mountain, sun, and cloud, and wind . . ."

and the rest of it.

From the *Panchatantra,* translated by Arthur W. Ryder (Chicago: Univercity of Chicago Press, 1925).

THE LION MAKERS

Scholarship is less than sense;
Therefore seek intelligence:
Senseless scholars in their pride
Made a lion; then they died.

IN A CERTAIN town were four Brahmans who lived in friendship. Three of them had reached the far shore of all scholarship but lacked sense. The other found scholarship distasteful; he had nothing but sense.

One day they met for consultation. "What is the use of attainments," said they, "if one does not travel, win the favor of kings, and acquire money? Whatever we do, let us all travel."

But when they had gone a little way the eldest of them said, "One of us, the fourth, is a dullard, having nothing but sense. Now nobody gains the favorable attention of kings by simple sense without scholarship. Therefore we will not share our earnings with him. Let him turn back and go home."

Then the second said, "My intelligent friend, you lack scholarship. Please go home." But the third said, "No, no. This is no way to behave. For we have played together since we were little boys. Come along, my noble friend. You shall have a share of the money we earn."

With this agreement they continued their journey, and in a forest they found the bones of a dead lion. Thereupon one of them said, "A good opportunity to test the ripeness of our scholarship. Here lies some kind of creature, dead. Let us bring it to life by means of the scholarship we have honestly won."

Then the first said, "I know how to assemble the skeleton." The second said, "I can supply skin, flesh, and blood." The third said, "I can give it life."

So the first assembled the skeleton, the second provided the skin, flesh, and blood. But while the third was intent on giving the breath of life, the man of sense advised against it, remarking, "This is a lion. If you bring him to life, he will kill every one of us."

"You simpleton!" said the other, "it is not I who will reduce scholarship to a nullity."

"In that case," came the reply, "wait a moment, while I climb this convenient tree."

When this had been done the lion was brought to life, rose up, and killed all three. But the man of sense, after the lion had gone elsewhere, climbed down and went home.

And that is why I say:

"Scholarship is less than sense . . ."

and the rest of it.

From the *Panchatantra.*

THE LOYAL MUNGOOSE

THERE was once a Brahman named Godly in a certain town. His wife mothered a single son and a mungoose. And as she loved little ones, she cared for the mungoose also like a son, giving him milk from her breast, and salves, and baths, and so on. But she did not trust him, for she thought, "A mungoose is a nasty kind of creature. He might hurt my boy." Yes, there is sense in the proverb:

> A son will ever bring delight,
> Though bent on folly, passion, spite,
> Though shabby, naughty, and a fright.

One day she tucked her son in bed, took a water jar, and said to her husband, "Now, Professor, I am going for water. You must protect the boy from the mungoose." But when she was gone the Brahman went off somewhere himself to beg food, leaving the house empty.

While he was gone a black snake issued from his hole and, as fate would have it, crawled toward the baby's cradle. But the mungoose, feeling him to be a natural enemy and fearing for the life of his baby brother, fell upon the vicious serpent halfway, joined battle with him, tore him to bits, and tossed the pieces far and wide. Then, delighted with his own heroism, he ran, blood trickling from

his mouth, to meet the mother; for he wished to show what he had done.

But when the mother saw him coming, saw his bloody mouth and his excitement, she feared that the villain must have eaten her baby boy, and without thinking twice she angrily dropped the water jar upon him, which killed him the moment that it struck. There she left him without a second thought and hurried home, where she found the baby safe and sound, and near the cradle a great black snake, torn to bits. Then overwhelmed with sorrow because she had thoughtlessly killed her benefactor, her son, she beat her head and breast.

At this moment the Brahman came home with a dish of rice gruel which he had got from someone in his begging tour, and saw his wife bitterly lamenting her son, the mungoose. "Greedy! Greedy!" she cried. "Because you did not do as I told you, you must now taste the bitterness of a son's death, the fruit of the tree of your own wickedness." Yes, this is what happens to those blinded by greed. For the proverb says:

> Indulge in no excessive greed
> (A little helps in time of need)–
> A greedy fellow in the world
> Found on his head a wheel that whirled.

From the *Panchatantra.*

THE BRAHMAN AND THE POT OF RICE

THERE lived in a certain place a Brahman, whose name was Svabhavakripana, which means a born miser. He had collected a quantity of rice by begging, and after having dined off it, he filled a pot with what was left over. He hung the pot on a peg on the wall, placed his couch beneath, and looking intently at it all the night, he thought, "Ah, that pot is indeed brimful of rice. Now if there should be a famine, I should certainly make a hundred rupees by it. With this I shall buy a couple of goats. They will have young ones every six months, and thus I shall have a whole herd of goats. Then with the goats I shall buy cows. As soon as they have calved, I shall sell the calves. Then with the cows I shall buy buffaloes; with the buffaloes, mares. When the mares have foaled, I shall have plenty of horses; and when I sell them, plenty of gold. With that gold I shall get a house with four wings. And then a Brahman will come to my house and will give me his beautiful daughter, with a large dowry. She will have a son, and I shall call him Somasarman. When he is old enough to be danced on his father's knee, I shall sit with a book at the back of the stable, and while I am reading the boy will see me, jump from his mother's lap, and run toward me to be danced on my knee. He will come too near the horse's hoof, and full of anger I shall call to my wife, 'Take the baby, take him!' But she, distracted by some domestic work, does not hear me. Then I get up, and give her such a kick with my foot."

While he thought this, he gave a kick with his foot and broke the pot. All the rice fell over him and made him quite white.

Therefore I say, "He who makes foolish plans for the future will be white all over, like the father of Somasarman."

From the *Panchatantra*, translated by Max Müller in *Chips From a German Workshop.*

THE MICE THAT ATE IRON

ONCE on a time there was a merchant's son who had spent all his father's wealth and had only an iron balance left. Now the balance was made of a thousand *palas* of iron; and depositing it in the care of a certain merchant, he went to another land. When, on his return, he went to that merchant to get back his balance, the merchant said, "It has been eaten by mice." And he repeated, "The iron of which it was composed was particularly sweet, and so the mice ate it." This he said with an outward show of sorrow, although laughing inwardly.

Thereupon the merchant's son asked him for some food, and the other one, being in a good temper, consented to give him some. Then the merchant's son went to bathe, taking with him the other's son, a mere child, whom he persuaded to come with him by offering him a dish of *amalakas*. And after he had bathed, the wise merchant's son deposited the boy in the house of a friend and returned alone to the house of the merchant. And the latter said to him, "Where is that son of mine?" Whereupon the merchant's son replied, "A hawk swooped down from the air and carried him off."

The merchant in a rage said, "You have concealed my son." And so he took him into the king's judgment hall; and there the merchant's son repeated his original statement. The officers of the court said, "This is impossible. How could a hawk carry off a boy?"

So the merchant's son answered, "In a country where a large balance of iron was eaten by mice, a hawk might easily carry off an elephant." When the officers heard that, they inquired further and, on being told the entire story, made the merchant restore the balance to the owner, and he, for his part, restored the merchant's son.

Adapted from Somadeva's *Katha Sarit Sagara*, translated by C. H. Tawney (Calcutta: Baptist Mission Society, 1880–1884).

DEVABHUTI AND THE FOOLISH MAGISTRATE

THERE lived in Panchala, of old time, a Brahman named Devabhuti, and that Brahman, who was learned in the Vedas, had a chaste wife named Bhogadatta. One day when he had gone to bathe, his wife went into the kitchen garden to get vegetables but found that a washerman's donkey was devouring them. So she took up a stick and ran after the donkey, and the animal, trying to escape, fell into a pit and broke its hoof. When its master heard of that, he came in a passion, beat the Brahman woman with a stick and kicked her. As a result of the beating, she, being pregnant, had a miscarriage. The washerman returned home with his donkey.

The woman's husband, hearing of it, came home after bathing, and, seeing his wife, went in his distress and complained to the chief magistrate of the town. The foolish magistrate immediately had the washerman brought before him, and, after hearing the pleadings of both parties, delivered this judgment.

"Since the donkey's hoof is broken, let the Brahman carry the donkey's load for the washerman until the donkey is again fit for work. And let the washerman make the Brahman's wife pregnant again, since he made her miscarry. Let this be the punishment of the two parties respectively."

When the Brahman heard this, he and his wife, in their despair, took poison and died. And when the king heard of it, he put to death that inconsiderate judge.

Adapted from the *Katha Sarit Sagara*.

THE THREE FASTIDIOUS MEN

THERE is a great tract of land assigned to Brahmans in the country of Anga. In it there lived a rich, sacrificing Brahman named Vishnusvamin. And he had a wife equal to himself in birth. And by her he had three sons, who were distinguished by their extraordinary sensitivity. One day, when he had begun a sacrifice, he sent the brothers to the sea to fetch a turtle. So off they went, and when they had found a turtle the eldest said to his two brothers, "Let one of you take the turtle. I cannot take it because it is so slimy."

When the eldest brother said this, the two younger ones answered him, "If you hesitate about taking it, why should not we?" When the eldest heard that, he said, "You two must take the turtle; if you do not you will have obstructed our father's sacrifice, and then you and he will certainly sink down to hell." When he told the younger brothers this, they laughed and said to him, "If you see our duty so clearly, why do you not see that your own is the same?" Then the eldest said, "What! do you not know how fastidious I am? I am most fastidious about eating, and I cannot be expected to touch what is repulsive." The middle brother, when he heard this speech, said to his brother, "Then I am even more fastidious than you, for I am a most particular connoisseur of women." When the middle one said this, the eldest went on to say, "Then let the younger of you two take the turtle!" Then the youngest brother frowned and in his turn said, "You fools, I am the most fastidious of us all, for I am fastidious even about beds."

So the three brothers fell to quarreling with one another, and, being completely under the dominion of conceit, they left that turtle and went off immediately to the court of the king of that country in order to have the dispute decided. There they had themselves announced by the warder, and went in, and gave the king a circumstantial account of their case. The king said, "Wait here, and I will put you all in turn to the proof."

And at the time that the king took his meal, he had them conducted to a seat of honor and given food that was fit for a king, possessing all the six flavors. And while all were feasting around him, the Brahman who was fastidious about eating, alone of all the company, did not eat, but sat there with his face puckered up with disgust. The king himself asked the Brahman why he did not eat his food, though it was sweet and fragrant, and the Brahman slowly answered him, "I perceive in this cooked rice an evil smell of corpses, so I cannot bring myself to eat it, however delicious it may seem."

Then the king reflected, and proceeded to inquire into the matter, and found out from his officers that the food had been made from rice which had been grown in a field near the burning *ghat* of a certain village. Then the king was much astonished, and he said to the Brahman, "In truth you are very particular as to what you eat; so eat of some other dish."

After they had finished the dinner the king dismissed the Brahmans to their apartments and sent for the loveliest lady of his court. That evening he sent her, splendidly adorned, to the second Brahman, who was so squeamish about the fair sex. And that matchless kindler of Kama's flame, with a face like the full moon of midnight, went, escorted by the king's servants, to the chamber of the Brahman. But when she entered, lighting up the chamber with her brightness, that gentleman, who was so fastidious about the fair sex, felt quite faint and, stopping his nose with his left hand, said to the king's servants, "Take her away. If you do not, I am a dead man. A smell comes from her like that of a goat."

When the king's servants heard this, they took the bewildered fair one to their sovereign and told him what had taken place. And the king immediately had the squeamish gentleman sent for and said to him, "How can this lovely woman, who has perfumed herself with sandalwood, camphor, black aloes, and other splendid scents, so that she diffuses exquisite fragrance through the whole world, smell like a goat?" But though the king used such arguments with the squeamish gentleman, he stuck to his point. And then the king began to have his doubts on the subject, and at last, by artfully framed questions, he elicited from the lady herself that, having been separated in her childhood from her mother and nurse, she had been brought up on goat's milk.

Then the king was much astonished, and praised highly the discernment of the man who was fastidious about the fair sex, and immediately had given to the third Brahman, who was fastidious about beds, a bed composed of seven mattresses placed upon a bedstead. White smooth sheets and coverlets were laid upon the bed, and the fastidious man slept on it in a splendid room. But before half a watch of the night had passed, he rose up from that bed with his hand pressed to his side, screaming in an agony of pain. And the king's officers, who were there, saw a crooked red mark on his side, as if a hair had been pressed deep into it. And they went and told the king, and the king said to them, "Look and see if there is not something under the mattresses."

So they went and examined the bottom of the mattresses one by one, and they found a hair in the middle of the bedstead underneath them all. And they took it and showed it to the king; and they also brought the man who was fastidious about beds, and when the king saw the state of his body, he was astonished. And he spent the whole night in wondering how a hair could have made so deep an impression on his skin through seven mattresses.

And the next morning the king gave three hundred thousand gold pieces to those three fastidious men, because they were persons of wonderful discernment and refinement. And they remained in great comfort in the king's court.

Adapted from the *Katha Sarit Sagara.*

THE KING WHO WAS FRIED

ONCE upon a time, a very long time ago indeed, there lived a king who had made a vow never to eat bread or break his fast until he had given away a hundredweight of gold in charity.

So every day, before King Karan—for that was his name—had his breakfast, the palace servants would come out with baskets and baskets of gold pieces to scatter amongst the crowds of poor folk, who, you may be sure, never forgot to be there to receive the alms. Then, when the last golden piece had been fought for, King Karan would sit down to his breakfast and enjoy it as a man who has kept his word should do.

Now when people saw the king lavishing his gold in this fashion they naturally thought that sooner or later the royal treasuries must give out, the gold come to an end, and the king—who was evidently a man of his word—die of starvation. But, though months and years passed by, every day, just a quarter of an hour before breakfast time, the servants came out of the palace with baskets and baskets of gold; and as the crowds dispersed they could see the king sitting down to his breakfast in the royal banqueting hall, as jolly, and fat, and hungry as could be.

Now, of course, there was some secret in all this, and this secret I shall now tell you. King Karan had made a compact with a holy and very hungry old fakir who lived at the top of the hill; and the compact was this: on condition that King Karan would allow himself to be fried and eaten for breakfast every day, the fakir would give him a hundred weight of pure gold.

Of course, had the fakir been an ordinary sort of person the compact would not have lasted long, for once King Karan had been fried and eaten, there would have been an end of the matter. But the fakir was a very remarkable fakir indeed, and when he had eaten the king, and picked the bones quite quite clean, he just put them together, said a charm or two, and, hey presto! there was King Karan as fat and jolly as ever, ready for the next morning's breakfast. In fact, the fakir made no bones at all over the affair, which, it must be confessed, was very convenient both for the breakfast and the breakfast eater. Nevertheless, it was of course not pleasant to be popped alive every morning into a great frying pan of boiling oil; and for my part I think King Karan earned his hundredweight of gold handsomely. But after a time he got accustomed to the process, and would go up quite cheerfully to the holy and hungry one's house, where the biggest frying pan was spitting and sputtering over the sacred fire. Then he would just pass the time of day to the fakir, to make sure he was punctual, and step gracefully into his hot oil bath. How he sizzled and fizzled! When he was crisp and brown, the fakir ate him, picked the bones, set them together, sang a charm, and finished the business by bringing out his dirty old ragged coat, which he shook and shook, while the bright golden pieces came tumbling out of the pockets onto the floor.

So that was the way King Karan got his gold, and if you think it very extraordinary, so do I!

Now, in the great Mansarobar Lake, where, as of course you

know, all the wild swans live when they leave us, and feed upon seed pearls, there was a great famine. Pearls were so scarce that one pair of swans determined to go out into the world and seek for food. So they flew into King Bikramajit's garden, at Ujjayin. Now, when the gardener saw the beautiful birds, he was delighted, and, hoping to induce them to stay, he threw them grain to eat. But they would not touch it, nor any other food he offered them; so he went to his master and told him there were a pair of swans in the garden who refused to eat anything.

Then King Bikramajit went out and asked them in birds' language (for, as everyone knows, Bikramajit understood both beasts and birds) why it was that they ate nothing.

"We don't eat grain!" said they, "nor fruit, nor anything but fresh unpierced pearls!"

Whereupon King Bikramajit, being very kindhearted, sent for a basket of pearls; and every day, when he came into the garden, he fed the swans with his own hand.

But one day, when he was feeding them as usual, one of the pearls happened to be pierced. The dainty swans found it out at once, and, coming to the conclusion that King Bikramajit's supply of pearls was running short, they made up their minds to go farther afield. So, despite his entreaties, they spread their broad white wings and flew up into the blue sky, their outstretched necks pointing straight toward home on the great Mansarobar Lake. Yet they were not ungrateful, for as they flew they sang the praises of Bikramajit.

Now King Karan was watching his servants bring out the baskets of gold when the wild swans came flying over his head; and when he heard them singing, "Glory to Bikramajit! Glory to Bikramajit!" he said to himself, "Who is this whom even the birds praise? I let myself be fried and eaten every day in order that I may be able to give away a hundredweight of gold in charity, yet no swan sings *my* song!"

So, being jealous, he sent for a birdcatcher, who snared the poor swans with lime and put them in a cage.

Then Karan hung the cage in the palace and ordered his servants to bring every kind of birds' food; but the proud swans only curved their white necks in scorn, saying, "Glory to Bikramajit! He gave us pearls to eat!"

Then King Karan, determined not to be outdone, sent for pearls; but still the scornful swans would not touch anything.

"Why will ye not eat?" quoth King Karan wrathfully. "Am I not as generous as Bikramajit?"

Then the swan's wife answered and said, "Kings do not imprison the innocent. Kings do not war against women. If Bikramajit were here, he would at any rate let me go!"

So Karan, not to be outdone in generosity, let the swan's wife go, and she spread her broad white wings and flew southward to Bikramajit and told him how her husband lay a prisoner at the court of King Karan.

Of course Bikramajit, who was, as everyone knows, the most generous of kings, determined to release the poor captive; and bidding the swan fly back and rejoin her mate, he put on the garb of a servant, and taking the name of Bikru, journeyed northward till he came to King Karan's kingdom. Then he took service with the king, and helped every day to carry out the baskets of gold pieces. He soon saw there was some secret in King Karan's endless wealth, and never rested until he had found it out. So, one day, hidden close by, he saw King Karan enter the fakir's house and pop into the boiling oil. He saw him frizzle and sizzle, he saw him come out crisp and brown, he saw the hungry and holy fakir pick the bones, and, finally, he saw King Karan, fat and jolly as ever, go down the mountainside with his hundredweight of gold!

Then Bikru knew what to do! So the very next day he rose very early and, taking a carving knife he slashed himself all over. Next he took some pepper and salt, spices, pounded pomegranate seeds, and pea flour; these he mixed together into a beautiful curry stuff and rubbed himself all over with it—right into the cuts in spite of the smarting. When he thought he was quite ready for cooking, he just went up the hill to the fakir's house and popped into the frying pan. The fakir was still asleep, but he soon awoke with the sizzling and the fizzling and said to himself, "Dear me! how uncommonly nice the king smells this morning!"

Indeed, so appetizing was the smell that he could hardly wait until the king was crisp and brown, but then how he gobbled him up!

You see, he had been eating plain fried so long that a deviled king was quite a change. He picked the bones ever so clean, and it is my belief would have eaten them too if he had not been afraid of killing the goose that laid the golden eggs.

Then, when it was all over, he put the king together again and said, with tears in his eyes, "What a breakfast that was, to be sure! Tell me how you managed to taste so nice, and I'll give you anything you ask."

Whereupon Bikru told him the way it was done and promised to devil himself every morning if he might have the old coat in return. "For," said he, "it is not pleasant to be fried! And I don't see why I should in addition have the trouble of carrying a hundredweight of gold to the palace every day. Now if *I* keep the coat, I can shake it down there."

To this the fakir agreed, and off went Bikru with the coat.

Meanwhile King Karan came toiling up the hill, and was surprised, when he entered the fakir's house, to find the fire out, the frying pan put away, and the fakir himself as holy as ever but not in the least hungry.

"Why, what is the matter?" faltered the king.

"Who are you?" asked the fakir, who, to begin with, was somewhat shortsighted, and, in addition, felt drowsy after his heavy meal.

"Who! Why, I'm King Karan, come to be fried! Don't you want your breakfast?"

"I've had my breakfast!" sighed the fakir regretfully. "You tasted very nice when you were deviled, I can assure you!"

"I never was deviled in my life!" shouted the king. "You must have eaten somebody else!"

"That's just what I was saying to myself!" returned the fakir sleepily. "I thought—it couldn't—be only—the spices—that—" Snore, snore, snore!

"Look here!" cried King Karan in a rage, shaking the fakir, "you must eat me too!"

"Couldn't!" nodded the holy but satisfied fakir. "Really—not another morsel—no, thanks!"

"Then give me my gold!" shrieked King Karan. "You're bound to do that, for I'm ready to fulfill my part of the contract!"

"Sorry I can't oblige, but the devil—I mean the other person—went off with the coat!" nodded the fakir.

Hearing this, King Karan returned home in despair and ordered the royal treasurer to send him gold; so that day he ate his breakfast in peace.

And the next day also, by ransacking all the private treasuries, a hundredweight of gold was forthcoming; so King Karan ate his breakfast as usual, though his heart was gloomy.

But the third day the royal treasurer arrived with empty hands and, casting himself on the ground exclaimed, "May it please Your Majesty! there is not any more gold in Your Majesty's domains!"

Then King Karan went solemnly to bed, without any breakfast, and the crowd, after waiting for hours expecting to see the palace doors open and the servants come out with the baskets of gold, melted away, saying it was a great shame to deceive poor folk in that way!

By dinnertime poor King Karan was visibly thinner; but he was a man of his word, and though the wily Bikru came and tried to persuade him to eat, by saying he could not possibly be blamed, he shook his head and turned his face to the wall.

Then Bikru, or Bikramajit, took the fakir's old coat and, shaking it before the king, said, "Take the money, my friend; and what is more, if you will set the wild swans you have in that cage at liberty, I will give you the coat into the bargain!"

So King Karan set the wild swans at liberty, and as the pair of them flew away to the great Mansarobar Lake, they sang as they went, "Glory to Bikramajit! the generous Bikramajit!"

Then King Karan hung his head and said to himself, "The swans' song is true! Bikramajit is more generous than I; for if I was fried for the sake of a hundredweight of gold and my breakfast, he was deviled in order to set a bird at liberty!"

From *Wide-awake Stories,* collected by Flora Annie Steel and R. C. Temple (Bombay: Education Society's Press; and London: Trübner and Company, 1884).

Irish

Deirdre

FEW FOLK tales represent the collective imagination of a people more adequately than do those of the Irish. They may of course give this impression because many of the most gifted of Ireland's professional writers since 1875 have drawn so heavily on them and contributed so heavily to them. One hardly knows where the spirit of popular tradition leaves off and that of William Butler Yeats, Douglas Hyde, J. M. Synge, Standish O'Grady, Lady Gregory, Lady Wilde, and James Stephens begins.

But it is undoubtedly the traditional stories of Deirdre, Cuchullin, and the heroes of Ulster that have given us the vision of a twilit realm in which pagan heroes eliminate each other by force or cunning while their queenly women read omens or raise their voices in poetic lament. They are the source of the conception of Cuchullin as Ulster's Achilles, fighting against fatal odds and dying young, of Deirdre as Ulster's Helen, leaving her royal husband for one of the sons of Usnach and spreading doom everywhere, and finally of all Ulster forever ranged in fierce struggle against the rest of Ireland.

But the Irish are rich in humor, capable of turning on the somber themes of their ancient tales and making light of them. "A Legend of Knockmany," with its jaunty manner and its blithe juxtaposing of the heroic Cuchullin, who dates from about the first century B.C., and the equally heroic Finn, who belongs to another cycle of Irish tales and does not come on the scene until several centuries later, is an amusing example of such a parody.

Probably the richest contribution the dreaming Celt has made to mankind's reserves of fancy is the *aes sidhe*, or shee–the fairy folk. Antiquarians say that they are descended from the gods of pagan Ireland (described in the great story cycle of the *Tuatha De Danān*) and that when the gods were no longer worshiped they dwindled until each was only a few spans in height. Country folk used to insist that the shee were really fallen angels. Either interpretation helps to explain the two-sided nature of "the little people" of modern Irish and British lore. (For the British species see "The Piskeys of Selena Moor.") In "The Field of Boliauns" the cluricaune—blood brothers to the leprechaun—are rather amiable creatures, almost living up to the name of "the good folk" with which fearful country people seek to placate them. Usually the mischievous goblin strain is dominant in them, and then it is apparently their pleasure to plague mortal men with the sort of ghoulishly humorous torment visited on Teig O'Kane.

DEIRDRE

THERE was a man in Ireland once who was called Malcolm Harper. The man was a right good man, and he had a goodly share of this world's goods. He had a wife but no family. What did Malcolm hear but that a soothsayer had come home to the place, and as the man was a right good man, he wished that the soothsayer might come near them. Whether it was that he was invited or that he came of himself, the soothsayer came to the house of Malcolm.

"Are you doing any soothsaying?" says Malcolm.

"Yes, I am doing a little. Are you in need of soothsaying?"

"Well, I do not mind taking soothsaying from you, if you had soothsaying for me, and you would be willing to do it."

"Well, I will do soothsaying for you. What kind of soothsaying do you want?"

"Well, the soothsaying I wanted was that you would tell me my lot or what will happen to me, if you can give me knowledge of it."

"Well, I am going out, and when I return I will tell you."

And the soothsayer went forth out of the house, and he was not long outside when he returned.

"Well," said the soothsayer, "I saw in my second sight that it is on account of a daughter of yours that the greatest amount of blood shall be shed that has ever been shed in Erin since time and race began. And the three most famous heroes that ever were found will lose their heads on her account."

After a time a daughter was born to Malcolm. He did not allow a living being to come to his house, only himself and the nurse. He asked this woman, "Will you yourself bring up the child to keep her in hiding far away where eye will not see a sight of her nor ear can hear a word about her?"

The woman said she would, so Malcolm got three men, and he took them away to a large mountain, distant and far from reach, without the knowledge or notice of anyone. He caused there a hillock, round and green, to be dug out of the middle, and the hole was thus made to be covered carefully over, so that a little company could dwell there together. This was done.

Deirdre and her foster mother dwelt in the bothy mid the hills without the knowledge or the suspicion of any living person about them, and without anything occurring, until Deirdre was sixteen years of age. Deirdre grew like the white sapling, straight and trim as the rash on the moss. She was the creature of fairest form, of loveliest aspect, and of gentlest nature that existed between earth and heaven in all Ireland–whatever color of hue she had before, there was nobody that looked into her face but she would blush fiery red over it.

The woman that had charge of her gave Deirdre every information and skill of which she herself had knowledge and skill. There was not a blade of grass growing from root, nor a bird singing in the wood, nor a star shining from heaven, but Deirdre had a name for it. But one thing, she did not wish her to have either part or parley with any single living man of the rest of the world. But on a gloomy winter night, with black, scowling clouds, a hunter of game was wearily traveling the hills, and what happened but that he missed the trail of the hunt and lost his course and companions. A drowsiness came upon the man as he wearily wandered over the hills, and he laid down by the side of the beautiful green knoll in which Deirdre lived, and he slept. The man was faint from hunger and wandering and benumbed with cold, and a deep sleep fell upon him. When he lay down beside the green hill where Deirdre was, a troubled dream came to the man, and he thought that he enjoyed the warmth of a fairy broch, the fairies being inside playing music. The hunter shouted out in his dream if there was anyone in the broch, to let him in for the Holy One's sake.

Deirdre heard the voice and said to her foster mother, "O foster mother, what cry is that?" "It is nothing at all, Deirdre–merely the birds of the air astray and seeking each other. But let them go past to the bosky glade. There is no shelter or house for them here." "O foster mother, the bird asked to get inside for the sake of the God of the Elements, and you yourself tell me that anything that is asked in His name we ought to do. If you will not allow the bird that is being benumbed with cold, and done to death with hunger, to be let in, I do not think much of your language or your faith. But since I give credence to your language and to your faith, which you taught me, I will myself let in the bird."

And Deirdre arose and drew the bolt from the leaf of the door, and she let in the hunter. She placed a seat in the place of sitting, food in the place for eating, and drink in the place for drinking, for the man who came to the house. "Oh, for this life and raiment, you man that came in, keep restraint on your tongue!" said the old woman. "It is not a great thing for you to keep your mouth shut and your tongue quiet when you get a home and shelter of a hearth on a gloomy winter's night." "Well," said the hunter, "I may do that—keep my mouth shut and my tongue quiet, since I came to the house and received hospitality from you; but by the hand of thy father and grandfather, and by your own two hands, if some other of the people of the world saw this beauteous creature you have here hid away, they would not long leave her with you, I swear."

"What men are these you refer to?" said Deirdre.

"Well, I will tell you, young woman," said the hunter. "They are Naois, son of Uisnech, and Allan and Arden his two brothers."

"What like are these men when seen, if we were to see them?" said Deidre.

"Why, the aspect and form of the men when seen are these," said the hunter. "They have the color of the raven on their hair, their skin like swan on the wave in whiteness, and their cheeks as the blood of the brindled red calf, and their speed and their leap are those of the salmon of the torrent and the deer of the gray mountainside. And Naois is head and shoulders over the rest of the people of Erin."

"However they are," said the nurse, "be you off from here and take another road. And, King of Light and Sun! in good sooth and certainty, little are my thanks for yourself or for her that let you in!"

The hunter went away and went straight to the palace of King Connachar. He sent word in to the king that he wished to speak to him if he pleased. The king answered the message and came out to speak to the man. "What is the reason of your journey?" said the king to the hunter.

"I have only to tell you, O king," said the hunter, "that I saw the fairest creature that ever was born in Erin, and I came to tell you of it."

"Who is this beauty, and where is she to be seen, when she was not seen before till you saw her, if you did see her?"

"Well, I did see her," said the hunter. "But, if I did, no man else can see her unless he get directions from me as to where she is dwelling."

"And will you direct me to where she dwells? And the reward of your directing me will be as good as the reward of your message," said the king.

"Well, I will direct you, O King, although it is likely that this will not be what they want," said the hunter.

Connachar, king of Ulster, sent for his nearest kinsmen, and he told them of his intent. Though early rose the song of the birds mid the rocky caves and the music of the birds in the grove, earlier than that did Connachar, king of Ulster, arise, with his little troop of dear friends, in the delightful twilight of the fresh and gentle May; the dew was heavy on each bush and flower and stem as they went to bring Deirdre forth from the green knoll where she stayed. Many a youth was there who had a lithe, leaping, and lissom step when they started whose step was faint, failing, and faltering when they reached the bothy on account of the length of the way and roughness of the road. "Yonder, now, down in the bottom of the glen is the bothy where the woman dwells, but I will not go nearer than this to the old woman," said the hunter.

Connachar with his band of kinsfolk went down to the green knoll where Deirdre dwelt and he knocked at the door of the bothy. The nurse replied, "No less than a king's command and a king's army could put me out of my bothy tonight. And I should be obliged to you, were you to tell who it is that wants me to open my bothy door." "It is I, Connachar, king of Ulster." When the poor woman heard who was at the door she rose with haste and let in the king and all that could get in of his retinue.

When the king saw the woman that was before him that he had been in quest of, he thought he never saw in the course of the day nor in the dream of night a creature so fair as Deirdre, and he gave his full heart's weight of love to her. Deirdre was raised on the topmost of the heroes' shoulders, and she and her foster mother were brought to the court of King Connachar of Ulster.

With the love that Connachar had for her, he wanted to marry Deirdre right off there and then, will she nill she marry him. But she said to him, "I would be obliged to you if you will give me the respite of a year and a day." He said, "I will grant you that, hard though it is, if you will give me your unfailing promise that you will marry me at the year's end." And she gave the promise. Connachar got for her a woman teacher and merry modest maidens fair that would lie down and rise with her, that would play and speak with her. Deirdre was clever in maidenly duties and wifely understanding, and Connachar thought he never saw with bodily eye a creature that pleased him more.

Deirdre and her women companions were one day out on the hillock behind the house, enjoying the scene and drinking in the sun's heat. What did they see coming but three men a-journeying. Deirdre was looking at the men that were coming and wondering at them. When the men neared them Deirdre remembered the language of the huntsman, and she said to herself that these were the three sons of Uisnech, and that this was Naois, he having what was above the bend of the two shoulders above the men of Erin all. The three brothers went past without taking any notice of them, without even glancing at the young girls on the hillock. What happened but that love for Naois struck the heart of Deirdre, so that she could not but follow after him. She girded up her raiment and went after the men that went past the base of the knoll, leaving her women attendants there. Allan and Arden had heard of the woman that Connachar, king of Ulster, had with him, and they thought that if Naois, their brother, saw her, he would have her himself, more especially as she was not married to the king. They perceived the woman coming and called on one another to hasten their step as they had a long distance to travel and the dusk of night was coming on. They did so. She cried, "Naois, son of Uisnech, will you leave me?" "What piercing, shrill cry is that—the most melodious my ear ever heard, and the shrillest that ever struck my heart of all the cries I ever heard?" "It isn't anything else but the wail of the wave swans of Connachar," said his brothers. "No! yonder is a woman's cry of distress," said Naois, and he swore he would not go farther until he saw from whom the cry came, and Naois turned back. Naois and Deirdre met, and Deirdre kissed Naois three times, and a kiss each to his brothers. With the confusion that she was in, Deirdre went into a crimson blaze of fire, and her color came and went as rapidly as the movement of the aspen by the stream side. Naois thought he never saw a fairer creature, and Naois gave Deirdre the love that he never gave to thing, to vision, or to creature but to herself.

Then Naois placed Deirdre on the topmost height of his shoulder and told his brothers to keep up their pace, and they kept up their pace. Naois thought that it would not be well for him to remain in Erin on account of the way in which Connachar, king of Ulster, his uncle's son, had gone against him because of the woman, though he had not married her; and he turned back to Alba, that is, Scotland. He reached the side of Loch Ness and made his habitation there. He could kill the salmon of the torrent from out his own door, and the deer of the gray gorge from out his window. Naois and Deirdre and Allan and Arden dwelt in a tower, and they were happy so long a time as they were there.

By this time the end of the period came in which Deirdre had to marry Connachar, king of Ulster. Connachar made up his mind to take Deirdre away by the sword whether she was married to Naois or not. So he prepared a great and gleeful feast. He sent word far and wide through Erin to all his kinspeople to come to the feast. Connachar thought to himself that Naois would not come though he should bid him, and the scheme that arose in his mind was to send for his father's brother, Ferchar Mac Ro, and to send him on an embassy to Naois. He did so; and Connachar said to Ferchar, "Tell Naois, son of Uisnech, that I am setting forth a great and gleeful feast to my friends and kinspeople throughout the wide extent of Erin all, and that I shall not have rest by day nor sleep by night if he and Allan and Arden be no partakers of the feast."

Ferchar Mac Ro and his three sons went on their journey, and reached the tower where Naois was dwelling by the side of Loch Etive. The sons of Uisnech gave a cordial, kindly welcome to Ferchar Mac Ro and his three sons and asked of him the news of Erin. "The best news that I have for you," said the Hardy Hero, "is that Connachar, king of Ulster, is setting forth a great sumptuous feast to his friends and kinspeople throughout the wide extent of Erin all, and he has vowed by the earth beneath him, by the high heaven above him, and by the sun that wends to the west, that he will have no rest by day nor sleep by night if the sons of Uisnech, the sons of his own father's brother, will not come back to the land of their home and the soil of their nativity, and to the feast likewise, and he has sent us as embassy to invite you."

"We will go with you," said Naois.

"We will," said his brothers.

But Deirdre did not wish to go with Ferchar Mac Ro, and she tried every prayer to turn Naois from going with him. She said, "I saw a vision, Naois, and do you interpret it to me," said Deirdre; then she sang:

"O Naois, son of Uisnech, hear
What was shown in a dream to me.

There came three white doves out of the south
Flying over the sea,
And drops of honey were in their mouth
From the hive of the honey bee.

O Naois, son of Uisnech, hear
What was shown in a dream to me.

I saw three gray hawks out of the south
Come flying over the sea,
And the red drops they bare in their mouth
They were dearer than life to me."

Said Naois:

"It is nought but the fear of woman's heart
And a dream of the night, Deirdre.

"The day that Connachar sent the invitation to his feast will be unlucky for us if we don't go, O Deirdre."

"You will go there," said Ferchar Mac Ro, "and if Connachar show kindness to you, show ye kindness to him; and if he will display wrath toward you, display ye wrath toward him, and I and my three sons will be with you."

"We will," said Daring Drop. "We will," said Hardy Holly. "We will," said Fiallan the Fair.

"I have three sons, and they are three heroes, and in any harm or danger that may befall you, they will be with you, and I myself will be along with them." And Ferchar Mac Ro gave his vow and his word in presence of his arms that, in any harm or danger that came in the way of the sons of Uisnech, he and his three sons would not leave head on live body in Erin, despite sword or helmet, spear or shield, blade or mail, be they ever so good.

Deirdre was unwilling to leave Alba, but she went with Naois. Deirdre wept tears in showers and she sang:

"Dear is the land, the land over there,
Alba full of woods and lakes;
Bitter to my heart is leaving thee,
But I go away with Naois."

Ferchar Mac Ro did not stop till he got the sons of Uisnech away with him, despite the suspicion of Deirdre.

The coracle was put to sea,
The sail was hoisted to it;
And the second morrow they arrived
On the white shores of Erin.

As soon as the sons of Uisnech landed in Erin, Ferchar Mac Ro sent word to Connachar, king of Ulster, that the men whom he wanted were come, and let him now show kindness to them. "Well," said Connachar, "I did not expect that the sons of Uisnech would come, though I sent for them, and I am not quite ready to receive them. But there is a house down yonder where I keep strangers, and let them go down to it today, and my house will be ready before them tomorrow."

But he that was up in the palace felt it long that he was not getting word as to how matters were going on for those down in the house of the strangers. "Go you, Gelban Grednach, son of Lochlin's king, go you down and bring me information as to whether her former hue and complexion are on Deirdre. If they be, I will take her out with edge of blade and point of sword, and if not, let Naois, son of Uisnech, have her for himself," said Connachar.

Gelban, the cheering and charming son of Lochlin's king, went down to the place of the strangers, where the sons of Uisnech and Deirdre were staying. He looked in through the bicker-hole on the door-leaf. Now she that he gazed upon used to go into a crimson blaze of blushes when anyone looked at her. Naois looked at Deirdre and knew that someone was looking at her from the back of the door-leaf. He seized one of the dice on the table before him, and fired it through the bicker-hole, and knocked the eye out of Gleban Grednach the Cheerful and Charming, right through the back of his head. Gelban returned back to the palace of King Connachar.

"You were cheerful, charming, going away, but you are cheerless, charmless, returning. What has happened to you, Gelban? But have you seen her, and are Deirdre's hue and complexion as before?" said Connachar.

"Well, I have seen Deirdre, and I saw her also truly, and while I was looking at her through the bicker-hole on the door, Naois, son of Uisnech, knocked out my eye with one of the dice in his hand. But of a truth and verity, although he put out even my eye, it were my desire still to remain looking at her with the other eye, were it not for the hurry you told me to be in," said Gelban.

"That is true," said Connachar. "Let three hundred brave heroes go down to the abode of the strangers, and let them bring hither to me Deirdre, and kill the rest."

Connachar ordered three hundred active heroes to go down to the abode of the strangers, and to take Deirdre up with them and kill the rest.

"The pursuit is coming," said Deirdre.

"Yes, but I will myself go out and stop the pursuit," said Naois.

"It is not you, but we that will go," said Daring Drop, and Hardy Holly, and Fiallan the Fair. "It is to us that our father entrusted your defense from harm and danger when he himself left for home." And the gallant youths, full noble, full manly, full handsome, with beauteous brown locks, went forth girt with battle arms fit for fierce fight and clothed with combat dress for fierce contest fit, which was burnished, bright, brilliant, bladed, blazing, on which were many pictures of beasts and birds, and creeping things, lions, and lithe-limbed tigers, brown eagle, and harrying hawk, and adder fierce; and the young heroes laid low three-thirds of the company.

Connachar came out in haste and cried with wrath, "Who is there on the floor of fight, slaughtering my men?"

"We, the three sons of Ferchar Mac Ro."

"Well," said the king, "I will give a free bridge to your grandfather, a free bridge to your father, and a free bridge each to you three brothers, if you come over to my side tonight."

"Well, Connachar, we will not accept that offer from you, nor thank you for it. Greater by far do we prefer to go home to our father, and tell the deeds of heroism we have done, than accept anything on these terms from you. Naois, son of Uisnech, and Allan and Arden are as nearly related to yourself as they are to us, though you are so keen to shed their blood, and you would shed our blood also, Connachar." And the noble, manly, handsome youths, with beauteous brown locks, returned inside. "We are now," said they, "going home to tell our father that you are now safe from the hands of the king." And the youths, all fresh and tall and lithe and beautiful, went home to their father to tell that the sons of Uisnech were safe. This happened at the parting of the day and night in the morning twilight time, and Naois said they must go away, leave that house, and return to Alba.

Naois and Deirdre, Allan and Arden, started to return to Alba. Word came to the king that the company he was in pursuit of were gone. The king then sent for Duanan Gacha Druid, the best magician he had, and he spake to him as follows: "Much wealth have I expended on you, Duanan Gacha Druid, to give schooling and learning and magic mystery to you. I'll hold you to account if these people get away from me today without care, without consideration or regard for me, without chance of overtaking them, and without power to stop them."

"Well, I will stop them," said the magician, "until the company you send in pursuit return." And the magician placed a wood before them through which no man could go, but the sons of Uisnech marched through the wood without halt or hesitation, and Deirdre held on to Naois's hand.

"What is the good of that? That will not do yet," said Connachar. "They are off without bending of their feet or stopping of their step, without heed or respect to me, and I am without power to keep up to them, or opportunity to turn them back this night."

"I will try another plan on them," said the druid; and he placed before them a gray sea instead of a green plain. The three heroes stripped and tied their clothes behind their heads, and Naois placed Deirdre on the top of his shoulder.

They stretched their sides to the stream,
    And sea and land were to them the same,
The rough gray ocean was the same
    As meadowland green and plain.

"Though that be good, O Duanan, it will not make the heroes return," said Connachar. "They are gone without regard for me, and without honor to me, and without power on my part to pursue them, or to force them to return this night."

"We shall try another method on them, since yon one did not stop them," said the druid. And the druid froze the gray-ridged sea into hard rocky knobs, the sharpness of sword being on the one edge and the poison power of adders on the other. Then Arden cried that he was getting tired and nearly giving over. "Come you, Arden, and sit on my right shoulder," said Naois. Arden came and sat on Naois's shoulder. Arden was not long in this posture when he died; but though he was dead Naois would not let him go. Allan then cried out that he was getting faint and well-nigh giving up. When Naois heard his prayer, he gave forth the piercing sigh of death, and asked Allan to lay hold of him and he would bring him to land. Allan was not long when the weakness of death came on him, and his hold failed. Naois looked around, and when he saw his two well-beloved brothers dead, he cared not whether he lived or died, and he gave forth the bitter sigh of death, and his heart burst.

"They are gone," said Duanan Gacha Druid to the king, "and I have done what you desired me. The sons of Uisnech are dead, and they will trouble you no more; and you have your wife hale and whole to yourself."

"Blessings for that upon you, and may the good results accrue to me, Duanan. I count it no loss what I spent in the schooling and teaching of you. Now dry up the flood and let me see if I can behold Deirdre," said Connachar. And Duanan Gacha Druid dried up the flood from the plain, and the three sons of Uisnech were lying together dead, without breath of life, side by side on the green meadow plain and Deirdre bending above showering down her tears.

Then Deirdre said this lament: "Fair one, loved one, flower of beauty; beloved, upright, and strong; beloved, noble, and modest warrior. Fair one, blue-eyed, beloved of thy wife; lovely to me at the trysting place came thy clear voice through the woods of Ireland. I cannot eat or smile henceforth. Break not today, my heart: soon enough shall I lie within my grave. Strong are the waves of sorrow, but stronger is sorrow's self, Connachar."

The people then gathered round the heroes' bodies and asked Connachar what was to be done with the bodies. The order that he gave was that they should dig a pit and put the three brothers in it side by side.

Deirdre kept sitting on the brink of the grave, constantly asking the gravediggers to dig the pit wide and free. When the bodies of the brothers were put in the grave, Deirdre said:

> "Come over hither, Naois, my love,
> Let Arden close to Allan lie;
> If the dead had any sense to feel,
> Ye would have made a place for Deirdre."

The men did as she told them. She jumped into the grave and lay down by Naois, and she was dead by his side.

The king ordered the body to be raised from out the grave and to be buried on the other side of the loch. It was done as the king bade, and the pit closed. Thereupon a fir shoot grew out of the grave of Deirdre and a fir shoot from the grave of Naois, and the two shoots united in a knot above the loch. The king ordered the shoots to be cut down, and this was done twice, until, at the third time, the wife whom the king had married caused him to stop this work of evil and his vengeance on the remains of the dead.

From *Celtic Fairy Tales*, selected and edited by Joseph Jacobs (New York: G. P. Putnam's Sons, n.d.).

THE FIELD OF BOLIAUNS

ONE FINE day in harvest—it was indeed Lady-day in harvest, that everybody knows to be one of the greatest holidays in the year—Tom was taking a ramble through the country, and went sauntering along the sunny side of a hedge . . . when all of a sudden he heard a clacking sort of noise a little before him in the hedge.

"Dear me," said Tom, "but isn't it surprising to hear the stonechatters singing so late in the season?" So Tom stole on, going on the tops of his toes to try if he could get a sight of what was making the noise, to see if he was right in his guess. The noise stopped; but as Tom looked sharply through the bushes, what should he see in a nook of the hedge but a brown pitcher that might hold about a gallon and a half of liquor; and by and by a little wee diny dony bit of an old man, with a little *motty* of a cocked hat stuck upon the top of his head, and a deeshy daushy leather apron hanging before him, pulled out a little wooden stool, and stood up upon it, and dipped a little piggin into the pitcher, and took out the full of it, and put it beside the stool, and then sat down under the pitcher, and began to work at putting a heel piece on a bit of a brogue just fit for himself.

"Well, by the powers," said Tom to himself, "I often heard tell of the cluricaune, and, to tell God's truth, I never rightly believed in them—but here's one of them in real earnest. If I go knowingly to work, I'm a made man. They say a body must never take their eyes off them, or they'll escape."

Tom now stole on a little farther, with his eye fixed on the little man just as a cat with a mouse. So when he got up quite close to him, "God bless your work neighbor," said Tom.

The little man raised up his head, and "Thank you kindly," said he.

"I wonder you'd be working on the holiday!" said Tom.

"That's my own business, not yours," was the reply.

"Well, maybe you'd be civil enough to tell *us* what you've got in the pitcher there?" said Tom.

"That I will, with pleasure," said he. "It's good beer."

"Beer!" said Tom. "Thunder and fire! where did you get it?"

"Where did I get it, is it? Why, I made it. And what do you think I made it of?"

"Devil a one of me knows," said Tom, "but of malt, I suppose. What else?"

" 'Tis there you're out. I made it of heath."

"Oh, heath!" said Tom, bursting out laughing. "Sure you don't think me such a fool as to believe that?"

"Do as you please," said he, "but what I tell you is the truth. Did you never hear tell of the Danes?"

"Well, what about them?" said Tom.

"Why, all the about them there is, is that when they were here they taught us to make beer out of the heath, and the secret's in my family ever since."

"Will you give a body a taste of your beer?" said Tom.

"I'll tell you what it is, young man—it would be fitter for you to be looking after your father's property than to be bothering decent, quiet people with your foolish questions. There now, while you're idling away your time here, there's the cows have broken into the oats and are knocking the corn all about."

Tom was taken so by surprise with this that he was just on the very point of turning round when he recollected himself; so, afraid that the like might happen again, he made a grab at the cluricaune and caught him up in his hand; but in his hurry he upset the pitcher and spilled all the beer, so that he could not get a taste of it to tell what sort it was. He then swore what he would not do to him if he did not show him where his money was. Tom looked so wicked and so bloody-minded that the little man was quite frightened; so says he, "Come along with me a couple of fields off, and I'll show you a crock of gold."

So they went, and Tom held the cluricaune fast in his hand, and never took his eyes from off him, though they had to cross hedges and ditches and a crooked bit of bog, till at last they came to a great field all full of *boliauns* [ragweed], and the cluricaune pointed to a big *boliaun*, and says he, "Dig under that *boliaun*, and you'll get the great crock all full of guineas."

Tom in his hurry had never thought of bringing a spade with him, so he made up his mind to run home and fetch one; and that he might know the place again he took off one of his red garters and tied it round the *boliaun*.

"I suppose," said the cluricaune very civilly, "you have no further occasion for me?"

"No," says Tom. "You may go away now, if you please, and God speed you, and may good luck attend you wherever you go."

"Well, good-by to you, Tom Fitzpatrick," said the cluricaune, "and much good may it do you, with what you'll get."

So Tom ran for dear life, till he came home and got a spade, and then away with him, as hard as he could go, back to the field of *boliauns*; but when he got there, lo and behold! not a *boliaun* in the field but had a red garter, the very model of his own, tied about it; and as to digging up the whole field, that was all nonsense, for there were more than forty good Irish acres in it. So Tom came home again with his spade on his shoulder, a little cooler than he went, and many's the hearty curse he gave the cluricaune every time he thought of the neat turn he had served him.

Adapted from *Fairy Legends and Traditions of the South of Ireland*, by T. Crofton Croker (London, 1862).

CUCHULLIN AND FARDIA

THEN arose Cuchullin, the unconquerable, striding through the forest, and he wondered which of the great champions of Meave should be brought against him that day; and when he came out into the open, he beheld the whole south country filled with a vast multitude, as it had been the Aenech of Taylteen or the great Feis of Tara when the authority of the Ard-Rie is supreme, and all the tribes of Erin gather together with their kings. But he saw not at first who was the champion that had come out against him, and he advanced through the willows, and came to the edge of the ford, and looked across, and he saw Fardia, son of Daman, of the Fir-bolgs, and Fardia looked upon Cuchullin, and Cuchullin looked upon Fardia.

Then Cuchullin blushed, and his neck and face above, and his temples waxed fiery red, and then again, paler than the white flower of the thorn, and his underjaw fell, and he stood like one stupefied; but Fardia held his shield unmoved, with his spears resting on the ground, and beneath the heavy cathbarr his brows stronger than brass.

But Cuchullin sent forth a voice hoarse and untuned, and said, "Is it Fardia Mic Daman of the Fir-bolgs, for there is a mist before my eyes?"

But Fardia answered not.

Then said Cuchullin, "Art thou come out to meet me in arms today, seeking to slay me?"

And Fardia answered sternly, "Go back, O Cuchullin, to thy own people, and cease to bar the gates of the north against our host, and I shall not slay thee or dishonor thee; but if thou remainest, I shall slay thee here at the ford. Therefore I bid thee go back into the province."

But Cuchullin answered him, and his voice became like the voice of a young girl, or the accents of one seeking an alms. "And is it thou alone of all this great host that has come out against thy friend, seeking to slay me or dishonor me? There are the battle standards of all the warrior tribes of Erin, save only the Ultonians, the banners of the children of Ith and Heber, all the far-spreading clans of Herēmon, the children of Amargin and Brega of Donn and Biela, and the Desie of Temair; there are the warlike clans of the Fomoroh, and the remnant of the people of Partholân, the Clanna Nemedh from the great harbor southward, the children of Orba, the Ernai, and the Osree, the Gamaradians, and the Clan Dega. Could not champion be sought out of this great host that covers the green plains of Conaul Murthemney to the limits of the farthest hills to come out against me, but that thou alone shouldst stand forth against thy friend? Persist not, O son of Daman, but retire, and I will meet three champions instead of one from this day forward. We parted with mutual gifts and with tears; why does thy spear now thirst after my blood, and why dost thou seek to dishonor me?"

And Fardia made answer, "Other champions, by their prowess, bear away many gifts, why should I ever have my hands empty? Bright as the sun is the brooch of Meave, which she has given me, the royal brooch of Cruhane, emblem of sovereignty amongst the Gaeil. Gems glitter along the rim. Like a level sunbeam in the forest is the shining delg of it. I shall have honor while I live, and my clan after me shall be glorious to the end of time. Therefore prepare for battle, O son of Sualtam; I remember thee not at all, or as one whom years since I met, and straight again forgot. Therefore prepare thyself for battle, or I shall slay thee off thy guard."

And Cuchullin said, "O Fardia, I believe thee not. Full well dost thou remember. Beneath the same rug we slept, and sat together at the feast, and side by side we went into the red battle. Together we consumed cities, and drove away captives. Together we practiced feats of arms before the warrior queens, grieving when either got any hurt. Together we kept back the streaming foe in the day of disaster, when the battle torrent roared over us, either guarding the other more than himself."

Then beneath his lowering brows the hot tears burst forth from the eyes of the son of Daman, and fell continuously from his beard, and he answered with a voice most stern, but that held within it a piteous tone like a vessel in which the careless eye sees not the hidden flaw, but at a touch, lo! it is broken. So sounded the stern voice of the warrior.

"Go back now, O Cuchullin, to thy pleasant Dûn–Dûn Dalgan upon the sea. Go back now, for I would not slay thee, and rule over Murthemney and the rough headland of thy sires, and Meave will not waste thy territory or injure aught that is thine. And care no more for the Red Branch, for they have forsaken thee, and given thee over to destruction, who have conspired against thee, trusting in thy great heart that thou wouldst be slain on the marches of the province, holding the gates of the north against their foes, for Hound is thy name and Royal Hound thy nature. Therefore, go back, O Cuchullin, and save thy young life; return now to thy infant son and thy sweet bride. Go back, O Cuchullin, for sweet is life, the life of the warrior, and very dark and sorrowful and empty is the grave."

"I will not go back, O Fardia Mic Daman, but here on the marches, while there is blood in my veins, and while reason like a king rebelled against but unsubdued holds the sovereignty of my mind, shall I contest the borders of my nation, though forsaken and alone. My people have indeed abandoned me and conspired for my destruction; but there is no power in Erin to dissolve my knightship to the son of Nessa and my kinship with the Crave Rue. Though they hate me, yet cannot I eject the love out of my heart. And not the kings alone and the might of the Crave Rue, but the women and the young children of Ulla, are under my protection, and all the unwarlike tribes, and this the sacred soil of Ulla upon which I stand. And this too well I know, that no power in the earth or in the air can keep the Red Branch my foe forever, and that loud and deep will be their sorrow when the red pyre flames beneath me. And seek not to terrify me with death, O son of Daman, for of yore, too, our minds did not agree, for dark and sorrowful death is not but a passage to the land of the ever young, the Tiernanóg. There shall I see the Tuatha face to face, and there the heroic sons of Milith and himself, a mighty shade, and there all the noblest of the earth. There hatred and scorn are not known, nor the rupturing of friendships, but sweet love rules over all."

"Go back, O Cuchullin, go back now again, for I would not slay thee. Think no more of the son of Nessa and the Red Branch, than whom the race of Milith hath produced naught fiercer or more baleful. Rooted out and cast down shall be the Red Branch in this foray, whether thou, O Cuchullin, survivest or art slain. Go back, O son of Sualtam, return to thine own Dûn. Once indeed thou wast obedient to me and served me, and polished my armor, and tied up my spears submissive to my commands. Therefore go back; add not thy blood to the bloody stream."

"Revilest thou my nation, O son of Daman. Talk no more now, but prepare thyself for battle and for death. I will not obey thee or retire before thee, nor shalt thou at all dishonor me as thou has most foully dishonored thyself. This indeed I well know, that I shall be slain at the ford when my strength has passed away, or my mind is overthrown; but by thee, O son of Daman, I shall not meet my death. Once indeed I was subservient to thee, because I was younger than thee. Therefore was I then as a servant unto thee, but not now; and which of us twain shall die I know, and it is thou, O Fardia, son of Daman."

Therewith then they fought, and Cuchullin had no weapon save only his colg, for the Gae Bulg, the rude spear which he had fashioned, he dropped upon the shore, and Fardia discharged his javelins at the same time, for he was ambidexter, and quick as lightning. Cuchullin avoided them, and they stuck trembling in the thither bank, and quick to right and left Cuchullin severed the leathern thongs rushing forward. Then drew Fardia his mighty sword that made a flaming crescent as it flashed most bright and terrible, and rushed headlong upon Cuchullin, and they met in the midst of the ford. But straightway there arose a spray and a mist from the trampling of the heroes, and through the mist their forms moved hugely, like two giants of the Fomoroh contending in a storm. But the war demons too contended around them, fighting, the Bocanahs and Bananahs, the wild people of the glens and the demons of the air, and the fiercer and more bloodthirsty of the Tuatha de Danán, and screeched in the clamor of the warriors, the clash of the shields and the clatter of land and meeting colg. But the warriors of Meave turned pale, and the war steeds brake loose, and flew through the plain with the war cars, and the women and camp followers brake forth and fled, and the upper water of the divine stream gathered together for fear, and reared itself aloft like a steed that has seen a specter, with jags of torn water and tossing foam. But Cuchullin was red all over, like a garment raised out of a dyeing vat, and Fardia's great sword made havoc in his unarmored flesh. Three times Cuchullin closed with the Fir-bolg, seeking to get within the ponderous shield, and three times the son of Daman cast him off, as the cliffs of Eyrus cast off a foaming billow of the great sea; but when the fourth time he was rushing on like a storm, he heard as it were the voice of Laeg, the son of Riangowra, taunting and insulting him, and himself he saw, standing in the river ford on the left, for he was accustomed to revile Cuchullin. Yet this time too the Fir-bolg cast him off, and advanced upon Cuchullin to slay him. Then stepped back Cuchullin quickly, and the men of Meave shouted, for Cuchullin's shield was falling to pieces. But again rushed forward the hound of Ulla, stooping, with the Gae Bulg in his hand, using it like a spearman in the battle, and he drove Fardia through the ford, and upon the hither bank, pressing against the shield, but Fardia himself too retreated back. But when the Fir-bolgs saw what was done, they feared mightily for their champion, and raised a sudden howl of lamentation and rage, and rushed forward, breaking through the guards. Which when Fergus Mac Roy beheld, he sprang down from his chariot shouting dreadfully, and put his hand into the hollow of his shield, and took out his battlestone, and smote Imchall, the son of Dega, with the battlestone upon the head,

and he fell rushing forward amongst the first. But Cormac Conlingas and Mainey Lamgarf ran thither with the queen's spearmen, restraining the Fir-bolgs.

But, meantime, Cuchullin lifted suddenly the Gae Bulg above his head, and plunged it into Fardia; but it passed through the upper rim of the brazen shield, and through the strong bones of his breast beneath his beard, and he fell backward with a crash, and grasped with outstretched hands at the ground, and his spirit went out of him, and he died.

But Cuchullin plucked out the spear, and stood above him, panting, as a hound pants returning from the chase, and the war demons passed out of him, and he looked upon Fardia, and a great sorrow overwhelmed him, and he lamented and moaned over Fardia, joining his voice to the howl of the people of Fardia, the greathearted children of Mac Erc, and he took off the cathbarr from the head of Fardia, and unwound his yellow hair, tress after bright tress, most beautiful, shedding many tears, and he opened the battledress and took out the queen's brooch—that for which his friend had come to slay him—and he cursed the lifeless metal, and cast it from him into the air, southward over the host, and men saw it no more.

From *Standish O'Grady: Selected Essays and Passages* (Dublin: Talbot Press; and London: T. Fisher Unwin, 1917).

A LEGEND OF KNOCKMANY

WHAT Irish man, woman, or child has not heard of our renowned Hibernian Hercules, the great and glorious Fin M'Coul? Not one, from Cape Clear to the Giant's Causeway, nor from that back again to Cape Clear. And by the way, speaking of the Giant's Causeway brings me at once to the beginning of my story. Well, it so happened that Fin and his gigantic relatives were all working at the Causeway, in order to make a bridge, or what was still better, a good stout pad-road, across to Scotland; when Fin, who was very fond of his wife Oonagh, took it into his head that he would go home and see how the poor woman got on in his absence. . . . So he pulled up a fir tree, and, after lopping off the roots and branches, made a walking stick of it, and set out on his way to Oonagh.

Oonagh, or rather Fin, lived at this time on the very tiptop of Knockmany Hill, which faces a cousin of its own called Cullamore, that rises up, half-hill, half-mountain, on the opposite side—east-east by south, as the sailors say when they wish to puzzle a landsman.

Now, the truth is, for it must come out, that honest Fin's affection for his wife, though cordial enough in itself, was by no manner of means the real cause of his journey home. There was at that time another giant, named Cuchullin—some say he was Irish, and some say he was Scotch—but whether Scotch or Irish, sorrow doubt of it, but he was a *targer*. No other giant of the day could stand before him;

and such was his strength that, when well vexed, he could give a stamp that shook the country about him. The fame and name of him went far and near; and nothing in the shape of a man, it was said, had any chance with him in a fight. Whether the story is true or not I cannot say, but the report went that, by one blow of his fists, he flattened a thunderbolt and kept it in his pocket in the shape of a pancake, to show to his enemies when they were about to fight him.

Undoubtedly he had given every giant in Ireland a considerable beating, barring Fin M'Coul himself; and he swore by the solemn contents of Moll Kelly's Primer that he would never rest, night or day, winter or summer, till he would serve Fin with the same sauce, if he could catch him. Fin, however, who no doubt was cock of the walk on his own dunghill, had a strong disinclination to meet a giant who could make a young earthquake or flatten a thunderbolt when he was angry; so he accordingly kept dodging about from place to place, not much to his credit as a Trojan, to be sure, whenever he happened to get the hard word that Cuchullin was on the scent of him. This, then, was the marrow of the whole movement, although he put it on his anxiety to see Oonagh; and I am not saying but there was some truth in that too. However, the short and long of it was, with reverence be it spoken, that he heard Cuchullin was coming to the Causeway to have a trial of strength with him; and he was naturally enough seized, in consequence, with a very warm and sudden fit of affection for his wife, poor woman, who was delicate in her health, and leading, besides, a very lonely, uncomfortable life of it (he assured them) in his absence. He accordingly pulled up the fir tree as I said before, and, having *snedded* it into a walking stick, set out on his affectionate travels to see his darling Oonagh on the top of Knockmany, by the way.

In truth, to state the suspicions of the country at the time, the people wondered very much why it was that Fin selected such a windy spot for his dwelling house, and they even went so far as to tell him as much.

"What can you mane, Mr. M'Coul," said they, "by pitching your tent upon the top of Knockmany, where you never are without a breeze, day or night, winter or summer, and where you're often forced to take your nightcap without either going to bed or turning up your little finger; ay, an' where, besides this, there's the sorrow's own want of water?"

"Why," said Fin, "ever since I was the height of a round tower I was known to be fond of having a good prospect of my own; and where the dickens, neighbors, could I find a better spot for a good prospect than the top of Knockmany? As for water I am sinking a pump, and, plase goodness, as soon as the Causeway's made, I intend to finish it."

Now this was more of Fin's philosophy; for the real state of the case was that he pitched upon the top of Knockmany in order that he might be able to see Cuchullin coming toward the house, and, of course, that he himself might go to look after his distant transactions in other parts of the country rather than—but no matter, we do not wish to be too hard on Fin. All we have to say is, that if he wanted a spot from which to keep a sharp lookout—barring Slieve Croob, or Slieve Donard, or its own cousin, Cullamore—he could not find a neater or more convenient situation for it in the sweet and sagacious province of Ulster.

"God save all here!" said Fin good-humoredly on putting his honest face into his own door.

"Musha Fin, avick, an' you're welcome home to your own Oonagh, you darlin' bully." Here followed a smack that is said to have made the waters of the lake at the bottom of the hill curl, as it were, with kindness and sympathy.

"Faith," said Fin, "beautiful; an' how are you, Oonagh—and how did you sport your figure during my absence, my bilberry?"

"Never a merrier—as bouncing a grass widow as ever there was in sweet 'Tyrone among the bushes.'"

Fin gave a short, good-humored cough and laughed most heartily, to show her how much he was delighted that she made herself happy in his absence.

"An' what brought you home so soon, Fin?" said she.

"Why, avourneen," said Fin, putting in his answer in the proper way, "never the thing but the purest of love and affection for yourself. Sure you know that's truth, anyhow, Oonagh."

Fin spent two or three happy days with Oonagh and felt himself very comfortable, considering the dread he had of Cuchullin. This, however, grew upon him so much that his wife could not but perceive something lay on his mind which he kept altogether to himself. Let a woman alone, in the meantime, for ferreting or wheedling a secret out of her good man when she wishes. Fin was a proof of this.

"It's this Cuchullin," said he, "that's troubling me. When the fellow gets angry, and begins to stamp, he'll shake you a whole townland;

and it's well known that he can stop a thunderbolt, for he always carries one about him in the shape of a pancake, to show to anyone that might misdoubt it."

And as he spoke he clapped his thumb in his mouth, which he always did when he wanted to prophesy or to know anything that happened in his absence; and the wife, who knew what he did it for, said, very sweetly, "Fin, darling, I hope you don't bite your thumb at me, dear?"

"No," said Fin, "but I bite my thumb, acushla," said he.

"Yes, jewel, but take care and don't draw blood," said she. "Ah, Fin! don't, my bully, don't!"

"He's coming," said Fin. "I see him below Dungannon."

"Thank goodness, dear! An' who is it, avick? Glory be to God!"

"That baste Cuchullin," replied Fin. "And how to manage I don't know. If I run away, I am disgraced; and I know that sooner or later I must meet him, for my thumb tells me so."

"When will he be here?" said she.

"Tomorrow, about two o'clock," replied Fin with a groan.

"Well, my bully, don't be cast down," said Oonagh. "Depend on me, and maybe I'll bring you better out of this scrape than ever you could bring yourself, by your rule o' thumb."

This quieted Fin's heart very much, for he knew that Oonagh was hand and glove with the fairies; and, indeed, to tell the truth, she was supposed to be a fairy herself. If she was, however, she must have been a kindhearted one, for, by all accounts, she never did anything but good in the neighborhood.

Now it so happened that Oonagh had a sister named Granua, living opposite them, on the very top of Cullamore, which I have mentioned already, and this Granua was quite as powerful as herself. The beautiful valley that lies between them is not more than about three or four miles broad, so that of a summer's evening Granua and Oonagh were able to hold many an agreeable conversation across it, from the one hilltop to the other. Upon this occasion Oonagh resolved to consult her sister as to what was best to be done in the difficulty that surrounded them.

"Granua," said she, "are you at home?"

"No," said the other, "I'm picking bilberries in Althadhawan" (*Anglicé*, the Devil's Glen).

"Well," said Oonagh, "get up to the top of Cullamore, look about you, and then tell us what you see."

"Very well," replied Granua; after a few minutes, "I am there now."

"What do you see?" asked the other.

"Goodness be about us!" exclaimed Granua, "I see the biggest giant that ever was known coming up from Dungannon."

"Ay," said Oonagh, "there's our difficulty. That giant is the great Cuchullin; and he's now comin' up to leather Fin. What's to be done?"

"I'll call to him," she replied, "to come up to Cullamore and refresh himself, and maybe that will give you and Fin time to think of some plan to get yourselves out of the scrape. But," she proceeded, "I'm short of butter, having in the house only half a dozen firkins, and as I'm to have a few giants and giantesses to spend the evenin' with me, I'd feel thankful, Oonagh, if you'd throw me up fifteen or sixteen tubs, or the largest miscaun you have got, and you'll oblige me very much."

"I'll do that with a heart and a half," replied Oonagh; "and, indeed, Granua, I feel myself under great obligations to you for your kindness in keeping him off us till we see what can be done; for what would become of us all if anything happened to Fin, poor man?"

She accordingly got the largest miscaun of butter she had—which might be about the weight of a couple of dozen millstones, so that you may easily judge of its size—and, calling up to her sister, "Granua," said she, "are you ready? I'm going to throw you up a miscaun, so be prepared to catch it."

"I will," said the other. "A good throw now, and take care it does not fall short."

Oonagh threw it; but, in consequence of her anxiety about Fin and Cuchullin, she forgot to say the charm that was to send it up, so that, instead of reaching Cullamore, as she expected, it fell about halfway between the two hills, at the edge of the Broad Bog near Augher.

"My curse upon you!" she exclaimed. "You've disgraced me. I now change you into a gray stone. Lie there as a testimony of what has happened; and may evil betide the first living man that will ever attempt to remove or injure you!"

And, sure enough, there it lies to this day, with the mark of the four fingers and thumb imprinted in it, exactly as it came out of her hand.

"Never mind," said Granua. "I must only do the best I can with Cuchullin. If all fail, I'll give him a cast of heather broth to keep the wind out of his stomach, or a panada of oak bark to draw it in a bit; but, above all things, think of some plan to get Fin out of the scrape he's in; otherwise he's a lost man. You know you used to be sharp and ready-witted; and my own opinion, Oonagh, is, that it will go hard with you, or you'll outdo Cuchullin yet."

She then made a high smoke on the top of the hill, after which she put her finger in her mouth and gave three whistles, and by that Cuchullin knew he was invited to Cullamore—for this was the way that the Irish long ago gave a sign to all strangers and travelers, to let them know they were welcome to come and take share of whatever was going.

In the meantime Fin was very melancholy and did not know what to do or how to act at all. Cuchullin was an ugly customer, no doubt, to meet with; and, moreover, the idea of the confounded "cake," aforesaid, flattened the very heart within him. What chance could he have, strong and brave though he was, with a man who could, when put in a passion, walk the country into earthquakes and knock thunderbolts into pancakes? The thing was impossible; and Fin knew not on what hand to turn him. Right or left, backward or forward, where to go he could form no guess whatsoever.

"Oonagh," said he, "can you do nothing for me? Where's all your invention? Am I to be skivered like a rabbit before your eyes, and to have my name disgraced forever in the sight of all my tribe, and me the best man among them? How am I to fight this man-mountain—this huge cross between an earthquake and a thunderbolt with a pancake in his pocket that was once—"

"Be easy, Fin," replied Oonagh. "Troth, I'm ashamed of you. Keep your toe in your pump, will you? Talking of pancakes, maybe we'll give him as good as any he brings with him—thunderbolt or otherwise. If I don't treat him to as smart feeding as he's got this many a day, never trust Oonagh again. Leave him to me, and do just as I bid you."

This relieved Fin very much; for, after all, he had great confidence in his wife, knowing, as he did, that she had got him out of many a quandary before. The present, however, was the greatest of all; but still he began to get courage and was able to eat his victuals as usual. Oonagh then drew the nine woolen threads of different colors, which she always did to find out the best way of succeeding in anything of importance she went about. She then platted them into three plats with three colors in each, putting one on her right arm, one around her heart, and the third round her right ankle, for then she knew that nothing could fail with her that she undertook.

Having everything now prepared, she sent round to the neighbors and borrowed one-and-twenty iron griddles, which she took and kneaded into the hearts of one-and-twenty cakes of bread, and these she baked on the fire in the usual way, setting them aside in the cupboard according as they were done. She then put down a large pot of new milk, which she made into curds and whey, and gave Fin due instructions how to use the curds when Cuchullin should come. Having done all this, she sat down quite contented, waiting for his arrival on the next day about two o'clock, that being the hour at which he was expected—for Fin knew as much by the sucking of his thumb. Now this was a curious property that Fin's thumb had; but, notwithstanding all the wisdom and logic he used to suck out of it, it could never have stood to him here were it not for the wit of his wife. In this very thing, moreover, he was very much resembled by his great foe, Cuchullin; for it was well known that the huge strength he possessed all lay in the middle finger of his right hand, and that, if he happened by any mischance to lose it, he was no more, notwithstanding his bulk, than a common man.

At length, the next day, he was seen coming across the valley, and Oonagh knew that it was time to commence operations. She immediately made the cradle and desired Fin to lie down in it and cover himself up with the clothes.

"You must pass for your own child," said she. "So just lie there snug and say nothing but be guided by me." This, to be sure, was wormwood to Fin—I mean going into the cradle in such a cowardly manner—but he knew Oonagh well; and, finding that he had nothing else for it, with a very rueful face he gathered himself into it and lay snug, as she had desired him.

About two o'clock, as he had been expected, Cuchullin came in. "God save all here!" said he. "Is this where the great Fin M'Coul lives?"

"Indeed it is, honest man," replied Oonagh. "God save you kindly—won't you be sitting?"

"Thank you, ma'am," says he, sitting down. "You're Mrs. M'Coul, I suppose?"

"I am," said she, "and I have no reason, I hope, to be ashamed of my husband."

"No," said the other. "He has the name of being the strongest and bravest man in Ireland; but, for all that, there's a man not far from you that's very desirous of taking a shake with him. Is he at home?"

"Why, then, no," she replied. "And if ever a man left his house in a fury, he did. It appears that someone told him of a big basthoon of a giant called Cuchullin being down at the Causeway to look for him, and so he set out there to try if he could catch him. Troth, I hope for the poor giant's sake he won't meet with him, for if he does, Fin will make paste of him at once."

"Well," said the other, "I am Cuchullin, and I have been seeking him these twelve months, but he always kept clear of me; and I will never rest night or day till I lay my hands on him."

At this Oonagh set up a loud laugh, of great contempt, by the way, and looked at him as if he were only a mere handful of a man.

"Did you ever see Fin?" said she, changing her manner all at once.

"How could I?" said he. "He always took care to keep his distance."

"I thought so," she replied. "I judged as much. And if you take my advice, you poor-looking creature, you'll pray night and day that you may never see him, for I tell you it will be a black day for you when you do. But, in the meantime, you perceive that the wind's on the door, and as Fin himself is from home, maybe you'd be civil enough to turn the house, for it's always what Fin does when he's here."

This was a startler even to Cuchullin; he got up, however, and, after pulling the middle finger of his right hand until it cracked three times, he went outside, and, getting his arms about the house, completely turned it as she had wished. When Fin saw this he felt a certain moisture oozing out through every pore of his skin; but Oonagh, depending upon her woman's wit, felt not a whit daunted.

"Arrah, then," said she, "as you are so civil, maybe you'd do another obliging turn for us, as Fin's not here to do it himself. You see, after this long stretch of dry weather we've had, we feel very badly off for want of water. Now Fin says there's a fine spring well somewhere under the rocks behind the hill here below, and it was his intention to pull them asunder; but, having heard of you, he left the place in such a fury that he never thought of it. Now if you try to find it, troth, I'd feel it a kindness."

She then brought Cuchullin down to see the place, which was then all one solid rock; and, after looking at it for some time, he cracked his right middle finger nine times, and, stooping down, tore a cleft about four hundred feet deep and a quarter of a mile in length, which has since been christened by the name of Lumford's Glen. This feat nearly threw Oonagh herself on her guard; but what won't a woman's sagacity and presence of mind accomplish?

"You'll now come in," said she, "and eat a bit of such humble fare as we can give you. Fin, even though he and you are enemies, would scorn not to treat you kindly in his own house; and, indeed, if I didn't do it even in his absence, he would not be pleased with me."

She accordingly brought him in and, placing half a dozen of the cakes we spoke of before him, together with a can or two of butter, a side of boiled bacon, and a stack of cabbage, she desired him to help himself—for this, be it known, was long before the invention of potatoes. Cuchullin, who, by the way, was a glutton as well as a hero, put one of the cakes in his mouth to take a huge whack out of it, when both Fin and Oonagh were stunned with a noise that resembled something between a growl and a yell. "Blood and fury!" he shouted. "How is this? Here are two of my teeth out! What kind of bread is this you gave me?"

"What's the matter?" said Oonagh coolly.

"Matter!" shouted the other again. "Why, here are the two best teeth in my head gone."

"Why," said she, "that's Fin's bread—the only bread he ever eats when at home; but, indeed, I forgot to tell you that nobody can eat it but himself, and that child in the cradle there. I thought, however, that, as you were reported to be rather a stout little fellow of your size, you might be able to manage it, and I did not wish to affront a man that thinks himself able to fight Fin. Here's another cake—maybe it's not so hard as that."

Cuchullin at the moment was not only hungry but ravenous, so he accordingly made a fresh set at the second cake, and immediately another yell was heard twice as loud as the first. "Thunder and giblets!" he roared. "Take your bread out of this, or I will not have a tooth in my head—there's another pair of them gone!"

"Well, honest man," replied Oonagh, "if you're not able to eat the bread, say so quietly, and don't be wakening the child in the cradle there. There, now, he's awake upon me."

Fin now gave a skirl that startled the giant, as coming from such a youngster as he was represented to be. "Mother," said he, "I'm hungry—get me something to eat." Oonagh went over, and, putting into his hand a cake that had no griddle in it, Fin, whose appetite in the meantime was sharpened by what he saw going forward, soon made it disappear. Cuchullin was thunderstruck and secretly thanked his stars that he had the good fortune to miss meeting Fin, for, as he said to himself, "I'd have no chance with a man who could eat such bread as that, which even his son that's but in his cradle can munch before my eyes."

"I'd like to take a glimpse of the lad in the cradle," said he to Oonagh, "for I can tell you that the infant who can manage that nutriment is no joke to look at, or to feed of a scarce summer."

"With all the veins of my heart," replied Oonagh. "Get up, acushla, and show this decent little man something that won't be unworthy of your father, Fin M'Coul."

Fin, who was dressed for the occasion as much like a boy as possible, got up, and, bringing Cuchullin out, "Are you strong?" said he.

"Thunder an' ounds!" exclaimed the other, "what a voice in so small a chap!"

"Are you strong?" said Fin again. "Are you able to squeeze water out of that white stone?" he asked, putting one into Cuchullin's hand. The latter squeezed and squeezed the stone, but to no purpose; he might pull the rock of Lumford's Glen asunder and flatten a thunderbolt, but to squeeze water out of a white stone was beyond his strength. Fin eyed him with great contempt as he kept straining and squeezing and squeezing and straining till he got black in the face with the efforts.

"Ah, you're a poor creature!" said Fin. "You a giant! Give me the stone here, and when I'll show what Fin's little son can do, you may then judge of what my daddy himself is."

Fin then took the stone, and, slyly exchanging it for the curds, he squeezed the latter until the whey, as clear as water, oozed out in a little shower from his hand.

"I'll now go in," said he, "to my cradle; for I scorn to lose my time with anyone that's not able to eat my daddy's bread or squeeze water out of a stone. Bedad, you had better be off out of this before he comes back; for if he catches you, it's in flummery he'd have you in two minutes."

Cuchullin, seeing what he had seen, was of the same opinion himself; his knees knocked together with the terror of Fin's return, and he accordingly hastened in to bid Oonagh farewell, and to assure her, that from that day out, he never wished to hear of, much less to see, her husband. "I admit fairly that I'm not a match for him," said he, "strong as I am; tell him I will avoid him as I would the plague, and that I will make myself scarce in this part of the country while I live."

Fin, in the meantime, had gone into the cradle, where he lay very quietly, his heart at his mouth with delight that Cuchullin was about to take his departure without discovering the tricks that had been played off on him.

"It's well for you," said Oonagh, "that he doesn't happen to be here, for it's nothing but hawk's meat he'd make of you."

"I know that," says Cuchullin; "divil a thing else he'd make of me; but before I go, will you let me feel what kind of teeth they are that can eat griddle bread like *that*?" And he pointed to it as he spoke.

"With all pleasure in life," said she. "Only, as they're far back in his head, you must put your finger a good way in."

Cuchullin was surprised to find such a powerful set of grinders in one so young; but he was still much more so on finding, when he took his hand from Fin's mouth, that he had left the very finger upon which his whole strength depended behind him. He gave one loud groan and fell down at once with terror and weakness. This was all Fin wanted, who now knew that his most powerful and bitterest enemy was completely at his mercy. He instantly started out of the cradle, and in a few minutes the great Cuchullin, that was for such a length of time the terror of him and all his followers, lay a corpse before him. Thus did Fin, through the wit and invention of Oonagh, his wife, succeed in overcoming his enemy by stratagem, which he never could have done by force: and thus also is it proved that the women, if they bring us *into* many an unpleasant scrape, can sometimes succeed in getting us *out* of others that are as bad.

From *Tales and Stories of the Irish Peasantry*, by William Carleton (Dublin, 1845), and reprinted in *Irish Fairy and Folk Tales*, selected and edited by William Butler Yeats. (London: Walter Scott; and New York: Thomas Whitaker, 1888).

HUDDEN AND DUDDEN AND DONALD O'NEARY

There was once upon a time two farmers, and their names were Hudden and Dudden. They had poultry in their yards, sheep on the uplands, and scores of cattle in the meadowland alongside the river. But for all that they weren't happy. For just between their two farms there lived a poor man by the name of Donald O'Neary. He had a hovel over his head and a strip of grass that was barely enough to keep his one cow, Daisy, from starving, and, though she did her best, it was but seldom that Donald got a drink of milk or a roll of butter from Daisy. You would think there was little here to make Hudden and Dudden jealous, but so it is, the more one has the more one wants, and Donald's neighbors lay awake of nights scheming how they might get hold of his little strip of grassland. Daisy, poor thing, they never thought of; she was just a bag of bones.

One day Hudden met Dudden, and they were soon grumbling as usual, and all to the tune of "If only we could get that vagabond Donald O'Neary out of the country."

"Let's kill Daisy," said Hudden at last. "If that doesn't make him clear out, nothing will."

No sooner said than agreed; and it wasn't dark before Hudden and Dudden crept up to the little shed where lay poor Daisy trying her best to chew the cud, though she hadn't had as much grass in the day as would cover your hand. And when Donald came to see if Daisy was all snug for the night, the poor beast had only time to lick his hand once before she died.

Well, Donald was a shrewd fellow, and, downhearted though he was, began to think if he could get any good out of Daisy's death. He thought and he thought, and the next day you could have seen him trudging off early to the fair, Daisy's hide over his shoulder, every penny he had jingling in his pockets. Just before he got to the fair he made several slits in the hide, put a penny in each slit, walked into the best inn of the town as bold as if it belonged to him, and, hanging the hide up to a nail in the wall, sat down.

"Some of your best whisky," says he to the landlord. But the landlord didn't like his looks. "Is it fearing I won't pay you, you are?" says Donald. "Why, I have a hide here that gives me all the money I want." And with that he hit it a whack with his stick and out hopped a penny. The landlord opened his eyes, as you may fancy.

"What'll you take for that hide?"

"It's not for sale, my good man."

"Will you take a gold piece?"

"It's not for sale, I tell you. Hasn't it kept me and mine for years?" And with that Donald hit the hide another whack and out jumped a second penny.

Well, the long and the short of it was that Donald let the hide go, and, that very evening, who but he should walk up to Hudden's door?

"Good evening, Hudden. Will you lend me your best pair of scales?"

Hudden stared and Hudden scratched his head, but he lent the scales.

When Donald was safe at home he pulled out his pocketful of bright gold and began to weigh each piece on the scales. But Hudden had put a lump of butter at the bottom, and so the last piece of gold stuck fast to the scales when he took them back to Hudden.

If Hudden had stared before, he stared ten times more now, and no sooner was Donald's back turned than he was off as hard as he could pelt to Dudden's.

"Good evening, Dudden. That vagabond, bad luck to him——"

"You mean Donald O'Neary?"

"And who else should I mean? He's back here weighing out sackfuls of gold."

"How do you know that?"

"Here are my scales that he borrowed, and here's a gold piece still sticking to them."

Off they went together, and they came to Donald's door. Donald had finished making the last pile of ten gold pieces. And he couldn't finish because a piece had stuck to the scales.

In they walked without an "If you please" or "By your leave."

"Well, *I* never!" that was all they could say.

"Good evening, Hudden. Good evening, Dudden. Ah! you thought you had played me a fine trick, but you never did me a better turn in all your lives. When I found poor Daisy dead I thought to myself, 'Well, her hide may fetch something'; and it did. Hides are worth their weight in gold in the market just now."

Hudden nudged Dudden, and Dudden winked at Hudden.

"Good evening, Donald O'Neary."

"Good evening, kind friends."

The next day there wasn't a cow or a calf that belonged to Hudden or Dudden but her hide was going to the fair in Hudden's biggest cart drawn by Dudden's strongest pair of horses.

When they came to the fair each one took a hide over his arm, and there they were, walking through the fair, bawling at the top of their voices, "Hides to sell! Hides to sell!"

Out came the tanner. "How much for your hides, my good men?"

"Their weight in gold."

"It's early in the day to come out of the tavern." That was all the tanner said, and back he went to his yard.

"Hides to sell! Fine fresh hides to sell!"

Out came the cobbler. "How much for your hides, my men?"

"Their weight in gold."

"Is it making game of me you are! Take that for your pains!" And the cobbler dealt Hudden a blow that made him stagger.

Up the people came running from one end of the fair to the other. "What's the matter? What's the matter?" cried they.

"Here are a couple of vagabonds selling hides at their weight in gold," said the cobbler.

"Hold 'em fast! Hold 'em fast!" bawled the innkeeper, who was the last to come up, he was so fat. "I'll wager it's one of the rogues who tricked me out of thirty gold pieces yesterday for a wretched hide."

It was more kicks than halfpence that Hudden and Dudden got before they were well on their way home again, and they didn't run the slower because all the dogs of the town were at their heels.

Well, as you may fancy, if they loved Donald little before, they loved him less now.

"What's the matter, friends?" said he as he saw them tearing along, their hats knocked in, and their coats torn off, and their faces black and blue. "Is it fighting you've been? Or mayhap you met the police, ill luck to them?"

"We'll police you, you vagabond. It's mighty smart you thought yourself, deluding us with your lying tales."

"Who deluded you? Didn't you see the gold with your own two eyes?"

But it was no use talking. Pay for it he must, and should. There was a meal sack handy, and into it Hudden and Dudden popped Donald O'Neary, tied him up tight, ran a pole through the knot, and off they started for the Brown Lake of the Bog, each with a pole-end on his shoulder, and Donald O'Neary between.

But the Brown Lake was far, the road was dusty, Hudden and Dudden were sore and weary and parched with thirst. There was an inn by the roadside.

"Let's go in," said Hudden. "I'm dead beat. It's heavy he is for the little he had to eat."

If Hudden was willing, so was Dudden. As for Donald, you may be sure his leave wasn't asked, but he was lumped down at the inn door for all the world as if he had been a sack of potatoes.

"Sit still, you vagabond," said Dudden. "If we don't mind waiting, you needn't."

Donald held his peace, but after a while he heard the glasses clink and Hudden singing away at the top of his voice.

"I won't have her, I tell you! I won't have her!" said Donald. But nobody heeded what he said.

"I won't have her, I tell you! I won't have her!" said Donald. And this time he said it louder; but nobody heeded what he said.

"I won't have her, I tell you! I won't have her!" said Donald, and this time he said it as loud as he could.

"And who won't you have, may I be so bold as to ask?" said a farmer, who had just come up with a drove of cattle and was turning in for a glass.

"It's the king's daughter. They are bothering the life out of me to marry her."

"You're the lucky fellow. I'd give something to be in your shoes."

"Do you see that now! Wouldn't it be a fine thing for a farmer to be marrying a princess, all dressed in gold and jewels?"

"Jewels, do you say? Ah, now, couldn't you take me with you?"

"Well, you're an honest fellow, and as I don't care for the king's daughter, though she's as beautiful as the day and is covered with jewels from top to toe, you shall have her. Just undo the cord and let me out; they tied me up tight, as they knew I'd run away from her."

Out crawled Donald, in crept the farmer.

"Now lie still, and don't mind the shaking. It's only rumbling over the palace steps you'll be. And maybe they'll abuse you for a vagabond, who won't have the king's daughter; but you needn't mind that. Ah! it's a deal I'm giving up for you, sure as it is that I don't care for the princess."

"Take my cattle in exchange," said the farmer. And you may guess it wasn't long before Donald was at their tails driving them homeward.

Out came Hudden and Dudden, and the one took one end of the pole, and the other the other.

"I'm thinking he's heavier," said Hudden.

"Ah, never mind," said Dudden, "it's only a step now to the Brown Lake."

"I'll have her now! I'll have her now!" bawled the farmer from inside the sack.

"By my faith and you shall though," said Hudden, and he laid his stick across the sack.

"I'll have her! I'll have her!" bawled the farmer, louder than ever.

"Well, here you are," said Dudden, for they were now come to the Brown Lake, and, unslinging the sack, they pitched it plump into the lake.

"You'll not be playing your tricks on us any longer," said Hudden.

"True for you," said Dudden. "Ah, Donald, my boy, it was an ill day when you borrowed my scales."

Off they went, with a light step and an easy heart, but when they were near home, whom should they see but Donald O'Neary, and all around him the cows were grazing, and the calves were kicking up their heels and butting their heads together.

"Is it you, Donald?" said Dudden. "Faith, you've been quicker than we are."

"True for you, Dudden, and let me thank you kindly; the turn was good, if the will was ill. You'll have heard, like me, that the Brown Lake leads to the Land of Promise. I always put it down as lies, but it is just as true as my word. Look at the cattle."

Hudden stared, and Dudden gaped; but they couldn't get over the cattle; fine fat cattle they were too.

"It's only the worst I could bring up with me," said Donald O'Neary. "The others were so fat there was no driving them. Faith, too, it's little wonder they didn't care to leave, with grass as far as you could see, and as sweet and juicy as fresh butter."

"Ah, now, Donald, we haven't always been friends," said Dudden, "but, as I was just saying, you were ever a decent lad, and you'll show us the way, won't you?"

"I don't see that I'm called upon to do that; there is a power more cattle down there. Why shouldn't I have them all to myself?"

"Faith, they may well say, the richer you get, the harder the heart. You always were a neighborly lad, Donald. You wouldn't wish to keep the luck all to yourself?"

"True for you, Hudden, though 'tis a bad example you set me. But I'll not be thinking of old times. There is plenty for all there, so come along with me."

Off they trudged, with a light heart and an eager step. When they came to the Brown Lake the sky was full of little white clouds, and, if the sky was full, the lake was as full."

"Ah, now, look, there they are," cried Donald, as he pointed to the clouds in the lake.

"Where? Where?" cried Hudden, and "Don't be greedy!" cried Dudden, as he jumped his hardest to be up first with the fat cattle. But if he jumped first, Hudden wasn't long behind.

They never came back. Maybe they got too fat, like the cattle. As for Donald O'Neary, he had cattle and sheep all his days to his heart's content.

From *Celtic Fairy Tales.*

TEIG O'KANE AND THE CORPSE

THERE was once a grown-up lad in the County Leitrim, and he was strong and lively, and the son of a rich farmer. His father had plenty of money, and he did not spare it on the son. Accordingly, when the boy grew up he liked sport better than work, and, as his father had no other children, he loved this one so much that he allowed him to do in everything just as it pleased himself. He was very extravagant, and he used to scatter the gold money as another person would scatter the white. He was seldom to be found at home, but if there was a fair, or a race, or a gathering within ten miles of him, you were dead certain to find him there. And he seldom spent a night in his father's house, but he used to be always out rambling, and, like Shawn Bwee long ago, there was "the love of every girl in the breast of his shirt," and it's many's the kiss he got and he gave, for he was very handsome, and there wasn't a girl in the country but would fall in love with him, only for him to fasten his two eyes on her, and it was for that someone made this *rann* [stanza] on him:

> Look at the rogue, it's for kisses he's rambling,
> It isn't much wonder, for that was his way;
> He's like an old hedgehog, at night he'll be scrambling
> From this place to that, but he'll sleep in the day.

At last he became very wild and unruly. He wasn't to be seen day nor night in his father's house, but always rambling or going on his *kailee* [night visit] from place to place and from house to house, so that the old people used to shake their heads and say to one another, "It's easy seen what will happen to the land when the old man dies; his son will run through it in a year, and it won't stand him that long itself."

He used to be always gambling and card playing and drinking, but his father never minded his bad habits and never punished him. But it happened one day that the old man was told that the son had ruined the character of a girl in the neighborhood, and he was greatly angry, and he called the son to him and said to him, quietly and sensibly, "Avic," says he, "you know I loved you greatly up to this, and I never stopped you from doing your choice thing whatever it was, and I kept plenty of money with you, and I always hoped to leave you the house and land, and all I had after myself would be gone; but I heard a story of you today that has disgusted me with you. I cannot tell you the grief that I felt when I heard such a thing of you, and I tell you now plainly that unless you marry that girl I'll leave house and land and everything to my brother's son. I never could leave it to anyone who would make so bad a use of it as you do yourself, deceiving women and coaxing girls. Settle with yourself now whether you'll marry that girl and get my land as a fortune with her, or refuse to marry her and give up all that was coming to you; and tell me in the morning which of the two things you have chosen."

"Och! *Domnoo Sheery!* Father, you wouldn't say that to me, and I such a good son as I am! Who told you I wouldn't marry the girl?" says he.

But his father was gone, and the lad knew well enough that he would keep his word too; and he was greatly troubled in his mind, for as quiet and as kind as the father was, he never went back of a word that he had once said, and there wasn't another man in the country who was harder to bend than he was.

The boy did not know rightly what to do. He was in love with the girl indeed, and he hoped to marry her some time or other, but he would much sooner have remained another while as he was and follow on at his old tricks—drinking, sporting, and playing cards; and, along with that, he was angry that his father should order him to marry and should threaten him if he did not do it.

"Isn't my father a great fool!" says he to himself. "I was ready enough, and only too anxious, to marry Mary; and now since he threatened me, faith, I've a great mind to let it go another while."

His mind was so much excited that he remained between two notions as to what he should do. He walked out into the night at last to cool his heated blood and went on to the road. He lit a pipe, and as the night was fine he walked and walked on, until the quick pace made him begin to forget his trouble. The night was bright, and the moon half full. There was not a breath of wind blowing, and the air was calm and mild. He walked on for nearly three hours, when he suddenly remembered that it was late in the night and time for him to turn. "Musha! I think I forgot myself," says he. "It must be near twelve o'clock now."

The word was hardly out of his mouth when he heard the sound of many voices and the trampling of feet on the road before him. "I don't know who can be out so late at night as this, and on such a lonely road," said he to himself.

He stood listening, and he heard the voices of many people talking through other, but he could not understand what they were saying. "Oh, *wirra!*" ["Oh, Mary!"] says he, "I'm afraid. It's not Irish or English they have; it can't be they're Frenchmen!" He went on a couple of yards farther, and he saw well enough by the light of the moon a band of little people coming toward him, and they were carrying something big and heavy with them.

"Oh, murder!" says he to himself, "sure it can't be that they're the good people that's in it!" Every *rib* [a single hair] that was on his head stood up, and there fell a shaking on his bones, for he saw that they were coming to him fast.

He looked at them again and perceived that there were about twenty little men in it, and there was not a man at all of them higher than about three feet or three feet and a half, and some of them were gray and seemed very old. He looked again, but he could not make out what was the heavy thing they were carrying until they came up to him, and then they all stood round about him. They threw the heavy thing down on the road, and he saw on the spot that it was a dead body.

He became as cold as the Death, and there was not a drop of blood running in his veins when an old little gray *maneen* came up to him and said, "Isn't it lucky we met you, Teig O'Kane?"

Poor Teig could not bring out a word at all, nor open his lips, if he were to get the world for it, and so he gave no answer.

"Teig O'Kane." said the little gray man again, "isn't it timely you met us?"

Teig could not answer him.

"Teig O'Kane," says he, the third time, "isn't it lucky and timely that we met you?"

But Teig remained silent, for he was afraid to return an answer, and his tongue was as if it was tied to the roof of his mouth.

The little gray man turned to his companions, and there was joy in his bright little eye. "And now," says he, "Teig O'Kane hasn't a word, we can do with him what we please. Teig, Teig," says he, "you're living a bad life, and we can make a slave of you now, and you cannot withstand us, for there's no use in trying to go against us. Lift that corpse."

Teig was so frightened that he was only able to utter the two words "I won't"; for as frightened as he was, he was obstinate and stiff, the same as ever.

"Teig O'Kane won't lift the corpse," said the little *maneen* with a wicked little laugh, for all the world like the breaking of a *lock* of dry *kippeens* [rods], and with a little harsh voice like the striking of a cracked bell. "Teig O'Kane won't lift the corpse—make him lift it"; and before the word was out of his mouth they had all gathered round poor Teig, and they all talking and laughing through other.

Teig tried to run from them, but they followed him, and a man of them stretched out his foot before him as he ran, so that Teig was thrown in a heap on the road. Then before he could rise up the fairies caught him, some by the hands and some by the feet, and they held him tight, in a way that he could not stir, with his face against the ground. Six or seven of them raised the body then, and pulled it over to him, and left it down on his back. The breast of the corpse was squeezed against Teig's back and shoulders, and the arms of the corpse were thrown around Teig's neck. Then they stood back from him a couple of yards and let him get up. He rose, foaming at the mouth and cursing, and he shook himself, thinking to throw the corpse off his back. But his fear and his wonder were great when he found that the two arms had a tight hold round his own neck, and that the two legs were squeezing his hips firmly, and that, however strongly he tried, he could not throw it off, any more than a horse can throw off its saddle. He was terribly frightened then, and he thought he was lost. "*Ochone!* forever," said he to himself, "it's the bad life I'm leading that has given the good people this power over me. I promise to God and Mary, Peter and Paul, Patrick and Bridget, that I'll mend my ways for as long as I have to live, if I come clear out of this danger–and I'll marry the girl."

The little gray man came up to him again and said he to him, "Now, Teigeen," says he, "you didn't lift the body when I told you to lift it, and see how you were made to lift it; perhaps when I tell you to bury it you won't bury it until you're made to bury it!"

"Anything at all that I can do for your honor," said Teig, "I'll do it," for he was getting sense already, and if it had not been for the great fear that was on him he never would have let that civil word slip out of his mouth.

The little man laughed a sort of laugh again. "You're getting quiet now, Teig," says he. "I'll go bail but you'll be quiet enough before I'm done with you. Listen to me now, Teig O'Kane, and if you don't obey me in all I'm telling you to do, you'll repent it. You must carry with you this corpse that is on your back to Teampoll-Démus, and you must bring it into the church with you, and make a grave for it in the very middle of the church, and you must raise up the flags and put them down again the very same way, and you must carry the clay out of the church and leave the place as it was when you came, so that no one could know that there had been anything changed. But that's not all. Maybe that the body won't be allowed to be buried in that church; perhaps some other man has the bed, and, if so, it's likely he won't share it with this one. If you don't get leave to bury it at Teampoll-Démus, you must carry it to Carrick-fhad-vic-Orus, and bury it in the churchyard there; and if you don't get it into that place, take it with you to Teampoll-Ronan; and if that churchyard is closed on you, take it to Imlogue-Fada; and if you're not able to bury it there, you've no more to do than to take it to Kill-Breedya, and you can bury it there without hindrance. I cannot tell you what one of those churches is the one where you will have leave to bury that corpse under the clay, but I know that it will be allowed you to bury him at some church or other of them. If you do this work rightly, we will be thankful to you, and you will have no cause to grieve; but if you are slow or lazy, believe me, we shall take satisfaction of you."

When the gray little man had done speaking his comrades laughed and clapped their hands together. "Glic! Glic! Hwee! Hwee!" they all cried. "Go on, go on, you have eight hours before you till day-break, and if you haven't this man buried before the sun rises you're lost." They struck a fist and a foot behind on him, and drove him on in the road. He was obliged to walk, and to walk fast, for they gave him no rest.

He thought himself that there was not a wet path, or a dirty *boreen* [lane], or a crooked, contrary road in the whole country that he had not walked that night. The night was at times very dark, and whenever there would come a cloud across the moon he could see nothing, and then he used often to fall. Sometimes he was hurt, and sometimes he escaped, but he was obliged always to rise on the moment and to hurry on. Sometimes the moon would break out clearly, and then he would look behind him and see the little people following at his back. And he heard them speaking amongst themselves, talking and crying out, and screaming like a flock of sea gulls; and if he was to save his soul he never understood as much as one word of what they were saying.

He did not know how far he had walked when at last one of them cried out to him, "Stop here!" He stood, and they all gathered round him.

"Do you see those withered trees over there!" says the old boy to him again. "Teampoll-Démus is among those trees, and you must go in there by yourself, for we cannot follow you or go with you. We must remain here. Go on boldly."

Teig looked from him, and he saw a high wall that was in places half broken down, and an old gray church on the inside of the wall, and about a dozen withered old trees scattered here and there around it. There was neither leaf nor twig on any of them, but their bare, crooked branches were stretched out like the arms of an angry man when he threatens. He had no help for it, but was obliged to go forward. He was a couple of hundred yards from the church, but he walked on, and never looked behind him until he came to the gate of the churchyard. The old gate was thrown down, and he had no difficulty in entering. He turned then to see if any of the little people were following him, but there came a cloud over the moon, and the night became so dark that he could see nothing. He went into the churchyard, and he walked up the old grassy pathway leading to the church. When he reached the door he found it locked. The door was large and strong, and he did not know what to do. At last he drew out his knife with difficulty and stuck it in the wood to try if it were not rotten, but it was not

"Now," said he to himself, "I have no more to do; the door is shut, and I can't open it."

Before the words were rightly shaped in his own mind a voice in his ear said to him, "Search for the key on the top of the door or on the wall."

He started. "Who is that speaking to me?" he cried, turning round; but he saw no one. The voice said in his ear again, "Search for the key on the top of the door or on the wall."

"What's that?" said he, and the sweat running from his forehead. "Who spoke to me?"

"It's I, the corpse, that spoke to you," said the voice.

"Can you talk?" said Teig.

"Now and again," said the corpse.

Teig searched for the key, and he found it on the top of the wall He was too much frightened to say any more, but he opened the door wide, and as quickly as he could, and he went in, with the corpse on his back. It was as dark as pitch inside, and poor Teig began to shake and tremble.

"Light the candle," said the corpse.

Teig put his hand in his pocket, as well as he was able, and drew out a flint and steel. He struck a spark out of it and lit a burned rag he had in his pocket. He blew it until it made a flame, and he looked around him. The church was very ancient, and part of the wall was broken down. The windows were blown in or cracked, and the timber of the seats was rotten. There were six or seven old iron candlesticks left there still, and in one of these candlesticks Teig found the stump of an old candle, and he lit it. He was still looking round him on the strange and horrid place in which he found himself when the cold corpse whispered in his ear, "Bury me now, bury me now; there is a spade and turn the ground." Teig looked from him, and he saw a spade lying beside the altar. He took it up, and he placed the blade under a flag that was in the middle of the aisle, and, leaning all his weight on the handle of the spade, he raised it. When the first flag was raised it was not hard to raise the others near it, and he moved three or four of them out of their places. The clay that was under them was soft and easy to dig, but he had not thrown up more than three or four shovelfuls when he felt the iron touch something soft like flesh. He threw up three or four more shovelfuls from around it, and then he saw that it was another body that was buried in the same place.

"I am afraid I'll never be allowed to bury the two bodies in the same hole," said Teig in his own mind. "You, corpse, there on my back," says he, "will you be satisfied if I bury you down here?" But the corpse never answered him a word.

"That's a good sign," said Teig to himself. "Maybe he's getting quiet," and he thrust the spade down in the earth again. Perhaps he hurt the flesh of the other body, for the dead man that was buried there stood up in the grave and shouted an awful shout. "Hoo! Hoo! Hoo! Go! Go! Go! or you're a dead, dead, dead man!" And then he fell back in the grave again. Teig said afterward that of all the wonderful things he saw that night that was the most awful to him. His hair stood upright on his head like the bristles of a pig, the cold sweat ran off his face, and then came a tremor over all his bones, until he thought that he must fall.

But after a while he became bolder, when he saw that the second corpse remained lying quietly there, and he threw in the clay on it again, and he smoothed it overhead, and he laid down the flags carefully as they had been before. "It can't be that he'll rise up any more," said he.

He went down the aisle a little farther, and drew near to the door, and began raising the flags again, looking for another bed for the corpse on his back. He took up three or four flags and put them aside, and then he dug the clay. He was not long digging until he laid bare an old woman without a thread upon her but her shirt. She was more lively than the first corpse, for he had scarcely taken any of the clay away from about her when she sat up and began to cry, "Ho, you *bodach* [clown]! Ha, you *bodach!* Where has he been that he got no bed?"

Poor Teig drew back, and when she found that she was getting no answer, she closed her eyes gently, lost her vigor, and fell back quietly and slowly under the clay. Teig did to her as he had done to the man—he threw the clay back on her and left the flags down overhead.

He began digging again near the door, but before he had thrown up more than a couple of shovels full, he noticed a man's hand laid bare by the spade. "By my soul, I'll go no farther then," said he to himself. "What use is it for me?" And he threw the clay in again on it and settled the flags as they had been before.

He left the church then, and his heart was heavy enough, but he shut the door and locked it and left the key where he found it. He sat down on a tombstone that was near the door and began thinking. He was in great doubt what he should do. He laid his face between his two hands and cried for grief and fatigue, since he was dead certain at this time that he never would come home alive. He made another attempt to loosen the hands of the corpse that were squeezed round his neck, but they were as tight as if they were clamped; and the more he tried to loosen them, the tighter they squeezed him. He was going to sit down once more when the cold, horrid lips of the dead man said to him, "Carrick-fhad-vic-Orus," and he remembered the command of the good people to bring the corpse with him to that place if he should be unable to bury it where he had been.

He rose up and looked about him. "I don't know the way," he said.

As soon as he had uttered the word the corpse stretched out suddenly its left hand that had been tightened around his neck and kept it pointing out, showing him the road he ought to follow. Teig went in the direction that the fingers were stretched and passed out of the churchyard. He found himself on an old rutty, stony road, and he stood still again, not knowing where to turn.

The corpse stretched out its bony hand a second time and pointed out to him another road—not the road by which he had come when approaching the old church. Teig followed that road, and whenever he came to a path or road meeting it, the corpse always stretched out its hand and pointed with its fingers, showing him the way he was to take.

Many was the crossroad he turned down, and many was the crooked *boreen* he walked, until he saw from him an old burying ground at last, beside the road, but there was neither church nor chapel nor any other building in it. The corpse squeezed him

tightly, and he stood. "Bury me, bury me in the burying ground," said the voice.

Teig drew over toward the old burying place, and he was not more than about twenty yards from it when, raising his eyes, he saw hundreds and hundreds of ghosts—men, women, and children—sitting on the top of the wall round about, or standing on the inside of it, or running backward and forward, and pointing at him, while he could see their mouths opening and shutting as if they were speaking, though he heard no word nor any sound amongst them at all.

He was afraid to go forward, so he stood where he was, and the moment he stood, all the ghosts became quiet and ceased moving. Then Teig understood that it was trying to keep him from going in, that they were. He walked a couple of yards forward, and immediately the whole crowd rushed together toward the spot to which he was moving, and they stood so thickly together that it seemed to him that he never could break through them, even though he had a mind to try. But he had no mind to try it. He went back broken and dispirited, and when he had gone a couple of hundred yards from the burying ground he stood again, for he did not know what way he was to go. He heard the voice of the corpse in his ear, saying, "Teampoll-Ronan," and the skinny hand was stretched out again, pointing him out the road.

As tired as he was he had to walk, and the road was neither short nor even. The night was darker than ever, and it was difficult to make his way. Many was the toss he got, and many a bruise they left on his body. At last he saw Teampoll-Ronan from him in the distance, standing in the middle of the burying ground. He moved over toward it, and thought he was all right and safe when he saw no ghosts nor anything else on the wall, and he thought he would never be hindered now from leaving his load off him at last. He moved over to the gate, but as he was passing in he tripped on the threshold. Before he could recover himself something that he could not see seized him by the neck, by the hands, and by the feet, and bruised him, and shook him, and choked him, until he was nearly dead; and at last he was lifted up, and carried more than a hundred yards from that place, and then thrown down in an old dyke, with the corpse still clinging to him.

He rose up, bruised and sore, but feared to go near the place again, for he had seen nothing the time he was thrown down and carried away.

"You, corpse, up on my back," said he, "shall I go over again to the churchyard?" But the corpse never answered him.

"That's a sign you don't wish me to try it again," said Teig.

He was now in great doubt as to what he ought to do, when the corpse spoke in his ear and said, "Imlogue-Fada."

"Oh, murder!" said Teig, "must I bring you there? If you keep me long walking like this, I tell you I'll fall under you."

He went on, however, in the direction the corpse pointed out to him. He could not have told, himself, how long he had been going when the dead man behind suddenly squeezed him and said, "There!"

Teig looked from him, and he saw a little low wall that was so broken down in places that it was no wall at all. It was in a great wide field, in from the road; and only for three or four great stones at the corners, that were more like rocks than stones, there was nothing to show that there was either graveyard or burying ground there.

"Is this Imlogue-Fada? Shall I bury you here?" said Teig.

"Yes," said the voice.

"But I see no grave or gravestone, only this pile of stones," said Teig.

The corpse did not answer, but stretched out its long, fleshless hand to show Teig the direction in which he was to go. Teig went on accordingly, but he was greatly terrified, for he remembered what had happened to him at the last place. He went on, "with his heart in his mouth," as he said himself afterward; but when he came to within fifteen or twenty yards of the little low, square wall, there broke out a flash of lightning, bright yellow and red, with blue streaks in it, and went round about the wall in one course, and it swept by as fast as the swallow in the clouds, and the longer Teig remained looking at it the faster it went, till at last it became like a bright ring of flame round the old graveyard, which no one could pass without being burned by it. Teig never saw, from the time he was born, and never saw afterward, so wonderful or so splendid a sight as that was. Round went the flame, white and yellow and blue sparks leaping out from it as it went, and although at first it had been no more than a thin, narrow line, it increased slowly until it was at last a great broad band, and it was continually getting broader and higher, and throwing out more brilliant sparks, till there was never a color on the ridge of the earth that was not to be seen in that fire; and lightning never shone and flame never flamed that was so shining and so bright as that.

Teig was amazed; he was half dead with fatigue, and he had no courage left to approach the wall. There fell a mist over his eyes, and there came a *soorawn* [vertigo] in his head, and he was obliged to sit down upon a great stone to recover himself. He could see nothing but the light, and he could hear nothing but the whir of it as it shot round the paddock faster than a flash of lightning.

As he sat there on the stone the voice whispered once more in his ear, "Kill-Breedya"; and the dead man squeezed him so tightly that he cried out. He rose again, sick, tired, and trembling, and went forward as he was directed. The wind was cold, and the road was bad, and the load upon his back was heavy, and the night was dark. and he himself was nearly worn out, and if he had had very much farther to go he must have fallen dead under his burden.

At last the corpse stretched out his hand and said to him, "Bury me there."

"This is the last burying place," said Teig in his own mind; "and the little gray man said I'd be allowed to bury him in some of them, so it must be this; it can't be but they'll let him in here."

The first faint streak of the *ring of day* was appearing in the east, and the clouds were beginning to catch fire, but it was darker than ever, for the moon was set and there were no stars.

"Make haste, make haste!" said the corpse; and Teig hurried forward as well as he could to the graveyard, which was a little place on a bare hill, with only a few graves in it.

He walked boldly in through the open gate, and nothing touched him, nor did he either hear or see anything. He came to the middle of the ground, and then stood up and looked round him for a spade or shovel to make a grave. As he was turning round and searching, he suddenly perceived what startled him greatly—a newly dug grave right before him. He moved over to it and looked down, and there at the bottom he saw a black coffin. He clambered down into the hole and lifted the lid and found that (as he thought it would be) the coffin was empty. He had hardly mounted up out of the hole, and was standing on the brink, when the corpse, which had clung to him for more than eight hours, suddenly relaxed its hold of his neck, and loosened its shins from round his hips, and sank down with a plop! into the open coffin.

Teig fell down on his two knees at the brink of the grave and gave thanks to God. He made no delay then, but pressed down the coffin lid in its place and threw in the clay over it with his two hands; and when the grave was filled up, he stamped and leaped on it with his feet, until it was firm and hard, and then he left the place.

The sun was fast rising as he finished his work, and the first thing he did was to return to the road and look out for a house to rest himself in. He found an inn at last, and lay down upon a bed there, and slept till night. Then he rose up, and ate a little, and fell asleep again till morning. When he awoke in the morning he hired a horse and rode home. He was more than twenty-six miles from home where he was, and he had come all that way with the dead body on his back in one night.

All the people at his own home thought that he must have left the country, and they rejoiced greatly when they saw him come back. Everyone began asking him where he had been, but he would not tell anyone except his father.

He was a changed man from that day. He never drank too much; he never lost his money over cards; and especially he would not take the world and be out late by himself of a dark night.

He was not a fortnight at home until he married Mary, the girl he had been in love with; and it's at their wedding the sport was, and it's he was the happy man from that day forward, and it's all I wish that we may be as happy as he was.

Contributed by Douglas Hyde to *Irish Fairy and Folk Tales.*

Italian

The Cunning Cat

CONSIDERABLY before Perrault and the French storywriters made fairy tales a literary fashion in Europe, Giovanni Francesco Straparola, a Venetian of the early sixteenth century—when Venice was still a channel for Eastern ideas as well as merchandise—and Giambattista Basile, an early seventeenth-century Neapolitan, had made collections of popular tales. Although neither writer hesitated, when it suited his purpose, to give his own interpretation of a traditional tale, Straparola's *Pleasant Nights* and Basile's *Pentamerone* are, as the Grimms pointed out, storehouses of authentic folk story.

In a style that the *Decameron's* country-dallying young Florentines had made popular, the stories in both the *Pleasant Nights* and the *Pentamerone* are told by fashionable citizens, and although Basile's is ostensibly a collection for children, both mingle elegance and coarseness as only writers who straddled the Middle Ages and the Renaissance could mingle them. From Straparola comes "The Cunning Cat," which anticipates the French "Puss in Boots" by two hundred and fifty years, and "The Untamed Shrew," which, like the tale from *Conde Lucanor* (page 712) and Shakespeare's famous play, deals with one of the most popular themes of the age—how to rule a roost. From Basile we get "The Merchant," a folk-tale comedy of errors, "The Ignorant Youth," an amusing Italian version of the Gifted Companions story ("The Seven Simeons" on page 639 is a Russian version), and "Pinto Smalto," a reversed Pygmalion and Galatea. Although bedecked with conceits in the prevailing literary mode, and with bombastic catalogues that no doubt owe much to Rabelais, the stories from the *Pentamerone* reprinted here are essentially traditional; and elsewhere in Basile's big book one can find many other tales, including "Cinderella," that the French "Mother Goose" later made famous.

From latter-day Venice comes "Bastianelo," on the theme of the Three Sillies, and from modern Sicily come both "The Thoughtless

Abbot," an analogue of the old English ballad of King John and the Abbot of Canterbury, and "Scissors They Were," an immemorial jest on the ultimate in female obstinacy.

THE UNTAMED SHREW

NO GREAT time ago there lived in Corneto, a village near Rome, situated in the patrimony of St. Peter, two men who were sworn brothers; indeed, the love between them was just as great as it would have been supposing they had been born of the same womb. Of these one was called Pisardo and the other Silverio, and both one and the other followed the calling of arms and were in the pay of the Pope; wherefore a great love and friendship sprang up between them though they did not dwell in the same house. Silverio, who was the younger in years and under no family restraint, took to wife a certain Spinella, the daughter of a tailor, a very fair and lovely maiden, but somewhat over-flighty in humor. After the wedding was over and the bride brought home, Silverio found himself so completely inflamed and dominated by the power of her beauty that it seemed to him she must be beyond comparison, and straightway he fulfilled any demand that she might make upon him. Thus it came to pass that Spinella grew so arrantly haughty and masterful that she took little or no reck of her husband. And in time the doting fool fell into such a state that if he should ask his wife to do one thing, she would forthwith do something else, and whenever he told her to come here, she went there, and laughed at everything he said. Because the foolish fellow saw nothing except through his own foolish eyes, he could not pluck up heart of grace enough to reprove her, nor seek a remedy for his mistake, but let her go her own way and work her own will in everything, according to her pleasure.

Before another year had passed away Pisardo took to wife Fiorella, the other daughter of the tailor, a damsel no less comely of person than Spinella, nor less sprightly in her disposition. When the wedding feast was over, and the wife taken home to her husband's house, Pisardo brought forth a pair of men's breeches and two stout sticks and said, "Fiorella, you see here this pair of men's breeches. Now you take hold of one of these sticks and I will take hold of the other, and we will have a struggle over the breeches as to who shall wear them. Which one of us shall get the better of the other in this trial shall be the wearer, and the one who loses shall henceforth yield obedience to the winner." When Fiorella heard this speech of her husband's she answered without aught of hesitation in a gentle voice, "Ah, my husband! what do you mean by such words as these? What is it you say? Are not you the husband, and I the wife, and ought not the wife always to bear herself obediently toward her husband? And, moreover, how could I ever bring myself to do such a foolish trick as this? Wear the breeches yourself, for assuredly they will become you much better than they will become me." "I, then," said Pisardo, "am to wear the breeches and to be the husband, and you, as my dearly beloved wife, will always hold yourself obedient to me. But take good care that you keep the same mind and do not hanker after taking the husband's part for yourself and giving me the wife's, for such license you will never get from me." Fiorella, who was a very prudent woman, confirmed all that she had hitherto said, and the husband, on his part, handed over to her the entire governance of his house and committed all his chattels to her keeping, making known to her the order he desired to have observed in his household.

A little time after this Pisardo said to his wife, "Fiorella, come with me. I wish to show you my horses and to point out to you the right way to train them in case you should at any time have to put your hand to such work." And when they were come into the stable he said, "Now, Fiorella, what do you think of these horses of mine? Are they not handsome? Are they not finely tended?" And to this Fiorella replied that they were. "But now see," said Pisardo, "how docile and handy they are." Then picking up a whip he gave a touch now to this and now to that, saying, "Go over there! Come here!" And then the horses, putting their tails between their legs, went all together into a group obedient to their master's word. Now Pisardo had amongst his other horses a certain one, very beautiful to look upon, but at the same time vicious and lazy—a beast upon which he set but little store. He went up to this horse and, dealing it a sharp cut with the whip, cried out, "Come here! Go over there!" But the beast, sluggish and sullen by nature, took no heed of the whip and refused to do anything his master ordered, lashing out vigorously now with one leg, now with the other, and now with both together. Whereupon Pisardo, remarking the brute's stubborn humor, took a tough, stout stick and began to baste its hide there-with so vigorously that he was soon out of breath with fatigue. However, the horse, now more stubborn than ever, let Pisardo lay on as he would and refused to budge an inch; so Pisardo, seeing how persistent was the obstinacy of the brute, flew into a violent rage, and, grasping the sword which he wore by his side, he slew it forthwith.

Fiorella, when she saw what her husband had done, was mightily moved with pity for the horse and cried out, "Alas, my husband! Why have you killed your horse, seeing that he was so shapely to look upon? Surely it is a great pity to have slain him thus." To this Pisardo replied, with his face strongly moved by passion, "Know then that all those who eat my bread and refuse to do my will must look to be paid in exactly the same coin." Fiorella, when she heard this speech, was greatly distressed and said to herself, "Alas! what a wretched miserable woman I am! What an evil day it was for me when I met this man! I believed I had chosen a man of good sense for my husband, and lo! I have become the prey of this brutal fellow. Behold how, for little or no fault, he has killed this beautiful horse!" And thus she went on, grieving sorely to herself, for she knew not to what end her husband had spoken in this wise.

On account of what had passed Fiorella fell into such a taking of fear and terror of her husband that she would tremble all over at the very sound of his footstep, and whenever he might demand any service of her she would carry out his wishes straightway. Indeed, she would understand his meaning almost before he might open his mouth, and never a cross word passed between them. Silverio, who, on account of the friendship he felt for Pisardo, would often visit the house of the latter, and dine and sup there, remarked the manners and carriage of Fiorella, and, being much astonished thereat, said to himself, "Great God! why was it not my lot to have Fiorella for my wife, as is the good luck of my brother Pisardo? See how deftly she manages the house, and goes about her business without any uproar! See how obedient she is to her husband, and how she carries out every wish of his! But my wife, miserable wight that I am, does everything to annoy me, and uses me in as vile a fashion as possible."

One day it chanced that Silverio and Pisardo were in company together, talking of various things, when the former spake thus: "Pisardo, my brother, you are aware of the love that there is between us. Now, on this account, I would gladly learn what is the method you have followed in the training of your wife, seeing that she is altogether obedient to you and treats you in such loving wise. Now I, however gently I may ask Spinella to do anything, find that she always stubbornly refuses to answer me, and, beyond this, does the exact opposite to what I ask her to do." Whereupon Pisardo, smiling, set forth word by word the plan and the means he had adopted when first he brought his wife home, and counseled his friend to go and do likewise, and to see whether he might not also succeed, adding that in case this remedy should not be found efficient, he would not know what other course to recommend.

Silverio was much pleased with this excellent counsel, and, having taken his leave, he went his way. When he reached his house he called his wife at once, and brought out a pair of his breeches and two sticks, following exactly the same course as Pisardo had recommended. When Spinella saw what he was doing she cried out, "What new freak is this of yours? Silverio, what are you about? What ridiculous fancy has got into your head? Surely you are gone stark mad! Don't you think everybody knows that men, and not women, should wear the breeches? And what need is there now to set about doing things which are beside all purpose?" But Silverio made no answer and went on with the task he had begun, laying down all sorts of rules for the regulation of his household. Spinella, altogether astonished at this humor of her husband, said in a mocking way, "Peradventure, Silverio, it seems to you that I know not how to manage a house rightly, since you make all this ado about letting your meaning be known?" But still the husband kept silence, and, having taken his wife with him into the stable, he did with the horses everything which Pisardo had done, and in the end slew one of them. Spinella, when she saw this fool's work, was convinced in her own mind that her husband had in truth lost his wits and spake thus: "By your faith, tell me, husband, what crazy humors are these that have risen to your head? What is the true meaning of all this foolishness you are doing without thinking of the issue? Perhaps it is your evil fate to have gone mad." Then answered Silverio, "I am not mad, but I have made up my mind that anyone who lives at my charges and will not obey me shall be treated in such fashion as you have seen me use this morning toward my horses."

Whereupon Spinella, when she perceived the drift of her besotted husband's brutal deed, said, "Ah, you wretched dolt! it must be clear enough to you that your horse was nothing but a poor beast to allow himself to be killed in this manner. What is the full meaning of this whim of yours? Perhaps you think you can deal with me as you have dealt with the horse? Certes, if such is your belief, you are hugely mistaken, and you put your hand much too late to the task of setting things in order after the fashion you desire. The bone is become too hard, the sore is now all ulcerated, and there is no cure at hand. You should have been more prompt in compassing the righting of these curious wrongs of yours. You fool! You brainless idiot! Do you not see what damage and disgrace must come upon you through these doltish deeds out of number of which you have been guilty? And what profit do you deem you will get from them? None, as I am a living woman."

Silverio, when he listened to the words of his shrewd wife, knew in his heart that his effort, through the doting affection he had hitherto spent on Spinella, had miserably failed; so he made up his mind, greatly to his chagrin, to put up patiently with his wretched lot till death should come to release him. And Spinella, when she perceived how little her husband's plan had turned out to his advantage, resolved that if in the past she had worked her own will with a finger she would henceforth work it with an arm; for a woman headstrong by nature would sooner die a thousand times than go aside aught from the path which she has deliberately marked out for herself.

The Second Fable from Night VIII of *The Nights of Straparola*, a translation by W. G. Waters of the *Piacevoli Notti* of Giovanni Francesco Straparola (London: privately printed, 1894).

THE CUNNING CAT

THERE was once upon a time in Bohemia a woman, Soriana by name, who lived in great poverty with her three sons, of whom one was called Dusolino, and another Tesifone, and the third Costantino Fortunato. Soriana had naught of any value in the way of household goods save three things, and these were a kneading trough of the kind women use in the making of bread, a board such as is used in the preparation of pastry, and a cat. Soriana, being now borne down with a very heavy burden of years, saw that death was approaching her, and on this account made her last testament, leaving to Dusolino, her eldest son, the kneading trough, to Tesifone the paste board, and to Costantino the cat. When the mother was dead and duly buried, the neighbors round about would borrow now the kneading trough and now the paste board, as they might happen to want them, and as they knew that the young men were very poor, they gave them by way of repayment a cake, which Dusolino and Tesifone ate by themselves, giving nothing of it to Costantino, the youngest brother. And if Costantino chanced to ask them to give him aught they would make answer by bidding him to go to his cat, who would without fail let him have what he wanted, and on this account poor Costantino and his cat underwent much suffering.

Now it chanced that this cat of Costantino's was a fairy in disguise, and the cat, feeling much compassion for him and anger at his two brothers on account of their cruel treatment of him, one day said to him, "Costantino, do not be cast down, for I will provide for your well-being and sustenance, and for my own as well." Whereupon the cat sallied forth from the house and went into the fields, where it lay down and feigned to be asleep so cleverly that an unsuspecting leveret came close up to where it was lying, and was forthwith seized and killed.

Then, carrying the leveret, the cat went to the king's palace, and, having met some of the courtiers who were standing about it, said that it wanted to speak to the king. When the king heard that a cat had begged an audience with him, he bade them bring it into his presence, and, having asked it what its business was, the cat replied that Costantino, its master, had sent a leveret as a present to the king and begged his gracious acceptance of the same. And with these words it presented the leveret to the king, who was pleased to accept it, asking at the same time who this Costantino might be. The cat replied that he was a young man who for virtue and good looks had no superior, and the king, on hearing this report, gave the cat a kindly welcome and ordered them to set before it meat and drink of the best. The cat, when it had eaten and drunk enough, dexterously filled the bag in which it had brought the leveret with all sorts of good provender, when no one was looking that way, and, having taken leave of the king, carried the spoil back to Costantino.

The two brothers, when they saw Costantino making good cheer over the victuals, asked him to let them have a share, but he paid them back in their own coin and refused to give them a morsel, wherefore on this account the brothers hereafter were tormented with gnawing envy of Costantino's good fortune. Now Costantino, though he was a good-looking youth, had suffered so much privation and distress that his face was rough and covered with blotches, which caused him much discomfort; so the cat, having taken him one day down to the river, washed him and licked him carefully with its tongue from head to foot and tended him so well that in a few days he was quite freed from his ailment. The cat still went on carrying presents to the royal palace in the fashion already described, and by these means got a living for Costantino.

But after a time the cat began to find these journeyings to and from the palace somewhat irksome, and it feared, moreover, that the king's courtiers might become impatient thereanent; so it said to Costantino, "My master, if you will only do what I shall tell you, in a short time you will find yourself a rich man." "And how will you manage this?" said Costantino. Then the cat answered, "Come with me, and do not trouble yourself about anything, for I have a plan for making a rich man of you which cannot fail." Whereupon the cat and Costantino betook themselves to a spot on the bank of the river which was hard by the king's palace, and forthwith the cat bade its master to strip off all his clothes and to throw himself into the river. Then it began to cry and shout in a loud voice, "Help, help, run, run, for Messer Costantino is drowning!" It happened that the king heard what the cat was crying out, and, bearing in mind what great benefits he had received from Costantino, he immediately sent some of his household to the rescue. When Costantino had been dragged out of the water and dressed by the attendants in seemly garments, he was led into the presence of the king, who gave him a hearty welcome and inquired of him how it was that he found himself in the water; but Costantino, on account of his agitation, knew not what reply to make; so the cat, who always kept at his elbow, answered in his stead, "You must know, O king! that some robbers, who had learned by the agency of a spy that my master was taking a great store of jewels to offer them to you as a present, laid wait for him and robbed him of his treasure, and then, wishing to murder him, they threw him into the river; but by the aid of these gentlemen he has escaped death." The king, when he heard this, gave orders that Costantino should enjoy the best of treatment, and, seeing that he was well made and handsome, and believing him to be very rich, he made up his mind to give him his daughter Elisetta to wife, and to endow her with a rich dowry of gold and jewels and sumptuous raiment.

When the nuptial ceremonies were completed and the festivities at an end, the king bade them load ten mules with gold and five with the richest garments, and sent the bride, accompanied by a great concourse of people, to her husband's house. Costantino, when he saw himself so highly honored and loaded with riches, was in sore perplexity as to where he should carry his bride, and took counsel with the cat thereanent. Said the cat, "Be not troubled over this business, my master; we will provide for everything." So as they were all riding on merrily together the cat left the others and rode on rapidly in advance, and after it had left the company a long way behind it came upon certain cavaliers whom it thus addressed: "Alas! you poor fellows, what are you doing here? Get hence as quickly as you can, for a great body of armed men is coming along this road and will surely attack and despoil you. See, they are now quite near. Listen to the noise of the neighing horses." Whereupon the horsemen, overcome with fear, said to the cat, "What then shall we do?" and the cat made answer, "It will be best for you to act in this wise. If they should question you as to whose men you are, you must answer boldly that you serve Messer Costantino, and then no one will molest you." Then the cat left them, and, having ridden on still farther, came upon great flocks of sheep and herds of cattle, and it told the same story and gave the same counsel to the shepherds and drovers who had charge of these. Then, going on still farther, it spake in the same terms to whomsoever it chanced to meet.

As the cavalcade of the princess passed on, the gentlemen who were accompanying her asked of the horsemen whom they met the name of their lord, and of the herdsmen who might be the owner of all these sheep and oxen, and the answer given by all was that they served Messer Costantino. Then the gentlemen of the escort said to the bridegroom, "So, Messer Costantino, it appears we are now entering your dominions?" And Costantino nodded his head in token of assent, and in like manner he made answer to all their interrogations, so that all the company on this account judged him to be enormously rich.

In the meantime the cat had ridden on and had come to a fair and stately castle, which was guarded by a very weak garrison, and these defenders the cat addressed in the following words: "My good men, what is it you do? Surely you must be aware of the ruin which is about to overwhelm you." "What is the ruin you speak of?" demanded the guards. "Why, before another hour shall have gone by," replied the cat, "your place will be beleaguered by a great company of soldiers, who will cut you in pieces. Do you not already hear the neighing of the horses and see the dust in the air? Wherefore, unless you are minded to perish, take heed of my advice, which will bring you safely out of all danger. For if anyone shall demand of you whose this castle is, say that it belongs to Messer Costantino Fortunato." And when the time came the guards gave answer as the cat had directed; for when the noble escort of the bride had arrived at the stately castle, and certain gentlemen had inquired of the guards the name of the lord of the castle, they were answered that it was Messer Costantino Fortunato; and when the whole company had entered the castle they were honorably lodged therein.

Now the lord of this castle was a certain Signor Valentino, a very brave soldier, who only a few days ago had left his castle to bring back thereto the wife he had recently espoused, but as ill fortune would have it, there happened to him on the road, somewhile before he came to the place where his beloved wife was abiding, an unhappy and unforeseen accident by which he straightway met his death. So Costantino Fortunato retained the lordship of Valentino's castle. Not long after this Morando, king of Bohemia, died, and the people by acclamation chose Costantino Fortunato for their king, seeing that he had espoused Elisetta, the late king's daughter, to whom by right the succession to the kingdom belonged. And by these means Costantino rose from an estate of poverty or even beggary to be a powerful king, and lived long with Elisetta his wife, leaving children by her to be the heirs of his kingdom.

The First Fable of Night XI of *The Nights of Straparola.*

THE MERCHANT

THERE lived in Naples city a rich merchant, Antoniello hight, who had two sons named Cienzo and Meo; and they so much resembled one another that one could hardly tell which was one and which the other. Now Cienzo, who was the eldest, was playing with the son of the king at throwing stones when it chanced that he struck and broke the prince's head; and Cienzo's sire, hearing of the mishap, said, "Bravo! thou hast done a good deed. Write now to thy country, boast of thy doings, bag of emptiness, and I will unpick thee. Mount on thy high horse, for thou hast gained that which is worth six soldi: thou hast broken the head of the prince. Hadst thou not the measure, son of a goatherd? Now what will become of thee? I would not give three farthings for thy skin, for thou hast cooked thy soup badly; even shouldst thou enter the womb whence thou camest forth, I would not answer that thou wouldst escape the king's wrath: thou knowest that king's arms are long and reach far, and he is certain to do something that will stink."

Cienzo listened patiently to his father's saying, and when he had ended, thus rejoined, "O my father, I have always heard it said that it is better to go to a court of justice than to have the doctor in the house. Would it not have been worse if he had broken my head? I was provoked: we are but children, and we quarreled; it is a first crime, and the king is a just man; at worst, what will it matter in a hundred years? Who will not give me the mother may give me the daughter, and who will not send me cooked food may send it uncooked; all the world is a country, and he that is afraid may become a constable." Antoniello answered, "What can he do to thee? He can send thee out of the world; he can send thee for a change of air; he can make thee a schoolmaster in a twenty-four-feet galley [slave ship], to be a horse for the fishes, so that thou mayest teach them to speak; he can send thee a three-feet collar well starched [for hanging], so that thou mayest enjoy thyself with the widow: and instead of touching the hand of the bride, thou shalt touch the feet of the groomsman. Therefore stand not with thy skin between the cloth and the cloth-shearer; but march at this same step, that we may never hear tidings, neither old nor new, of thee and thy doings, so that thou mayest not be caught by the foot. For it is better to be a bird in the wilderness than a bird in a cage. Here, take this gold, and go to the stable, and mount one of the two charmed steeds I have therein; and take a bitch which is also ensorcelled, and wait for nothing more. It is better to lift thine heel than to be caught by the heel; it is better to carry thy legs than to put thy neck under thy legs; it is better to walk a thousand feet than to remain with a rope three feet long. If thou takest not thy saddlebags, neither Baldo nor Bartolo will help thee."

Cienzo begged his father to give him his blessing, and, mounting horse and taking the bitch on his arm, journeyed away from the city; but as soon as he fared forth from the Capuan gate, turning his head backward, he began saying, "I am going to leave thee, O my beautiful Naples; who knoweth if I evermore will see thee, O thou whose bricks are sugar, and whose walls are made of sweet soft pastry, where the stones are manna, and the beams are of sugar cane, and the doors and the windows are of sweet cakes? Alas! separating myself from thee, O beautiful Apennine, it seems to me as if I fared away with the standard; withdrawing myself from thee, O thou Great Place, my soul is straitened; removing myself from thee, Ermo's Place, my spirit is ready to depart from this body; dividing myself from you, Lancers, I feel the stroke of a Catalan lance in my side. Where shall I ever find another harbor like thine, the sweetest harbor in all the world? Where shall I find another hole, receptacle of all virtuous men, where another lodge where dwelleth all that pleaseth and enticeth the taste? Alas! and woe is me, I cannot leave thee, O dear bay mine, if I do not let mine eyes run a sea of tears; I cannot leave thee, O market, without deep grief burning in my breast; in leaving thee, O beautiful Chiaja, I must bear in my heart a thousand wounds. Farewell, sweet carrots, and cabbages, and cauliflowers! Adieu, dear tripe and lovely trots! Adieu, tarantella and elegant ladies! Adieu, flower of the city and Talia's luxury, Cupid of Europe and Ass of the World! Farewell, Naples, where ends all virtue, and all grace abideth! I go, and shall be forever a widower of married pottage; I fare away from this beauteous country, where I leave all my strength and peace."

And thus saying, he made a winter of tears and a summer of sighs, and journeyed onward, and never ceased faring till the evening, when he came to a forest, where he sighted an old house at the foot of a strong tower. He knocked at the door, but the master, fearing brigands, it being a dark night, would not open to him; and Cienzo was obliged to take refuge in a dilapidated part of the old house: and, tethering the horse in the adjacent field, he lay with the bitch by his side on some straw he found there. But hardly had he closed his eyes when he started up at the barking of the bitch; and, listening, he heard footsteps creeping around. Now Cienzo was brave and courageous, and he drew his sword and began to lunge and plunge in the dark; but finding that he caught no one, and that he fought with the wind, he lay down once more. But after a little while he felt someone pulling him gently by the foot; and, again rising and drawing his sword, he cried, "Ho, there, whoever thou art, thou annoyest me now; it is no good playing hide-and-seek: if thou art valiant, let me see thee, and if thou wilt fight, let us fight, for thou hast found the shape for thy shoe." In answer to this he heard a light laugh, and a muffled voice said, "Come down here, and I will tell thee who I am." Cienzo fearlessly replied, "Wait a minute, and I will be with thee"; and he crept in the dark, feeling about till he found a staircase descending to the cellar; and he went down, and perceived, by the light of a small lantern, three gnomes who were weeping bitterly and crying, "O beautiful treasure, how can we lose thee?" Cienzo at the sight began also to weep and lament, to keep them company; and after bemoaning for some time, and the moon being high amidst the heavens, the three gnomes said to him, "Go and take this treasure: it was decreed by the Decreer that it should be thine; take it, and know how to use it." And having spoken thus, they disappeared.

Now as soon as Cienzo beheld a ray of the sun from a little fissure, he tried to find the stairs to mount; but he could see no mode of exit, at which case he began to cry out so very loud that the master of the tower, who had entered those ruins to make water, heard him, and, asking him what he was doing there and hearing how it fortuned, went to fetch a ladder, and, in descending thereon, found the hoard, which he wished to share with Cienzo. But Cienzo would accept none of it; and, taking the bitch on his arm, he mounted his steed and fared on. After a while he came to another forest, very dark and gloomy; and there at the seashore he found a fairy, who, being enamored of the shade and its coolness, liked to spend her time in the wood in the shape of a serpent: and she was persecuted by several others who desired to slay her, which Cienzo seeing, he laid hand on sword and sliced right and left, thus saving the fairy's life and honor. Then she appeared to him as a beauteous lady, and thanked him, and complimented him on his valor, and invited him to her palace, which was not very distant, for that she desired to show him proof of her gratitude. But Cienzo said to her, "There is no need; a thousand thanks! Another time I will accept thy favor; now I cannot, for I am pressed for time"; and, taking leave of her, he fared on for some time, and he came to a king's palace, all tapestried in mourning, so that it made the very heart be darkened to look upon it.

Cienzo went forward and inquired the cause of this mourning; and they answered him that into that country had come a dragon with seven heads, the most terrible that could be seen in the world. On each head he had a cock's comb and a cat's face, eyes of fire, a dog's mouth, a bat's jaws, and he had a bear's paws and a serpent's tail. And this dragon ate a human being each day, and so it had been for some time; and now, by decree of the Decreer, it had come to the turn of Menechiella, the king's daughter, to serve as food for the monster. "And this is the reason why the king's palace is in mourning," continued they, "because the loveliest and most graceful creature in this country must serve as food for this horrible monster." As Cienzo heard this he stood aside, and beheld Menechiella coming dressed all in mourning, and followed by the young ladies of the court and by all the women of the land, who buffeted their faces, and struck at their breasts, and tore their hair, and wept and wailed, bemoaning the lot of the unhappy princess, saying, "Who could have dreamed that this poor child should give up all the joys and pleasures of life in the body of this hideous beast? If anyone had told us that this pretty bird should serve as food for this dragon, we could not have believed it; we could not dream that this bright young angel would lose her life in this monster's belly"; and as they spake thus, behold! out of a hidden place came the dragon. O mother mine, how hideous! The sun would hide its face behind the clouds for fear, and the sky would darken. And the hearts of all beholders shriveled up, and the trembling was such that a pig's head could not have made its way into the crowd.

Cienzo, beholding this sight, hent sword in hand and came forward and sliced at the dragon; and, tiff and taff, down went one of the dragon's heads. But the dragon, rubbing the fallen head on some grass which grew hard by, stuck it on again, like a lizard glueing on its tail. But Cienzo, seeing this, said, "Who followeth not up his work will fail," and, tightening his lips, lifted his sword and gave such a powerful blow that all the seven heads fell at a single stroke; and they jumped to a distance like beans from a wooden spoon. Taking hold of them, and wrenching their tongues, and putting them aside, he carried them about a mile's distance, for fear that they should cleave together again; and, taking a handful of the grass with which the dragon had glued on his head, he put it carefully by;

then he sent Menechiella back to her father's house, and he went to take some rest at a tavern.

When the king beheld his daughter his joy and gladness knew no bounds, and, hearing how she had been delivered, he sent the public crier round the city to publish an edict "that whosoever had killed the dragon, by the king's command, should come and wed the princess." A cunning rustic, hearing the crier, went and picked up the dragon's seven heads and fared to the presence, and, after paying due homage to the king, presented him the heads and said, "My prowess saved Menechiella, and these hands saved our land from direst ruin. Here are the heads as witnesses of the deed; and every promise is a debt." The king, hearing this, took off the crown from his head and put it on the clown's; and it looked like an exile's head on the top of a pillar. The news went round like wildfire in all the land, till it reached the ears of Cienzo, who said to himself, "I am in very sooth an ass; I held Fortune by the hair, and I let her slip from my grasp; the master of the tower offered me a moiety of the treasure, and I refused, holding it of such account as a German does water; the fairy invited me to her palace, desiring to do some deed of kindness, and I took so much heed of it as the ass doth of the fly; and now I am sent for to wear a crown, and I behave as a drunkard doth with the spindle, allowing that a clodhopper should set his hairy foot before me and bear away from me this beautiful being by a dishonest gambling to his advantage." And thus saying, he searched for pen, ink, and paper, and began to write:

"To the most beauteous jewel, above all women, Menechiella, Infanta of King Pierdisinno.

"Having, by the sun's grace, saved thy life, I find that another is enjoying the fruit of my labor; another beareth the honors for the service which I rendered thee; therefore I ask of thee, that wert present and a witness of my doings, to undeceive the king thy sire, and let him know the truth, and do not thou consent that another should win thee, when I imperiled my life to gain thy safety. And this is written so that thou shouldst bestow upon me with thy queenly grace the guerdon due to my valor; and I end this kissing thy lily-white hands.

"From the Pot Tavern today, Sunday."

Having written and sealed this letter, he put it in the bitch's mouth, saying to her, "Haste thee, and tarry not till thou hast taken this missive to the king's daughter; and let no one have it but herself, and let her hand take it, my princess, with her face like a silvern moon." The bitch went to the palace nearly flying, and, ascending the stairs, entered the saloon, where she beheld the king paying great homage to the bridegroom. And when they sighted the bitch with a letter in her mouth, they ordered that it should be taken from her, but the bitch would not let anyone touch her till she reached the princess, and laid it in her hands. And Menechiella arose and read it, and, bowing low to the king, laid it in his hands, so that he might see it. And the king, having read it, ordered some of his officers to follow the bitch wherever she went and bring back with them her master.

The officers and courtiers followed the bitch to the tavern, where

they found Cienzo; and, delivering their message from the king, they returned, and Cienzo with them, to the royal presence. The king asked him, "How canst thou boast of having killed the dragon, if this man, who is crowned here by my side, brought the seven heads?" And Cienzo rejoined, "This clodhopper deserveth rather a paper hat than a crown, and he hath been so impudent as to make thee believe that bladders are lanthorns; and to prove to thee that it was I that delivered thy daughter, and not this tow-bearded villain, let the dragon's heads be brought here, and thou wilt see that not one of them can bear witness against me, as they are tongueless, and I have brought the tongues to the judgment." Saying thus, he drew forth the seven tongues and showed them to the king; and the rustic stood still as if carved in stone, hardly knowing what had happened to him. And Menechiella came forward and said, "O my sire, this is the one that saved me," and, turning to the boor, said, "Ah, accursed dog and villain, I had nearly believed thee."

The king, hearing and seeing all this, took off the crown from the head of that hardened hind and put it on Cienzo's head; and would have sent the clown to the galleys, but Cienzo besought the king to be gracious and forgive him, desiring to heap coals of fire upon his head, punishing his indiscretion with generosity and kindness. And the king married his daughter to Cienzo, and tables were spread, and abundance of victuals was brought, and all ate and were satisfied; and when all was ended, the bride and bridegroom retired to a perfumed bed, where Cienzo, lifting the trophy of his victory over the dragon, entered in triumph into love's capital. But as morning dawned, when the sun, having drawn his sword of light, chaseth away the stars, crying, "Stand back, canaille," Cienzo donned his raiment and looked out of the window; and in a house opposite he beheld a beautiful lady at the window and, turning to Menechiella, said to her, "What a pretty thing that is opposite our palace!" "And what dost thou want with it?" answered his wife; and pursued she, "Hast thou opened thine eyes already? Art thou in a bad humor? Hast thy good surfeited thee? Doth it not suffice thee what thou hast at home?" Cienzo bowed his head like a cat which hath done some damage, and said nothing; but, pretending to go out on some business, fared forth from the palace and entered the house of that young lady, who was in sooth a choice morsel, a curdled milk, a sugar cane, a sweet paste. She never turned her eyes without ensnaring a thousand hearts, and she never opened her lips without setting fire to all breasts, and never moved a foot without crushing down the hopes of her adorers. But, besides such grace and comeliness, she had the power through sorcery to charm, chain, and tie all men with her hair, as she did with Cienzo, that no sooner did he put foot where she abode than he was tethered like unto a pony. Such was his case.

Now his younger brother Meo, receiving no news from Cienzo, begged leave of his father to go and search for him, and he let him go willingly, giving him another steed and a bitch, as he had done to his elder son. And Meo, bidding farewell to his sire, departed, and fared on the same road whither his brother had forewent him, till he reached the tower. The master, believing him to be Cienzo, received him and welcomed him with joy and affection and offered him some money, which Meo refused; but, seeing himself so well entreated, he bethought him that his brother must have been there before him, and he waxed more hopeful of finding him. But as soon as Luna, with her enmity to poets, turned her shoulders to the sun, he fared on once more, and never ceased faring till he arrived at the fairy's palace; and when she saw him, believing him to be Cienzo, she welcomed him with joy and gladness, saying to him, "Be thou welcome and well come, O youth mine, thou who hast saved my life." Meo thanked her for her kindness and said, "Forgive me if I do not stay longer, as I have some pressing matters to attend to; I will come and visit thee on my return"; and joying in himself at having thus perceived traces of his brother, he pursued the same road, and never ceased wayfaring till he came to the king's palace.

On the evening of the day on which Cienzo had been ensorcelled Meo entered the palace and was received with great honor by the officers, and guards, and pages, and servants, and was embraced by the bride with great affection; and she said to him, "Welcome, my darling, to thy wife! This morning thou wentest, and this evening thou returnest; when every bird seeketh for food the owl sleepeth. Where hast thou been so long, O Cienzo mine? How canst thou stay so long away from Menechiella? Thou hast saved me from the dragon's mouth and cast me deep into suspicion's chasm; and thou holdest me not as the light of thine eyes." Meo, who was sharp-witted, understood at once that the one who thus addressed him was no other than his brother's wife, and, turning toward her, said, "Pray, excuse me for being away so long"; and he embraced her and went with her to take food. But when the moon, like a breeding fowl, calleth the stars to enjoy the dews, they rose to go to their rest, and Meo, who respected his brother's honor, divided the bed linen, so that there should be no chance of his touching his sister-in-law; and she, beholding this new system, with a darkened face and wrathful mien said to him, "O my love, since when? What game are we playing at? Are we two disputants, that thou hast put a division? Are we two belligerent armies, that thou hast dug a trench? Are we two strange horses, that thou dividest the manger?" Meo, who knew well how to count till thirteen, rejoined, "Do not be angry with me, O my dear love, but I do so by the doctor's orders; it is he that hath advised me this diet, fearing that chasing too much would make me powerless."

Menechiella knew naught of troubled waters, and swallowed this pear, and peacefully went to sleep. But when night, exiled by the sun, took her flight, Meo arose and began dressing near the same window where heretofore his brother had looked out, and beheld the same sorceress in whose bonds was Cienzo; and she pleased him and, turning to Menechiella, he said, "Who may that girl be?" And the princess answered in wrath, "Ah! that is it. And if it be so, the thing is ours. Yesterday thou didst sing the same song to me about that dogfish, and I fear me that the tongue goeth where the tooth acheth; thou oughtest to show respect unto me, for, after all, I am a king's daughter. Was it not enough that last night thou play'dst at eagle imperial shoulder to shoulder, deeming not sufficient thy withdrawal of expense? I hear thee; the diet of our bed is convincing proof to me of a banquet in the house of others; but if I find this to be true, I will do some mad deed and will not heed what evil may come."

Meo, who was a youth who had eaten bread from several bakers, soothed her with kind words, and sware an oath, and said that for the handsomest leman in the world he would not exchange what was at his home, and that she alone was engrafted in his heart and entrails. Menechiella, comforted by these words, retired to her chamber and sent for her tirewomen to dress her hair, and to paint her eyebrows, and to anoint her face, and have recourse to all arts so as to look bewitching to her lord; whilst Meo, suspecting by her words that Cienzo might be at the house of that sorceress, fared forth, taking the bitch with him, and, entering the house of the sorceress, came to the saloon, where no sooner did she behold him than she said, "O my hair, bind him fast!" And Meo rejoined readily, "O my bitch, eat this witch!" And the bitch, obedient to her master's words, swallowed the sorceress just as if she had been the yolk of an egg. Then he fared from room to room till he came to the chamber where lay his brother, ensorcelled by the witch. And Meo took a few hairs from the bitch's tail and burned them over him, when Cienzo awakened as from a deep sleep; and when he beheld his brother, he joyed with exceeding joy and asked how he came there. And Meo related to him how he had decided to come in search of him, and how he had fared on his journey, and, lastly, how he came to the palace, and how Menechiella had mistaken him for her husband, and how he had slept with her; and he was about to continue his narrative and explain to his brother how he had divided the bed linen when Cienzo harshly interrupted him, and, tempted by the demon of jealousy, he took up an old sword which lay near at hand and cut off his brother's head. At the noise and cries the king came with his daughter and looked out of the window; and they beheld Cienzo, who had cut off the head of someone very like him, at which sight they inquired of him the cause; and Cienzo made answer, "Inquire of it thyself, thou who hast slept with my brother, believing that thou didst sleep with me, and for this reason have I slain him."

"Alas! how many are slain and punished wrongfully," exclaimed Menechiella. "A fine deed hast thou done! Thou wast not worthy to have such a brother; he did find himself in the same bed with me, and so great was his respect for thee that he divided the bed linen, so as not to come in contact with me." Cienzo, hearing these words, repented with deep repentance of having committed such a direful error, born of a rash judgment, and fathered by crass stupidity, and buffeted his face, and tore his hair, and plucked his beard. But after a little while, remembering the herb used by the dragon, he rubbed his brother's neck with it and stuck his head on again. And he at once became whole, hale, and hearty, as he was before, and embracing him with exceeding joy and pleasure, and begging him to forgive him his hastiness in thus sending him out of the world without listening to the end of his say, they entered the palace, and the king sent a messenger to bring hither Antoniello, and all his family and belongings. And when he arrived he became very dear unto the king, who made him his companion, and he beheld verified in the person of his son the old saw:

A ship sailing crossways reacheth harbor straightway.

From *Il Pentamerone: or The Tale of Tales*, by Giovanni Battista Basile, translated by Sir Richard Burton (London: Henry and Company, 1893).

PINTO SMALTO

THERE was once a merchant with an only daughter, for whom he greatly desired to find a husband, but whenever he struck the chords of this lute, he found her a hundred miles off his prelude. This thoughtless girl, like some feminine ape, hated the idea of a tail; like enclosed land reserved for shooting, she resented the approach of any man; she wished that it might always be fair day at her tribunal, always holidays at her school, and always court feast for her bank, so that her father was the most miserable and afflicted man in the world.

One day, when he was going to market, he asked Betta (such was his daughter's name) what she would like him to bring her back on his return, and she answered, "Papa, if you love me, bring me half a quintal of Palermo sugar and half of ambrosian almonds and five or six flagons of scented water and a little musk and amber and also about two score pearls, two sapphires, a handful of garnets and rubies with a little spun gold, and, above all, a modeling bowl and a silver scalpel."

Her father was amazed at this extravagant request, but, not wishing to disoblige her, he went to the fair, and on his return brought her just what she had asked for. As soon as she had received them, she shut herself into a room and began to make a great quantity of paste with the sugar and almonds, mixed with the rose water and perfumes, and with this she started to model a handsome youth, giving him locks of spun gold, eyes of sapphire, teeth of pearls, lips of rubies, and all this with such grace and beauty that only speech was lacking.

Betta had heard that a statue had once come to life through the prayers of a certain king of Cyprus, so, when she had finished her work, she prayed so earnestly to the Goddess of Love that her statue began to open its eyes and then to breathe, and following breath came out words, and at last, disengaging its limbs, it began to walk.

Betta was more overjoyed than if she had won a kingdom; she threw her arms round him and kissed him; then, taking him by the hand, she led him to her father and said, "My good papa, you have always said you wanted to see me married; so to please you I have chosen the husband of my heart."

When her father saw this handsome young man, whom he had not previously seen enter, coming out of his daughter's room, he was filled with amazement; but when he perceived his marvelous beauty which one would willingly pay a grain a head for admission to gaze at, he decided to consent to the marriage.

At the splendid feasts held to celebrate the wedding there chanced to be a great queen, incognita among the many others who came to take part. She was so struck with admiration at the beauty of Pinto Smalto (such was the name Betta had given him) that she was seized with an unfeigned love for him. Pinto Smalto, whose eyes had opened to the wickedness of the world but three hours before, knew no troubled waters; so when, as his bride directed him, he accompanied the departing guests to the foot of the stairs and was in this way escorting the strange lady, she took him by the hand and led him gently to her carriage, with its six horses, which was waiting in the courtyard, and drew him in. She ordered the coachman to drive off at a gallop in the direction of her lands, where the simple Pinto Smalto, not knowing what had befallen him, became her husband.

Betta waited some time for him, then, seeing that he did not return, she sent down to the courtyard to find out if anyone was holding him in conversation. She sent, too, to the roof terrace, in case he had gone there for a breath of air, and she herself sought him elsewhere. But he was nowhere to be found, so she imagined that he had been stolen away from her because of his great beauty. She had the usual proclamations spread abroad, but since no one came forward to reveal his hiding place, she determined to go in search of him herself, disguised as a beggar.

She set out on her way, and after several months she came to the house of a good old woman, who received her with great kindness. She was so sorry for Betta when she heard of her misfortunes and saw that she was pregnant, that she taught her three words. The first was "*Tricche-varlacche*, for the house is raining"; and the second, "*Anola tránola, pizza fontánola*"; and the third, "*Tafaro tamburo, pizze 'ngongole e cemmino*"; and added that if she spoke these words in any moment of dire need, she would receive succor.

Although Betta was amazed at such a worthless gift, yet she said to herself, "He who spits in your face, does not wish you dead, and he who takes does not wither: every prick helps. Who knows what good fortune is hidden in these words!" So she thanked the old woman and went on her way.

After journeying a long time she reached a fine city called Monterotondo and went straight to the royal palace, where she asked in heaven's name for shelter, even in a stable, seeing that she was near the time of delivery.

The ladies of the court had pity on her and brought her into a little room under the stairs, and while she was there, the unhappy girl saw Pinto Smalto pass by; such was the weight of her joy that she nearly slipped down the tree of life.

Betta felt that this was indeed an hour of need, so, to test the first words taught her by the old woman, she said, "*Tricche-varlacche*, for the house is raining!" And at once there appeared before her a beautiful little golden cart glittering with gems, which ran by itself all round the room and was a marvel to behold.

The ladies who had seen this told the queen about it, and she, without a moment's delay, ran to Betta's room and, admiring her magnificent jewel, asked if she would sell it, because she would be paid any sum she demanded. But Betta answered that she held her own pleasures dearer than all the gold in the world, and that if the queen wanted the little cart she must allow her to sleep one night with her husband.

The queen was greatly surprised at the madness of this poor ragged girl, who for a whim gave away such riches. She made up her mind to win this tasty morsel, and, by giving Pinto Smalto a dose of opium, content the girl and yet pay her ill. At nightfall, when the stars of heaven and the fireflies on earth come forth to show themselves, the queen gave Pinto Smalto a sleeping draught and sent him, obedient as he was, to sleep with Betta. But the young man, as soon as his head touched the pillow, was sleeping as fast as any dormouse.

The unhappy Betta, who had thought that night to repay herself for all her past woes, saw that she had not obtained a hearing; she began to lament unceasingly and reproached him with all that she had done for his good. But the sleeper did not once open his eyes, and the sorrowing girl did not once shut her mouth until the sun came up with his resin water to divide the shadows from the light; then the queen entered and, taking Pinto Smalto by the hand, said to Betta, "Now you are satisfied!"

"May you too have such satisfaction all the days of your life!" said Betta to herself, "for I have passed such a bad night that I shan't forget it for many a day."

But she could not resist the urge of her longing, so she tried the second phrase, saying, "*Anola tránola, pizza fontánola!*" And there appeared to her a golden cage with a most lovely bird made from gold and precious stones, which sang like any nightingale.

It all fell out as before: the ladies saw the wonderful object and told the queen, and she in her turn went to see it, and made the same request, and received the same answer; she thought she had discovered the girl to be an easy gull, so she promised to let her sleep with her husband, and so carried off the cage and bird. When night came she gave the same soporific to Pinto Smalto and sent him to Betta in the same room, where she had had a magnificent bed set up. When poor Betta saw him sleeping as if he were dead, she again took up her lament, saying things that would have moved even the stones to pity, and so, groaning and weeping and tearing her hair, she passed another night of torment. At daybreak the queen came in to reclaim her husband, and left the miserable Betta cold and frozen, biting her hands in anger at the trick that had been played her a second time.

The same morning Pinto Smalto went to pick some figs in a garden outside the city gates, where he met a cobbler, who lived next to Betta's room, and had heard every word she said through the walls. The cobbler repeated exactly the weeping and wailing and lamentation of the unhappy beggar. On hearing this, the king, who was already beginning to gather his wits, cast about in his mind to guess how this had chanced, so he decided that if he were sent another time to sleep with the poor girl he would not swallow the potion that the queen had set before him.

Betta made her third trial and said, "*Tafaro tamburo, pizze 'ngongole e cemmino!*" And there appeared a quantity of silks and cloth of gold and embroidered linen with a golden cradle, so that even the queen herself would not have been able to show such finery. The ladies saw them and told their mistress, and she tried to bargain for them in the same way, and at Betta's third request she said to herself, "What do I lose by contenting this silly girl if I gain all these fine things?" So she took the riches that Betta offered her and, when night came, because the deed of contract with sleep and rest had been liquidated, she gave Pinto Smalto the sleeping draught. But he kept it in his mouth and, pretending to answer a call of nature, he spat it out. When he was in bed, Betta, who was at his side, began again her lament, saying how she had with her own hands modeled him from sugar and almonds, how she had given him golden hair and eyes and mouth of precious stones, and how he was in her debt for the life that the gods had given him because of her prayers, how he had been stolen from her so that she had gone, heavy with child, in search of him through the world, suffering such hardships as she prayed heaven to keep all other Christian souls from, and, moreover, how she had already slept two nights with him, and twice given away treasures in payment, and not one single word had he given her; this, then, would be the last night of her hopes and the last hour of her life.

Pinto Smalto was awake and heard her words; he recalled as if in a dream all that had happened, and, embracing Betta, tried to console her as best he could. Then, since night in her black mask was directing the dance of the stars, he crept out of bed and went very quietly to the queen's room, where he found her sunk in sleep. He took all the things she had torn from Betta and all the finery and jewels that were in the chest to repay them their past troubles and returned to his wife, and they both went away at once and traveled on until they passed the frontiers of that kingdom. They rested in a handsome lodging until Betta had given birth to her son, and as soon as she could leave her bed, they set off toward her father's house. They found him alive and in good health, and he was so overjoyed to see his daughter again that he lost years of his life and became like a boy of fifteen. The queen, when she found that her husband and the beggar and her jewels had disappeared, tore her hair in rage and despair. But there were some who did not forbear to tell her:

That he who deceives must not complain of deceit.

From *The Pentamerone of Giambattista Basile,* translated by Benedetto Croce, edited by N. M. Penzer (London: John Lane; and New York: E. P. Dutton & Co., 1932).

BASTIANELO

ONCE upon a time there was a husband and wife who had a son. The son grew up, and said one day to his mother, "Do you know, mother, I would like to marry!" "Very well, marry! Whom do you want to take?" He answered, "I want the gardener's daughter." "She is a good girl; take her; I am willing."

So he went and asked for the girl, and her parents gave her to him. They were married, and when they were in the midst of the dinner the wine gave out. The husband said, "There is no more wine!" The bride, to show that she was a good housekeeper, said, "I will go and get some." She took the bottles and went to the cellar, turned the cock, and began to think, "Suppose I should have a son, and we should call him Bastianelo, and he should die. Oh, how grieved I should be! Oh, how grieved I should be!" And thereupon she began to weep and weep; and meanwhile the wine was running all over the cellar.

When they saw that the bride did not return, the mother said, "I will go and see what the matter is." So she went into the cellar, and saw the bride, with the bottle in her hand, and weeping, while the wine was running over the cellar. "What is the matter with you that you are weeping?" "Ah! my mother, I was thinking that if I had a son, and should name him Bastianelo, and he should die, oh, how I should grieve! Oh, how I should grieve!" The mother too began to weep, and weep, and weep; and meanwhile the wine was running over the cellar.

When the people at the table saw that no one brought the wine, the groom's father said, "I will go and see what is the matter. Certainly something bad has happened to the bride." He went and saw the whole cellar full of wine, and the mother and bride weeping. "What is the matter?" he said. "Has anything wrong happened to you?" "No," said the bride, "but I was thinking that if I had a son and should call him Bastianelo, and he should die, oh, how I should grieve! Oh, how I should grieve!" Then he too began to weep, and all three wept; and meanwhile the wine was running over the cellar.

When the groom saw that neither the bride, nor the mother, nor the father came back, he said, "Now I will go and see what the matter is that no one returns." He went into the cellar and saw all the wine running over the cellar. He hastened to stop the cask, and then asked, "What is the matter, that you are all weeping, and have let the wine run all over the cellar?" Then the bride said, "I was thinking that if I had a son and called him Bastianelo and he should die, oh, how I should grieve! Oh, how I should grieve!" Then the groom said, "You stupid fools! Are you weeping at this and letting all the wine run into the cellar? Have you nothing else to think of? It shall never be said that I remained with you! I will roam about the world, and until I find three fools greater than you I will not return home."

He had a bread cake made, took a bottle of wine, a sausage, and some linen, and made a bundle, which he put on a stick and carried over his shoulder. He journeyed and journeyed, but found no fools. At last he said, worn out, "I must turn back, for I see I cannot find a greater fool than my wife." He did not know what to do, whether to go on or to turn back. "Oh," he said, "it is better to try and go a little farther." So he went on, and shortly he saw a man in his shirt-sleeves at a well, all wet with perspiration and water. "What are you doing, sir, that you are so covered with water and in such a sweat?" "Oh, let me alone!" the man answered, "for I have been here a long time drawing water to fill this pail and I cannot fill it." "What are you drawing the water in?" he asked him. "In this sieve," he said. "What are you thinking about, trying to draw water in a sieve? Just wait!" He went to a house near by and borrowed a bucket, with which he returned to the well and filled the pail. "Thank you, good man. God knows how long I should have had to remain here!"

"Here is one," the traveler said, "who is a greater fool than my wife."

He continued his journey, and after a time he saw at a distance a man in his shirt who was jumping from a tree. He drew near and saw a woman under the same tree holding a pair of breeches. He asked them what they were doing, and they said they had been there a long time, and that the man was trying on the breeches and did not know how to get into them. "I have jumped and jumped," said the man, "until I am tired out, and I cannot imagine how to get into those breeches." "Oh," said the traveler, "you might stay here as long as you wished, for you would never get into them in this way. Come down and lean against the tree." Then he took the man's legs and put them in the breeches, and after he had done so he said, "Is that right?" "Very good, bless you; for if it had not been for you, God knows how long I should have had to jump."

Then the traveler said to himself, "I have seen two greater fools than my wife."

Then he went his way, and as he approached a city he heard a great noise. When he drew near he asked what it was, and was told it was a marriage, and that it was the custom in that city for brides to enter the city gate on horseback, and that there was a great discussion on this occasion between the groom and the owner of the horse, for the bride was tall and the horse high, and they could not get through the gate; so that they must either cut off the bride's head or the horse's legs. The groom did not wish his bride's head cut off, and the owner of the horse did not wish his horse's legs cut off, and hence this disturbance. Then the traveler said, "Just wait," and came up to the bride and gave her a slap that made her lower her head, and then he gave the horse a kick, and so they passed through the gate and entered the city. The groom and the owner of the horse asked the traveler what he wanted, for he had saved the groom his bride and the owner of the horse his horse.

The traveler answered that he did not wish anything and said to himself, "Two and one makes three! That is enough; now I will go home." He did so and said to his wife, "Here I am, my wife; I have seen three greater fools than you; now let us remain in peace and think about nothing else." They renewed the wedding and always remained in peace. After a time the wife had a son whom they named Bastianelo, and Bastianelo did not die, but still lives with his father and mother.

From *Italian Popular Tales*, translated by Thomas Frederick Crane (Boston: Houghton Mifflin Company, 1885). A Venetian tale collected by Dom. Giuseppe Bernoni.

THE THOUGHTLESS ABBOT

THERE was once in a city a priest who became an abbot, and because of his wealth had carriages, horses, grooms, steward, secretary, valet, and many other servants. This abbot thought only of eating, drinking, and sleeping. All the priests and laymen were jealous of him and called him "the thoughtless abbot."

One day the king happened to pass that way and stopped, and all the abbot's enemies went to him straightway and accused the abbot, saying, "Your Majesty, in this town there is a person happier than you, very rich, and lacking nothing in the world, and he is called 'the thoughtless abbot.' "

After reflection the king said to the accusers, "Gentlemen, depart in peace, for I will soon make this abbot think." The king sent directly for the abbot, who had his carriage made ready and went to the king in his coach and four. The king received him kindly, made him sit at his side, and talked about various things with him. Finally he asked him why they called him "the thoughtless abbot," and he replied that it was because he was free from care and that his servants attended to his interests.

Then the king said, "Well, then, Sir Abbot, since you have nothing to do, do me the favor of counting all the stars in the sky, and this within three days and three nights; otherwise you will surely be beheaded." The poor thoughtless abbot, on hearing these words, began to tremble like a leaf, and, taking leave of the king, returned home in mortal fear for his neck.

When mealtime came he could not eat on account of his great anxiety and went out at once on the terrace to look at the sky, but the poor man could not see a single star. When it grew dark, and the stars came out, the abbot began to count them and write it down. But it grew dark and light again without the abbot succeeding in his task. The cook, the steward, the secretaries, the grooms, the coachmen, and everyone else in the house became thoughtful when they saw that their master did not eat or drink and always watched the sky. Not knowing what else to think, they believed that he had gone mad. To make the matter short, the three days passed without the abbot succeeding in counting the stars, and the poor man did not know how to present himself to the king, for he was sure he would behead him. Finally, the last day, an old and trusty servant begged him so long that he told him the whole matter and said, "I have not been able to count the stars, and the king will cut my head off this morning." When the servant had heard all he said, "Do not fear, leave it to me; I will settle everything."

He went and bought a large ox hide, stretched it on the ground, and cut off a piece of the tail, half an ear, and a small piece out of the side, and then said to the abbot, "Now let us go to the king; and when he asks Your Excellency how many stars there are in heaven,

Your Excellency will call me; I will stretch the hide on the ground, and Your Excellency will say, 'The stars in heaven are as many as the hairs on this hide; and as there are more hairs than stars, I have been obliged to cut off part of the hide.' "

After the abbot had heard him, he felt relieved, ordered his carriage, and took his servant to the king. When the king saw the abbot he saluted him and then said, "Have you fulfilled my command?"

"Yes, Your Majesty," answered the abbot, "the stars are all counted."

"Then tell me how many they are."

The abbot called his servant, who brought the hide and spread it on the ground, while the king, not knowing how the matter was going to end, continued his questioning.

When the servant had stretched out the hide the abbot said to the king, "Your Majesty, during these three days I have gone mad counting the stars, and they are all counted."

"In short, how many are they?"

"Your Majesty, the stars are as many as the hairs of this hide, and those that were in excess I have had to cut off, and they are so many hundreds of millions; and if you don't believe me, have them counted, for I have brought you the proof."

Then the king remained with his mouth open and had nothing to answer; he said only, "Go and live as long as Noah, without thoughts, for your brains are enough for you." And so speaking, he dismissed him, thanking him, and remaining henceforth his best friend.

The abbot returned home with his servant, delighted and rejoicing. He thanked his servant, made him his steward and intimate friend, and gave him more than an ounce of money a day to live on.

From *Italian Popular Tales.* A Sicilian tale collected by Giuseppe Pitrè.

SCISSORS THEY WERE

ONCE upon a time there was a husband and a wife. The husband was a tailor; so was the wife, and in addition was a good housekeeper. One day the husband found some things in the kitchen broken —pots, glasses, plates. He asked, "How were they broken?"

"How do I know?" answered the wife.

"What do you mean by saying 'How do I know?' Who broke them?"

"Who broke them? I, with the scissors," said the wife in anger.

"With the scissors?"

"With the scissors!" (for she had the scissors in her hand).

"Are you telling the truth? I want to know what you broke them with. If you don't tell me, I will beat you."

"With the scissors!"

"Scissors, do you say?"

"Scissors they were!"

"Ah! what do you mean? Wait a bit; I will make you see whether it was with the scissors." So he tied a rope around her and began to lower her into the well, saying, "Come, how did you break them? Tell me, or I'll keep on lowering you into the well."

"It was the scissors!"

The husband, seeing her so obstinate, lowered her into the well; and she, for all that, did not hold her tongue. "How did you break them?" said the husband

"It was the scissors."

He lowered her until she was halfway down. "What did you do it with?"

"It was the scissors!"

Then he lowered her until her feet touched the water. "What did you do it with?"

"It was the scissors!"

Then he let her down into the water to her waist. "What did you do it with?"

"It was the scissors!"

"Take care!" cried her husband, enraged at seeing her so obstinate, "it will need but little to put you under the water. You had better tell what you did it with; it will be better for you. How is it possible to break pots and dishes with the scissors! What has become of the pieces, if they were cut?"

"It was the scissors! the scissors!"

He let go the rope, and splash! his wife was under water. "Are you satisfied now? Do you still say it was with the scissors?"

The wife could not speak any more, for she was under the water; so what did she do? She stuck her hand up out of the water and with her fingers began to make signs as if she were cutting with the scissors.

What could the poor husband do? He said, "I am losing my wife, and I shall have to go after her." So he pulled her out, and then of course there was no way of making her tell with what she had broken all those things in the kitchen.

From *Italian Popular Tales*. A Sicilian tale collected by Giuseppe Pitré.

Jewish

Pinya of Helm

THE KEYNOTES of Jewish folk story are wisdom, humor, and piety, and its favorite form is the parable. It is plainly the product of a society that was in its early days priestly and in its later days persecuted. Rare are the mighty, muscular heroes (Samson was one, of course, but David against Goliath and Judith against Holofernes seem much more characteristic); nor are there any authentic fire-breathing dragons or broom-riding witches. The heroes of the Jews are wise kings, learned rabbis, or rogues who live by their wits; their dragons are the Devil and the Temptations; their witches are those who have historically oppressed them. Even their humor is of a worldly-wise or satiric sort; and their sillies, the Wise Men of Helm, are not so much numskulls as absent-minded philosophers, men whose heads are filled with more than is commonly useful.

No one can say how much of a sage Solomon really was; what matters is that the Jews have glorified him as "the Wise" and attributed to him almost every traditional instance of shrewd, or seeming-shrewd, judgment. Equally significant is the way their folk tales, or *ma'asehs*, cherish the qualities of the humble and scholarly men who wrote those elaborate biblical commentaries known as the Talmud, and the illustrative tales that make up much of that section of the Talmud known as the Agada.

Whatever the origin of the Old Testament stories themselves, they have given rise among the Jews to legends and tales so numerous that collections many times the size of the Bible can do little more than sample them. The folk-story account of Joseph's relations with Potiphar's wife, based on no more than a dozen verses in the Bible itself, is only one part of an elaborate Joseph cycle among such legends. (For an analogous Egyptian tale, see "Anpu and Bata," page 200.)

From the conclusion of the Passover Service comes "The Song of the Kid" (*Had Gadya*), a chant that is said by some to have an elaborate allegorical significance but is identified by others as simply an old cumulative tale, perhaps the earliest in the tradition that includes "The House that Jack Built," "The Old Woman and the Pig," and countless others.

ABRAHAM AND THE IDOLS

TERAH, the father of Abraham, says tradition, was not only an idolater but a maker of idols, which he used to put on sale. Being obliged one day to go out on business, he asked Abraham to superintend for him. Abraham obeyed reluctantly.

"What is the price of that god?" asked an old man who had just entered the place of sale, pointing to an idol to which he took a fancy.

"Old man," said Abraham, "may I ask thine age?"

"Threescore years," replied the idolater.

"Threescore years!" exclaimed Abraham, "and thou wouldst worship a thing that has been fashioned by the hands of my father's slaves within the last four-and-twenty hours? Strange that a man of sixty should be willing to bow down his gray head to a creature of a day!"

The man was overwhelmed with shame and went away. After this there came a sedate and grave matron, carrying in her hand a large dish containing flour.

"Here," said she, "have I brought an offering to the gods. Place it before them, Abraham, and bid them favor me."

"Place it before them thyself, foolish woman!" said Abraham. "Thou wilt soon see how greedily they will devour it."

She did so. In the meantime Abraham took a hammer, broke the idols in pieces—all except the largest, in whose hands he placed the instrument of destruction.

Terah returned, and with the utmost surprise and consternation beheld the havoc amongst his favorite gods.

"What is all this, Abraham! What profane wretch has dared to use our gods in this manner?" exclaimed the infatuated and indignant Terah.

"Why should I conceal anything from my father?" replied the pious son. "During thine absence there came a woman with yonder offering for the gods. She placed it before them. The younger gods, who, as may well be supposed, had not tasted food for a long time,

greedily stretched forth their hands and began to eat before the old god had given them permission. Enraged at their boldness, he rose, took the hammer, and punished them for their want of respect."

"Dost thou mock me? Wilt thou deceive thy aged father?" exclaimed Terah in a great rage. "Do I not know that they can neither eat, nor stir, nor move?"

"And yet," rejoined Abraham, "thou payest them divine honors, adorest them, and wouldst have me worship them!"

A translation from the Midrash, in *Hebrew Tales* by Hyman Hurwitz (London, 1826).

THE LORD HELPETH MAN AND BEAST

DURING his march to conquer the world Alexander the Macedonian came to a people in Africa who dwelt in a remote and secluded corner in peaceful huts and knew neither war nor conqueror. They led him to the hut of their chief, who received him hospitably and placed before him golden dates, golden figs, and bread of gold.

"Do you eat gold in this country?" said Alexander.

"I take it for granted," replied the chief, "that thou wert able to find eatable food in thine own country. For what reason, then, art thou come amongst us?"

"Your gold has not tempted me hither," said Alexander, "but I would become acquainted with your manners and customs."

"So be it," rejoined the other. "Sojourn among us as long as it pleaseth thee."

At the close of this conversation two citizens entered, as into their court of justice. The plaintiff said, "I bought of this man a piece of land, and as I was making a deep drain through it, I found a treasure. This is not mine, for I bargained only for the land, and not for any treasure that might be concealed beneath it; and yet the former owner of the land will not receive it."

The defendant answered, "I hope I have a conscience, as well as my fellow citizen. I sold him the land with all its contingent, as well as existing, advantages, and consequently the treasure inclusively."

The chief, who was at the same time their supreme judge, recapitulated their words, in order that the parties might see whether or not he understood them aright. Then, after some reflection, he said, "Thou hast a son, friend, I believe?"

"Yes."

"And thou," addressing the other, "a daughter?"

"Yes."

"Well, then, let thy son marry *thy* daughter, and bestow the treasure on the young couple for a marriage portion."

Alexander seemed surprised and perplexed.

"Think you my sentence unjust?" the chief asked him.

"Oh, no!" replied Alexander, "but it astonishes me."

"And how, then," rejoined the chief, "would the case have been decided in your country?"

"To confess the truth," said Alexander, "we should have taken both parties into custody and have seized the treasure for the king's use."

"For the king's use!" exclaimed the chief. "Does the sun shine on that country?"

"Oh, yes!"

"Does it rain there?"

"Assuredly."

"Wonderful! But are there tame animals in the country, that live on the grass and green herbs?"

"Very many, and of many kinds."

"Aye, that must then be the cause," said the chief. "For the sake of those innocent animals the all-gracious Being continues to let the sun shine and the rain drop down on your own country; since its inhabitants are unworthy of such blessings."

A translation from the Talmud by Samuel Taylor Coleridge, reprinted in *Hebrew Tales.*

THE PRINCESS AND RABBI JOSHUAH

RABBI JOSHUAH, the son of Cha-nan-yah, was one of those men whose minds are far more beautiful than their bodies. He was so dark that people often took him for a blacksmith, and so plain as almost to frighten children. Yet his great learning, wit, and wisdom had procured him not only the love and respect of the people, but even the favor of the Emperor Trajan. Being often at court, one of the princesses rallied him on his want of beauty.

"How comes it," said she, "that such glorious wisdom is inclosed in so mean a vessel?"

The rabbi, no ways dismayed, requested her to tell him in what sort of vessels her father kept his wine.

"Why, in earthen vessels, to be sure," replied the princess.

"Oh," exclaimed the rabbi, "this is the way that ordinary people do. An emperor's wine ought to be kept in more precious vessels."

The princess, thinking him in earnest, ordered a quantity of wine to be emptied out of the earthen jars into gold and silver vessels; but to her great surprise found it in a very short time sour and unfit to drink.

"Very fine advice, indeed, Joshuah, hast thou given me!" said the princess the next time she saw him. "Do you know the wine is sour and spoiled?"

"Thou art then convinced," said the rabbi, "that wine keeps best in plain and mean vessels. It is even so with wisdom."

"But," continued the princess, "I know many persons who are both wise and handsome."

"True," replied the sage, "but they would, most probably, be still wiser, were they less handsome."

A translation from the Talmud, in *Hebrew Tales.*

THE WIFE'S ONE WISH

A CERTAIN Israelite of Sidon, having been married above ten years without being blessed with offspring, determined to be divorced from his wife. With this view he brought her before Rabbi Simon, son of Jo-cho-e. The rabbi, who did not favor divorces, tried at first to dissuade him. Seeing him, however, unwilling to accept his advice, he addressed him and his wife thus:

"My children, when you were first joined in the holy bands of wedlock, were ye not rejoiced? Did ye not make a feast and entertain your friends? Now, since ye are resolved to be divorced, let your separation be like your union. Go home, make a feast, entertain your friends, and on the morrow come to me, and I will comply with your wishes."

So reasonable a request, and coming from such authority, could not, with any degree of propriety, be rejected. They accordingly went home, prepared a sumptuous entertainment, to which they invited their several friends. During the hours of merriment the husband, being elated with wine, thus addressed his wife:

"My beloved, we have lived together happily these many many years; it is only the want of children that makes me wish for a separation. To convince thee, however, that I bear thee no ill will, I give thee permission to take with thee out of my house anything thou likest best."

"Be it so," rejoined the woman.

The cup went round, the people were merry; and, having drunk rather freely, most of the guests fell asleep; and amongst them the master of the feast. The lady no sooner perceived this than she ordered him to be carried to her father's house, and to be put into a bed prepared for the purpose. The fumes of the wine having gradually evaporated, the man awoke. Finding himself in a strange place, he wondered and exclaimed, "Where am I? How came I here? What means all this?"

His wife, who had waited to see the issue of her stratagem, stepped from behind a curtain and, begging him not to be alarmed, told him that he was now in her father's house.

"In thy father's house!" exclaimed the still astonished husband. "How should I come in thy father's house?"

"Be patient, my dear husband," replied the prudent woman. "Be patient and I will tell thee all. Recollect, didst thou not tell me last night I might take out of thy house whatever I valued most? Now, believe me, my beloved, amongst all thy treasures there is not one I value so much as I do thee."

The husband, overcome by so much kindness, embraced her and was reconciled to her; and they lived thenceforth very happily together.

A translation from the Midrash, in *Hebrew Tales.*

THE THOUGHTFUL FATHER

A RICH Israelite who dwelt at a considerable distance from Jerusalem had an only son whom he sent to the Holy City for education. During his absence the father was suddenly taken ill. Seeing his end approaching, he made his will, by which he left all his property to a slave whom he named on condition that he should permit his son to select out of that property any single thing he might choose.

No sooner was the master dead than the slave, elated with the prospect of so much wealth, hastened to Jerusalem, informed the son of what had taken place, and showed him the will. The young Israelite was plunged into the deepest sorrow by this unexpected intelligence. He rent his clothes, strewed ashes on his head, and lamented the loss of a parent whom he tenderly loved and whose memory he still revered. As soon as the first transports of grief were over, and the days allotted for mourning had passed, the young man began seriously to consider the situation in which he was left. Born in affluence, and grown up under the expectation of receiving, after his father's demise, those possessions to which he was so justly entitled, he saw, or imagined he saw, his expectations disappointed and his worldly prospects blighted.

In this state of mind he went to his instructor, a man famous for his piety and wisdom, acquainted him with the cause of his affliction, made him read the will, and in the bitterness of distress ventured to express his thoughts that his father, by making such a strange disposition of his property, neither showed good sense nor affection for his only child.

"Say nothing against thy father, young man!" said the pious instructor. "Thy father was both a wise man and an affectionate parent —the most convincing proof of which he gave by this very will."

"By this will!" exclaimed the young man. "By this will! Surely, my honored master, thou art not in earnest. I can see neither wisdom in bestowing his property on a slave nor affection in depriving his only son of his legal rights."

"Thy father has done neither," rejoined the learned instructor, "but like a just, loving parent, has by this very will secured the property to thee, if thou hast sense enough to avail thyself of it."

"How! How!" exclaimed the young man in utmost astonishment.

"Listen, then," said the friendly instructor. "Listen, young man, and thou wilt have reason to admire thy father's prudence. When he saw his end approaching, and that he must go in the way in which all mortals must sooner or later go, he thought within himself, 'Behold, I must die; my son is too far off to take immediate possession of my estate; my slaves will no sooner be certain of my death than they will plunder my property; and, to avoid detection, will conceal my death from my beloved child and thus deprive him even of the melancholy consolation of mourning for me.' To prevent the first, he bequeathed his property to his slave, whose apparent interest it would be to take care of it. To insure the second, he made it a condition that thou shouldst be allowed to select something out of that property. This slave, thought he, in order to secure his apparent legal claim would not fail to give thee speedy information as indeed he has done."

"Well," exclaimed the young man rather impatiently, "what benefit is all this to me? Will this restore me the property of which I have so unjustly been deprived?"

"Ah," replied the good man, "I see that wisdom resides only with the aged. Knowest thou not that whatever a slave possesses belongs to his lawful master? And has not thy father left thee the power of selecting out of his property any one thing thou mightest choose? What hinders thee, then, from choosing that very slave as thy portion; and by possessing him, thou wilt of course be entitled to the whole property. This, no doubt, was thy father's intention."

The young Israelite, admiring his father's wisdom, no less than his master's sagacity, chose the slave as his portion and took possession of his father's estates.

A translation from the Midrash, in *Hebrew Tales.*

RABBI ELIEZER ENJOYS AN EXCEPTION

RABBI ELIEZER, who was as much distinguished by the greatness of his mind as by the extraordinary size of his body, once paid a friendly visit to Rabbi Simon. The learned Simon received him most cordially and, filling a cup with wine, handed it to him. Eliezer took it and drank it off at a draught. Another was poured out—it shared the same fate.

"Brother Eliezer," said Simon jestingly, "rememberest thou not what the wise men have said on this subject?"

"I well remember," answered the corpulent Eliezer, "the saying of our Instructors—that people ought not to take a cup at one draught; but," added he jocosely, "the wise men have not so defined their rule as to admit of no exception. And in this instance, friend Simon, there are no less than three: the cup is small, the receiver large, and your wine delicious!"

A translation from the Talmud, in *Hebrew Tales.*

KNOW BEFORE YOU CRITICIZE

A YOUNG, half-baked Talmudic student, while talking to his rabbi, expressed a heretical view about prophets and the nature of prophecy.

The rabbi bristled with indignation. "Shame on you!" he cried. "How can you speak that way about the Holy Prophets?"

"But that's not my own opinion, Rabbi," the student apologized. "I'm only quoting the Rambam. It's written in the *Guide to the Perplexed*."

The rabbi smiled wryly. "Let me tell you a parable," he began. "A merchant once came to buy goods in a large wholesale establishment.

Quite by accident he broke the glass in a showcase. This filled him with confusion.

" 'I'm terribly sorry about this,' he said.

" 'Oh, that's all right—it's only a trifle,' said the proprietor, minimizing the loss. 'May no worse damage happen to me. Thank God none of the flying glass hurt you! Tell you what—let's have a drink of *schnapps* on it.'

"So the two drank in very friendly fashion, as if nothing unpleasant had occurred.

"Now there was a simpleton who saw all this happen with his own eyes. He was very much impressed and said to himself, 'If for breaking a single pane of glass the proprietor gives this customer a glass of *schnapps*—what will he give me for breaking his big front window? He'll feel so sorry when he sees how upset I am about it that, likely as not, he'll have me drink a whole bottle of *schnapps* with him!'

"So he picked up a rock and, with all his might, threw it at the front window, smashing it. Thereupon the clerks in the store who had seen him do this ran out and gave him a good trouncing.

" 'Stop, stop, you fools! Why do you hit me?' yelled the simpleton. 'Your employer gave that customer a glass of *schnapps* to quiet his nerves, and me you hit?'

" '*Schlemihl!*' answered the proprietor. 'That man is my best customer. If he broke a pane—*nu*, so what? But you, idiot, who broke my front store window—what profit do I get from you?' "

The rabbi then concluded, "It's the same with you and the Rambam, my son. About Rabbi Moses ben Maimon, it has been said, 'From Moses our teacher to Moses ben Maimon, there has been no Moses like unto this Moses.' He was a prince in Israel. He wrote wonderful books with deep meanings. It was perfectly all right for him to express a heresy, so to speak—to break a windowpane. But you, ignoramus, what have you done for the world to allow yourself the luxury of breaking the store-front window of our faith?"

From *A Treasury of Jewish Folklore,* edited by Nathan Ausubel, (New York: Crown Publishers, 1948).

THE WISE ROGUE

A MAN who was once caught stealing was ordered by the king to be hanged. On the way to the gallows he said to the governor that he knew a wonderful secret, and it would be a pity to allow it to die with him, and he would like to disclose it to the king. He would put a seed of a pomegranate in the ground, and through the secret taught to him by his father he would make it grow and bear fruit overnight. The thief was brought before the king, and on the morrow the king, accompanied by the high officers of state, came to the place where the thief was waiting for them. There the thief dug a hole and said, "This seed must be put in the ground only by a man who has never stolen or taken anything which did not belong to him. I being a thief cannot do it." So he turned to the vizier who, frightened, said that in his younger days he had retained something which did not belong to him. The treasurer said that in dealing with large sums he might have entered too much or too little, and even the king owned that he had kept a necklace of his father's. The thief then said, "You are all mighty and powerful and want nothing, and yet you cannot plant the seed, whilst I who have stolen a little because I was starving am to be hanged." The king, pleased with the ruse of the thief, pardoned him.

From *The Exempla of the Rabbis*, by Moses Gaster (London and Leipzig: The Asia Publishing Co., 1924).

THE HELM GOAT MYSTERY

THE RABBI of Helm once fell gravely sick. While he could work wonders for others, he refused to use his supernatural powers for himself—such a saint he was! So they had to do the next best thing and call the doctor.

The doctor examined the holy man and shook his head. "Bad, bad!" he muttered to the *rebbitzen*. "There's only one thing that can help him—a steady supply of fresh goat's milk. But for this you've got to own a goat. My advice to you is: buy a goat."

So the *rebbitzen* asked two of the rabbi's disciples to go to the next village and buy a good nanny goat at a reasonable price.

"Trust us!" cried the disciples. "We'll bring you the best goat in goatland!"

So they went to the next village and bought a white nanny goat.

"Are you sure it's a good nanny goat?" the disciples asked the dealer, just to make sure.

"Is it a good nanny goat?" cried the dealer, offended. "Why, it gushes milk like a fountain!"

Delighted with their purchase, the disciples started for home, leading the goat by a rope.

"With such an animal the rabbi will surely get well!" they rejoiced.

On the way they came to an inn. Already in high spirits the disciples said, "Let's drink to the health of our rabbi and his nanny goat!"

So, after tying their goat to a post in the stable, they went into the inn and ordered some drinks.

Made talkative by the *schnapps*, they began to boast before the innkeeper.

"Some goat we've just bought for our rabbi! It's positively the best goat in goatland—it gushes milk like a fountain! There isn't another like it in Helm!"

"You don't say so!" replied the innkeeper with amazement.

Now this innkeeper was an irreverent rogue; he had a hearty dislike for wonder-working rabbis as well as for all the people of Helm. Therefore he plotted a mischievous prank against the rabbi's disciples. While they were merrily celebrating, he quietly slipped out into the stable. He untied the wonderful white nanny goat they had bought and in its place he tied his own white billy goat.

When the disciples had sobered up a bit they paid the innkeeper, untied their goat, and continued on their homeward journey.

They arrived in Helm toward nightfall. In their eagerness to show off their purchase they ran to the rabbi's house, with the goat galloping behind them and a crowd of curious children trotting after the goat. When they reached the rabbi's house the disciples called, "*Rebbitzen*, quick, come out and look at the wonderful goat we bought for you!"

"Really a fine goat!" said the *rebbitzen* judiciously. "The question is, does she give a lot of milk?"

"Don't ask! Just milk her and you'll see for yourself!" said the disciples, beaming.

The *rebbitzen* went for a stool and a pot and sat down to milk. She tried and tried but no milk came.

"May such a misfortune happen to my enemies!" she burst out angrily. "What kind of a goat did you buy? She doesn't give a drop!"

"Don't be so hasty, *Rebbitzen*," they implored her. "The Torah says specifically, 'Everything has to be done with knowledge and with understanding.' Since you have never owned a goat before, let's call in a goat expert."

So they called in a goat expert, who took one look at the goat and cried out in surprise, "This is no nanny goat! This is a billy goat!"

The disciples grew bitter. "That enemy of Israel!" they cried, referring to the dealer in goats. "Tomorrow we'll take this wretched beast back to him and tell him a thing or two for this swindle."

Early the next morning the disciples, boiling with anger, started out with the goat. Again they passed the wayside inn.

"Let's go in and cheer ourselves up with a drink," one suggested. "After all, we don't have to make ourselves miserable on account of a flea-bitten goat!"

So, after tying the goat in the stable, they went into the inn and ordered drinks.

"What kind of a swindle do you suppose that dog of a goat dealer put over on us?" they said to the innkeeper. "Gave us a billy instead of a nanny!"

"Tsk, tsk!" exclaimed the innkeeper commiseratingly. "The trouble with you scholars is that you're so unwordly. You believe everything you're told. Why don't you keep your eyes open when you buy something?"

To drown their humiliation the disciples drank heavily, and, while they were at it, the innkeeper went quietly into the stable, removed his own billy, and in its place he tied the nanny that he had taken from the disciples the day before. Through with their drinking, the disciples untied their goat and departed.

"Enemy of Israel!" they called out with rage when they saw the goat dealer. "Don't think you can swindle honest folk so easily!"

"What's wrong, what's wrong?" murmured the dealer in confusion.

"What's wrong? You said you sold us a nanny! And what do you suppose we found when we got home—a billy!"

"I swear, you're crazy!" cried the dealer as he took but one look at the goat.

"Malke!" he called to his wife. "Just milk this nanny for these fine scholars!"

The woman brought a stool and a pot and began to milk the goat. The disciples stood by, their eyes popping out of their heads. There, right before their very eyes, the goat was streaming milk like a fountain, just as the dealer had told them she would'

"*Nu, schlemihls*, are you satisfied now?" he asked scornfully.

Muttering their apologies, the rabbi's disciples took their goat and started for home.

Elated, they burst into song. When they passed the inn again one said, "Now we should really celebrate! Our goat is some gusher!"

Into the inn they went and ordered a big bottle of *schnapps*, and, while they were drinking to the health of the rabbi and the goat, sure enough, that rascal of an innkeeper stole away and once more exchanged the goats.

Unsuspectingly the happy disciples returned home. But the same thing happened this time as before. When the *rebbitzen* sat down to milk the goat she discovered it was a billy.

"There's witchcraft in this!" cried the disciples, horrified. "With our own eyes we saw the dealer's wife milk this goat. We must tell the whole story to the rabbi!"

Breathlessly they went to the sick rabbi and told him all that had happened.

"It's clear to me that the dealer is a swindler," was the rabbi's judicious opinion. "There's only one thing left for you to do. Return immediately to the dealer with the goat and summon him to Rabbi Shmul in his town. Demand a signed document from the rabbi that the goat you finally leave with is a nanny and not a billy."

The following day, bright and early, the disciples started out again with the goat. As they had done every time before, they went into the inn to cheer themselves up. When he heard their story the innkeeper said, "You're a bunch of *schlemihls!* If your goat dealer had played a trick on me like that I'd have broken every bone in his body!"

"Never fear!" promised the disciples. "We'll fix him so he'll see his dead grandmother!"

And, while they were drinking to give themselves courage for the final encounter with the goat dealer, the sly innkeeper again exchanged the goats.

The disciples left in high spirits to call on the dealer.

"Swindler!" they cried. "Do you expect us to spend the rest of our lives traveling from Helm to your cursed village with this miserable animal? Here's your goat. Now show us, before we make you join your dead grandmother, how much milk you can squeeze out of your gusher!"

Without a word the dealer sat down and milked the animal.

The disciples looked on stunned. They could hardly believe their eyes. The milk was pouring into the pot in a foaming stream.

"To your rabbi! Take us to your rabbi!" they now demanded. "We want a document from him that this is a genuine nanny!"

The goat dealer shrugged his shoulders disdainfully and went with them to the rabbi, who carefully examined the goat and pronounced it a nanny. He gave them a signed and sealed document attesting to that effect.

Now the disciples were certain that all their troubles were over, so they started for home in a merry mood. To crown their triumph they again went into the inn for a round of drinks. Once more the innkeeper exchanged the goats.

When the disciples reached the rabbi's house they cried joyfully, "*Rebbitzen!* Just come out and see! It's a genuine nanny this time. Here you have Rabbi Shmul's written word for it!"

Eagerly the *rebbitzen* ran for her pot and stool and sat down to milk the goat. With a cry she leaped up and screamed, "Numskulls! Lunatics! What sort of game do you think you're playing with me?"

She then made them go with her to the rabbi's room.

"Here you have Rabbi Shmul's document!" cried the disciples in bewilderment. "Tell us, what does all this mean? Do you perhaps see the Evil Eye in it, Rabbi?"

"Bring me my spectacles!" ordered the rabbi.

They brought him his spectacles. He put them on and carefully read Rabbi Shmul's document.

For a long time the rabbi sat deliberating, his brow furrowed, his eyes far away. Then he spoke. "This is my opinion: Rabbi Shmul is a wise and upright man. He never writes anything that is not true. If he tells us that the goat is a nanny you can rest assured that it is not a billy. Now, you will ask: how is it that the goat he tells us is a nanny turns out to be a billy? The answer is very simple: true, the goat he examined and testified to was a nanny. But such is the confounded luck of us Helm *schlimazls* that, by the time a nanny goat finally reaches our town, it's sure to turn into a billy!"

From *A Treasury of Jewish Folklore.*

HIGHER MATHEMATICS IN HELM

TWO WISE men of Helm lay sweating in the steam bath one day. To drive away the boredom of doing nothing they began to discuss deep mathematical problems.

The first one said, "If, for instance, it takes four hours to drive to Dvinsk with one horse, wouldn't it be right to say that if I drove with two horses it would only take me two hours?"

"Correct as gold," answered the other sage, filled with admiration.

"Now, why couldn't I drive to Dvinsk with four horses so I'd get there in no time?" continued the mathematician.

"Why trouble to go to Dvinsk at all?" exclaimed the other. "Just harness your four horses and stay right here."

From *A Treasury of Jewish Folklore.*

PINYA OF HELM

WHEN the Helmites were seeking a wise man to send to Warsaw to find out how fires were put out in that great city, they chose Pinya the Philosopher.

At the break of day Pinya awoke, recited his prayers, breakfasted, packed some food for the journey, and set out for Warsaw.

Pinya walked. The road was dusty, the day was hot, and Pinya thought, "A drink of cold water would surely be refreshing." But the road was long and dusty and there was no water.

So Pinya walked farther. Soon he came to a hill. Pinya groaned and went on. Going uphill was hard. He climbed slowly, puffing and panting all the way to the top. On the hilltop it was cooler, and near by there was a little grove. In the grove, close to the road, stood a large shade tree. Underneath the tree was a big rock, and from beneath the rock gushed a spring of clear cold water.

Pinya stopped, cast off his coat, wiped the sweat from his brow, and sat down. Then he took a long drink from the icy spring, washed, and ate. Growing sleepy, he took another drink from the spring, yawned slowly and murmured, "To lie down in the shade of this tree would be pleasant. It is cool and comfortable here."

Making a pillow of his coat, he was soon ready for sleep. But Pinya was not called "the Philosopher" for nothing, and soon his shrewd brain posed a question: "A fine thing! Here am I going to sleep, but when I awake, how will I know which way is Warsaw?"

Then Pinya had an idea. He took off his shoes and placed them out on the road with the toes pointing toward Warsaw. Now he could go safely to sleep, and when he awoke his shoes would tell him just which way to go. And without further ado Pinya lay down and was soon fast asleep.

Not long afterward a stranger happened to pass, saw Pinya sleeping under the tree, and noticed the shoes out in the middle of the road. They looked so funny standing there that, for no reason at all, the stranger just had to turn them around. Then he went on his way, whistling a merry tune.

Pinya the Philosopher slept long and soundly. When he awoke he yawned contentedly and said to himself, "God is good to me. I have eaten well, I have slept soundly, and there are my shoes pointing the way to Warsaw. God is truly good to me."

He put on his shoes and continued on his way. One hour passed, then two, and suddenly he glimpsed a town in the distance. The first thing he saw was the cemetery, and then there appeared the roofs of the houses. Pinya clucked his tongue and marveled—from the distance Warsaw looked exactly like Helm. But Pinya was a Philosopher, and he reasoned, "To be sure, isn't it written in the Great Books that the world is the same everywhere? Naturally, *that* is why Warsaw looks like Helm."

The nearer he approached the place the more he marveled. The streets looked exactly like the streets of Helm. Even the Town Baths looked the same. And an identical Town Hall. Why, there was a post for the watchman's horse, just like the post near the

Town Hall in Helm. And imagine, there, in the middle of the market place, stood a pear tree, just like in Helm. Pinya couldn't get over it. "True," he said to himself, "it is written that the world is the same everywhere, but I never expected it to be *so much* the same. That just goes to show you. When the Great Books say something, they know what they're talking about."

Pinya walked on. He gasped as he rounded the next corner. "Well, well, just such a street in Warsaw as my street in Helm." He continued walking. "Look, there is a house exactly the same as mine and standing just where mine does in Helm."

Pinya stood and stared and wondered. He stroked his curly little black beard and murmured, "Lo and behold, the whole world is like Helm!"

And as he stood there he heard a woman inside the house, shouting, "Moishe, stop that noise. Your father leaves, and I think I'll get a little peace, so now *you* begin. Go bring in the goat. And don't say 'Later' or I'll—"

By this time Pinya was really impressed. Will God's wonders never cease? A scolding wife just like mine, nagging a disobedient son named Moishe, just like mine, in a house on a street just like mine. And imagine, as if all this weren't wonder enough, this Moishe says "Later" when told to do something—just like mine.

Standing with mouth agape, he scrutinized the house, the porch, the gate, when suddenly out came his wife Zlota. When she saw Pinya she clasped her hands in amazement and shrieked, "Pinya, back so soon from Warsaw?"

Pinya nearly dropped from shock. How does this strange woman know that I am called Pinya and what does she mean when she says "Back so soon from Warsaw?" After all, I *am* in Warsaw.

When Zlota saw her Philosopher standing there with his mouth open wide enough for a cat to walk in, she began to scold, "Why are you standing there like a dummy, staring at me with two glass eyes? Fool! Go to the synagogue or you'll be late for evening prayers."

All his life Pinya had obeyed his wife Zlota. So now, without another thought, he obeyed this strange woman who was so much like his Zlota, and went off to the synagogue.

There the Helmites greeted him with surprise and joy. After the services they crowded around him, exclaiming, "Back so soon?

Now there's a messenger for you! Goes to Warsaw in the morning and is back in Helm by evening!"

Pinya became very angry, but not being a Philosopher for nothing he controlled himself and said calmly, "I know that the Jews of Warsaw are clever, but surely that doesn't give you the right to laugh at a stranger."

"Look here, Pinya," replied the rabbi. "You may be a great Philosopher, but that's no reason for you to talk in riddles. Please tell us how they put out fires in Warsaw."

Spluttered Pinya, "What are you talking about? I am in Warsaw!"

The Helmites became indignant. "Why are you making fun of us?" they cried. "You know you're back in Helm."

Still calm, Pinya answered, "Jews of Warsaw, I am not called Pinya the Philosopher for nothing. I am in Warsaw and I have proof of it."

Whereupon Pinya told them how before he had gone to sleep he had carefully placed his shoes on the road with the toes pointing toward Warsaw.

When the Helmites heard *this*, a hue and cry arose: if that's the case, then Pinya must be right and they are in Warsaw! A pretty kettle of fish! The women and children in Helm, and they, the menfolk, in Warsaw, all of a sudden! Something had to be done!

Once again timid Berel the Beadle spoke up in a piping voice, "I think I know how we can tell where we are. Remember how I painted *Zeh Hashul Shayech Lechelem* [This Synagogue belongs to Helm], on the outside of the synagogue. Let's go out and see if it's there. If it is, we're in Helm. If not, we're in Warsaw.

Being Berel's idea, it was naturally ridiculed, but the Helmites went out anyway. Happily it was a bright, moonlit night, and, sure enough, there was the inscription on the synagogue, clear and plain for anyone to see. It was as though a stone had been lifted from their hearts.

But not so with Pinya the Philosopher. He stood his ground, stroked his curly red beard, and asked, "How can you explain the testimony of the shoes?"

At that moment they caught sight of their angry wives, coming to fetch them, as their suppers were getting cold. Then and there Berel the Beadle said, "We must be in Helm—there can't be two sets of wives such as ours!"

And though it was against their better judgment to agree with the sentiments of Berel, who was not quite wise in the measure of Helm, to this indeed they had to agree—there couldn't be two such sets of wives as theirs! Truly, it was certain they were in Helm!

From *The Wise Men of Helm*, by Solomon Simon (New York: Behrman House, 1945).

KING SOLOMON AND THE QUEEN OF SHEBA

ONCE the Queen of Sheba accompanied King Solomon on horseback outside Jerusalem. When they came near Mount Lebanon they dismounted and sat down on the grass to rest.

"Listen!" said the queen. "Do you hear a woman singing? But I do not understand her words."

"This is a farmer's wife," answered the king. "She sings that her husband Abiezer works in the fields, that her son Ahiezer is grazing his flock in the pasture, and that she herself is doing the housework. She sings that, although so humble, she is happier than I, Solomon, King of Israel, is in his palace."

"What a good woman!" cried the queen, enchanted. "Just see how unjust you were when you wrote that among a thousand men one may find one who is good, but that among all women you have found not even one who is virtuous."

"I still hold to that opinion," answered King Solomon.

To this the Queen of Sheba replied, "I will not believe you until you have proven this woman."

"Very well," said King Solomon. "Let us now go to the house where this virtuous woman lives, and we will test her."

So they went to the house of Abiezer and stood before the door. When the farmer's wife saw them she bowed low and invited them to enter her lowly home. When the royal guests had entered she placed before them a pitcher of cold water, milk, butter, and sweet cakes. She begged them to eat, and they ate. And the Queen of Sheba said to King Solomon, "See, I have found a virtuous woman, but where will you find a virtuous man among a thousand?"

King Solomon laughed and said, "Let us not keep this woman from her housework, for soon her husband and her son will return tired and hungry from their work in the fields, and she must prepare their noonday meal."

As they left the house King Solomon said, "As you wish me to test this woman's virtue I will do so, although I have no desire to disturb the tranquil life of this family."

Then the king went back to his horse and returned carrying a little casket. He unlocked it and asked the Queen of Sheba to look inside. She saw in it a little white mouse and a tiny dish of seeds. The king then locked the casket and said, "With this I will test the virtue of this woman. If she withstands the temptation I am placing before her, then I will admit that I am in error."

At that King Solomon and the Queen of Sheba returned to the farmhouse, where they met Abiezer and his son. The farmer immediately recognized the king, because he had seen him on several occasions when he had gone to Jerusalem on pilgrimages.

Then King Solomon said to the wife of Abiezer, "I am leaving this little casket with you for three days. Place it in that corner there, and under no circumstances must you move or open it. If you do as I bid you I will give you many fine gifts, but if you disobey me, you, your husband and your son will have to pay with your lives."

The king then gave the key to the box to Abiezer. He blessed him, his wife, and his son and returned to Jerusalem with the Queen of Sheba.

When they were eating their evening meal Abiezer's wife said to him, "The Lord only knows what's inside this little box! Maybe the king has filled it with gems. It also might be that it is an enchanted box."

"Better let us not think or speculate about this box," urged Abiezer. "Let it rest there in the corner until the king comes back for it in three days."

Abiezer then went to bed, and early in the morning he arose for his daily labors. When he returned home for the noon meal his wife placed it before him, but she herself would not touch any of it. When he asked her whether she was ill or had received evil tidings from the home of her father, she answered, "I have not slept all night long, dear husband, thinking about that little box. Even when

I dozed off for a little while I had nightmares. Oh, if I only knew what is inside of that locked box!"

"Stop talking about that box!" Abiezer said angrily. "Remember what the king said, and don't trifle with our lives!"

Then he returned to his work.

When he came home in the evening he found his wife in bed, groaning and moaning.

"What ails you?" cried Abiezer in a fright.

"Let me be!" wailed his wife. "Now I see that you think more of the little box than of me."

Abiezer tried to comfort and soothe her, but to no avail. She persisted, "If you love me truly and wish me to get well, then let us both look through the keyhole of the box. I must confess that while you were at work I wished to get near the box, but a terrible fright came over me. I have no doubt that the king has hidden a little demon inside."

His wife tormented Abiezer so long with her nagging that finally he was obliged to give in to her, saying, "Very well. Get out of bed and come with me to the box, but remember, you must not touch it with your hands!"

"Have no anxiety on that score," his wife answered. "Even if I were to touch it no harm would come of it. What King Solomon meant was that we should not move it from the corner. He never said anything about not touching it."

And so she looked through the keyhole of the box, but she saw nothing. Thereupon she was filled with disappointment and said bitterly, "The king has concealed his secret only too well. We will never know what's inside that box unless we open it."

Hearing these words, Abiezer began to tremble and cried out with fright, "What a terrible thought! Do not speak about opening that box unless you wish to forfeit our lives!"

Then he led her back to her bed, saying, "You must rest now and try to calm yourself. In the morning you will get up feeling better. You'll begin doing your housework again and will forget all about that box."

Then they went to bed.

When the morning star appeared in the sky Abiezer arose. He made his ablutions and said the morning prayers. Afterward he went to labor in the fields.

He had been at work only a short while when he saw his son

Ahiezer hastening to him. "Quick father, come home!" cried Ahiezer. "Mother is near death, and she wants to see you before she dies!"

When Abiezer heard this he exclaimed, "Woe is me! All these years I have lived in peace and contentment, then the king had to come and bring this misfortune upon us!"

Abiezer hurried home and found his wife in bed. He said to her, "Take heart, my wife, and arise!"

But she answered, "It is already two days that I have taken neither food nor drink, and my body is altogether weakened. I had a frightful dream last night. I quake even now when I think of it. In my dream I saw many demons and devils float out of this box until they filled the house. They danced and whirled about me, raised a great lamentation, and gnashed their teeth with rage. One devil sprang upon my bed and said to me, 'If you do not open the box and liberate us we will again come tomorrow night and choke you. We will tear you limb from limb. We will burn you, grind you to dust, and cast you to all the seven winds!' And when the devil finished speaking he spat in my face and disappeared. I awoke trembling with fright. I called you but you did not answer."

And Abiezer's wife did not cease her weeping. "Soon," she said, "the devils will come and choke me. Therefore I've sent for you that you should prepare my grave for me."

"Why do you tell me your foolish dreams?" Abiezer reproached her. "Don't you know that dreams are false and ridiculous? If there really were demons and devils in the box, as you say, then it wouldn't be you but *me* that they would try to scare, because the key to the box is in my possession. Therefore your dream has no meaning. You dreamed it because you were thinking about the box all the time."

When the wife of Abiezer saw that he was resolute not to open the box, she got out of bed and fell weeping at his feet.

"Do me only one small favor," she pleaded. "Give me the key, and I will open the box only the tiniest bit. I will peep into it for just one instant, then I will close it quickly, and nobody will ever know about it."

"Dear wife!" Abiezer cried. "How drawn and pinched your face looks! Come and eat and you will feel better and calmer. Then you will recall what the king said to us, and you will stop thinking about the box."

Abiezer then helped her out of bed. He placed food before her and urged her to eat. She ate, but no sooner had she finished when again she resumed her wailing, saying, "Oh, Abiezer, my loving husband! Have pity on me! The king does not have to know anything about this. I will be very careful and swear that I will take only one little peep."

And so she carried on until evening, until Abiezer could no longer endure her nagging. So he arose and said, "Very well, we will open the box. But remember—for only one instant, just as you promise."

So Abiezer inserted the key, and no sooner did he turn it in the lock when the box sprang open and the little white mouse that was inside jumped out and disappeared.

Abiezer and his wife were congealed with terror. She rent her garments and cried bitterly, "It is you Abiezer who will be the cause of our death. Had you been careful the mouse would not have jumped out! How many times did I have to tell you to open the lid just the tiniest bit, and you had to go and open it altogether!"

"Why do you reproach me?" replied Abiezer resentfully. "If you had not pestered me to open the box nothing would have happened."

"It was all your fault!" lamented his wife. "Had you only been a real man and had will-power you would not have allowed yourself to be governed by a woman. You would not have given in to me, and we would have avoided misfortune."

But Abiezer said bitterly, "Of what use now are lamentations and tears! We cannot undo our mistake that way. Better let us pray to the Almighty to aid us."

On the third day, as Abiezer and his wife sat grieving, King Solomon and the Queen of Sheba arrived. The guilty woman fell at the feet of the king and cried, "By your life, O my Lord the King, know that it was I who opened the box! Have mercy and spare my life!"

"Why did you disobey me, Abiezer?" asked the king sternly.

And Abiezer answered, "It is I who am the guilty one, O King, because I allowed my wife to wheedle me into doing such a thing. Now I beseech you, have mercy on my wife and let her live. If you wish to punish us, it is me you should kill!"

Gently King Solomon answered, "Peace be to you both, my children! Be assured I wish you no harm. I only wished to prove you."

The Queen of Sheba then asked Abiezer to tell her all that had happened, and when Abiezer had finished his story King Solomon exclaimed, "One man among a thousand have I found; but a woman among all those have I not found."

Adapted from the Midrash, by Nathan Ausubel, in *A Treasury of Jewish Folklore.*

THE BURIED MONEY

IN THE time of King Solomon three Jewish merchants started out together on a business journey. One Friday evening they came into a forest, where they were separated and lost sight of one another. One of them continued his journey and came to a distant country to buy goods. Then he thought, "What shall I do? I am a stranger in a strange land and know no one to whom I can entrust my money." So he went out into the fields and, looking round to see that nobody was watching, he buried the money in a hollow in the ground, where corn was stored during the winter. But the man to whom the granary belonged saw from a distance the merchant hiding the money, and as soon as the merchant went away he took it out.

After three or four days the merchant came back to fetch his money and found it was gone. Then he cried out and said, "Woe is me! What shall I do? There was no one around, and yet the money has disappeared." So he went to King Solomon and complained to him. King Solomon replied, "Find out to whom the hole belongs, and go to him and tell him that you are a stranger and that you brought a great deal of money with you. Then say to him, 'I buried a part of it, but I still have a great deal with me and do not know what to do with it. Shall I bury the rest in the same place, or shall I give it to an honest man to take care of, or shall I bury it separately?' His reply will be, 'Take my advice. If the place where the other money is hidden is a safe hiding place, put the rest of your money there too.' And he will put the stolen money back, for he will reflect that when you find the other money gone you will not put any more money there. Then you can go and recover the stolen money."

The merchant found out to whom the hole belonged and went to him for advice. And he advised him to put the rest of his money in the same place. The merchant said that he would follow his advice, and went to town for a walk. The man who had stolen the money thought, "If the merchant finds that his money is gone, he will not put any more there. I will therefore restore the money I have taken and then I will get the entire amount." But he did not know that the matter had been prearranged. Accordingly he put the money back, and the merchant recovered his loss and went his way. The thief came back to steal the whole amount but found nothing. Thus the merchant recovered his money through the advice of King Solomon.

From the *Ma'aseh Book,* edited and translated by Moses Gaster (Philadelphia: Jewish Publication Society of America, 1934).

ALONE WITH GOD

RABBI SUSSYA of Annipole, who was one of the most humble of men despite the greatness of his reputation for devotion, once visited Rabbi Mordecai of Nizchot.

It came about that in the middle of the night Rabbi Sussya arose from his bed and in a voice overflowing with holy fervor cried out, "O God, my soul! I love you so, yet have I found no way of expressing my adoration." Then he paced up and down his room, repeating over and over again his passionate outburst.

Meanwhile his host, Rabbi Mordecai, and a friend, having heard the sound of his voice in the night, came to his door and stood outside it, listening in wonder. For a time there was no sound, and then they heard Rabbi Sussya cry out, "O my creator! It has come to me at last how I may express to you the devotion that fills me to bursting. I can whistle. It is a small thing—of no importance—but it is all I can do, and so I will do it for you and for your glorification."

And Rabbi Sussya began to whistle, pouring himself out in a sound beautiful and awesome to hear. Hearing it from where he stood outside the door, Rabbi Mordecai was seized with fear and trembling, and, turning to his companion, said, "Come, let us fly from here before the fire of this holiness consumes us."

Adapted from "Mit Gott allein!" in *Priester der Liebe, Die Welt der Chassidim*, by Chajim Bloch (Vienna: Amalthea-Verlag, 1930).

JOSEPH AND POTIPHAR'S WIFE

THE SAYING is, "Throw the stick up in the air and it will always return to its original place." Like Rachel his mother, Joseph was a ravishing beauty, and the wife of his master Potiphar was filled with invincible passion for him. Her feeling was heightened by the astrologic forecast that she was destined to have descendants through Joseph. This was true, but not in the sense in which she understood the prophecy. Joseph married her daughter Asenath later on, and she bore him children, thus fulfilling what had been read in the stars.

In the beginning she did not confess her love to Joseph. She tried first to seduce him by artifice. On the pretext of visiting him, she would go to him at night, and, as she had no sons, she would pretend a desire to adopt him. Joseph then prayed to God in her behalf, and she bore a son. However, she continued to embrace him as though he were her own child, yet he did not notice her evil designs. Finally, when he recognized her wanton trickery, he mourned many days, and endeavored to turn her away from her sinful passion by the word of God. She, on her side, often threatened him with death, and surrendered him to castigations in order to make him amenable to her will, and when these means had no effect upon Joseph, she sought to seduce him with enticements. She would say, "I promise thee, thou shalt rule over me and all I have, if thou wilt but give thyself up to me, and thou shalt be to me the same as my lawful husband." But Joseph was mindful of the words of his fathers, and he went into his chamber, and fasted, and prayed to God that He would deliver him from the toils of the Egyptian woman.

In spite of the mortifications he practiced, and though he gave the poor and the sick the food apportioned to him, his master thought he lived a luxurious life, for those that fast for the glory of God are made beautiful of countenance.

The wife of Potiphar would frequently speak to her husband in praise of Joseph's chastity in order that he might conceive no suspicion of the state of her feelings. And, again, she would encourage Joseph secretly, telling him not to fear her husband, that he was convinced of Joseph's purity of life, and though one should carry tales to him about Joseph and herself, Potiphar would lend them no credence. And when she saw that all this was ineffectual, she approached him with the request that he teach her the word of God, saying, "If it be thy wish that I forsake idol worship, then fulfill my desire, and I will persuade that Egyptian husband of mine to abjure the idols, and we shall walk in the law of thy God." Joseph replied, "The Lord desireth not that those who fear Him shall walk in impurity, nor hath He pleasure in the adulterer."

Another time she came to him and said, "If thou wilt not do my desire, I will murder the Egyptian and wed with thee according to the law." Whereat Joseph rent his garment, and he said, "O woman, fear the Lord, and do not execute this evil deed, that thou mayest not bring destruction down upon thyself, for I will proclaim thy impious purposes to all in public."

When Zuleika could not prevail upon him or persuade him, her desire threw her into a grievous sickness, and all the women of Egypt came to visit her and they said unto her, "Why art thou so languid and wasted, thou that lackest nothing? Is not thy husband a prince great and esteemed in the sight of the king? Is it possible that thou canst want aught of what thy heart desireth?" Zuleika answered them, saying, "This day shall it be made known unto you whence cometh the state wherein you see me."

She commanded her maidservants to prepare food for all the women, and she spread a banquet before them in her house. She placed knives upon the table to peel the oranges, and then ordered Joseph to appear, arrayed in costly garments, and wait upon her guests. When Joseph came in, the women could not take their eyes off him, and they all cut their hands with the knives, and the oranges in their hands were covered with blood, but they, not knowing what they were doing, continued to look upon the beauty of Joseph without turning their eyes away from him.

Then Zuleika said unto them, "What have ye done? Behold, I set oranges before you to eat, and you have cut your hands." All the women looked at their hands, and lo, they were full of blood, and it flowed down and stained their garments. They said to Zuleika, "This slave in thy house did enchant us, and we could not turn our eyes away from him on account of his beauty." She then said, "This happened to you that looked upon him but a moment, and you could not restrain yourselves! How, then, can I control myself in whose house he abideth continually, who see him go in and out day after day? How, then, should I not waste away, or keep from languishing on account of him!" And the women spake, saying "It is true, who can look upon this beauty in the house, and deny her feelings? But he is thy slave! Why dost thou not disclose to him that which is in thy heart, rather than suffer thy life to perish through this thing?" Zuleika answered them, "Daily do I endeavor to persuade him, but he will not consent to my wishes. I promised him everything that is fair, yet have I met with no return from him, and therefore I am sick, as you may see."

Her sickness increased upon her. Her husband and her household suspected not the cause of her decline, but all the women that were her friends knew that it was on account of the love she bore Joseph, and they advised her all the time to try to entice the youth. On a certain day, while Joseph was doing his master's work in the house, Zuleika came and fell suddenly upon him, but Joseph was stronger than she, and he pressed her down to the ground. Zuleika wept, and in a voice of supplication, and in bitterness of soul, she said to Joseph, "Hast thou ever known, seen, or heard of a woman my peer in beauty, let alone a woman with beauty exceeding mine? Yet I try daily to persuade thee, I fall into decline through love of thee, I confer all this honor upon thee, and thou wilt not hearken unto my voice! Is it by reason of fear of thy master, that he punish thee? As the king liveth, no harm shall come upon thee from thy master on account of this thing. Now, therefore, I pray thee, listen to me, and consent unto my desire for the sake of the honor that I have conferred upon thee, and take this death away from me. For why should I die on account of thee?" Joseph remained as steadfast under these importunities as before.

Zuleika, however, was not discouraged; she continued her solicitations unremittingly, day after day, month after month, for a whole year, but always without the least success, for Joseph in his chastity did not permit himself even to look upon her, wherefore she resorted to constraint. She had an iron shackle placed upon his chin, and he was compelled to keep his head up and look her in the face.

Seeing that she could not attain her object by entreaties or tears, Zuleika finally used force, when she judged that the favorable chance had come. She did not have long to wait. When the Nile overflowed its banks, and, according to the annual custom of the Egyptians, all repaired to the river, men and women, people and princes, accompanied by music, Zuleika remained at home under the pretense of being sick. This was her long-looked-for opportunity, she thought. She rose up and ascended to the hall of state, and arrayed herself in princely garments. She placed precious stones upon her head, onyx stones set in silver and gold, she beautified her face and her body with all sorts of things for the purifying of women, she perfumed the hall and the whole house with cassia and frankincense, spread myrrh and aloes all over, and afterward sat herself down at the entrance to the hall, in the vestibule leading to the house, through which Joseph had to pass to his work.

And behold, Joseph came from the field, and he was on the point of entering the house to do his master's work, but when he reached the place where Zuleika sat, and saw all she had done, he turned back. His mistress, perceiving it, called out to him, "What aileth thee, Joseph? Go to thy work, I will make room for thee, that thou mayest pass by to thy seat." Joseph did as she bade him, he entered the house, took his seat, and set about his master's work as usual. Then Zuleika stood before him suddenly in all her beauty of person and magnificence of raiment, and repeated the desire of her heart. It was the first and the last time that Joseph's steadfastness deserted him, but only for an instant. When he was on the point of complying with the wish of his mistress, the image of his mother Rachel appeared before him, and that of his aunt Leah, and the image of his father Jacob. The last addressed him thus: "In time to come the names of thy brethren will be graven upon the breastplate of the high priest. Dost thou desire to have thy name appear with theirs? Or wilt thou forfeit this honor through sinful conduct. For know, he that keepeth company with harlots wasteth his substance." This vision of the dead, and especially the image of his father, brought Joseph to his senses, and his illicit passion departed from him.

Joseph fled forth, away from the house of his mistress, the same house in which aforetime wonders had been done for Sarah, kept a captive there by Pharaoh. But hardly was he outside when the sinful passion again overwhelmed him, and he returned to Zuleika's chamber. Then the Lord appeared unto him, holding the *Eben Shetiyah* in His hand, and said to him, "If thou touchest her, I will cast away this stone upon which the earth is founded, and the world will fall to ruin." Sobered again, Joseph started to escape from his mistress, but Zuleika caught him by his garment, and she said, "As the king liveth, if thou wilt not fulfill my wish, thou must die," and while she spoke thus, she drew a sword with her free hand from under her dress, and, pressing it against Joseph's throat, she said, "Do as I bid thee, or thou diest." Joseph ran out, leaving a piece of his garment in the hands of Zuleika as he wrenched himself loose from the grasp of the woman with a quick, energetic motion.

Zuleika's passion for Joseph was so violent that, in lieu of its owner, whom she could not succeed in subduing to her will, she kissed and caressed the fragment of cloth left in her hand. At the same time she was not slow to perceive the danger into which she had put herself, for, she feared, Joseph might possibly betray her conduct, and she considered ways and means of obviating the consequences of her folly.

Meanwhile her friends returned from the Nile festival, and they came to visit her and inquire after her health. They found her looking wretchedly ill, on account of the excitement she had passed through and the anxiety she was in. She confessed to the women what had happened with Joseph, and they advised her to accuse him of immorality before her husband, and then he would be thrown into prison. Zuleika accepted their advice, and she begged her visitors to support her charges by also lodging complaints against Joseph, that he had been annoying them with improper proposals.

But Zuleika did not depend entirely upon the assistance of her friends. She planned a ruse, besides, to be sure of convincing her husband of Joseph's guilt. She laid aside her rich robes of state, put on her ordinary clothes, and took to her sickbed, in which she had been lying when the people left to go to the festival. Also, she took Joseph's torn garment and laid it out next to her. Then she sent a little boy to summon some of the men of her house, and to them she told the tale of Joseph's alleged outrage, saying, "See the Hebrew slave, whom your master hath brought in unto my house, and who attempted to do violence to me today! You had scarcely gone away to the festival when he entered the house and, making sure that no one was here, he tried to force me to yield to his lustful desire. But I grasped his clothes, tore them, and cried with a loud voice. When he heard that I lifted up my voice and cried, he was seized with fear, and he fled, and got him out, but he left his garment by me." The men of her house spake not a word, but, in a rage against Joseph, they went to their master and reported to him what had come to pass. In the meantime the husbands of Zuleika's friends had also spoken to Potiphar, at the instigation of their wives, and complained of his slave, that he molested their wives.

Potiphar hastened home, and he found his wife in low spirits, and though the cause of her dejection was chagrin at not having succeeded in winning Joseph's love, she pretended that it was anger at the immoral conduct of the slave. She accused him in the following words: "O husband, mayest thou not live a day longer if thou dost not punish the wicked slave that hath desired to defile thy bed, that hath not kept in mind who he was when he came to our house, to demean himself with modesty, nor hath he been mindful of the favors he hath received from thy bounty. He did lay a privy design to abuse thy wife, and this at the time of observing a festival, when thou wouldst be absent." These words she spoke at the moment of conjugal intimacy with Potiphar, when she was certain of exerting an influence upon her husband.

Potiphar gave credence to her words, and he had Joseph flogged unmercifully. While the cruel blows fell upon him, he cried to God, "O Lord, Thou knowest that I am innocent of these things, and why should I die today on account of a false accusation by the hands of these uncircumcised impious men?" God opened the mouth of Zuleika's child, a babe of but eleven months, and he spoke to the men that were beating Joseph, saying, "What is your quarrel with this man? Why do you inflict such evil upon him? Lies my mother doth speak, and deceit is what her mouth uttereth. This is the true tale of that which did happen," and the child proceeded to tell all that had passed—how Zuleika had tried first to persuade Joseph to act wickedly, and then had tried to force him to do her will. The people listened in great amazement. But the report finished, the child spake no word, as before.

Abashed by the speech of his own infant son, Potiphar commanded his bailiffs to leave off from chastising Joseph, and the matter was brought into court, where priests sat as judges. Joseph protested his innocence and related all that had happened according to the truth, but Potiphar repeated the account his wife had given him. The judges ordered the garment of Joseph, which Zuleika had in her possession, to be brought before them, and they examined the tear therein. It turned out to be on the front part of the mantle, and they came to the conclusion that Zuleika had tried to hold him fast, and had been foiled in her attempt by Joseph, against whom she was now lodging a trumped-up charge. They decided that Joseph had not incurred the death penalty, but they condemned him to incarceration, because he was the cause of a stain upon Zuleika's fair name.

Potiphar himself was convinced of Joseph's innocence, and when he cast him into prison, he said to him, "I know that thou art not guilty of so vile a crime, but I must put thee in durance, lest a taint cling to my children."

From *The Legends of the Jews*, by Louis Ginzberg, translated by Henrietta Szold (Philadelphia: Jewish Publication Society of America, 1910).

FATHER BIRD AND FLEDGLINGS

WE SHOULD, I say, put ourselves to great pains for our children, for on this the world is built, yet we must understand that if children did as much for their parents, the children would quickly tire of it.

A bird once set out to cross a windy sea with its three fledglings. The sea was so wide and the wind so strong, the father bird was forced to carry his young, one by one, in his strong claws. When he was halfway across with the first fledgling the wind turned to a gale, and he said, "My child, look how I am struggling and risking my life in your behalf. When you are grown up, will you do as much for me and provide for my old age?"

The fledgling replied, "Only bring me to safety, and when you are old I shall do everything you ask of me."

Whereat the father bird dropped his child into the sea, and it drowned, and he said, "So shall it be done to such a liar as you."

Then the father bird returned to shore, set forth with his second fledgling, asked the same question, and, receiving the same answer, drowned the second child with the cry, "You, too, are a liar."

Finally he set out with the third fledgling, and when he asked the same question, the third and last fledgling replied, "My dear father,

it is true you are struggling mightily and risking your life in my behalf, and I shall be wrong not to repay you when you are old, but I cannot bind myself. This though I can promise: when I am grown up and have children of my own, I shall do as much for them as you have done for me."

Whereupon the father bird said, "Well spoken, my child, and wisely; your life I will spare, and I will carry you to shore in safety."

From *The Memoirs of Glückel of Hameln,* translated by Marvin Lowenthal (New York: Harper & Brothers, 1932).

SONG OF THE KID

One only kid, one only kid, which my father bought for two zuzim—one only kid, one only kid.

And a cat came and devoured the kid, which my father bought for two zuzim—one only kid, one only kid.

And a dog came and bit the cat, which had devoured the kid, which my father bought for two zuzim—one only kid, one only kid.

Then a staff came and smote the dog, which had bitten the cat, which had devoured the kid, which my father bought for two zuzim—one only kid, one only kid.

Then a fire came and burned the staff, which had smitten the dog, which had bitten the cat, which had devoured the kid, which my father bought for two zuzim—one only kid, one only kid.

Then water came and extinguished the fire, which had burned the staff, which had smitten the dog, which had bitten the cat, which had devoured the kid, which my father bought for two zuzim—one only kid, one only kid.

Then the ox came and drank the water, which had extinguished the fire, which had burned the staff, which had smitten the dog, which had bitten the cat, which had devoured the kid, which my father bought for two zuzim—one only kid, one only kid.

Then the slaughterer came, and slaughtered the ox, which had drunk the water, which had extinguished the fire, which had burned the staff, which had smitten the dog, which had bitten the cat, which had devoured the kid, which my father bought for two zuzim—one only kid, one only kid.

Then the angel of death came, and slew the slaughterer, who had slaughtered the ox, which had drunk the water, which had extinguished the fire, which had burned the staff, which had smitten the dog, which had bitten the cat, which had devoured the kid, which my father bought for two zuzim—one only kid, one only kid.

Then came the Most Holy One, blessed is He, and slew the angel of death, who had slain the slaughterer, who had slaughtered the ox, which had drunk the water, which had extinguished the fire, which had burned the staff, which had smitten the dog, which had bitten the cat, which had devoured the kid, which my father bought for two zuzim—one only kid, one only kid.

From the traditional Passover service.

Latin American

Repaying Good with Evil

TWO SPRINGS feed the reservoirs of Central and South American folk story, one from Europe, the other welling up from native races, ancient and modern. The former brings old stories, particularly from Spain and Portugal, and submits them to reshaping by whatever New World culture adopts them. Thus some of the Mexican tales assembled here—for example, "A Time for Everything" and "Repaying Good with Evil"—echo continental originals in form as well as theme; but others, if not completely new, at least abound in qualities that seem peculiarly Mexican. Such a one is "Lesson for Lesson," although it might be added that the collector's feeling for local speechways and pungent detail goes far toward giving this narrative its effectiveness. Another is "The Legend of Agustín Lorenzo," which is typical of the many naïve and wishful tales that sprang up like sunflowers around the memory of Lorenzo, Pancho Villa, Emiliano Zapata, and other popular heroes of Mexico's Revolutionary period. Although, like all legends, it pretends to be historical, it everywhere prefers wish to fact, miracle to recorded deed.

The other source of South and Central American story is native Indian, both modern tribes and the ancient civilizations of the Incas of Peru, the Aztecs of Mexico, and the Mayans of Central America. Curiously, three of the Indian tales, "The Incubus" (from the Argentine), "Ayaymama" (from Peru), and "The Yara" (from the Brazilian Amazon), deal with demonic visitors who lure earthly men and women to strange fates; this resemblance in theme may be partly coincidental, but the darkly fantastic atmosphere that surrounds all three is surely significant. The mysteries lurking in forest or jungle, the sense of powerful corruption working on helpless innocence, the loveliness of the women, all remind one forcibly of Hudson's celebrated *Green Mansions*, and convey a total impression of bizarre enchantment that is almost unique in folk literature. The fact that the particular versions reprinted here were set down respectively by Ricardo Rojas, formerly president of the University of Buenos Aires, Ciro Alegría, well-known

Peruvian novelist, and Affonso Arinhos de Melo Franco, distinguished Brazilian historian and journalist, may have something to do with the sense of form and the felicity of phrase they display, but it can hardly account for their fundamental beauty of theme and conception.

LESSON FOR LESSON

ONE TIME a young *charro* who wished to travel into the world was presented by his father with a fine palomino horse that trod nothing but the pure air, his mane of silk curling into waves at every step, his ears alert every minute, and his bottom as deep as his *ánimo* was high; also with a new saddle, the horn inlaid with a hundred pieces of lucent woods and the leather parts ornamented with little alligators, a silverplated bridle, spurs that rang like bells, a beautiful Saltillo serape that water could not go through and as bright as the rainbow, sombrero embroidered all over with horseshoes and eagles, *chaparreras* on which the silver weighed as much as the leather, an eight-ply reata in which the rawhide strands were plaited as smoothly as the strains of a waltz, a thirty-thirty rifle of radiant blue—everything new, beautiful, and *muy fino*. He was fitted out like a twenty-four.

So he went riding away, looking at his shadow and singing for another reason than to scare away sorrows. And within himself this young man was as bright and sound as he was without. He had no tail for anybody to step upon, and he wore his hat *a media cabeza*. Only he was without experience and expected to find the bounty of God wrapped in a tortilla.

Then at a gate in the mountains, overlooking a valley of fields, the young *charro* met an old man driving a burro loaded with roasting ears. As to fatness, this burro looked like the horse that died just as he was learning how not to eat.

"*Buenos días*," the *charro* said.

"*Buenos días, caballero*, and how do you find yourself?"

"Well, well. Three rocks and one tick."

"Thanks be to God," the old man said. "And my heart, that is a fine outfit you have. Would you let me look at your lovely new rifle in its beautifully stamped scabbard?"

"Why not?" the young man answered. "With pleasure," and he pulled the bright thirty-thirty out of its scabbard and passed it to the old one.

The old one took it by the stock, threw a cartridge out of the magazine into the barrel, and pointed the gun straight at the owner, full-cocked. "Now," he said, "step right over there to my burro, get six ears of corn, and eat them."

"That is a good joke," said the *charro*. "I ate *elotes* for breakfast just about an hour ago. I am fond of them, but I could not contain any more right now. Barrel full and heart content. Thank you for your offer just the same."

"The burro is the one who will thank me," the old man growled, "for lightening his load. You'll find that you can eat, for every growing youth has a lobo in his belly. I am not playing."

"Nor I either," the *charro* said. "Take your music to another house."

Now he was angry and he reached to get back his gun, but the old one's finger was on the trigger.

"Move yourself," he said. "Here there'll be no long track between the word and the act. Eat those ears of corn and eat them quick. Eat them raw, and if you wait a minute longer you'll have to eat the shucks! Go in a trot! Hurry! Be sudden!"

When a closed head declares that his horse mule is a mare mule, nobody can argue with him. So the *charro* gnawed the grains of corn off six cobs and swallowed them down into his already well-filled stomach. They nearly choked him. Then the old man removed the cartridge from the barrel of the rifle and in a very agreeable way handed it back to its owner.

"Let this be a lesson to you," he said, "not to trust everybody you meet. Perhaps now you'll not offer your arm again to be twisted. *Adiós*."

"Not so fast, my uncle," the young man called. "Your burro still has too heavy a load." Then he gave a jerk to the lever of his rifle, threw a cartridge into the barrel, and aimed right at the heart of the old man. "Now," he said, "I'm going to give you a sop of your own chocolate. You eat six *elotes*. Pick big ones."

"Now," the old man cackled, "you are making a good comedy. Nevertheless, I have just come from the field, where we had a fire and roasted so many *elotes* that after we had eaten I had to give three of them to my burro. How he likes toasted corn!"

"It is the other burro's time to eat again," the *charro* said. "And instead of six ears, just for your delay you'll eat eight. The cart belongs to you. Pull it."

The old one saw that the other meant business and, considering that it is better to say "Here a hen ran" than "Here a cock died," he mashed his gums on the corn and at last had it all down.

When he was through the *charro* put his gun back in the scabbard but kept his hand on it. Before he gave his palomino the spur, he said, "Let this be a lesson to you not to be offering advice to everybody you meet. As sure as you spit against the sky, the spittle will fall back in your face."

From *Tongues of the Monte,* by J. Frank Dobie (Boston: Little, Brown & Co., 1947).

THE INCUBUS

AN ARGENTINE TALE

THE WOMAN and her man lived in a remote spot of the forest they knew so well. Far from the neighboring villages, the crags and brambles constituted their happiness. The wilderness presented no obstacles to his strength and bravery. Bird and animal fell victim to his skill. She, young and beautiful, sometimes accompanied him or waited for him in their cabin until he returned at night with his bag of the day. They were happy in their remote retreat, living on the honey and game that sufficed for their simple meals. Some afternoons the man came home, ax in one hand, and in the other a white "flower of the air," the silken glory that hangs from the gnarled quebrachos; the woman repaid the flower with her kisses. The days rolled by, and the couple lived a life of love in the lap of fecund nature. A son was born to them, and the new being brought still more joy to their lives. Seated under the eaves of the cabin, the father would ride him on his knee, pointing out to him, when he was old enough to understand, the *tuca-tuca* that passed overhead, slashing the blue of the rustling night, or entertaining him with the heavenly bodies.

"See the moon, little one?"

"I thee it."

"And you see the donkey?"

"I thee it."

"And the Virgin with the God-child in her arms?"

"Yeth."

Then the father would point to a star, a constellation, the Milky Way—*Cielu-mayu*—river of the sea, in whose silvery waters flowing between banks of shadow he showed him the little yellow ducks, like those the child was already throwing stones at in a near-by brook.

This happiness was to end, and the day it happened the woman saw a stranger coming down the narrow gorge that led to the rustic

dwelling. She wanted to turn away but was unable to; the stranger advanced toward her as she stood motionless, held there by a fascination against which she was powerless. The rider's strong breast gave her a foretaste of his embraces, a wanton breeze came laden with intoxicating wild perfumes, sensations of pleasure fluttered along her spine. At the same time the image of her husband, off gathering honey, rose up before her.

"Cross, cross, Devil." Her lips would have formed the words of the exorcism if she had suspected that she was in the presence of Zupay, or she would have held before him a knife, its hilt forming a cross, but she did nothing. The stranger was standing beside her; she was swooning from the poison of the lying visions; the sun disappeared behind the clouds, as though hastening to hide the scene in darkness; the dog slunk along on its belly, unable to bark. And the stranger, as he moved away, murmured in the ear of the woman that was already his, "I shall be waiting for you; when the night bird calls, follow it. It will guide your steps through the darkness—"

When night descended, the man, wearied with his day's work, fell into a heavy sleep. She lay awake, watching through the open window the twinkling of the distant stars. Suddenly an owl on the ridgepole of the house hooted, and then the flapping of its wings could be heard in the vast silence. The woman slipped from the bed and, crawling on hands and knees, left the house. The eyes of the bird were shining overhead and led her down paths she had never trod to a spring of transparent waters, where the lover was waiting who had dragged her from her house in pursuit of a chimera.

"Let us go farther into the woods," he undoubtedly said to her. They would make their way to some hidden nook, where happiness, wealth, delight, awaited them; the grass would be their bridal bed, the leaves their canopy. But before they went she must leave her eyes in a gleaming magic caldron, where, when they returned, she would find them more beautiful and shining than before.

They set out. She followed blindly, the sockets of her eyes empty. On both sides of the path the thick forest stretched, invisible to the unhappy creature, although she could hear, like the sound of distant crowds, the echo of the whispering foliage. In the heavens all was peace; the world was drenched in moonlight. And beside her went not the handsome youth she had known, but Zupay in his pristine satyr's shape.

Hours later the gaucho awoke and noticed anxiously that his beloved wife was gone. He got up quickly, and, distracted, not knowing where to look, unable to understand the mystery of what had happened, set out through the darkness of the wood. Wandering about, he came by chance on the fountain. He sensed that something horrible had happened there. And to his horror, as he looked into it, he saw his wife's eyes gleaming in the magic caldron. He picked them up, looked at them, and, clasping them to his breast as though defending a priceless treasure, he kept on through the forest, beside himself with fear and anger, suspecting a crime, and waiting for the dawn to reveal some bloody tragedy.

Before the day began to break the adulterous couple returned to the fountain. When Zupay saw that the eyes were gone he fled like a frightened coward, as though to escape the coming light. The woman, deserted and blind, ran wildly about the forest. Later a party of honey gatherers found her body crumpled at the foot of a clump of huge *quebrachos*. Meanwhile the gaucho had returned to his cabin, crushed with sorrow, still holding the pupils in his hand, his happiness gone forever, for in the mirror of the eyes' dark pupils he had seen the imprisoned visions of lust and death.

From *El páis de la selva* by Ricardo Rojas, translated by Harriet de Onis, in *The Golden Land* (New York: Alfred A. Knopf, Inc., 1948).

THE COYOTE AND JUAN'S MAGUEY

This was a country fellow very poor named Juan. He had no other crops except one maguey plant. His jacal was the same size as the others in this same region; but, standing near this maguey plant, it looked like a child's house for dolls, because this maguey was the largest one in all the country. It held its blades curving over the roof in the manner of the branches of a tree.

Juan was very proud of this giant maguey, which gave him his living; he tended it with care and affection. He did not use a gourd and straw to suck out the *agua miel*, as the honey water is extracted from ordinary magueys. He bailed the honey water out from the hollow in the center of the great maguey with a gourd dipper and stored it in jars. The plant gave so much honey water that he had plenty to sell and plenty left over to make pulque to drink during the plant's period of resting.

And now, after many mornings of good harvest from his great plant, came Juan just at sunup out of his house toward his maguey, gourd and jar in hand. He was singing a *cantina*, a barroom song, that he had composed out of his own head, about this maguey of his, the greatest in the world.

Mi novia, mi maguey
Nunca falla, nunca falla,
Con su dulzura,

Nunca falla
Con el agua miel.

My sweetheart, my maguey
Never fails, never fails,
With its sweetness,
Never fails
With its honey water.

Hardly looking at all into the hollow among the great leaves in the trunk of the plant where the sweet liquid always collected without fail, he dipped his gourd down and presently stopped his song and became somewhat sober. The hole was dry.

On his hands and knees Juan looked for tracks, and right away he saw them. They were of the little hands and feet of Coyote.

"This thief must be caught," said Juan to himself. "He will continue this custom and tell all his *compadres* how sweet and delicious is this *agua miel.*"

So all day Juan cut long poles with his machete and sharpened them on the ends and drove them into the ground very close to each other around the great plant. By dusk he had built a round corral almost as high as his head about the maguey. Close to the ground he made a little door just large enough for Coyote to enter. He filled the hollow up with *agua miel* and put a little pulque in there also and walked away past his house toward the hill just as darkness was dropping little by little from the sky. Juan did this so that if Coyote were watching him the animal would think the man was nowhere around because he could not smell him.

Before the dark could all come, the moon showed its rounded section above the near-by hilltop, and then the world got lighter and lighter until the whole round moon was very brilliant; and here in the moonlight came Coyote trotting straight up to the maguey.

From the moon shadows where he was hiding, Juan watched Coyote stop in surprise when he saw the fence. But he must have been very thirsty for the *agua miel*, because he went around the corral till he saw the little door. Then he quickly entered.

And here came Juan, stooping low in a creeping run on his *guarache*-shod feet, fingering in his hand a stout stick. As he approached the corral he could hear Coyote already saying "Slup, slup; gulp, gulp."

"Drink well, my fearless devil," Juan whispered as he stepped close against the corral, leaning directly over the little door. "Drink well, shameless one. For it is your last drink." So saying, he drew a deep breath and tore the air, shrill and loud, with a *vaquero's* Indian yell.

From outside the corral Juan saw Coyote jump backward out of the hollow straight up into the air into the moonlight and begin running with his feet while still in the air. Down he came and went flying around and around the inside wall of the corral so fast that he could neither stop nor see the little door. Juan thought that this was the funniest thing he had ever seen in his life and fell immediately

into an insane fit of laughter: "Hua, hue, huee-haaa! What a fright I gave him. Hua, hua, haee!"

Finally, while Juan was laughing so loudly and bragging about the terrible fright he had given Coyote, the animal found the door and stuck his head through to come out.

In this moment Juan raised his club, still laughing, to bring it down upon Coyote's head; but there he stood, holding his club aloft in the air like a statue, paralyzed with laughing while Coyote came through the hole in the corral and escaped, running past Juan's front door. Juan tried to throw his club at Coyote just as he turned the corner of his house, but no. All he could do was stand there laughing and saying, "What a fright I gave him!" Not until Coyote was out of danger in the night was Juan able to stop his laughing and begin cursing, in his frenzy stamping on his sombrero.

Juan, at that time, threw upon himself the blame for failing to kill Coyote, but if he has any more sense now than he had then, he knows that Coyote, through certain powers as a magician, simply chose this method of casting him under a spell of witchcraft.

From "The Little Animals of Mexico," contributed by Dan Storm to *Coyote Wisdom* (Texas Folk-Lore Society Publications, No. XIV, 1938).

REPAYING GOOD WITH EVIL

THIS was a wise man who, while walking along the trail, found a serpent in a trap.

"Let me out," begged the serpent. "It's wrong to keep me here."

"You are right," said the wise man. "It is wrong to keep one trapped." Thereupon he released the snake.

Immediately the serpent coiled about his benefactor and prepared to eat him.

"This is not right," said the wise man. "It is wrong to repay good with evil."

"Perhaps," replied the serpent, "but I am hungry."

"That I regret," said the wise man. "It is wrong to repay good with evil. Before you devour me, let's ask the opinion of someone else."

"That would only prolong your worry, for he would agree with me," said the serpent. "However, to please you, we will call a judge."

They spied a horse passing near. "Come here," called the wise man. "Come here, *Señor Caballo*. We want your opinion in a serious dispute."

The horse approached and heard impartially the pleas of each. "It is indeed not right for one to repay good with evil," said he. Then, fearing the wrath of the serpent, he added, "But on the other hand, *es la costumbre* [it is the custom] that good be repaid with evil. Behold myself, for example. Once I was young, had the best of food, and was happy, and it was with my energy that my master became a rich man. Now that I am old, he has turned me out to starve. Yes, *es la costumbre* to repay good with evil."

Then they called the ox. "Brother Ox," said the serpent, "we have called you to hear our cause and give an opinion. My friend here contends that it is wrong to repay good with evil. What is your judgment?"

The ox looked the facts calmly in the face and meditated and chewed his cud. Then with a tired sigh he said, "Whether it is right or wrong is not the case. *Es la costumbre* to repay good with evil."

"Fine," said the serpent to the wise man. "Now I shall devour you."

"We are but little wiser than we were," pleaded the wise man. "Grant that we hear the opinion of one more judge."

Thereupon they called the coyote. "*'Mano* [brother] Coyote," said the wise man, "my friend the serpent contends that it is right to repay good with evil. *Qué dices?*"

"I had rather not say without due thought. I am just *gente corriente* (common folks), a wild animal from the chaparral. My judgment at best may be of little use. What is the trouble?"

The story was told how the snake was released by the wise man and then how the former was wanting to devour the latter when the wise man said that it was not right to repay good with evil.

"That is not enough," said *'Mano Coyote*. "I desire to study the case more in detail. Now just how was the serpent trapped? Show me where and show me the trap and show me just how he was fastened, for it might be that he was never trapped at all."

The serpent feared the suggestion that the trap was only a trick. He placed himself as the wise man had found him.

"Now is that really the way you were fastened in, Mr. Snake?" asked the coyote.

"It is," said the snake.

"Is that really the way he was caught?" he asked the wise man.

"It is," said the wise man.

"Then it is my judgment that the situation as it stands is better than it was when I found it. That is all."

"But it isn't right to leave him to die," said the wise man.

"If it isn't," said the coyote, "it's his own affair."

The wise man and the coyote walked away. When out of hearing, the coyote said to the wise man, "Brother Wise Man, you will not deny that I have saved your life."

"No," said the wise man. "Though your decision was not definite, at least you saved my life. Look! I own a ranch near here. Come there at eight every morning from now on after I have tied up the dog and I shall give you a hen."

"Good!" said the coyote. "That is better; that is repaying good with good."

The coyote found life so easy he became lazy and took to strong drink, insisting that his appetite was bad and that he needed a *traguito* each morning before eating a hen. Then within a few days he complained that the *traguito* of *sotol* increased his appetite so much that one hen would not do. The wise man was compelled to add a bottle of *sotol* and another hen to the daily menu.

"It seems," meditated the wise man, "that, after all, good is repaid with evil. It was right to give the coyote something, but now my friend is resorting to blackmail."

"And that isn't all," growled the dog. "Ere long he will call for another hen. I know him; he lives by his wits."

"That would be my ruin," said the wise man. "What should one do?"

"Put him off one day," said the dog; "then put me in the sack with the hens, and when he calls for another chicken, let me out. I will attend to him."

Before long the coyote began to hint that one bottle of *sotol* and two hens were poor pay for the saving of a life. "It seems you have forgotten that good must be repaid with good," said he to the wise man.

"It seems, '*Mano* Coyote," answered the latter, "that you have forgotten that at one time you said one hen a day was enough."

"But time changes all. The first contract is now unsatisfactory," answered the coyote. "It is my desire now that I be paid three bottles of *sotol* and three hens daily."

"Very well," said the wise man, "tomorrow I shall begin the new arrangements."

The following morning at the appointed time the wise man came to the meeting place with three bottles of *sotol* and three sacks.

"*Ay, carray!* Toss me out a hen."

This the wise man did. The coyote devoured her, feathers and all, and then drank another bottle of *sotol*.

"*Ay, qué carray*," he shouted. "Toss me out another hen."

The wise man released another hen. The coyote pounced upon her and ate her quicker than the first.

"*Caramba!*" he said, "with age and experience my appetite grows. Now give me the other bottle of *sotol*."

After finishing the third bottle, he shouted, "Let her out."

The wise man released the dog from the sack. The poor coyote was too drunk and stuffed to run. He was caught, but before the fangs of the dog had found their mark he called to the wise man, "It isn't right to repay good with evil. Call off your dog."

"Perhaps it isn't right," answered the wise man, "but *es la costumbre*."

From "A Pack Load of Mexican Tales," by Riley Aiken, in *Puro Mexicano*, edited by J. Frank Dobie (Texas Folk-Lore Society Publications, No. XII, 1935).

A TIME FOR EVERYTHING

"*Mamacita*, tell us a story," said Juanito.

"This is no time for stories, *hijito*," responded the mother. "For instance, it is about time that you fill this tub with water so I can finish the washing and get the clothes on the bushes to dry."

"First a story, *mamacita*, then the water," teased the boy.

"This is no time for stories, Juanito. You must learn to be patient." Then, with a laugh, she continued, "If once upon a time people had been patient, none of us would have to die and stay dead, but, just as a worm changes into a butterfly, we would come from death slightly changed but would still continue to live."

"*Más, madrecita;* tell the rest of it," said Juanito.

"Well, Solomon, the wisest of all men, discovered just how it could be done. He told his most faithful servant that on a certain day he would die. 'You must wrap me in a certain way, and after I have been three weeks in the grave you must dig me up and unwrap me. After having spent that time in the sleep of death, I shall come alive again,' said Solomon.

"*Bueno, pues*, the people missed Solomon. They asked questions and wanted to know why he was no longer on his throne.

" 'He is visiting another kingdom,' said the faithful servant. 'Within three weeks he will return.'

"At first the people were satisfied with the answer to their questions, but soon a rumor swept the kingdom like a plague. It was told that the servant had murdered their ruler, and before he could escape from the kingdom to wait for the three weeks to pass, he was captured by a mob. The people demanded to see their king without delay.

"Now, if you had been the servant, Juanito, what would you have done?"

"I would have told them all about it," said the boy.

"I forgot to tell that Solomon had asked that no one be told. In that case, Juanito, just what would you have done?"

"I don't know," said the boy.

"Very well, while you are thinking about it you may fill this tub with water," said the mother.

Juanito, very thoughtful, sat for a moment. Then he sprang to his feet and quickly filled the tub. "Now tell, *madrecita;* what did the faithful servant do?" he asked.

"He told the people it wasn't time for Solomon's return. They asked to know where the king had gone, and the servant, refusing to tell, was threatened with death.

" 'Tell us,' they said, 'or we shall kill you.'

"The servant realized that if he told them, Solomon would never come alive again. He knew too, that if he didn't tell, both he and his king would be dead forever. So he took them to the grave, showed them their ruler, and told them the story. The people were heartbroken and wept and prayed for forgiveness, but it was little good that this did. They had not been patient with time, and just for that the secret for coming alive from death was lost forever and ever.

"Now, if you had waited until some other time, this story would have been better," said the mother.

From "A Pack Load of Mexican Tales."

WINE AND THE DEVIL

THE WORLD had been made and God was preparing to plant the vineyard when the devil asked, "What are you doing?"

"I'm planting some grapes," said God. "There will be times in the life of man when he will need wine to cheer him up."

"Would you mind if I help?" asked the devil.

God meditated for a bit. "What is he up to now?" thought He. At last, feeling no harm could be done, He said, "All right, you may help."

"You will be surprised at my efficiency," said the devil.

He went to work immediately. First he killed a mockingbird and sprinkled the blood along the rows. Then he killed a lion, and then a swine, and sprinkled their blood too, from one end of the vineyard to the other.

"*A' 'sta listo*," said he. "Now we are ready and we shall see what happens."

We are all well aware what happened. When a man first begins drinking he feels the effects of the bird's blood and sings. He continues to drink until fired by the lion's blood; then he fights. His thirst increases until he has drunk as deep as the swine's blood, and the next thing we know he is in the gutter.

Ay, qué mala suerte! What ill fate!

From "A Pack Load of Mexican Tales."

AYAYMAMA

A PERUVIAN INDIAN LEGEND

LONG ago, a very long time ago, on the banks of a river that flowed into the Napo—which is a river that winds through the jungle and empties into the Amazon—lived the Secoya Indians whose chief was Coranke. Like all the natives, he had a cabin of palm-tree trunks, thatched over with leaves from the same plant. There he stayed with his wife, who was called Nara, and their little daughter. Yet to say he stayed there is just a manner of speaking, for Coranke was almost never at home. He was a strong, brave man who was always in the heart of the jungle engaged in fighting or hunting. Wherever he turned his eye, there his arrow flew, and he brandished his wooden club with a strength nobody could equal. Wild turkeys, tapirs, and deer fell, pierced through, and more than one jaguar, trying to spring on him by surprise, dropped to the ground, its skull crushed with a blow from his club. His enemies fled from him.

Nara was as beautiful and industrious as Coranke was strong and brave. Her eyes were deep like the river, her lips were red like ripe fruits, her hair was black as a raven's wing, and her skin was as smooth as cedar wood. She could weave cotton into tunics and blankets, and plait hammocks from the fiber of the *shambira* palm, which is very elastic, and mold pots and water jugs from clay, and cultivate the garden that lay beside the cabin, where corn, yuccas, and bananas flourished.

Their little daughter, who was still very small, had Coranke's strength and Nara's beauty, and was like a beautiful jungle flower.

But at this point Chullachaqui had to begin his meddling. He is the evil spirit of the forest, who looks like a man except for the fact that one of his feet is the hoof of a goat or a deer. There is no more perverse creature living. He is the scourge of the natives as well as of the white men who go into the jungle to cut mahogany or cedar, or to hunt lizards and anacondas for their skin, or to gather rubber. Chullachaqui drowns them in swamps or rivers, makes them lose their way in the maze of forest, or attacks them in the shape of wild animals. It is bad to cross his path, but it is worse if he crosses yours.

One day Chullachaqui happened to be passing in the neighborhood of the chief's cabin and saw Nara. To see her and fall in love with her was all one. And as he can take the form of any animal that he wants to, sometimes he changed himself into a bird, and at others into an insect, so as to be near her and to be able to look at her as much as he wanted to without frightening her.

But soon he tired of this and wanted to take Nara away with him. So he went into the forest, changed himself back to his own shape, and so as not to appear before her naked, he lay in wait for a poor Indian who was hunting there, killed him, and stole his tunic, which was long and covered up his goat foot. Disguised this way, he went to the river and took a canoe which a boy, who had been sent by his parents to gather some healing herbs, had left on the bank. He is so wicked that he did not mind killing the Indian in the forest or leaving the boy there in the jungle with no way to get home. He rowed along till he came to the chief's house, which was on one of the riverbanks.

"Nara, beautiful Nara, wife of Chief Coranke," he said as he drew in, "I am a hungry traveler. Give me food."

Beautiful Nara filled half a gourd shell with yuccas and sweet corn and bananas. Sitting at the door of the cabin Chullachaqui ate slowly, looking at Nara, and then said, "Beautiful Nara, I am not a hungry traveler, as you think, and I am here only because of you. I adore your beauty and I cannot live without it. Come with me!"

Nara answered, "I cannot leave Chief Coranke."

Then Chullachaqui began to plead and weep and weep and plead with Nara to go away with him.

"I will not leave Chief Coranke," said Nara.

Chullachaqui went sadly toward the canoe, very sadly got into it, and rowed down the river, disappearing in the distance.

Nara noticed the footprints the visitor had left in the sand and on the riverbank, and when she saw that one print was that of a foot and the other of a hoof, she exclaimed, "That was Chullachaqui."

But she did not say anything to Chief Coranke when he came back from his travels, so as not to expose him to the wrath of the Evil One.

Six months went by and, late in the afternoon of the last day of the six months, a mighty chief stopped his great canoe in front of the cabin. He wore a rich tunic, and his head was adorned with beautiful plumes, and his neck with heavy necklaces.

"Nara, beautiful Nara," he said, coming ashore and showing her a thousand gifts. "You can see that I am powerful. The jungle is my domain. Come with me and it will be yours."

He had brought the most beautiful flowers of the forest, and all the sweetest fruits, and all the most beautiful things—blankets, dishes, hammocks, tunics, necklaces of teeth and of seeds—that the different tribes of the jungle make. On one of Chullachaqui's hands sat a white parrot and on the other a wild turkey as black as night.

"I see and know that you are powerful," answered Nara, glancing at his footprints, which confirmed her suspicions. "But for nothing in the world will I leave Chief Coranke."

Then Chullachaqui called out, and the anaconda came out of the river; and he gave another cry, and the jaguar came out of the forest. And on his one side the anaconda rolled up its huge, flexible body, and the jaguar arched its back on the other.

"You see now," said Chullachaqui, "I am the master of the jungle and of the animals in the jungle. I will kill you if you do not come with me."

"I don't care," answered Nara.

"I will kill Chief Coranke," replied Chullachaqui.

"He would prefer to die," answered Nara.

Then the Evil One pondered a moment and said, "I could take you by force, but I don't want you to be sad with me for that would be unpleasant. I will return, as I have today, in six months, and if you refuse to come with me I will give you a terrible punishment."

The anaconda returned to the river and the jaguar to the jungle, and Chullachaqui went back to the canoe carrying away his gifts, sad, very sad, and got into it and disappeared once more down the river.

When Coranke returned from his hunting Nara told him everything, for she had to, and the chief decided he would stay home at the time Chullachaqui had promised to return, to protect Nara and their daughter. And so he did. He put a new cord on his bow, sharpened his arrows, and stayed around the cabin. Then one day, when Nara was out in the cornfield, Chullachaqui suddenly appeared before her.

"Come with me," he said. "It is the last time I'm going to ask you. If you don't come I will turn your daughter into a bird who will mourn forever in the forest and will be so timid that nobody can ever see her; for the day she is seen the spell will be broken, and she will resume her human shape. Come, come with me, I am asking you for the last time. If not–"

But Nara, mastering the fright the threat had caused her, began to cry out, "Coranke! Coranke!"

The chief came quickly with drawn bow and swift arrow, ready to pierce Chullachaqui's heart, but he had already fled into the jungle.

The parents ran to the spot where their little daughter lay sleeping, but the hammock was empty. And out of the rustling depths of the jungle they heard for the first time that mournful cry, "Ay, ay, mama," which gives its name to the enchanted bird.

Nara and Coranke grew old quickly and died from the sorrow of hearing the sad voice of their little daughter who had been changed to a bird so shy it could not even be seen.

The *ayaymama* still sings, especially on moonlit nights, and the men of the jungle always peer into the thick foliage in the hope of liberating this unfortunate human being. It is very sad that nobody has yet been able to see it.

From *Broad and Alien Is the World*, by Ciro Alegría, translated by Harriet de Onis (New York: Farrar & Rinehart, Inc., 1941).

BRER RABBIT, BUSINESSMAN

A COSTA RICAN TALE

Once Brer Rabbit raised a crop of a bushel of corn and a bushel of beans, and as he was such a rascal he made up his mind to sell them for as much as he could get.

So early one Wednesday morning he put on his big straw hat, slung his coat over his shoulder, and started down the road. He came to Sis Roach's house, and knock, knock. Sis Roach was roasting coffee, and she came out, throwing her shawl over her head to keep from taking a chill.

"Who's there? Oh, Brer Rabbit! How are things going with you? Come in and sit down." And Sis Roach wiped off the end of the bench with her apron.

"Can't complain," answered Brer Rabbit. "I was just going by and thought I'd drop in to see if we could do a little business. What would you say if I told you I was selling a bushel of corn and a bushel of beans for two dollars? Did you ever hear the like? But needs must when the devil drives!"

"Well, I'll think it over, Brer Rabbit. If I decide to take you up I'll come over and let you know."

"Oh, no, Sis Roach. You'll have to make up your mind right now, or I'll look for another customer. I came here first because you know how much I think of you. If you want them, come to my house on Saturday around seven in the morning, for I have to go to town."

"What the devil, it's a deal. I'll be over for them on Saturday with my wagon. But don't go. The coffee is almost ready, and I have some tamales I just took out of the oven."

Brer Rabbit sat down, and in a little while Sis Roach was back with a pot of fresh coffee and a nice chunk of tamale. With this to prop up his stomach, Brer Rabbit went on his way. He came to Sis Hen's house, and knock, knock.

"Who's there?" called out Sis Hen, who was busy getting lunch.

"It's me, Brer Rabbit. I've come to see if we can do a little business."

"Come in, come in, and sit down. Now, what kind of business is this?"

"I'm selling a bushel of corn and a bushel of beans for two dollars. Can you beat it? Just throwing the corn and the beans into the street, you might say. But I'm in a tight spot and I have to take what I can get. I came right over to your place, Sis Hen, because, when all is said and done, we're good friends, and I always like to favor a friend."

Sis Hen got up to turn the tortilla on the griddle, and as she went back and forth she decided it was a good bargain, and she promised Brer Rabbit she would be over on Saturday about eight o'clock for her corn and beans. And she gave him a cheese she had made to taste.

Brer Rabbit went on his way and came to the house of Sis Fox, who was picking some chickens.

"Morning, Sis Fox. How's the world treating you?"

"Bless my soul if it isn't Brer Rabbit! Shanks' mare is right lively this morning. Come in, come in. We're just getting ready to eat."

Brer Rabbit came in, told Sis Fox the same yarn about the corn and the beans, saying that she was the first one he had thought of, and here and there, and that if she wanted them she was to come around nine on Saturday, because he had to go to town. Sis Fox said all right, she would be there on Saturday with her money.

After a fine meal Brer Rabbit said good-by and went on his way. He came to the house of Brer Coyote, who was just taking a big kettle of preserves off the stove.

"Hi there, Brer Coyote. What you know?"

"Why, Brer Rabbit, haven't seen you in a coon's age. It's better to walk in at the right time than be invited. Come on in and taste these preserves."

While he licked up the dish of preserves Brer Rabbit offered Brer Coyote his bushel of corn and beans for two dollars. They made the deal, and Brer Coyote was to come for them with his wagon on Saturday at ten o'clock.

Brer Rabbit said good-by and went on his way. He came to the house of Hunter Man, who was sitting on the porch cleaning his gun.

"Hunter Man, you're going to think I've gone plumb-dumb crazy, offering you a bushel of corn and a bushel of beans for two dollars. But I'm in debt up to my ears."

Hunter Man thought it over and said he'd be over on Saturday with his two mules for the corn and the beans. Brer Rabbit told him to come about noon, because he had to go to town without fail that morning, and he wouldn't be back until around one. Then Brer Rabbit moseyed along home. Saturday he got up bright and early and sat himself on the fence. The sun was hardly up when he saw Sis Roach coming down the road with her wagon.

Brer Rabbit told her to leave the wagon at the back of the house. He showed her the corn and the beans; Sis Roach pulled out her handkerchief with the two dollars tied in it, untied it, and handed him the money. Then Brer Rabbit invited Sis Roach in, got down the hammock, which was hanging from one of the crossbeams, and said, "Come on, Sis Roach, and have yourself a little swing while you smoke this nice Havana cigar." And Sis Roach stretched herself out in the hammock and began to puff away.

Brer Rabbit was first in and then out of the house. Suddenly he rushed in with his hands to his head. "Lord have mercy, Sis Roach! Sis Hen is coming down the road, and she's headed this way!"

"Don't say that, Brer Rabbit," said Sis Roach, leaping out of the hammock. "God help me if she finds out I'm here! Hide me, hide me, Brer Rabbit! Oh, I can see myself in Sis Hen's craw!"

Brer Rabbit hid her in the oven and went out to meet Sis Hen. He told her to put her wagon in the shed, showed her the bushel of corn and beans, and received her two dollars. Then, winking and making signs, he pointed to the oven, and when she opened it, there was Sis Roach, who was down her crop before you could say amen. Then he invited her into the sitting-room, had her get into the hammock, and gave her a Havana cigar.

Sis Hen was having a high old time when in rushed Brer Rabbit with his hands to his head. "Lord have mercy on us, Sis Hen! Guess who's coming down the road?"

"Who, Brer Rabbit?"

"Sis Fox, and I don't know if she's coming for you or for me."

"For me, Brer Rabbit! Who would she be after? For mercy's sake, hide me!" And poor Sis Hen, scared out of her wits, rushed around, not knowing what to do.

Brer Rabbit hid her in the oven and went out to meet Sis Fox. He took her to the barn to leave her wagon, so she would not see the others, got her two dollars, and then did the same as before. Like the sly rascal he was, he kept pointing to the oven till Sis Fox opened it and finished off Sis Hen in the twinkling of an eye. While she lay rocking in the hammock, smoking a Havana cigar, Brer Rabbit was in and out, in and out, like a shuttle. One of these times he came in pretending he was scared to death.

"My God, Sis Fox, guess who's coming down the road!"

Sis Fox jumped out of the hammock. "Who, Brer Rabbit?"

"Brer Coyote. And I don't know if he's after you or after me."

"How can you be so dumb, Brer Rabbit? It's me he's after. Hide me, and please God he don't smell me!"

Brer Rabbit hid her in the oven and went out to meet Brer Coyote. After he got his two dollars he took him into the house.

"Stretch out in that hammock, Brer Coyote, and rest yourself while you smoke this nice little Havana. No need to be in a rush. You know how it is, we're here today and gone tomorrow, and nobody knows when the reaper cometh. For that reason I never hurry."

While he was puffing his cigar Brer Rabbit whispered in his ear, "Go take a look in the oven and see what I've got for you." Brer Coyote opened it, and there was Sis Fox playing possum. In a minute she was really dead, and Brer Coyote ate her up. He was still licking his chops when Brer Rabbit rushed in. "God be merciful to sinners, Brer Coyote! Guess who's coming down the road?"

"Who, Brer Rabbit?" yelled Brer Coyote, trembling at the look on Brer Rabbit's face.

"It's Hunter Man, with a gun this long. And I don't know if he's after you or after me!"

"Oh, Brer Rabbit, he's after me. He's got it in for me. For pity's sake, hide me!"

"Well, get in the oven, and I'll shut the door."

Brer Coyote crawled in, with his heart going like a triphammer, while Brer Rabbit went out to the gate to meet Hunter Man.

"I was beginning to think you weren't coming, Hunter Man," said the old whited sepulcher. "Come in, come in, and rest yourself in this hammock, for you must be worn out. Have a cigar, and then you can look at the corn and the beans."

After Hunter Man had rested himself, Brer Rabbit whispered in his ear, "Take your gun, Hunter Man, and have a look in the oven."

Hunter Man went to the oven, and what did he find there but Brer Coyote, whose shanks were knocking together so he couldn't stand up. Hunter Man took aim—bang—and good-by, Brer Coyote.

Then they went out and loaded the corn and beans on the mules, and Hunter Man was the only customer who got what he had paid for. Brer Rabbit had seven dollars and a half for his bushel of corn and beans, and four wagons and four yoke of oxen, and he felt very proud of himself.

From *Cuentos de mi tía Panchita* by Carmen Lyra, translated by Harriet de Onis in *The Golden Land* (New York: Alfred A. Knopf, Inc., 1948).

THE YARA

AN AMAZON INDIAN LEGEND FROM BRAZIL

JAGUARARI, the son of the chieftain of the Manáus, was as beautiful as a cool morning when the sun is shining on the waters of the Amazon. He was as strong and agile as the gold-black puma, the lord of the jungle, but he far surpassed him in his boldness as a hunter, and his daring in the face of the enemy. When he sailed his canoe, slipping so lightly over the still waters that the prow, like a bird's wing, hardly touched the surface, the shy herons, for the pleasure of seeing him, did not fly away from the bank, and the friendly *jacamins* came to greet him, fluttering along the ground.

In the great festivals with which the different villages of the Manáus, called together by the beating of the great drum made of a hollow tree trunk, celebrated the admission of the youths to the rank of warriors, none of the young braves equaled Jaguarari in pride of bearing, keenness of sight, and strength of arm. The unerring arrow from his tense bow halted the swift flight of the peccary, dropped the bounding ocelot in its tracks, and the dart from his blowgun brought the preying hawk to the ground.

The old men loved him, the girls dreamed of him at night, the braves admired him, and their songs foretold how Jaguarari—may the day be distant!—would go to receive his supreme reward in the Blue Mountains, where the brave have their eternal mansion.

When the leafy *mamaurana* flowered he would glide along the bank in his canoe under the green foliage shading the stream, and the playful breezes would shake the branches and shower down on the black hair of the chieftain's son a rain of blossoms.

But many a purple twilight his canoe, reddened by the glow of the setting sun and checkered by the flickering shadows of the trees that lined the stream, failed to return to Taruman point, but remained on the water, alone and silent, until midnight.

"What kind of fishing is this, my son, that lasts into the night, at an hour when only the Devil Anhangá goes about the land and the waters? Have you never heard his fearful voice carried on the howling wind? Son, my beloved son, Anhangá scatters upon the grass and the leaves of the bushes the seeds of the sorrows that kill."

These were the words of his sorrowing mother when she saw her son return to his home in the dead hours of the night and sit huddled in his hammock, his legs hanging, his elbows on his knees, unsleeping, his sad, sunken eyes gazing out on the darkness, the river, the night, the realm of darkness.

To these pathetic words of his mother Jaguarari responded with a brief glance, a glance from those sad, sunken eyes, contracted as with a vertigo of the depths.

"Son, it was not long ago, only a little while back, that happiness fluttered over your eyes like the wild ducks about the lake. Why did it fly away? Why did it go to build its nest so far from you and from me?"

"Mother," he murmured, in a voice so low as to be barely heard, with a helpless gesture. And his body, fresh and full of sap like a palm tree, withered away, withered away; the gnawing termites had stung him in the heart.

He still accompanied the chieftain on his hunting expeditions, and his arm did not tremble at the roar of the spotted leopard. But as the afternoon lengthened, he left the company of the young braves who were setting snares for wild birds and fled the company of those who followed the course of the river, casting their fishing nets.

Alone, he leaped into his little canoe and sped toward Taruman point, where from the distance his comrades could see him, his eyes fixed on the mirror of the waters, solitary and sad, like the pensive heron.

One day his mother, her heart heavy with sad forebodings, said, "Son, the evil spirits have poisoned the air you breathe, the *acanan* have been singing by the door. Your father wants to build another village for our people far from here. Only in that way will the bird of happiness flutter in your eyes again."

After a long silence Jaguarari answered, with a sigh, "Mother, I saw her. I saw her, mother, floating among the flowers like the water lilies on the lagoon. She is beautiful like the moon on a night when there is not a cloud in the sky. I saw her. Mother, her hair is the color of the flower of the *pau d'arco*, and gleams like the sun. Her face is pink like a flamingo's feathers and the flower of the coconut tree. The song of the birds that sing most sweetly cannot equal hers. Mother, no man in all the villages of the Amazon has ever seen or will ever see anything so beautiful as she. When she sings, the waterfall of Taruman hushes its roar to listen to her, I am sure. Oh, mother, she looks at me and holds out her arms to me. Then the waters divide, and she descends to her home that was left there by the sky, long, long ago, when the sky spread all around us like a flowery mead, before it rose to form an arch above our heads with its starry vault. But I want to see her again; I want to hear her song once more."

The terrified mother cried, "Oh, flee, flee that cursed spot! Never again let your canoe reach the point of Taruman. Flee, my son. You have seen the Yara. Her song is fatal. Flee, Jaguarari! It is the Yara. Death lurks in her green eyes."

And, sobbing, the old Indian woman threw herself on the ground.

The next day, at the hour in which the turtledoves fly high above the houses, cleaving the air as they seek their nocturnal haven, Jaguarari's canoe slipped swiftly down the waters of the black river. The lads of the tribe who saw him pass said, "There goes Jaguarari to fish for *tucunaré*."

But suddenly from a group of women who had gone to the river with their water jars there came a cry, "Come, everyone. Come and see."

The young men rushed to the spot and stood rooted to the ground, gazing into the horizon reddened by the setting sun. The canoe of the chieftain's son, all aglow, was cutting through the water, and Jaguarari was standing up, his arms outspread, like a wild bird about to take off in flight. The canoe seemed to be rushing straight toward the sun, as though it would hurl itself into the flaming disk. And beside the young warrior, clasping him like a vine, stood a white figure, of beautiful form, in a halo of silvery light that contrasted with the ruddy gleam of the setting sun, and crowned with long loose golden tresses.

"The Yara! The Yara!" they all shouted with one voice, the braves and the maidens of the Manáus, as they ran back to the village.

This was the last time anyone saw the chieftain's son sailing the dark waters of the river.

By Affonso Arinhos de Melo Franco, translated by Harriet de Onis in *The Golden Land* (New York: Alfred A. Knopf, Inc., 1948).

THE LEGEND OF AGUSTÍN LORENZO

OUR LITTLE Agustín was born just above this house. He was still much under fifteen years old when he was carrying the daily *gorditas* to his grandfather. This little grandfather of his was a peon on the hacienda of Zapacualco, down in Tierra Caliente. The five leagues there and five leagues back he walked alone every day, every day.

One day he arrived there to find his little grandfather bruised and bleeding outside the hacienda gates. The Señor Mayordomo had had him whipped. Resentment and a deep pain moved in the breast of Agustín Lorenzo. He said that he was a man now and that he was going to take his grandfather home on his back. But the grandfather would not let him, saying that it was better that he stay and work. But not so Agustín. He finally said that the little grandfather could stay if he liked, but that he, for his part, must dedicate himself to settling accounts.

That day on the long trail back to Tlamacuzapa, Agustín Lorenzo found a little snake. It was dead, cut in two among the sharp rocks on the path. And Agustín Lorenzo sat down and wept for it. He took the little snake in his hands and spoke to it. And then he took leaves of palm, the *cojollo*, and split them and wove a little casing, a sort of little serpent of palm. It was like those toys from Tlamacuzapa which you find of a Sunday in the market. He slipped it over the wounded parts of the animal. And he caressed the snake, and the little animal came alive, and he finally left him, moving off into the underbrush.

Eight days later when Agustín was passing the same spot he found a fine old man on a black mule. "Sweet child, where do you go?" he said. "I must talk with you." And Agustín said, "What, then?"

The old man said it was about his work for which he owed him. "But," said Agustín, "I have not worked yet." "But was it not you who revived the life of a little snake a week ago?" And Agustín said, "Well, yes, *Señor*." "Well, then," said the old man, "that was my son, and I owe you his life." "I ask nothing for that," said the boy.

But the old man said he could have anything that might please him. "Then," said Agustín, "let it be revenge, for that is what I desire more than money—and if I only had a horse!" "I will give you a horse," said the old man, "and you must only do as I say."

They had been walking through the forest when suddenly there appeared the palace of the old man. The old man went into the palace and came out with five silver pesos, which he placed in the hands of Agustín Lorenzo. "With this money you must buy twenty

reales worth of pulque, a little *panochita* [brown sugar] to put in the pulque, and *petates* of palm leaves. With the *petates* you must cover well the walls of your house so that no one may see in. For there you must keep and care for the horse." And then he embraced him and told him that in a week he would be a man; that for the moment he must go home and prepare his house and buy the pulque for the horse; that in three days time he should come back and he would give him a horse.

When Agustín went back three days later, there was the old man, and he gave him a horse the size of a cat. "Take this horse," he said, "beneath your blouse, and let no one see him. Take him to your house and guard him well, but remember to feed him only pulque with *panochita*. In four days you will be a man and the horse will be fit to carry you."

And then the old man gave him a saddle of snake skin, all trimmed with silver, and a quirt of a coral snake, and trappings of *zilcuate*, another kind of snake. And he said, "Prepare yourself. Take this pencil; it is mine and knows well how to write. With it you must write a letter to the mayordomo, who beat your little grandfather. With this pencil you will need neither pen nor ink nor schooling."

And so it was. The horse in one week became a great white mare, and Agustín saddled her, and he wrote a letter to the mayordomo, and then he mounted the white horse and he rode down to the gates of the hacienda.

"Who are you?" said the mayordomo. "It doesn't matter," said Agustín Lorenzo, "here is a letter." "You will have to wait until I have eaten," said the mayordomo. "But no," said Agustín Lorenzo, "you cannot play thus with me; take the letter." And the mayordomo took it and began to open it; and when he was opening it Agustín, with one mighty cut of his quirt, opened his face. And the mayordomo fell down dead.

Then the federals who were in the hacienda wanted to shoot Agustín Lorenzo, but the balls did not enter, and his white mare was off the ground in two great leaps and was flying through pure air.

They sent to tell the government, and the government moved itself. There were two thousand men, and they pursued him into these mountains. But not one of the federals returned. And Agustín got his men together and they took a vast load of silver away from the government at Iguala. And later they took much more, and they stored it safely in the caves of the canyon of Tepetlapa.

Then Agustín Lorenzo gathered all the old men of Tlamacuzapa, and he explained to them that the silver was for their people and that he put the silver in their care; that they should never touch it until there was great need.

There were years and years and years when the federals sought to vanquish Agustín Lorenzo. It was a constant war, and the government was constantly in the wrong. Agustín Lorenzo's was a charmed life. The states of Puebla, Oaxaca, Morelos, Mexico, and Michoacán were the scenes of innumerable exploits. Guerrero was his own land, and Tlamacuzapa, his house.

The charm never failed. He came and went as he pleased. If he was alone, with the federals closing in on him, he would reshoe his horses with the shoes backward, so that when he was going they thought he was coming. He had caves from one side of the country to the other. His caves communicated from Tlamacuzapa to Iguala, and from Huitztac to Teloloapan. And now there is no one who even knows the entrances!

Some say that at last he was betrayed; that the government paid a poor devil to join the forces of Agustín Lorenzo and then to stab him. But no one here believes that, because he is not dead. Too many of us here in Tlamacuzapa have heard the hoofs of his horse in the night. And certainly Agustín Lorenzo was never betrayed by the poor. He loved the poor and he defended them all his life.

What the federals really did was to send a girl, and certain it was that they paid her well. They dressed her with much silk, like those women of the capital. She was blond, something Agustín Lorenzo had never known. And she went and offered herself to Agustín Lorenzo, saying she hoped to please him. And so he took her with him to a little hut that he had in the mountains, a little house of adobe with a roof of palm. And he locked the door. And then they were both pleased enough. And Agustín slept. And while he slept, this girl unlocked the door and went out, and then they locked the door from the other side. The federals were on all sides of the house, and they set fire to it. And then while they waited for him to burn to death, Agustín Lorenzo came through the burning roof in one leap and with his machete killed three thousand federals before they could manage to tie him.

They took him to Mexico, and there in one of the palaces of the government they took the lead out of his body. And there were seven quarts of lead of *bala-de-onzo* which they took out. But Agustín Lorenzo still lived, and his horse was there waiting for him in the patio, and he leaped from the window of the hospital onto the horse's back and his horse flew off with him. . . . *Si Señor.*

From *A Treasury of Mexican Folkways*, edited by Frances Toor (New York: Crown Publishers, 1947). Recorded by William P. Spratling in the State of Guerrero.

Russian

The Seven Simeons

If Russian folk tales become—as the number of recent translations suggests—among the most popular of all, the explanation will be their promise of an inexhaustible fund of marvels poured forth as rapidly as language allows. Certainly the chief characteristic of *skazki* is their headlong pace. Rarely is there any building up of scenes or situations—only haphazard incidents in overwhelming profusion. There is no such fatalism as underlies many stories from regions farther to the east, but the reaction to the flow of events may be characterized only as resignation. The narrative is often vivid, even gorgeous, but the main interest seems to be the forward motion of things. The atmosphere in which events take place is one almost of sadness, and although there is humor it is never boisterous or rollicking. The cast of characters includes the usual quota of nobles, peasants, soldiers, and animals, but fairies, gnomes, and giants are notably absent. There are only a few supernatural beings, but two of these turn up repeatedly: bony-legged Baba Yaga, the old witch who lives in a hut that stands on cock's legs, and Koschey the Deathless, a vaguely baleful magician. If the reader gets any general impression of the mood of Russian story, it is likely to be that life is often unfortunate and always inscrutable.

The first of the stories in this section, "The Golden Cock," is, like the famous ballet "Le Coq d'Or," a descendant of Pushkin's "The Golden Cockerel"—a story which Pushkin, in turn, probably heard from his nurse. The theme of "The Seven Simeons," using the familiar motif of the Gifted Companions, is well known throughout Europe.

In the Caucasus mountains, at the southern tip of the Soviet hegemony—but Russian more by contiguity than culture—lies the ancient land of Georgia. On the highroad taken by marauding Romans, Byzantines, Arabs, and Mongols, it is a mixed civilization, half Christian and half Islamic, a link between East and West. From this region, according to Greek legend, came the myth of Prometheus the fire-bringer and the saga of the Argonauts. Reprinted in the following pages is a legend found in the Caucasus, "The Earth Will Have Its Own," a parable of ingratitude called "The Serpent and the Peasant," and several short pieces, including the delightful "The Khevsouri and the Eshmahkie."

THE GOLDEN COCK

LONG ago, before the days of thy great-grandsire or of his great-grandsire, the illustrious Tsar Dadón ruled his tsardom and guarded it against the invasions of his enemy. And if any dared oppose him, he girt his shining sword about him and went forth into battle and fell upon him with so great a slaughter that none remained alive save only one, whom the tsar spared that he might return to his country and bear with him the tale of the prowess of Dadón. So that all the neighboring rulers trembled at his name, and all the princes and boyars acclaimed him and bowed down before him. And whatever affront he chose to put upon them, they must suffer it in silence.

But the years came and withered his arm and dulled his eye. His head grew heavy with the weight of his power, and his shoulders drooped under their burden. Fain was he to abandon the rigors of warfare for ease and soft living, but his vigilant foes, biding their hour in the day of his strength, saw now that the day of his weakness was upon him. And straightway they assembled their armies and harried him upon all his borders, laying waste his lands and plundering his people and spreading desolation in their wake. And Dadón scourged his weary limbs to the attack, and multiplied his legions until their number was so great that none remained to till the soil or keep the vineyards, and a famine was all over the land.

And still he knew not how he should prevail over his adversary. For though his soldiers fought bravely and bravely perished, Dadón was confounded by the hordes of his enemy as a weary steed by the blows of a savage rider. Did he ride southward, swift couriers hastened to him with the tidings that an armed force approached him from the west. Did he turn westward, a flourish of trumpets sounded the alarm in the east. And Dadón knew neither joy in the morning nor peace by night.

Wherefore he sent his criers up and down throughout the country, to proclaim to all that whoso should find a way to bring destruction upon the enemy of Dadón the Tsar, upon him would Dadón heap honors and a mountain of golden rubles.

And a day and a night passed, and a second day and a night, and on the evening of the third day an ancient sorcerer passed through the city and came before the throne of the tsar. Black was his raiment, and white his beard as the breast of a swan. His face was withered as a dry leaf, and his eyes burned like coals in the gray ashes of a fire. And in his right hand he bore a bag, from whose depths he drew forth a golden cock and proffered it to Dadón, saying, "Majesty, thy word hath traveled even to that dusty corner of the earth wherein thy servant plies his humble arts. Behold this golden cock that I have fashioned for thy need! Faithful is he and vigilant and bold. Let him be set upon a pinnacle atop the loftiest dome of thy golden palace, and thou shalt need no other sentinel. For while thy foes lie harmless within their strongholds, he will rest motionless upon his height. But let the wind bear to him over the mountains the lightest breath of their approach, be it from the deserts of the west or from the southern seas or from the perfumed bazaars of the Orient, and my golden cock will ruffle his plumage, raise his crest, and, turning in the direction whence danger threatens, cry 'Kiri-ku-ku' in tones so sweet and shrill that they must reach thine ears, O Majesty, though thou wert buried beneath the snows of fifty winters."

And Dadón took up the golden cock into his hand and laughed with pleasure in him, saying, "O sage and savior of my tsardom, thou who hast served a prince shalt have a prince's guerdon. A mountain of gold shall be thine and a river of silver. And whatsoever thy desire may be, either now or in the fullness of time, it shall be as my own desire, and naught shall stay its fulfillment. This pledge do I pledge thee."

"As for gold and silver, Sire, what need have I of these, who am content with black bread for my hunger and clear water for my thirst? And as for my desires, they are not as the desires of other men. Yet who can say what lies hidden in the stars? It may be that one day I shall return to redeem thy pledge." So saying, the sorcerer bowed his head thrice to the ground, turned and left the palace, and was seen no more.

And the tsar ordered that the golden cock be set upon a pinnacle atop the loftiest dome of his golden palace. And while his enemies lay harmless within their strongholds, the little cock slumbered upon his height. But with the first stir of strife, however distant and however secret, he awoke, ruffled his golden plumage, raised his golden crest, and, turning in the direction whence danger threatened, cried, "Kiri-ku-ku! Kiri-ku-ku! Guard thy tsardom as I guard thy peace! Kiri-ku-koooo!" in tones so sweet and shrill that, whether he waked or slept, whether he walked in his garden or galloped afar in the chase, Dadón heard and led his legions against the enemy and mowed them down and scattered them to the four winds, so that his glory was proclaimed anew and none dared cross swords with him.

Thus did the golden cock keep watch over the tsardom of Dadón, and he arose in the morning with a quiet heart and with an untroubled spirit laid him down at nightfall. And peace dwelt upon his borders.

Thus passed three joyful years, and as the fourth year dawned Dadón lay one night in tranquil slumber. And it seemed to him that a faint far cry disturbed his rest, but so sweetly did he slumber that he gave it no heed, and did but sigh a piteous sigh and draw the purple coverlet closer about his head. And of a sudden a tumult arose in the city streets and drew nigh the palace walls and grew in volume and in fury. And the tsar awoke and cried, "Who dares disturb the slumber of Dadón the Tsar!"

And the voice of the commander of his army called to him, "Thou, O Tsar, father and defender of thy people, awake! Disaster is upon us. Awake, O Tsar, and look to thy tsardom!"

"Get ye back to your beds, ye foolish ones," cried Dadón, "and be at peace! Know ye not that the golden cock sleeps and no harm can come nigh you?"

"The golden cock wakes, Sire, and cries to the west, and thy people clamor to thee for protection."

And Dadón looked from the window to where the golden cock kept watch on his lofty pinnacle. And he saw that the bird beat his wings in a very frenzy and turned ever toward the west. And even as he gazed the cock raised his golden crest and cried, "Kiri-ku-ku! Kiri-ku-ku! Guard thy tsardom on the west! Kiri-ku-koooo!"

Thereupon the tsar donned his royal crown, and took his royal scepter, and went forth from the palace. And he commanded that an army be assembled, at whose head he placed his elder son, known through the length and breadth of the land as Igor the Valiant. Him he kissed upon either cheek and bade godspeed, saying, "For the head of mine enemy, half my kingdom."

And Igor the Valiant answered, "Thine enemy is mine, O Sire and Tsar," and mounted his steel-gray steed and rode away to the west. And his troops rode behind him. And the golden cock grew silent upon his pinnacle, and the tsar's people returned to their homes, and Dadón laid him down upon his royal couch and fell into tranquil slumber.

Thus passed eight days, and Dadón awaited tidings of the battle and of his son Igor. But though he gazed from his window until his eyes grew dim, no heralds approached from the west, nor could he learn aught of what had befallen.

And suddenly the golden cock on his pinnacle awoke, ruffled his plumage, raised his crest, and cried, "Kiri-ku-ku! Kiri-ku-ku! Guard thy tsardom on the west! Kiri-ku-kooo!"

And again a murmur arose among the dwellers in the city, and the murmur grew to a roar, and again they surrounded the palace of Dadón and prayed to him for protection.

Thereupon the tsar commanded that a second army be assembled, outnumbering the army of Igor the Valiant by a thousand legions, and at its head he placed his younger son, known far and wide as Oleg the Beautiful. Him he kissed upon either cheek and bade godspeed, saying, "For the head of mine enemy, half my kingdom."

And Oleg the Beautiful answered, "Thine enemy is mine, O Sire and Tsar," and mounted his milk-white steed and rode away to the west. And his troops rode behind him. And the golden cock grew silent upon his pinnacle, and the people returned to their homes, and Dadón slept.

Thus passed eight days, and Dadón watched the western sky for the first sight of the couriers of his son Oleg. But though he watched till his lids grew weary, there came neither courier nor any word from those who had gone forth to do battle with the tsar's enemies.

And the heart of Dadón grew heavy with dread, and the people of Dadón crept away into hidden places, and when they went forth they went in terror. And suddenly the golden cock on his pinnacle awoke, ruffled his plumage, raised his crest, and cried, "Kiri-ku-ku! Kiri-ku-ku! Guard thy tsardom on the west! Kiri-ku-kooo!"

And now the tsar commanded a third army to be assembled, outnumbering the armies of Igor the Valiant and of Oleg the Beautiful by countless legions, and he girt his shining sword about him and mounted his night-black steed and rode away to the west. And his troops rode behind him, and gray care rode by his side.

Onward they journeyed toward the setting sun, and the night fell and the dawn broke, and a second night and a second dawn, and still they rode without let or pause. And though they scanned earth and sky to north and to south of them, they saw neither the pitched tents of their friends nor the burial mounds of their enemies nor any bloodscarred battlefields.

"Surely this is an omen," thought Dadón, "but whether of good or evil who can tell me?"

Onward they journeyed through the dawn and the noon and the night. And the soldiers slept in their saddles and their horses stumbled for weariness. Seven days they journeyed and seven nights, and on the evening of the eighth day they came within sight of the purple hills, and through a cleft in the hills they beheld a silken tent; and Dadón said, "It is the tent of mine enemy." And over hills and valleys a deep silence lay.

And so they approached the cleft. And before it lay the body of one who had ridden with Igor the Valiant, and a great wound gaped in his side. And close by lay the body of one who had followed Oleg the Beautiful, and his head was struck from his shoulders. And Dadón looked about him and saw naught but the lifeless bodies of his soldiers stretched out upon every hand, but his sons he saw not.

Then he drew his sword from its sheath and rode toward the silken tent of his enemy. But his steed trembled and would bear him no farther. And in the distance he beheld the steeds of his two sons, and they galloped to and fro in their madness. But his sons he saw not.

Then he alighted and went on foot toward the silken tent, and before its portal he paused. For there he saw his sons, their shields cast from them, and the naked blade of each was lodged in the heart of his brother.

And the tsar flung himself upon the earth and rent his garments and lifted his voice in a loud lament, crying, "Woe, woe is me! Both my bright falcons snared in an evil net! Your death is mine, my sons, that should have lived to mourn for me!"

And all the hosts of his army wept with him, so that the very depths of the valleys trembled and the heart of the mountains was shaken with their cries.

And suddenly the portal of the tent was raised, and a maiden stepped forth whose beauty was as the beauty of the young dawn and of the radiant sun and of the shining stars. And when the tsar beheld her, he was as one bereft of the power of movement, and his heart grew quiet as a night bird at the break of day. And she smiled upon him, and straightway he forgot whence he had come or wherefore, and the memory of his two sons was strange to him. For this was she whose beauty blinded the sight of men and ravished their hearts, so that all dear and familiar things grew alien. And none could withstand the potency of her spell.

And she bowed her head before him and took his hand into her white hand and led him into her tent. And she placed him before a table, laden with rare foods and crimson wines, and ministered unto him. And he looked into her eyes and said, "The tent of mine enemy have I sought, and found the tent of my belovèd."

And she smiled but spake no word, and anointed his limbs with fragrant oils, and laid him to rest upon a couch of swansdown, and covered him with a coverlet of cloth of gold. And she sat beside him, and played sweet music on a golden lute, and Dadón slumbered.

And for eight days he dwelt with her in her tent, and ate and drank plentifully and slept softly, and knew not weariness nor regret. But on the evening of the eighth day he commanded that a chariot be brought, drawn by four stallions, and he said to the maiden, "Now shalt thou come with me to my golden palace which is eight days' journey from this place, and dwell with me there in love and joy as I have dwelt with thee in thy silken tent." And she stepped into the chariot, and Dadón sat beside her, and her white hand lay in his as a bird in its nest.

In this wise did they journey, and came at length within a *vyerstá* of the city gates. And the people of Dadón came forth to meet them with shouting and revelry. For the tidings of what had befallen had gone before them, and the people rejoiced that the golden cock slept on his pinnacle, and that their tsar who had ridden forth in peril had returned in safety, and with him a Tsarevna who was the most beautiful in all the tsardoms of the earth.

And the heart of Dadón grew big with pride, and he bowed to this side and to that, and doffed his plumèd hat, returning the greetings of his people. And the maiden smiled upon them.

And suddenly the throng parted, and the ancient sorcerer appeared before the chariot of the tsar. Black was his raiment; and white his beard as the breast of a swan. His face was withered as a dry leaf, and his eyes burned like coals in the gray ashes of a fire.

And the tsar greeted him, crying, "Health to thee, venerable father! And to the golden cock life without end! Peace hath he brought to my kingdom, and to mine arms my belovèd."

And the sorcerer bowed his head three times to the ground and answered, "Well for me, Majesty, that he hath found favor in thy sight. For I am come to redeem thy pledge. For the service of the golden cock thou didst swear that my desire should be as thy desire, and naught should stay its fulfillment."

"It is the word of the tsar."

"Give me, then, the maiden for my bride."

Then Dadón arose from his place, and his eyes flashed flame, and his voice rolled like thunder behind the hills. And upon all the shouting multitude a deep silence fell.

"Thou fool and knave! What madness is this? What fiend of darkness hath seized upon thee to turn thy wisdom to folly and thine honor to shame?"

"It is thy word, Sire."

"Yet have all things their measure, and the maid is not for thee."

"So is the tsar forsworn."

"And were he twenty times forsworn, thou shouldst not have her. Gold is thine for the asking, more than ten men can carry; the rarest of wines from the royal store; the swiftest stallion from the stables of the tsar; rank and honor and broad lands will I give thee even unto the half of my tsardom, and thou shalt be second to none save the tsar alone."

"My desire is for neither land nor riches, nor for honors nor swift steeds nor rare wines. My desire is for the maid. Do thou according to thy word and yield her up to me."

Then did the tsar's wrath wax exceeding great, and he spat upon the garment of the ancient man and cried, "Begone from out my sight lest harm befall thee!"

But the sorcerer would not, and Dadón cried, "Let him be taken away!"

And two soldiers stepped forward, but when they would have seized him to bear him from the sight of the tsar, their arms fell powerless to their sides.

And once again the sorcerer cried, "Thy word, Sire!" But the folly of him that would dispute with a monarch is greater than any other folly. For Dadón raised aloft his golden scepter and smote the ancient man upon the brow, and he fell upon the ground, and his black garments covered him, and his spirit left his body.

Then did the tsar's people avert their eyes one from the other, for their spirits were troubled as by a foreboding of evil. And the heart of Dadón was heavy with the weight of his sin. But the maiden, who knew not good nor evil, parted her red lips and laughed long and merrily, and Dadón, listening, was comforted. So they journeyed into the city, and the body of the ancient sorcerer lay by the wayside.

And as they neared the palace gates there sounded a sudden whirring as of the beat of wings, and in the sight of all the multitude the golden cock flew from his pinnacle and lit upon the head of Tsar Dadón. And every eye was fixed on him, but no hand was raised to

succor him, for all were bound as by the power of some strange enchantment.

And the golden cock drove his beak once through the head of Dadón and cried, "Kiri-ku-ku! Kiri-ku-ku! Evil on thy head as thou hast wrought evil! Kiri-ku-kooo!" and spread his golden wings and flew away beyond the knowledge and the sight of men.

But Dadón fell to the ground, groaned once, and died.

And as for the maiden, she vanished like a dream that is done.

The dreamer awakes,
The shadow goes by,
The cock is a myth,
The tale is a lie.

Yet ponder it well,
Good maiden, good youth,
Though the tale be a lie,
Its teaching is truth.

From *Skazki, Tales and Legends of Old Russia,* by Ida Zeitlin (New York: Farrar & Rinehart, Inc., 1926).

THE SOLDIER AND THE DEMONS

A SOLDIER served the Lord and the great tsar for five and twenty years, and all the meed of his services was three dry loaves. And he placed the loaves in his boot and left the palace, and as he went his way he pondered thus: "For five and twenty years I served the tsar, who gave me meat and drink, armor to cover me, and a faithful steed to bear me into battle. But now my service is ended. I hunger and go cold. I have neither steed to bear nor armor to cover me, but three dry loaves are all my scanty store."

And he went farther, and an aged mendicant approached him and bowed before him and humbly sued for alms in the Lord's name. And he drew forth a loaf and gave it to the aged man, and left two for his hunger. And the beggar blessed him, saying, "Go with God!"

And he went farther, and a second mendicant approached him and bowed before him and humbly sued for alms in the Lord's name. And he drew forth another loaf and gave it, leaving one for his hunger. And the beggar blessed him, saying, "Go with God!"

And he went farther, and a third mendicant approached him and bowed before him and humbly sued for alms in the Lord's name. And he drew forth the one loaf that remained and would have broken it in equal parts, but, taking counsel with himself, he thought, "If he should meet his brothers on the road and they should say to him, 'Thou hast but half a loaf and we the whole,' it may be he would grieve. Nay, I will give him all, and though I hunger, yet my arms are strong and my heart willing, and God will not forsake me." And he gave away the loaf.

And the beggar said, "God will reward thee, soldier, and I will lend thee aid upon thy way. Tell me whereof thou art in need, that I may fill the lack."

"Naught but thy blessing, venerable father. For what should I beg of thy poverty?"

"Regard it not, but speak out thy desire."

"Nay, I lack naught, but I will take from thee in memory of this hour the pack of cards that lies beneath thy habit."

And the old man drew forth the cards and gave them to the soldier, saying, "Play with this pack, and though thou play against the prince of gamesters, thou canst not choose but win. And take as well my knapsack. And if thou shouldst encounter on the road aught that thy fancy craves, or bird or beast or any living thing, open, and cry, 'Enter my knapsack, bird, beast,' or what thou wilt, and he will enter in."

And the soldier took the knapsack and the pack of cards and thanked the beggar and went his way. And whether the road was long or short, he came at length within sight of a lake, and three wild geese flew over it. And the soldier thought, "Now let me try the virtue of this gift," and, loosing the cord that bound its throat, he cried, "Enter my knapsack, ye wild geese that fly over the lake!" And the wild geese entered the knapsack, and he drew close the cord that bound its throat.

And he went farther, and in the end he came to a great city and knocked upon the portal of an inn. And the host bade him enter. And he drew forth the wild geese from his knapsack and said, "Garnish the first that I may sup thereof; for the second give me vodka to slake my thirst; the third is thine in barter for thy service."

And all was done according to his word, and the soldier feasted. And as he ate and drank and took his ease, he looked from the casement and saw a palace ravaged and despoiled, its crystals shattered and its golden domes tottering to their fall.

And he summoned the innkeeper and questioned him, saying, "What is this palace that rises desolate here in my sight?"

And he answered, "It is the palace of the prince who rules the city, and it is accurst. For seven long years it lies untenanted, save by the demons of the netherworld. Nightly they hold their impious revels within its walls, and feast and dance, carousing till the dawn. And many have striven to drive them forth, but all have striven in vain."

And the soldier sought audience of the prince, and when he was brought before him, he said, "My Lord and Prince, humbly I crave thy leave to sleep a single night beneath the roof of yon deserted palace."

And the prince made reply, "I wish thee well, brave soldier, and deny thy suit. For many before thee have essayed the task, and none came forth alive."

"Yet I would go, for the waters may not drown a Russian soldier nor the flames consume him. For five and twenty years I served the Lord and the great tsar, and no harm befell me. How can I perish, then, in thy domain in a single night?"

"Think upon those who went before thee, alive and in the flower of their strength, whom the dawn found a heap of moldering bones."

"I think upon them, and yet I would go."

"Go then, since thou wilt have it so, and God go at thy side."

And the soldier went to the palace and entered the hall of state. And he flung his knapsack into the corner and his saber against the wall, and, seating himself upon the prince's throne, he filled his pipe and smoked and was content.

And as the bells tolled midnight from the steeple of the church, straightway a horde of demons appeared from nowhere, and leaped and clamored and made merry, and all the air was noxious with their din.

And presently they spied the soldier and hailed him, crying, "Ho, soldier! Art thou come to join our revels? Say, wilt thou game with us?"

And the soldier answered, "That will I. But with my cards, good demons."

And he drew forth his pack and dealt the cards. And he won the first turn and dealt again. And he won the second and the third, and though the demons practiced all their wiles, they could not outplay the soldier, and all their gold lay heaped beneath his hand.

And the hoary demon who commanded them cried, "Let the bags of silver and of gold that lie in our treasure house be brought and staked against the cunning of the soldier."

And the imp who was their messenger descended to the netherworld and returned laden with a hundred bags of gold and silver.

And so they played again, and the soldier won. And the imp bore on his back the bags of silver and laid them at the soldier's feet. And he said to the hoary demon whom he served, "Grandsire, the silver pieces are gamed away."

"Then let us play the gold."

And the soldier dealt the cards, and they played again. And he won a bag of gold, and a second, and a third, until the fifty bags lay heaped beneath his feet.

And the demons gnashed their teeth in rage for their lost treasure and they cried, "Now we will rend thee, soldier, limb from limb, and so devour thee. And thy bones shall be laid upon the threshold for him that finds them."

And the soldier thought, "Is it so indeed, my friends? Then let me set a feast fit for your eating."

And from the corner of the hall he brought his knapsack and, opening it, cried, "What do you see in my hand, ye fiends of Satan?"

"Naught but a knapsack."

"Then by the Lord's will and the soldier's word, enter my knapsack." And they entered it. And so great was their number that each was pressed close on the other, and none could move by so much as the breadth of a hair. And the soldier drew fast the cord and hung the knapsack on the wall, and with a quiet heart he laid him down to rest.

And at the break of dawn the prince commanded his servants, "Go to the palace and bring me tidings of the gallant soldier who slept beneath its roof. And if he is slain by the hand of the Evil One, then gather his bones together and give them burial."

And they went to the palace and sought for the soldier's bones upon the threshold, but found them not. And fearfully they entered, and crept through the deserted corridors, and came at length into the hall of state. And there they beheld the soldier, who smoked his pipe and bided in peace their coming.

And they said, "May misfortune never visit thee, most valiant soldier! Surely thou art belovèd of the Lord, since thou has slept this night within the palace and lived to greet the dawn. Say, was thy slumber sweet? And how didst thou prevail upon the demons to spare thy life?"

"As for the demons, they are less than the smoke that issues from my pipe. But their store of gold and silver is worthy the ransom of a tsar, and all is mine." And the prince's servants marveled to see the shining heaps of treasure that lay on every hand.

But the soldier bade them hasten to do his bidding. "Go to the forge," he said, "and bring me hither two sturdy smiths, armed with stout sledges and an anvil wrought of iron."

And the servants did as he commanded and brought him two sturdy smiths, and they bore mighty sledges on their shoulders and on their backs an anvil wrought of iron.

And the soldier said, "Take yonder knapsack that hangs against the wall and lay it upon your anvil, and beat upon it with your sledges as worthy blacksmiths and as men of might."

And they took down the knapsack, and would have borne it upon their shoulders to the anvil. But all their strength sufficed not for the task, and they must needs draw it behind them to the ground. And they whispered one to the other, "It must be that the fiends themselves lie captive within this knapsack, and weigh it down with evil."

And the demons cried, "Yea! Yea! We lie within! Harm us not, little fathers! Harm us not!"

But they laid the knapsack upon the anvil and beat upon it with their heavy sledges, as worthy blacksmiths and as men of might. And the demons writhed in torment and begged for mercy and in the end they could endure no more.

And they cried, "Have pity, soldier, and release us that we may run free! Forever will we hold thy name in dread, but for this palace, no fiend will venture to set foot herein, though the prince himself should bear him company."

And the soldier bade the blacksmiths stay their hands and, opening the knapsack, he set the demons free. And they crept forth and went their way, nor paused to look behind them.

But the soldier seized by his cloven hoof the last to issue forth, and pricked him with his knife till the blood flowed, and said, "Seal me a covenant, demon, in thy blood, that thou wilt serve me without craft or guile." And the demon sealed the covenant in his blood and fled after his brothers.

And they reached the fiery furnace of the netherworld and beat upon the gates, and so sorry was their plight that terror seized upon the young and old that dwell in Satan's realm, and they placed sentinels at the four corners of their kingdom to keep close vigil, lest the soldier with his wondrous knapsack should knock at their portals.

But the soldier stood before the prince's throne and said, "Thus did I and thus did I, and thy palace is delivered of the demons' curse."

And the prince replied, "My love is thine, and thou shalt dwell beside me as my brother."

And so it came to pass. And the soldier was honored by the prince, and his wealth was plentiful as grain in harvest time.

And when a year had passed the soldier took unto himself a wife, and when another year had passed God blessed them with a son.

And it chanced upon a time that child sickened, and so grievous was his malady that no leech could heal him. And though the soldier summoned them from far and near, their simples were without the virtue of a copper coin.

And at length the soldier bethought himself of the covenant that lay hidden in his breast, and, drawing it forth, he cried, "Where dost thou bide, old demon, that didst pledge thy word in blood to serve me without craft or guile?"

And in a moment the demon stood before him and bowed to the ground and said, "What is my master's will?"

"Here lies my son, ill of a secret malady that none can heal. Heal thou my son."

And the demon drew forth a tumbler from the fold of his attire, and filled it with clear water, and placed it at the bedside of the child. And he said to the soldier, "Look within."

And the soldier looked into the tumbler, and the demon spoke again, saying, "What dost thou see?"

"I see Death standing at my son's white feet."

"Then count thyself a happy father, for thy son will be restored to thee in health. But if Death stood at his head, no power could save him." And the demon took water from the tumbler and besprayed the soldier's son and made him whole.

And the soldier said, "Give me the tumbler, and I will ask no further service of thee." And the demon gave him the tumbler, and took in return the covenant sealed in his blood, and went his way.

And the glory of the soldier's name spread over land and sea, for when he looked into the tumbler he knew what man would live and what man die, and great generals and boyars called him to the four corners of the world to heal their ills.

And so it happened that the prince himself was stricken, and the soldier was summoned to his side. And, filling the tumbler with clear water, he looked within and saw Death standing at the prince's head.

And the soldier said, "My Lord, no power can save thee. Death stands at thy head, and in three hours' time the tale of all thy days is at an end."

But the word of the soldier angered the prince, and he cried, "Great generals and boyars hast thou healed in the four corners of the world, and now wilt thou deny me succor? If it be so indeed, the scaffold shall be built for thee straightway, and I will see thee hang before I die."

And the soldier pondered long upon the prince's word, and in the end he parleyed thus with Death.

"Give to the prince my span of life, and take me in his stead. Early or late thy summons must be heard, and better far to go with thee in peace than perish on the scaffold."

And he looked again into the tumbler, and saw that Death stood at the prince's feet. And he besprayed the prince with water from the tumbler and made him whole. And he said to Death, "Grant me three hours that I may take leave of my wife and son." And Death gave him three hours, and the soldier set forth to his dwelling, but when he came there his limbs would bear him no longer and he laid him down upon his bed.

And Death stood by his side. "Now take leave of thy wife and son," he said, "for in three minutes thy life in this white world will reach its end."

And the soldier drew from beneath the pillow his wondrous knapsack, and opened it, and whispered, "What dost thou see in my hand, O friend of man?"

And Death replied, "A knapsack."

"Enter my knapsack, Death," the soldier said, and Death entered in. And the soldier sprang from his bed, restored to life, and drawing fast the cord that bound its throat, he bore the knapsack to the very heart of the great forest. And there he bound it to the topmost branch of a green aspen, and went his way.

And from that hour Death came to none, but life abounded over all the earth, and no soul departed.

And the years came and went, and it chanced that the soldier walked one day upon the highroad that led to the prince's city. And he met with an ancient crone, so withered that she bowed as the wind blew.

And he said, "Good morrow to thee, grandam. The mark of a great age is on thy brow. It must be that Death should have laid his hand upon thee long years ago."

"Long years, my son. For I had but a single hour to live when thou didst take him captive. And now I must live on, though my toilworn body cries for peace. But without Death how can I know the way? Thou hast sinned grievously against the Lord, good soldier, and thou must answer to Him for the sorrowing ones that droop beneath the burden of their years."

And the soldier answered, "I will set Death free, though he slay me. For my sins are thick upon my head, and better that I expiate them now, while I am in the fullness of my strength, than suffer the weight of the Lord's anger upon a back feeble and bent as thine."

And he went to the very heart of the great forest and stood beneath the aspen, upon whose topmost branch his knapsack swayed in the wind. And he cried, "Ho, Death! Dost thou still live?"

And Death answered, "I live, little father."

And the soldier brought down his knapsack and loosed the cord that bound its throat and set Death free. And he laid him down upon his bed and bade his wife and son farewell, and besought Death to take his soul away. But Death replied, "Thou hast offended me beyond forgiveness, and I will not serve thee. Let the fiends do with thee as they will." And he departed to bear peace to the weary, but the soldier he left in life.

And the soldier thought, "I will not tarry, but betake myself straightway to the netherworld, that the hosts of Satan may cast me into the fiery pit and purge me of my sins."

And he bade farewell to friend and foe, and took his knapsack on his back, and set forth on his journey to the netherworld. And he went a short way and he went a long way, and he went a deep way and a shallow way, but in the end he reached the borders of the netherworld. And sentinels kept watch at the four corners, but the soldier knocked upon the gate.

And the keeper of the gate cried, "Who goes there?"

"A sinful soul that would be purged of sin."

"What dost thou bear upon thy back?"

"Naught but a knapsack."

And now the keeper of the gate beat the alarm, and all the demons scampered to and fro and barred the casements and bolted the portals with bolts of iron.

And the soldier called aloud upon the Prince of Darkness. "Satan, be merciful! Cast me into the flames! I would do penance for my sins, and be at peace."

But Satan answered, "Return as thou hast come, for thou shalt not enter here."

"Then give me ere I go two hundred souls, and I will proffer them unto the Lord, that he may grant me pardon for their sake."

"I will add fifty to their number, so thou depart straightway, nor linger within the borders of my realm."

And it was done as he commanded.

And the soldier bore them to paradise and knocked upon the gate. And the keeper of the gate cried, "Who goes there?"

"A soldier and two hundred and fifty souls, delivered from the everlasting flames and proffered unto the Lord."

And the keeper of the gate said to the Lord, "A soldier and two hundred and fifty souls, delivered from the everlasting flames, seek entry into paradise."

And the Lord said, "Admit the souls, but drive the soldier forth."

And when the soldier heard the Lord's decree he gave his knapsack into the hands of the youngest soul and said, "When thou hast entered, open the knapsack, and cry, 'Enter my knapsack, soldier,' that I may enter and rejoice with thee in paradise."

And wide were flung the gates of paradise, and the souls entered in. And last to enter was the youngest soul who bore the soldier's knapsack in her hand. And the gates closed behind her, and when she found herself among the spirits of the blessed, so great was her joy that she thought no more upon the soldier's words.

And so he was shut out from paradise, and he must needs return again to earth, and live and live and live.

From *Skazki, Tales and Legends of Old Russia.*

THE SEVEN SIMEONS

THERE lived an old man and his old wife; they lived many years, to a great age. Then they began to pray to God to give them a child who in their old age might help them to work. They prayed a year, they prayed a second, they prayed a third and fourth, they prayed a fifth and a sixth, and did not receive a child; but in the seventh year the Lord gave them seven sons, and they called them all Simeon. When the old man with the old woman died, the Simeons were left orphans, each in his tenth year.

They plowed their own land and were not worse than their neighbors. It happened that one time Tsar Ador, the ruler of all that country, passed their village, and he saw the Seven Simeons working in the field. He wondered greatly that such small boys were plowing and harrowing. Therefore he sent his chief boyar to inquire whose children they were. When the boyar came to the Simeons he asked why they, such small children, were doing such heavy work.

The eldest Simeon answered that they were orphans, that there was no one to work for them, and said at the same time that they were all called Simeon. The boyar left them and told this to the tsar, who wondered greatly that so many small boys, brothers, should be called by one name. Therefore he sent the same boyar to take them to the palace. The boyar carried out the command of the tsar and took all the Simeons with him. When the tsar came to the palace he assembled the boyars and men of counsel and asked advice in the following words:

"My boyars and men of counsel, ye see these seven orphans who have no relatives: I wish to make of them men who may be grateful to me hereafter; therefore I ask counsel of you. In what science or art should I have them instructed?"

To this all answered as follows: "Most gracious Sovereign, as they are now grown somewhat and have reason, dost thou not think it well to ask each one of them separately with what science or art he would like to occupy himself?"

The tsar accepted this advice gladly and began by asking the eldest Simeon, "Listen to me, my friend: with whatever science or art thou wishest to occupy thyself, in that I will have thee instructed."

Simeon answered, "Your Majesty, I have no wish to occupy myself with any science or art; but if you would give command to build a forge in the middle of your courtyard, I would forge a pillar reaching to the sky."

The tsar saw that there was no reason to teach this Simeon, for he knew well enough the art of a blacksmith; still, he did not believe that the boy could forge a pillar to the very sky; therefore he gave command to build in quick time a forge in the middle of his courtyard. After the first he called the second Simeon. "And thou, my friend, whatever science or art thou wishest to study, in that will I give thee to be taught."

Then that Simeon answered, "Your Majesty, I do not wish to study any science or art; but if my eldest brother will forge a pillar to the sky, then I will climb that pillar to the top, and will look at all lands, and tell you what is going on in each one of them."

The tsar considered that there was no need to teach this Simeon either, because he was wise already. Then he asked the third Simeon, "Thou, my friend, what science or art dost thou wish to learn?"

Simeon answered, "Your Majesty, I do not wish to learn any science or art; but if my eldest brother will make me an ax, with the ax I will strike once, twice; that moment there will be a ship."

Then the tsar answered, "I need shipwrights, and thou shouldst not be taught anything else." Next he asked the fourth, "Thou, Simeon, what science or art dost thou wish to know?"

"Your Majesty," answered he, "I do not wish to know any science; but if my third brother should make a ship, and if it should happen to that ship to be at sea, and an enemy should attack it, I would seize it by the prow and take the ship to the underground kingdom; and when the enemy had gone away I would bring it back to the surface of the sea."

The tsar was astonished at these great wonders of the fourth Simeon, and he said, "There is no need to teach thee either." Then he asked the fifth Simeon, "And thou, Simeon, what science or art dost thou wish to learn?"

"I do not wish to learn any," said he; "but if my eldest brother will make me a gun, with that gun, if I see a bird, I will hit it, even one hundred versts distant."

"Well, thou wilt be a splendid sharpshooter for me," said the tsar. Then he asked the sixth Simeon, "Thou, Simeon, what science dost thou wish to begin?"

"Your Majesty," said Simeon, "I have no wish to begin any science or art; but if my fifth brother will shoot a bird on the wing, I will not let it reach the earth, but will catch it and bring it to you."

"Thou'rt very cunning," said the tsar; "thou wilt take the place of a retriever for me in the field." Then the tsar asked the last Simeon, "What art or science dost thou wish to learn?"

"Your Majesty," answered he, "I do not wish to learn any science or art, because I have a most precious craft."

"But what is thy craft? Tell me, if it please thee."

"I know how to steal dexterously," said Simeon, "so that no man can steal in comparison with me."

The tsar became greatly enraged, hearing of such an evil art, and said to his boyars and men of counsel, "Gentlemen, how do ye advise me to punish this thief Simeon? Tell me what death should he die?"

"Your Majesty," said they all to him, "Why put him to death? He is a thief in name, but a thief who may be needed on an occasion."

"For what reason?" asked the tsar.

"For this reason: Your Majesty is trying now these ten years to get Tsarevna Yelena the Beautiful, and you have not been able to get her; and, besides, have lost great forces and armies, and spent much treasure and other things. Mayhap this Simeon the thief may in some way be able to steal Yelena the Beautiful for Your Majesty."

The tsar said in answer, "My friends, ye tell me the truth." Then he turned to Simeon the thief and asked, "Well, Simeon, canst thou go to the thrice-ninth land, to the thirtieth kingdom, and steal for me Yelena the Beautiful? I am strongly in love with her, and if thou canst steal her for me I'll give thee a great reward."

"Stealing is my art, Your Majesty," answered the seventh Simeon, "and I will steal her for you; only give me the command."

"Not only do I give thee command, but I beg thee to do it; and delay no longer at my court, but take for thyself troops and money, whatever is needed."

"Neither troops nor treasure do I need," answered he. "Let all of us brothers go together, and I will get Tsarevna Yelena the Beautiful."

The tsar did not like to part with all the Simeons; still, though he regretted it, he was obliged to let them all go together. Meanwhile the forge was built in the court, and the eldest Simeon forged an iron pillar to the very sky; the second Simeon climbed on that pillar to the top and looked in the direction in which was the kingdom of the father of Yelena the Beautiful. After he had looked he cried from the top of the pillar, "Your Majesty, I see Yelena the Beautiful sitting beyond the thrice-ninth land in the thirtieth kingdom under a window; her marrow flows from bone to bone."

Now the tsar was still more enticed by her beauty and said to the Simeons in a loud voice, "My friends, start on your journey at once, for I cannot live without Yelena, the beautiful tsarevna."

The eldest Simeon made an ax for the third, and for the fifth he made a gun; and after that they took bread for the journey, and Simeon the Thief took a cat, and they went their way. Simeon the Thief had made the cat so used to him that she ran after him everywhere like a dog; and if he stopped on the road, or in any other place, the cat stood on her hind legs, rubbed against him, and purred. So the brothers went their way for some time, and at last came to the sea, which they had to cross, and there was nothing to cross upon. They walked along the shore and looked for a tree of some kind to make a vessel, and they found a very large oak. The third Simeon took his ax and cut the oak at the very root, and then with one stroke and another he made straightway a ship, which was rigged, and in the ship were various costly goods. All the Simeons sat on that ship and sailed on their journey.

In a few months they arrived safely at the place where it was necessary for them to go. When they entered the harbor they cast anchor at once. On the following day Simeon the Thief took his cat and went into the town, and, coming to the tsar's palace, he stood opposite the window of Yelena the Beautiful. At that moment the cat stood on her hind legs and began to rub against him and to purr. It is necessary to say that in that kingdom they knew nothing of cats and had not heard what kind of beast the cat is.

Tsarevna Yelena the Beautiful was sitting at the window; and, seeing the cat, sent straightway her nurses and maidens to ask Simeon what kind of beast that was, would he not sell it, and what price would he take. The maidens and nurses ran out in the street and asked Simeon what kind of beast that was and would he not sell it.

Simeon answered, "My ladies, be pleased to relate to Her Highness, Yelena the Beautiful, that this little beast is called a cat, that I will not sell it, but if she wishes to have it I will give it to her without price."

The maidens and nurses ran straight to the palace and told what they had heard from Simeon. Tsarevna Yelena the Beautiful was rejoiced beyond measure, ran out herself, and asked Simeon would he not sell the cat.

Simeon said, "Your Highness, I will not sell the cat; but if you like her, then I make you a present of her."

The tsarevna took the cat in her arms and went to the palace, and Simeon she commanded to follow. When she came to the palace the tsarevna went to her father, and showed him the cat, explaining that a certain foreigner had given it to her as a present.

The tsar, seeing such a wonderful little beast, was greatly delighted and gave orders to call Simeon the Thief; and when he came the tsar wished to reward him with money for the cat; but as Simeon would not take it, he said, "My friend, live for the time in my house, and meanwhile, in your presence, the cat will become better used to my daughter."

To this Simeon did not agree and said to the tsar, "Your Majesty, I could live with great delight in your house if I had not the ship on which I came to your kingdom, and which I cannot commit to anyone; but if you command me, I will come every day and teach the cat to know your daughter."

The tsar commanded Simeon to come every day. Simeon began to visit Tsarevna Yelena the Beautiful. One day he said to her, "Gracious lady, often have I come here; I see that you are not pleased to walk anywhere; you might come to my ship, and I would show you such costly brocades as you have never seen till this day."

The tsarevna went straightway to her father and began to beg permission to go to the ship wharf. The tsar permitted her, and told her to take nurses and maidens, and go with Simeon.

As soon as they came to the wharf Simeon invited her to his ship, and when she entered the ship Simeon and his brothers began to show the tsarevna various rich brocades. Then Simeon the Thief said to Yelena the Beautiful, "Now be pleased to tell your nurses and maidens to leave the ship, because I wish to show you things so costly that they should not see them."

The tsarevna commanded her maidens and nurses to leave the ship. As soon as they had gone Simeon the Thief ordered his brothers in silence to cut off the anchor and go to sea with all sail; meanwhile he showed the tsarevna rich goods and made her presents of some. About two hours had passed while he was showing the stuffs. At last she said it was time for her to go home, since the tsar her father would expect her for dinner. Then she went out of the cabin and saw that the ship was under sail and land no longer in sight.

She struck herself on the breast, turned into a swan, and flew off. The fifth Simeon took his gun that minute and wounded the swan; the sixth Simeon did not let her fall to the water, but brought her back to the ship, where she became a maiden as before.

The nurses and maidens who were at the wharf, seeing the ship move away from the shore with the tsarevna, ran straight to the tsar and told him of Simeon's deceit. Then the tsar sent a whole fleet in pursuit. When this fleet came up and was very near the ship of the Simeons, the fourth Simeon seized the prow and conducted the ship to the underground kingdom. When the ship had become entirely invisible, the commanders of the fleet thought it was lost, with the tsarevna; therefore they returned and reported to the tsar that Simeon's ship had gone to the bottom with Yelena the Beautiful.

The Simeons arrived at their own kingdom successfully, delivered Yelena the Beautiful to Tsar Ador, who for such a mighty service of the Simeons gave liberty to them all, and plenty of gold, silver, and precious stones, married Yelena the Beautiful himself, and lived with her many years.

From *Myths and Folk Tales of the Russians, Western Slavs, and Magyars*, by Jeremiah Curtin (Boston: Little, Brown & Co., 1890).

THE WONDROUS WONDER

ONCE there was a wealthy merchant who traded in rare and precious goods, traveling with his wares every year to foreign lands. One day he fitted out a ship, made ready for his voyage, and said to his wife, "Tell me, my joy, what shall I bring you as a gift from foreign lands?" The merchant's wife answered, "In your house I have all I want and enough of everything! But if you want to gladden my heart, buy me a wondrous wonder, a marvelous marvel." "Very well. If I find one, I shall buy it."

The merchant traveled beyond thrice nine lands, to the thrice tenth kingdom, sailed into a great and wealthy port, sold all of his cargo, bought a new one, and loaded his ship. Then he walked through the city and thought, "Where shall I find a wondrous wonder, a marvelous marvel?" He met an old man, who asked him, "What are you pondering about, what makes you so sad, my good young man?" "How can I help being sad?" answered the merchant. "I am looking for a wondrous wonder, a marvelous marvel, to buy for my wife, but I do not know where to find one." "Eh, you should have told me that in the first place! Come with me. I have a wondrous wonder, a marvelous marvel, and since you must have it, I will sell it to you."

The old man led the merchant to his house and said, "Do you see that goose walking in my yard?" "I do." "Now see what's going to happen to it. Hey, goose, come here!" And the goose came into the room. The old man took a roasting pan and again spoke to the goose, "Hey, goose, lie down in the roasting pan." And the goose lay down in the roasting pan. The old man put it in the oven, roasted the goose, took it out, and set it on the table. "Now, merchant," said the old man, "let us sit down and eat. Only do not throw the bones under the table; instead, gather them all into one pile." So they sat at the table and between them ate the whole goose. Then the old man took the picked bones, wrapped them in the tablecloth, threw them on the floor, and said, "Hey, goose! Get up, shake your wings, and go out into the yard!" The goose got up, shook its wings, and went into the yard as though it had never been in the oven! "Indeed, my host, yours is a wondrous wonder, a marvelous marvel," said the merchant, and began to bargain with him for the goose, which he finally bought for a high price. Then he took the goose with him aboard ship and sailed back to his native land.

He returned home, greeted his wife, gave her the goose, and told her that with this bird she could have a roast every day without spending a penny—"Just roast it, and it will come to life again!" Next day the merchant went to his stall in the bazaar, and in his absence his wife's lover came to see her. She welcomed him with great joy and offered to prepare a roast goose for him. She leaned out of the window and called, "Goose, come here!" And the goose came into the room. "Goose, lie down in the roasting pan!" But the goose refused. The merchant's wife grew angry and struck it with the roasting pan. As she did so, one end of the pan stuck to the goose and the other to her. It stuck so fast that she could not in any way pull herself loose from it. "Oh, sweetheart," cried the merchant's wife, "wrench me loose from this roasting pan! That accursed goose must be bewitched!" The lover grasped the merchant's wife with his two hands to wrench her loose from the roasting pan, but he himself stuck to her.

The goose ran out into the yard, then into the street, and dragged them both to the bazaar. The clerks saw their plight and rushed forward to separate them, but whoever touched them stuck to them. A crowd gathered to look at this wonder, and the merchant too came out of his stall. He saw that something was wrong. Who were all these new friends of his wife's? "Confess everything," he said, "otherwise you will stay stuck together like this forever." There was no way out of it, so the merchant's wife confessed her guilt. Then the merchant pulled them apart, soundly thrashed the lover, took his wife home and gave her a good hiding too, repeating with each blow, "Here is your wondrous wonder, your marvelous marvel!"

From *Russian Fairy Tales*, translated from A. N. Afanas'ev's collection by Norbert Guterman (New York: Pantheon Books, 1945).

THE EARTH WILL HAVE ITS OWN

A CAUCASIAN LEGEND

Once upon a time there was a widow who had one son. The boy grew up and saw that everyone around him, except himself, had a father.

"Mother," he asked one day, "why is it that every other boy has a father and I have none?" "Because your father is dead," answered his mother. "And will he never come back?" "No, my child, your father will never come back, but we will go to him. No one can escape death, we too must die and be buried in the earth." "I did not ask God for my life," answered the boy, "and if He has given it to me, why does He take it away again? I will go and look for a place where there is no death."

His mother tried her best to keep him from going forth into the world to look for such a place, but in vain. The boy set out on his wanderings. He wandered over the whole earth, but at every place he came to and asked, "Is there death here?" he received the same answer—"Yes, yes!" And he came to be twenty years old and had not yet found the Land of the Ever-Living.

One day he was walking over a field when he suddenly saw in front of him a stag whose great branching horns pierced the clouds and were lost to sight. The youth was pleased with the sight of these great antlers; he went up to the stag and said, "I pray you, in the name of the Creator of the world, tell me, is there a place where there is no death?" "I am God's messenger and fulfill His will," answered the stag. "I will live until my antlers reach the heavens, but then I must die. If you like, you can stay with me till my death; you shall want for nothing." "No," said the youth, "I will either live forever or not at all. Otherwise I could have stayed at home and not undertaken this pilgrimage."

With these words he left the stag and went on his way. Through deserts, steppes, and plains, through meadows and woods, he wandered till he came at last to an abyss; it seemed to him like hell, it yawned so bottomless before him. Round about the abyss great rocks reared themselves up into the sky, and on the pinnacle of one of them a raven sat motionless. The youth addressed it and said, "Raven, do you know a land where there is no death?" "I am a messenger of God," answered the raven, "and I will live till I have filled up this abyss. . . . If you like, you can stay with me; you shall want for nothing."

But the youth would have none of this and went on his way. He came to the brink of the sea without meeting anyone else. But he saw something shining in the distance, and as he drew near he saw it was a house built of glass. It had no doors, but on examining it closely he saw a line marked on the glass; he pressed on it, and the house opened before him. Within lay a maiden so beautiful that even the sun was jealous of her beauty and shone more dimly when she crossed the threshold. The youth too was struck by her beauty; he went up to her and asked her the same question he had asked the stag and the raven. "Such a land does not exist," she said, "but why do you seek it? Stay here with me!" "I did not leave my home," answered the youth, "to find you, but to find the land where there is no death." "Your search is vain," she replied, "The earth will have its own, you will not find the Land of the Ever-Living. Tell me, if you can, how old am I?" The youth looked at her; her youthful figure and the bloom on her cheeks enchanted him so that he forgot life and death. "You cannot be more than fifteen years old," he said.

"You are mistaken," she replied. "I was made on the first day of the Creation, and I am today as I was then. I am called Beauty; I will always be as I am now. You could have stayed with me always, but you are not worth immortality; everlasting life would become distasteful to you." But the youth vowed never to do anything against her will, and always to stay beside her.

The years flew by, one after the other; so quickly did they pass that they seemed like seconds. The earth was always changing, but the youth knew nothing of that change, and the maiden remained always the same. A century passed in this way.

Then the youth began to long for his home. He wanted to see his mother, his friends and acquaintances. "I must go home and see my mother and my friends," he said to the maiden. "You will not even find their bones now, so what is the use of going?" she replied. "What nonsense you are talking!" he interrupted. "I only came to you a short time ago; why should they be dead already?" "I told you at the beginning," said the maiden, "that you were not worthy of everlasting life. But do as you wish. Take these three apples with you, and when you get home, eat them."

The youth then left the maiden and journeyed back to his home. On the way he came to the old well-known places; the raven still sat on its rock, but it was dead, and the abyss was filled up. The youth's heart sank within him when he saw that; he wanted to turn back to the maiden, but something drove him forward. Over rocks and through woods and fields, he came at last to the stag; it still stood there, but it was dead, and the heavens supported themselves on its horns. Now for the first time the youth believed that many years had passed since he first traveled that way. But he was still impelled forward to his home. He entered his own village, but met no one he knew. He asked for his mother; no one knew anything about her, only one old couple told him there had once, according to an old tradition, been a woman of that name; but that was a thousand years ago, and her son could not possibly be living now.

No one would believe him, that he really was the son of that woman; they all thought he was a messenger from God. And so they all gathered round him and went on with him. At last he came to the place where his mother's house had stood; there were still ruins there, broken walls covered with moss and overgrown with nettles. And now the past all came back clearly before him; he thought of his mother and his childhood; bitter thoughts rose in his heart. Then he remembered the apples: he ate the first—and suddenly a white beard fell from his chin right over his chest. He ate the second—and his knees gave way, his powers forsook him. He became weak and frail. He felt ashamed of himself. He asked one of the boys round about him if he would be so good as to take the third apple out of his pocket and give it to him. And when he had eaten it, he gave up the ghost.

But the people of the village carried his body away and buried it in the name of Christ.

From *Caucasian Folk Tales*, selected and translated from the originals by Adolf Dirr and translated into English by Lucy Menzies (London and Toronto: J. M. Dent & Sons, Ltd., 1925).

THE SERPENT AND THE PEASANT

A GEORGIAN TALE

THERE was once a happy king. Great or small, maid or man, everyone was happy in his kingdom, everyone was joyful and glad.

Once this monarch saw a vision. In his dream there hung from the ceiling in his house a fox suspended by the tail. He awoke, he could not see what the dream signified. He assembled his viziers, but they also could not divine what this dream presaged.

Then he said, "Assemble all my kingdom together, perhaps someone may interpret it." On the third day all the people of his kingdom assembled in the king's palace. Among others came a poor peasant.

In one place he had to travel along a footpath. The path on both sides was shut in by rocky mountains. When the peasant arrived there he saw a serpent lying on the path, stretching its neck and putting out its tongue.

When the peasant went near the serpent called out, "Good day, where art thou going, peasant?" The peasant told what was the matter. The serpent said, "Do not fear him; give me thy word that what the king gives, thou wilt share with me, and I will teach thee." The peasant rejoiced, gave his word, and swore, saying, "I will bring thee all that the king presents to me if thou wilt aid me in this matter." The serpent said, "I shall divide it in halves, half will be thine; when thou seest the king, say, 'The fox meant this, that in the kingdom there is cunning, hypocrisy, and treachery.' "

The peasant went, he approached the king, and told even what the serpent had taught. The king was very much pleased and gave great presents. The peasant did not return by that way, so that he might not share with the serpent, but went by another path.

Time passed by and the king saw another vision: in his dream a naked sword hung suspended from the roof. The king this time sent a man quickly for the peasant and asked him to come. The peasant was very uneasy. There was nothing for the peasant to do but go by the same footpath as before.

He came to the place where he had seen the serpent before, but now he saw the serpent there no more. He cried out, "O serpent, come here one moment, I need thee." He ceased not until the serpent came. It said, "What dost thou want? What distresses thee?" The peasant answered, "Thus and thus is the matter, and I should like some aid." The serpent replied, "Go, tell the king that the naked sword means war—enemies are intriguing within and without, and he must prepare for battle and attack."

The peasant thanked the serpent and went. He came and told the king even as the serpent had commanded. The king was pleased, he began to prepare for war, and gave the peasant great presents. Now

the peasant went by the path where the serpent was waiting. The serpent said, "Now give me the half thou hast promised." The peasant replied, "Half, certainly not! I shall give thee a black stone and a burning cinder." He drew out his sword and pursued it. The serpent retreated into a hole, but the peasant followed it and cut off its tail with his sword.

Some time passed, and the king again saw a vision. In this vision a slain sheep was hanging from the roof. The king sent a man quickly for the peasant. The peasant was now very much afraid. And he said, "How can I approach the king?" Formerly the serpent had taught him, but now it could no longer do this; for its goodness he had wounded it with the sword.

Nevertheless he went by that footpath. When he came to the place where the serpent had been he cried out, "O serpent, come here one moment, I want to ask thee something." The serpent came. The man told his grief. The serpent said, "If thou givest me half of what the king gives thee, I shall tell thee." He promised and swore. The serpent said, "This is a sign that now everywhere peace falls on all; the people are become like quiet, gentle sheep."

The peasant thanked it and went his way. When he came to the king he spoke as the serpent had instructed him. The king was exceedingly pleased and gave him greater presents. The peasant returned by the way where the serpent was waiting. He came to the serpent, divided everything he had received from the king, and said, "Thou hast been patient with me, and now I will give thee even what was given me before by the king." He humbly asked forgiveness for his former offenses. The serpent said, "Be not grieved nor troubled; it certainly was not thy fault. The first time, when all the people were entirely deceitful, and there was treachery and hypocrisy in the land, thou too wert a deceiver, for, in spite of thy promise, thou wentest home by another way. The second time, when there was war everywhere, quarrels and assassination, thou, too, didst quarrel with me, and cut off my tail. But now, when peace and love have fallen on all, thou bringest the gifts and sharest all with me. Go, brother, may the peace of God rest with thee! I do not want thy wealth." And the serpent went away and cast itself into its hole.

From *Georgian Folk Tales*, translated by Marjory Wardrop (London: David Nutt, 1894).

A WITTY ANSWER

A GEORGIAN TALE

A CERTAIN king was angry with one of his lords and put him in prison; wishing to keep him there, he said he would only set him free if he could bring to the court a horse which was neither gray nor black, brown nor bay, white nor roan, dun, chestnut, nor piebald —and, in short, the king enumerated every possible color that a horse could be. The imprisoned lord promised to get such a horse if the king would set him free at once. As soon as he was at liberty the lord asked the king to send a groom for the horse, but begged that the groom might come neither on Monday nor Tuesday, Wednesday nor Thursday, Friday, Saturday, nor Sunday, but on any other day of the week that suited His Majesty.

From *Georgian Folk Tales.*

THE KHEVSOURI AND THE ESHMAHKIE

A GEORGIAN TALE

THERE was, there was, and yet there was not, there was once a Khevsouri who was mowing his hay with a scythe and minding his own business when, all at once, he saw an Eshmahkie on the other side of the field watching him.

The Khevsouri paid no attention to him but kept swinging the scythe.

To mock him, the Eshmahkie picked up a long stick for *his* scythe and pretended to cut hay too.

Naturally this annoyed the Khevsouri. He shook his fist at the Eshmahkie. The Eshmahkie shook his back.

"Go away," the Khevsouri said.

"Go away," the Eshmahkie echoed.

"Stop imitating me."

"Stop imitating me."

The Khevsouri swung his scythe a few more times. The Eshmahkie swung his stick.

The Khevsouri took out a whetstone and sharpened his blade. The Eshmahkie picked up a rock and ran it back and forth on his stick.

Now the Khevsouri was really furious. He had his pride like any other man and he didn't want an Eshmahkie to make fun of him. Especially in broad daylight and in his own field. He threw down his scythe. The Eshmahkie threw down his stick.

The Khevsouri pulled up handfuls of long grass and braided them into a rope.

So did the Eshmahkie.

The Khevsouri sat down and tied his grass rope tight around his own ankles.

So did the Eshmahkie.

Then the Khevsouri picked up his scythe, cut through the grass braid, jumped and ran toward the Eshmahkie.

The Eshmahkie grabbed his stick, but, of course, it was only a mock scythe and it could not cut the grass.

The Khevsouri caught the Eshmahkie and trimmed his fingernails short (because that is the way to keep an Eshmahkie in your power), and the Eshmahkie worked for the Khevsouri after this as his servant. At least he worked until his fingernails grew again, and then he ran away.

As he was running the Khevsouri called to him. "Tell me one thing before you go, Eshmahkie, to show there's no hard feelings."

"What do you want to know?" the Eshmahkie asked from the other side of the field.

"When I am sick what will cure me?"

"The same thing that made you sick. Only not so much of it," he said, and with that he disappeared.

At first the Khevsouri had a suspicion the Eshmahkie was making fun of him again. But after he thought it over he knew what the Eshmahkie meant.

Do you?

From *Yes and No Stories*, by George and Helen Papashvily (New York: Harper & Brothers, 1946).

Scandinavian

The Making of the Hammer

If Norse mythology is incomplete and unsystematic, the fragments are magnificent, and if its gods and heroes are sometimes misty, they are like peaks in the clouds. Compared with the myths of ancient Greece and India, those of the Northlanders are latecomers in the realm of mythology. The poetry of the Elder Edda introduced a number of them in the tenth century and the prose narratives of the Younger Edda, set down by the Icelandic scholar Snorri Sturluson, gave shape to others in the early thirteenth century. They were in fact written down so recently that in many passages the old pagan system of divinity has been almost completely overlaid by Christian ideas. But late as they may be, they have challenged Greek dominion in the realm of myth-making and hero-creating, contributing to the world's store the figures of Odin, Thor, Freya, Loki, Baldur, and Sigurd, such regions of mythlandia as Asgard, Jotunheim, and Valhalla, and such conceptions as Ygdrasil, the tree that binds heaven, earth, and hell, and Ragnarok, the final holocaust, the twilight of the gods.

At about the same time the Eddas were being written down, a Danish chronicler, Saxo Grammaticus, who is best remembered for the original story of Prince Hamlet the Dane, told a tale of a thane, Palnatoki, and his lord. That tale, retold here in "The Archer and the King," anticipates by several centuries the Swiss legend of William Tell—and may well have been a hoary tale when Saxo recorded it.

In the middle of the nineteenth century two Norwegians, P. C. Asbjörnsen and Jörgen Moe, made a collection of *Norske folkeeventyr* that earned them the name of "the Grimms of Scandinavia." It is from Sir George Dasent's old translations of these tales that we draw the traditional "Why the Sea Is Salt" with its magic quern (see the note on the magic sampo of the Finns on page 280) and "The Master Thief," one of the best versions of a tale that has been told from northernmost Europe to southernmost Asia. From Iceland comes "Bjarni Sveinnsen and his Sister Salvor," vividly conveying the feeling of a land of lonely reaches, and "Now I Should Laugh If I Were Not Dead," the well-traveled droll of the two wives who laid a wager on the stupidity of their husbands.

Two stories told—or, more accurately, retold—by Hans Andersen close this section. "The Princess on the Pea" is justly famous for its charm, but it is so far from being Danish, or original with Andersen, that Somadeva's twelfth-century Indian compilation, the *Katha Sarit Sagara*, contains two stories (one is "The Three Fastidious Men," on page 453) that are obviously its prototypes. And "The Tinderbox" is in part only a variation of the old story of Aladdin and his lamp. Nevertheless the Andersen stamp is everywhere evident on these tales. The themes belong to tradition, but the warmth, the ingratiating manner, the embellishments are Andersen's—as are, it is only fair to add, the occasional additions of a kind of sentiment now sometimes considered old-fashioned.

ODIN'S SEARCH FOR WISDOM

THE WONDERFUL ash tree, Ygdrasil, made a far-spreading shade against the fierce heat of the sun in summer and a stronghold against the piercing winds of winter. No man could remember when it had been young. Little children played under its branches, grew to be strong men and women, lived to be old and weary and feeble, and died; and yet the ash tree gave no signs of decay. Forever preserving its freshness and beauty, it was to live as long as there were men to look upon it, animals to feed under it, birds to flutter among its branches. This mighty ash tree touched and bound all the worlds together in its wonderful circle of life. One root it sent deep down into the sightless depths of hell, where the dead lived; another it fastened firmly in Jotunheim, the dreary home of the giants; and with the third it grasped Midgard, the dwelling place of men. Serpents and all kinds of worms gnawed continually at its roots but were never able to destroy them. Its branches spread out over the whole earth, and the topmost boughs swayed in the clear air of Asgard itself, rustling against the Valhalla, the home of the heroes who had done great deeds or died manfully in battle. At the foot of the tree sat the three Norns, wonderful spinners of fate, who weave the thread of every man's life, making it what they will; and a strange weaving it often was, cut off when the pattern was just beginning to show itself. And every day these Norns sprinkled the tree with the water of life from the Urdar fountain, and so kept it forever green. In the topmost branches sat an eagle singing a strange song about the birth of the world, its decay and death. Under its branches browsed all manner of animals; among its leaves every kind of bird made its nest; by day the rainbow hung under it; at night the pale northern light flashed over it; and as the winds swept through its rustling branches the multitudinous murmur of the leaves told strange stories of the past and of the future.

The giants were older than the gods and knew so much more of the past that the gods had to go to them for wisdom. After a time, however, the gods became wiser than the giants, or they would have ceased to be gods and been destroyed by the giants instead of destroying them. When the world was still young, and there were still many things which even the gods had to learn, Odin was so anxious to become wise that he went to a deep well whose waters touched the roots of Ygdrasil itself. The keeper of the well was a very old and very wise giant, named Mimir, or Memory, and he gave no draughts out of the well until he was well paid; for the well contained the water of wisdom, and whoever drank of it became straightway wonderfully wise.

"Give me a draught of this clear water, O Mimir," said Odin, when he had reached the well and was looking down into its clear, fathomless depths.

Mimir, the keeper, was so old that he could remember everything that had ever happened. His eyes were clear and calm as the stars, his face was noble and restful, and his long white beard flowed down to his waist.

"This water is only to be had at a great price," he said in a wonderfully sweet, majestic tone. "I cannot give to all who ask, but only to those who are able and willing to give greatly in return," he continued.

If Odin had been less of a god he would have thought longer and bargained sharper, but he was so godlike that he cared more to be wise and great than anything else.

"I will give you whatever you ask," he answered.

Mimir thought a moment. "You must leave an eye," he said at last.

Then he drew up a great draught of the sparkling water, and Odin quenched his divine thirst and went away rejoicing, although he had left an eye behind. Even the gods could not be wise without struggle and toil and sacrifice.

So Odin became the wisest in all the worlds, and there was no god or giant that could contend with him. There was one giant, however, who was called all-wise in Jotunheim, with whom many had contended in knowledge, with curious and difficult questions, and had always been silenced and killed, for then, as now, a man's life often depended on his wisdom. Of this giant, Vafthrudner, and his wisdom many wonderful stories were told, and even among the gods his fame was great. One day as Odin sat thinking of many strange things in the worlds, and many mysterious things in the future, he thought of Vafthrudner. "I will go to Jotunheim and measure wisdom with Vafthrudner, the wisest of the giants," said he to Frigga, his wife, who was sitting by.

Then Frigga remembered those who had gone to contend with the all-wise giant and had never come back, and a fear came over her that the same fate might befall Odin.

"You are wisest in all the worlds, All-Father," she said. "Why should you seek a treacherous giant who knows not half so much as you?"

But Odin, who feared nothing, could not be persuaded to stay, and Frigga sadly said good-by as he passed out of Asgard on his journey to Jotunheim. His blue mantle set with stars and his golden helmet he left behind him, and as he journeyed swiftly those who met him saw nothing godlike in him; nor did Vafthrudner when at last he stood at the giant's door.

"I am a simple traveler, Gangraad by name," he said as Vafthrudner came gruffly toward him. "I ask your hospitality and a chance to strive with you in wisdom." The giant laughed scornfully at the thought of a man coming to contend with him for mastery in knowledge.

"You shall have all you want of both," he growled, "and if you cannot answer my questions you shall never go hence alive."

He did not even ask Odin to sit down, but let him stand in the hall, despising him too much to show him any courtesy. After a time he began to ask questions.

"Tell me, if you can, O wise Gangraad, the name of the river which divides Asgard from Jotunheim."

"The river Ifing, which never freezes over," answered Odin quickly, as if it were the easiest question in the world; and indeed it was to him, although no man could have answered it. Vafthrudner looked up in great surprise when he heard the reply.

"Good," he said, "you have answered rightly. Tell me, now, the names of the horses that carry day and night across the sky."

Before the words were fairly spoken Odin replied, "Skinfaxe and Hrimfaxe." The giant could not conceal his surprise that a man should know these things.

"Once more," he said quickly, as if he were risking everything on one question; "tell me the name of the plain where the Last Battle will be fought."

This was a terrible question, for the Last Battle was still far off in the future, and only the gods and the greatest of the giants knew where and when it would come. Odin bowed his head when he heard the words, for to be ready for that battle was the divine work of his life, and then said, slowly and solemnly, "On the plain of Vigard, which is one hundred miles on each side."

Vafthrudner rose trembling from his seat. He knew now that Gangraad was some great one in disguise, and that his own life hung on the answers he himself would soon be forced to make.

"Sit here beside me," he said, "for, whoever you are, worthier antagonist has never entered these walls."

Then they sat down together in the rude stone hall, the mightiest of the gods and the wisest of the giants, and the great contest in wisdom, with a life hanging in either scale, went on between them. Wonderful secrets of the time when no man was and the time when no man will be, those silent walls listened to as Vafthrudner asked Odin one deep question after another, the answer coming swiftly and surely.

After a time the giant could ask no more, for he had exhausted his wisdom.

"It is my turn now," said Odin, and one after another he drew out from Vafthrudner the events of the past, then the wonderful things of the race of giants, and finally he began to question him of that dim, mysterious future whose secrets only the gods know; and as he touched these wonderful things Odin's eyes began to flash, and his form to grow larger and nobler, until he seemed no longer the humble Gangraad but the mighty god he was, and Vafthrudner trembled as he felt the coming doom nearing him with every question.

So hours went by, until at last Odin paused in his swift questioning, stooped down, and asked the giant, "What did Odin whisper in the ear of Baldur as he ascended the funeral pile?"

Only Odin himself could answer this question, and Vafthrudner replied humbly and with awe, "Who but thyself, All-Father, knoweth the words thou didst say to thy son in the days of old? I have brought my doom upon myself, for in my ignorance I have contended with wisdom itself. Thou art ever the wisest of all."

So Odin conquered, and wisdom was victorious, as she always has been even when she has contended with giants.

From *Norse Stories*, retold from the Eddas by Hamilton Wright Mabie (Boston: Roberts Brothers, 1882).

THE MAKING OF THE HAMMER

ONE DAY as Sif, Thor's beautiful wife, was sitting in the palace Bilskirner in Thrudvang, or Thunder-world, she fell asleep, with her long hair falling about her shoulders like a shower of gold. She made a very pretty picture as she sat there in the sunlight; at least Loki thought so as he passed by and saw her motionless, like the statue of a goddess in a great temple, instead of a living goddess in her own palace. Loki never saw anything beautiful without the wish that somehow he might spoil it; and when he noticed that Sif was asleep he thought it was a good time to carry off her golden hair, and so rob her of that which Thor was most proud. As noiselessly as he could, and more like a thief than a god, he stole into the palace, cut off the golden locks and carried them away, without leaving one behind as a trace of his evil deed. When Sif awoke and found her beautiful hair gone, she went and hid herself, lest Thor coming home should miss the beauty which had always been like light to his eyes.

And presently Thor came; but no Sif was there to meet him, making him forget with one proud look from her tender eyes the dangers and labors of his life. She had never failed to greet him at the threshold before; and the strong god's heart, which had never beat a second quicker at sight of the greatest giant in the world, grew faint with fear that in his absence some mishap had befallen her. He ran quickly from room to room in the palace, and at last he came upon Sif, hidden behind a pillar, her shorn head bowed, weeping bitterly. In a few broken words she told Thor what had happened, and as she went on, Thor's wrath grew hotter and hotter until he was terrible to behold. Lightnings flashed out of his deep-set eyes, the palace trembled under his angry strides, and it seemed as if his fury would burst forth like some awful tempest uprooting and destroying everything in its path.

"I know who did it," he shouted when Sif had ended her story. "It was that rascally Loki, and I'll break every bone in his thievish body"; and without as much as saying good-by to his sobbing wife, he strode off like a thundercloud to Asgard, and there, coming suddenly upon Loki, he seized him by the neck and would have killed him on the spot had not Loki confessed his deed and promised to restore the golden hair.

"I'll get the swarthy elves to make a crown of golden hair for Sif more beautiful than she used to wear," gasped Loki, in the iron grasp of the angry Thor; and Thor, who cared more for Sif's beauty than for Loki's punishment, let the thief go, having bound him by solemn pledges to fulfill his promise without delay.

Loki lost no time, but went far underground to the gloomy smithy of the dwarfs, who were called Ivald's sons, and who were wonderful workers in gold and brass.

"Make me a crown of golden hair," said Loki, "that will grow like any other hair, and I will give you whatever you want for your work."

The bargain was quickly made, and the busy little dwarfs were soon at their task, and in a little time they had done all that Loki asked, and more too; for in addition to the shining hair they gave Loki the spear Gungner and the famous ship Skidbladner.

With these treasures in his arms Loki came into Asgard and began boasting of the wonderful things he had brought from the smithy of Ivald's sons. "Nobody like the sons of Ivald to work in metal!" he said. "The other dwarfs are all stupid little knaves compared with them."

Now it happened that the dwarf Brok was standing by and heard Loki's boasting; his brother Sindre was so cunning a workman that most of the dwarfs thought him by far the best in the world. It made Brok angry, therefore, to hear the sons of Ivald called the best workmen, and he spoke up and said, "My brother Sindre can make more wonderful things of gold and iron and brass than ever the sons of Ivald thought of."

"Your brother Sindre," repeated Loki scornfully. "Who is your brother Sindre?"

"The best workman in the world," answered Brok.

Loki laughed loud and long. "Go to your wonderful brother Sindre," said he, "and tell him if he can make three such precious things as the spear, the ship, and the golden hair, he shall have my head for his trouble." And Loki laughed longer and louder than before.

Brok was off to the underworld before the laugh died out of his ears, determined to have Loki's head if magic and hard work could do it. He went straight to Sindre and told him of the wager he had laid with Loki, and in a little while Sindre was hard at work in his smithy. It was a queer place for such wonderful work as was done in it, for it was nothing but a great cavern underground, with tools piled up in little heaps around its sides, and thick darkness everywhere when the furnace fire was not sending its glow out into the blackness. If you had looked in now, you would have seen a broad glare of light streaming out from the furnace, for Brok was blowing the bellows with all his might, and the coals were fairly blazing with heat. When all was ready Sindre took a swine skin, put it into the furnace, and, telling Brok to blow the bellows until his return, went out of the smithy. Brok kept steadily at work, although a gadfly flew in, buzzed noisily about, and, finally settling on his hand, stung him so that he could hardly bear it. After a while Sindre came back and took out of the furnace a wonderful boar with bristles of pure gold.

Then Sindre took some gold, and, placing it in the furnace, bade Brok blow as if his life depended on it, and went out a second time. Brok had no sooner begun blowing than the troublesome gadfly came back and, fastening upon his neck, stung him so fiercely that he could hardly keep his hands away from his neck; but Brok was a faithful dwarf, who meant to do his work thoroughly if he died for it, and so he blew away as if it were the easiest thing in the world, until Sindre came back and took a shining ring from the fire. The third time Sindre put iron into the fire and, bidding Brok blow without ceasing, went out again. No sooner had he gone than the gadfly flew in and, settling between Brok's eyes, stung him so sharply that drops of blood ran down into his eyes, and he could not see what he was doing. He blew away as bravely as he could for some time, but the pain was so keen, and he was so blind, that at last he raised his hand quickly to brush the fly away. That very instant Sindre returned.

"You have almost spoiled it," he said as he took out of the glowing furnace the wonderful hammer Mjolner. "See how short you have made the handle! But you can't lengthen it now. So carry the gifts to Asgard, and bring me Loki's head."

Brok started off with the golden boar, the shining ring, and the terrible hammer.

When he came through the great gate of Asgard the gods were very anxious to see the end of this strange contest, and, taking their seats on their shining thrones, they appointed Odin, Thor, and Freya to judge between Loki and Brok, as to which had the most wonderful things. Then Loki brought out the spear Gungner, which never misses its mark, and gave it to Odin; and the golden hair he gave to Thor, who placed it on Sif's head, and straightway it began to grow like any other hair, and Sif was as beautiful as on the day when Loki saw her in Thor's palace and robbed her of her tresses; and to Freya he gave the marvelous ship Skidbladner, which always found a breeze to drive it wherever its master would go, no matter how the sea was running or from what quarter the wind was blowing, and which could be folded up and carried in one's pocket.

Then Loki laughed scornfully. "Bring out the trinkets which that wonderful brother of yours has made," he said.

Brok came forward and stood before the wondering gods with his treasures.

"This ring," said he, handing it to Odin, "will cast off, every ninth night, eight other rings as pure and heavy as itself. This boar," giving it to Freya, "will run more swiftly in the air, and on the sea, by night or by day, than the swiftest horse, and no night will be so dark, no world so gloomy, that the shining of these bristles shall not make it light as noonday. And this hammer," placing Mjolner in Thor's strong hands, "shall never fail, no matter how big nor how hard that which it smites may be; no matter how far it is thrown, it will always return to your hand; you may make it so small that it can be hidden in your bosom, and its only fault is the shortness of its handle."

Thor swung it round his head, and lightning flashed and flamed through Asgard, deep peals of thunder rolled through the sky, and mighty masses of cloud piled quickly up around him. The gods gathered around and passed the hammer from one to the other, saying that it would be their greatest protection against their enemies, and frost-giants, who were always trying to force their way into Asgard, and they declared that Brok had won the wager. Brok's swarthy little face was as bright as his brother's furnace fire, so delighted was he to have beaten the boastful Loki. But how was he to get his wager, now he had won it? It was no easy matter to take the head off a god's shoulders. Brok thought a moment. "I will take Loki's head," he said finally, thinking some of the other gods might help him.

"I will give you whatever you want in place of my head," growled Loki, angry that he was beaten and having no idea of paying his wager by losing his head.

"I will have your head or I will have nothing," answered the plucky little dwarf, determined not to be cheated out of his victory.

"Well, then, take it," shouted Loki; but by the time Brok reached the place where he had been standing, Loki was far away, for he wore shoes with which he could run through the air or over the water. Then Brok asked Thor to find Loki and bring him back, which Thor did promptly, for the gods always saw to it that people kept their promises. When Loki was brought back Brok wanted to cut his head off at once.

"You may cut off my head, but you have no right to touch my neck," said Loki, who was cunning as well as wicked. That was true, and of course the head could not be taken off without touching the neck, so Brok had to give it up.

But he determined to do something to make Loki feel that he had won his wager, so he took an awl and a thong and sewed his lips together so tightly that he could make no more boastings.

From *Norse Stories.*

HOW THOR FOUND HIS HAMMER

THE FROST-GIANTS were always trying to get into Asgard. For more than half the year they held the world in their grasp, locking up the streams in their rocky beds, hushing their music and the music of the birds as well, and leaving nothing but a wild waste of desolation under the cold sky. They hated the warm sunshine which stirred the wild flowers out of their sleep, and clothed the steep mountains with verdure, and set all the birds a-singing in the swaying treetops. They hated the beautiful god Baldur, with whose presence summer came back to the icebound earth, and, above all, they hated

Thor, whose flashing hammer drove them back into Jotunheim, and guarded the summer sky with its sudden gleamings of power. So long as Thor had his hammmer Asgard was safe against the giants.

One morning Thor started up out of a long, deep sleep and put out his hand for the hammer; but no hammer was there. Not a sign of it could be found anywhere, although Thor anxiously searched for it. Then a thought of the giants came suddenly in his mind; and his anger rose till his eyes flashed like great fires and his red beard trembled with wrath.

"Look, now, Loki," he shouted, "they have stolen Mjolner by enchantment, and no one on earth or in heaven knows where they have hidden it."

"We will get Freya's falcon-guise and search for it," answered Loki, who was always quick to get into trouble or to get out of it again. So they went quickly to Folkvang and found Freya surrounded by her maidens and weeping tears of pure gold, as she had always done since her husband went on his long journey.

"The hammer has been stolen by enchantment," said Thor. "Will you lend me the falcon-guise that I may search for it?"

"If it were silver, or even gold, you should have it and welcome," answered Freya, glad to help Thor find the wonderful hammer that kept them all safe from the hands of the frost-giants.

So the falcon-guise was brought, and Loki put it on and flew swiftly out of Asgard to the home of the giants. His great wings made broad shadows over the ripe fields as he swept along, and the reapers, looking up from their work, wondered what mighty bird was flying seaward. At last he reached Jotunheim, and no sooner had he touched ground and taken off the falcon-guise than he came upon the giant Thrym, sitting on a hill, twisting golden collars for his dogs and stroking the long manes of his horses.

"Welcome, Loki," said the giant. "How fares it with the gods and the elves, and what has brought you to Jotunheim?"

"It fares ill with both gods and elves since you stole Thor's hammer," replied Loki, guessing quickly that Thrym was the thief; "and I have come to find where you have hidden it."

Thrym laughed as only a giant can when he knows he has made trouble for somebody.

"You won't find it," he said at last. "I have buried it eight miles under ground, and no one shall take it away unless he gets Freya for me as my wife."

The giant looked as if he meant what he said, and Loki, seeing no other way of finding the hammer, put on his falcon-guise and flew back to Asgard. Thor was waiting to hear what news he brought, and both were soon at the great doors of Folkvang.

"Put on your bridal dress, Freya," said Thor bluntly after his fashion, "and we will ride swiftly to Jotunheim."

But Freya had no idea of marrying a giant just to please Thor; and, in fact, that Thor should ask her to do such a thing threw her into such a rage that the floor shook under her angry tread and her necklace snapped in pieces.

"Do you think I am a weak lovesick girl, to follow you to Jotunheim and marry Thrym?" she cried indignantly.

Finding they could do nothing with Freya, Thor and Loki called all the gods together to talk over the matter and decide what should be done to get back the hammer. The gods were very much alarmed, because they knew the frost-giants would come upon Asgard as soon as they knew the hammer was gone. They said little, for they did not waste time with idle words, but they thought long and earnestly, and still they could find no way of getting hold of Mjolner once more. At last Heimdal, who had once been a Van, and could therefore look into the future, said, "We must have the hammer at once or Asgard will be in danger. If Freya will not go, let Thor be dressed up and go in her place. Let keys jingle from his waist and a woman's dress fall about his feet. Put precious stones upon his breast, braid his hair like a woman's, hang the necklace around his neck, and bind the bridal veil around his head."

Thor frowned angrily. "If I dress like a woman," he said, "you will jeer at me."

"Don't talk of jeers," retorted Loki; "unless that hammer is brought back quickly the giants will rule in our places."

Thor said no more, but allowed himself to be dressed like a bride, and soon drove off to Jotunheim with Loki beside him disguised as a servant-maid. There was never such a wedding journey before. They rode in Thor's chariot, and the goats drew them, plunging swiftly along the way, thunder pealing through the mountains, and the frightened earth blazing and smoking as they passed. When Thrym saw the bridal party coming he was filled with delight.

"Stand up, you giants," he shouted to his companions. "Spread cushions upon the benches and bring in Freya, my bride. My yards are full of golden-horned cows, black oxen please my gaze whichever way I look, great wealth and many treasures are mine, and Freya is all I lack."

It was evening when the bride came driving into the giant's court in her blazing chariot. The feast was already spread against her coming, and with her veil modestly covering her face she was seated at the great table, Thrym fairly beside himself with delight. It wasn't every giant who could marry a goddess!

If the bridal journey had been so strange that anyone but a foolish giant would have hesitated to marry a wife who came in such a turmoil of fire and storm, her conduct at the table ought certainly to have put Thrym on his guard; for never had bride such an appetite before. The great tables groaned under the load of good things, but

they were quickly relieved of their burden by the voracious bride. She ate a whole ox before the astonished giant had fairly begun to enjoy his meal. Then she devoured eight large salmon, one after the other, without stopping to take breath; and having eaten up the part of the feast specially prepared for the hungry men, she turned upon the delicacies which had been made for the women, and especially for her own fastidious appetite.

Thrym looked on with wondering eyes, and at last, when she had added to these solid foods three whole barrels of mead, his amazement was so great that, his astonishment getting the better of his politeness, he called out, "Did anyone ever see such an appetite in a bride before, or know a maid who could drink so much mead?"

Then Loki, who was playing the part of a serving-maid, thinking that the giant might have some suspicions, whispered to him, "Freya was so happy in the thought of coming here that she has eaten nothing for eight whole days."

Thrym was so pleased at this evidence of affection that he leaned forward and raised the veil as gently as a giant could, but he instantly dropped it and sprang back the whole length of the hall before the bride's terrible eyes.

"Why are Freya's eyes so sharp?" he called to Loki. "They burn me like fire."

"Oh," said the cunning serving-maid, "she has not slept for a week, so anxious has she been to come here, and that is why her eyes are so fiery."

Everybody looked at the bride, and nobody envied Thrym. They thought it was too much like marrying a thunderstorm.

The giant's sister came into the hall just then and, seeing the veiled form of the bride sitting there, went up to her and asked for a bridal gift. "If you would have my love and friendship, give me those rings of gold upon your fingers."

But the bride sat perfectly silent. No one had yet seen her face or heard her voice.

Thrym became very impatient. "Bring in the hammer," he shouted, "that the bride may be consecrated, and wed us in the name of Var."

If the giant could have seen the bride's eyes when she heard these words he would have sent her home as quickly as possible and looked somewhere else for a wife.

The hammer was brought and placed in the bride's lap, and everybody looked to see the marriage ceremony; but the wedding was more strange and terrible than the bridal journey had been. No sooner did the bride's fingers close round the handle of Mjolner than the veil which covered her face was torn off and there stood Thor, the giant-queller, his terrible eyes blazing with wrath. The giants shuddered and shrank away from those flaming eyes, the sight of which they dreaded more than anything else in all the worlds; but there was no chance of escape. Thor swung the hammer round his head, and the great house rocked on its foundations. There was a vivid flash of lightning, an awful crash of thunder, and the burning roof and walls buried the whole company in one common ruin.

Thrym was punished for stealing the hammer, his wedding guests got crushing blows instead of bridal gifts, and Thor and Loki went back to Asgard, where the presence of Mjolner made the gods safe once more.

From *Norse Stories.*

THE ARCHER AND THE KING

NOR IS the following story to be wrapped in silence. A certain Palnatoki, for some time among King Harold's bodyguard, had made his bravery odious to very many of his fellow soldiers by the zeal with which he surpassed them in the discharge of his duty. This man, talking tipsily over his cups, boasted that he was so skilled an archer that at the first shot he could hit the smallest apple placed a long way off on a wand.

This talk, caught up by the ears of backbiters, soon came to the hearing of the king. Now mark how wickedly the king turned Palnatoki's confidence into a trial that imperiled the life of the soldier's son. The king commanded that the son, that dearest pledge of Palnatoki's life, should be used instead of the wand, with a threat that, unless Palnatoki could strike off the apple at the first flight of the arrow, he should pay the penalty of his boasting by the loss of his head.

Palnatoki's sterling courage, though caught in the snare of slander, did not suffer him to lay aside his firmness of heart; nay, he accepted the trial the more readily because it was hard. So Palnatoki warned the boy urgently when he took his stand to await the coming of the hurtling arrow with calm bearing and unbent head, lest by a slight turn of his body he should defeat the practiced skill of the bowman. Taking a further step to prevent fear, the boy turned away his face, lest he should be scared at the sight of the weapon. Then Palnatoki took three arrows from the quiver; but struck the mark with the first he fitted to the string.

When asked by the king why he had taken more than one arrow from the quiver, after it had been settled that he should only try the fortune of the bow *once,* Palnatoki made answer, "That I might avenge on thee any swerving of the first by the points of the rest, lest my innocence might have been punished while your violence escaped scot-free."

From a story in the *Gesta Danorum* of Saxo Grammaticus, translated by Sir George Webbe Dasent in his introduction to *Popular Tales from the Norse.*

WHY THE SEA IS SALT

ONCE on a time, but it was a long, long time ago, there were two brothers, one rich and one poor. Now, one Christmas eve, the poor one hadn't so much as a crumb in the house, either of meat or bread, so he went to his brother to ask him for something to keep Christmas with, in God's name. It was not the first time his brother had been forced to help him, and you may fancy he wasn't very glad to see his face, but he said, "If you will do what I ask you to do, I'll give you a whole flitch of bacon."

So the poor brother said he would do anything, and was full of thanks.

"Well, here is the flitch," said the rich brother, "and now go straight to hell."

"What I have given my word to do, I must stick to," said the other; so he took the flitch and set off. He walked the whole day, and at dusk he came to a place where he saw a very bright light.

"Maybe this is the place," said the man to himself. So he turned aside, and the first thing he saw was an old, old man, with a long white beard, who stood in a woodshed, hewing wood for the Christmas fire.

"Good even," said the man with the flitch.

"The same to you. Whither are you going so late?" said the man.

"Oh, I'm going to hell, if I only knew the right way," answered the poor man.

"Well, you're not far wrong, for this is hell," said the old man. "When you get inside they will be all for buying your flitch, for meat is scarce in hell; but mind you don't sell it unless you get the hand-quern which stands behind the door for it. When you come out, I'll teach you how to handle the quern, for it's good to grind almost anything."

So the man with the flitch thanked the other for his good advice, and gave a great knock at the Devil's door.

When he got in, everything went just as the old man had said. All the devils, great and small, came swarming up to him like ants round an anthill, and each tried to outbid the other for the flitch.

"Well," said the man, "by rights my old dame and I ought to have this flitch for our Christmas dinner; but since you have all set your hearts on it, I suppose I must give it up to you; but if I sell it at all, I'll have for it that quern behind the door yonder."

At first the Devil wouldn't hear of such a bargain and chaffered and haggled with the man; but he stuck to what he said, and at last the devil had to part with his quern. When the man got out into the yard, he asked the old woodcutter how he was to handle the quern; and after he had learned how to use it, he thanked the old man and went off home as fast as he could, but still the clock had struck twelve on Christmas eve before he reached his own door.

"Wherever in the world have you been?" said his old dame. "Here have I sat hour after hour, waiting and watching, without so much as two sticks to lay together under the Christmas brose."

"Oh," said the man, "I couldn't get back before, for I had to go a long way first for one thing, and then for another; but now you shall see what you shall see."

So he put the quern on the table and bade it first of all grind lights, then a tablecloth, then meat, then ale, and so on, till they had got everything that was nice for Christmas fare. He had only to speak the word, and the quern ground out what he wanted. The old dame stood by blessing her stars, and kept on asking where he had got this wonderful quern, but he wouldn't tell her.

"It's all one where I got it from; you see the quern is a good one, and the millstream never freezes, that's enough."

So he ground meat and drink and dainties enough to last out till Twelfth Day, and on the third day he asked all his friends and kin to his house, and gave a great feast. Now when his rich brother saw all that was on the table, and all that was behind in the larder, he grew quite spiteful and wild, for he couldn't bear that his brother should have anything.

" 'Twas only on Christmas eve," he said to the rest, "he was in such straits that he came and asked for a morsel of food in God's name, and now he gives a feast as if he were count or king." And he turned to his brother and said, "But whence, in hell's name, have you got all this wealth?"

"From behind the door," answered the owner of the quern, for he didn't care to let the cat out of the bag. But later on in the evening, when he had got a drop too much, he could keep his secret no longer, and brought out the quern, and said, "There, you see what has gotten me all this wealth!" And so he made the quern grind all kinds of things. When his brother saw it, he set his heart on having the quern, and, after a deal of coaxing, he got it; but he had to pay three hundred dollars for it, and his brother bargained to keep it till hay harvest, "for," he thought, "if I keep it till then, I can make it grind meat and drink that will last for years." So you may fancy the quern didn't grow rusty for want of work, and when hay harvest came the rich brother got it, but the other took care not to teach him how to handle it.

It was evening when the rich brother got the quern home, and next morning he told his wife to go out into the hayfield and toss, while the mowers cut the grass, and he would stay at home and get the dinner ready. So, when dinner time drew near, he put the quern on the kitchen table and said, "Grind herrings and broth, and grind them good and fast."

So the quern began to grind herrings and broth; first of all, all the dishes full, then all the tubs full, and so on till the kitchen floor was quite covered. Then the man twisted and twirled at the quern to get it to stop, but for all his twisting and fingering the quern went on grinding, and in a little while the broth rose so high that the man was like to drown. So he threw open the kitchen door and ran into the parlor, but it wasn't long before the quern had ground the parlor full too, and it was only at the risk of his life that the man could get hold of the latch of the house door through the stream of broth. When he got the door open, he ran out and set off down the road, with the stream of herrings and broth at his heels, roaring like a waterfall over the whole farm.

Now his old dame, who was in the field tossing hay, thought it a long time to dinner, and at last she said, "Well, though the master doesn't call us home, we may as well go. Maybe he finds it hard work to boil the broth and will be glad of my help."

The men were willing enough, so they sauntered homeward; but just as they had got a little way up the hill, what should they meet but herrings, and broth, and bread, all running and dashing and splashing together in a stream, and the master himself running before them for his life, and as he passed them he bawled out, "Would to heaven each of you had a hundred throats! But take care you're not drowned in the broth."

Away he went, as though the Evil One were at his heels, to his brother's house, and begged him, for God's sake, take back the quern that instant; for, said he, "If it grinds only one hour more, the whole parish will be swallowed up by herrings and broth."

But his brother wouldn't hear of taking it back till the other paid him down three hundred dollars more.

So the poor brother got both the money and the quern, and it wasn't long before he set up a farmhouse far finer than the one in which his brother lived, and with the quern he ground so much gold that he covered it with plates of gold; and as the farm lay by the seaside, the golden house gleamed and glistened far away over the sea. All who sailed by put ashore to see the rich man in the golden house, and to see the wonderful quern, the fame of which spread far and wide, till there was nobody who hadn't heard tell of it.

So one day there came a skipper who wanted to see the quern; and the first thing he asked was if it could grind salt.

"Grind salt!" said the owner. "I should just think it could. It can grind anything."

When the skipper heard that, he said he must have the quern, cost what it would; for if he only had it, he thought he should be rid of his long voyages across stormy seas for a lading of salt.

Well, at first the man wouldn't hear of parting with the quern; but the skipper begged and prayed so hard that at last he let him have it, but he had to pay many, many thousand dollars for it. Now when the skipper had got the quern on his back, he soon made off with it, for he was afraid lest the man should change his mind; so he had no time to ask how to handle the quern, but got on board his ship as fast as he could and set sail.

When he had sailed a good way off he brought the quern on deck and said, "Grind salt, and grind both good and fast."

Well, the quern began to grind salt so that it poured out like water; and when the skipper had got the ship full, he wished to stop the quern, but whichever way he turned it, and however much he tried, it was no good; the quern kept grinding on, and the heap of salt grew higher and higher, and at last down sunk the ship.

There lies the quern at the bottom of the sea, and grinds away at this very day, and that's why the sea is salt.

From *Popular Tales from the Norse,* a translation by Sir George Webbe Dasent of tales collected by Peter Asbjörnsen and Jörgen Moe.

THE MASTER THIEF

ONCE upon a time there was a poor cottager who had three sons. He had nothing to leave them when he died, and no money with which to put them to any trade, so that he did not know what to make of them. At last he said he would give them leave to take to anything each liked best, and to go whithersoever they pleased, and he would go with them a bit of the way; and so he did. He went with them till they came to a place where three roads met, and there each of them chose a road, and their father bade them good-by, and went back home. I have never heard tell what became of the two elder; but as for the youngest, he went both far and long, as you shall hear.

So it fell out one night as he was going through a great wood that bad weather overtook him. It blew and sleeted and drove so that he could scarce keep his eyes open; and in a trice, before he knew how it was, he got bewildered and could not find either road or path. But he went on and on, and at last he saw a glimmering of light far, far off in the wood. So he thought he would try and get to the light; and after a time he did reach it. There it was, in a large house, and the fire was blazing so brightly inside that he could tell the folk had not yet gone to bed; so he went in and saw an old dame bustling about and minding the house.

"Good evening!" said the youth.

"Good evening!" said the old dame.

"Hutetu! it's such foul weather out of doors tonight," said he.

"So it is," said she.

"Can I get leave to have a bed and shelter here tonight?" asked the youth.

"You'll get no good by sleeping here," said the old dame; "for if the folk come home and find you here, they'll kill both me and you."

"What sort of folk, then, are they who live here?"

"Oh, robbers! And a bad lot of them too," said the old dame. "They stole me away when I was little and have kept me as their housekeeper ever since."

"Well, for all that, I think I'll just go to bed," said the youth. "Come what may, I'll not stir out at night in such weather."

"Very well," said the old dame; "but if you stay it will be the worse for you."

With that the youth got into a bed which stood there, but he dared not go to sleep, and very soon after in came the robbers; so the old dame told them how a strange fellow had come in whom she had not been able to get out of the house again.

"Did you see if he had any money?" said the robbers.

"Such a one as he—money!" said the old dame. "The tramper! Why, if he had clothes to his back it was as much as he had."

Then the robbers began to talk among themselves what they should do with him—if they should kill him outright, or what else they should do. Meantime the youth got up and began to talk to them, and to ask if they didn't want a servant, for it might be that he would be glad to enter their service.

"Oh," said they, "if you have a mind to follow the trade that we follow, you can very well get a place here."

"It's all one to me what trade I follow," said the youth; "for when I left home father gave me leave to take to any trade I chose."

"Well, have you a mind to steal?" asked the robbers.

"I don't care," said the youth, for he thought it would not take long to learn that trade.

Now there lived a man a little way off who had three oxen. One of these he was to take to the town to sell, and the robbers had heard what he was going to do, so they said to the youth that if he were good enough to steal the ox from the man without his knowing it and without doing him any harm, they would give him leave to be their serving-man.

Well, the youth set off, and took with him a pretty shoe with a silver buckle on it; and he put the shoe in the road along which the man was going with his ox; and when he had done that, he went into the wood and hid himself under a bush. So when the man came by he saw the shoe at once.

"That's a nice shoe," said he. "If I only had the fellow to it, I'd take it home with me, and perhaps I'd put my old dame in a good humor for once." For you must know he had an old wife, so cross and snappish it was not long between each time that she boxed his ears. But then he bethought him that he could do nothing with the odd shoe unless he had the fellow to it; so he went on his way and let the shoe lie on the road.

Then the youth took up the shoe, and made all the haste he could to get before the man by a short cut through the wood, and laid it down before him in the road again. When the man came along with his ox, he got quite angry with himself for being so dull as to leave the fellow to the shoe lying in the road instead of taking it with him; so he tied the ox to the fence and said to himself, "I may just as well run back and pick up the other, and then I'll have a pair of good shoes for my old dame, and so, perhaps, I'll get a kind word from her for once."

So he set off, and hunted and hunted up and down for the shoe, but no shoe did he find; and at length he had to go back with the one he had. But, meanwhile, the youth had taken the ox and gone off with it; and when the man came and saw his ox gone, he began to cry and wail, for he was afraid his old dame would kill him outright when she came to know that the ox was lost. But just then it came to him that he would go home, take the second ox and drive it to town, and not let his old dame know anything about the matter. So he did this, and went home and took the ox without his dame's knowing it, and set off with it to the town. But the robbers knew all about it, and they said to the youth that if he could get this ox too, without the man's knowing it and without his doing him any harm, he should be as good as any one of them. If that were all, the youth said, he did not think it a very hard thing.

This time he took with him a rope and hung himself up under the armpits to a tree right in the man's way. So the man came along with his ox, and when he saw such a sight hanging there he began to feel a little queer.

"Well," said he, "whatever heavy thoughts you had who have hanged yourself up there, it can't be helped; you may hang for what I care! I can't breathe life into you again." And with that he went on his way with his ox. Down slipped the youth from the tree, and ran by a footpath, and got before the man, and hung himself up right in his way again.

"Bless me!" said the man, "were you really so heavy at heart that you hanged yourself up there—or is it only a piece of witchcraft that I see before me? Ay, ay! you may hang for all I care, whether you are a ghost, or whatever you are." So he passed on with his ox.

Now the youth did just as he had done twice before; he jumped down from the tree, ran through the wood by a footpath, and hung himself up right in the man's way again. But when the man saw this sight for the third time, he said to himself, "Well, this is an ugly business! Is it likely now that they should have been so heavy at heart as to hang themselves, all these three? No! I cannot think it is

anything else but a piece of witchcraft that I see. But now I'll soon know for certain; if the other two are still hanging there, it must be really so; but if they are not, then it can be nothing but witchcraft."

So he tied up his ox and ran back to see if the others were still really hanging there. But while he went and peered up into all the trees, the youth jumped down and took his ox and ran off with it. When the man came back and found his ox gone, he was in a sad plight, and, as anyone might know without being told, he began to cry and bemoan; but at last he began to take it easier, and so he thought, "There's no other help for it than to go home and take the third ox without my dame's knowing it, and to try and drive a good bargain with it, so that I may get a good sum of money for it."

So he went home and set off with the ox, and his old dame knew never a word about the matter. But the robbers knew all about it, and they said to the youth that if he could steal this ox as he had stolen the other two, then he should be master over the whole band. Well, the youth set off and ran into the wood; and as the man came by with his ox he set up a dreadful bellowing, just like a great ox in the wood. When the man heard that, you can't imagine how glad he was, for it seemed to him that he knew the voice of his big bullock, and he thought that now he should find both of them again; so he tied up the third ox and ran off from the road to look for them in the wood; but meantime the youth went off with the third ox. Now, when the man came back and found he had lost this ox too, he was so wild that there was no end to his grief. He cried and roared and beat his breast, and, to tell the truth, it was many days before he dared go home; for he was afraid lest his old dame should kill him on the spot.

As for the robbers, they were not very well pleased either when they had to own that the youth was master over the whole band. So one day they thought they would try their hands at something which he was not man enough to do; and they set off all together, every man Jack of them, and left him alone at home. Now the first thing that he did when they were all well clear of the house was to drive the oxen out to the road, so that they might run back to the man from whom he had stolen them; and right glad the man was to see them, as you may fancy. Next he took all the horses which the robbers had and loaded them with the best things he could lay his hands on—gold and silver and clothes and other fine things; and then he bade the old dame greet the robbers when they came back, and thank them for him, and say that now he was setting off on his travels and they would have hard work to find him again; and with that, off he started.

After a good bit he came to the road along which he had been going when he had fallen among the robbers, and when he got near home, and could see his father's cottage, he put on a uniform which he had found among the clothes he had taken from the robbers, and which was made just like a general's. So he drove up to the door as if he were any other great man. After that he went in and asked if he could have a lodging. No—that he couldn't at any price.

"However should I be able," said the man, "to make room in my house for such a fine gentleman—I who scarce have a rag to lie upon, and miserable rags too."

"You always were a stingy old hunks," said the youth, "and so you are still, when you won't take your own son in."

"What, you my son!" said the man.

"Don't you know me again?" said the youth. Well, after a little while he did know him again.

"But what have you been turning your hand to, that you have made yourself so great a man in such haste?" asked the man.

"Oh, I'll soon tell you," said the youth. "You said I might take to any trade I chose, and so I bound myself apprentice to a pack of thieves and robbers, and now I've served my time out, and am become a master thief."

Now there lived a squire close by to his father's cottage, and he had such a great house, and such heaps of money, he could not tell how much he had. He had a daughter too, and a smart and pretty girl she was. So the master thief set his heart upon having her to wife, and he told his father to go to the squire and ask for his daughter for him.

"If he asks by what trade I get my living, you can say I'm a master thief."

"I think you've lost your wits," said the man, "for you can't be in your right mind when you think of such stuff."

No, he had not lost his wits; his father must and should go to the squire and ask for his daughter. But his father was still loath to go; so he stepped after him, and rubbed him down with a good birch cudgel, and kept on till the man went crying and sobbing to the squire's door.

"How now, my man! what ails you?" said the squire.

So he told him the whole story; how he had three sons who set off one day, and how he had given them leave to follow whatever calling they chose. "And here now is the youngest come home, and has thrashed me till he has made me come to you and ask for your daughter for him to wife; and he bids me say, besides, that he's a master thief." And so he fell to crying and sobbing again.

"Never mind, my man," said the squire, laughing; "just go back and tell him from me he must prove his skill first. If he can steal the roast from the spit in the kitchen on Sunday, when all the household are looking after it, he shall have my daughter. Just go and tell him that."

So he went back and told the youth, who thought it would be an easy job. So he set about and caught three hares alive, and put them into a bag, and dressed himself in some old rags, until he looked so poor and filthy that it made one's heart bleed to see; and then he stole into the passage at the back door of the squire's house on the Sunday forenoon, with his bag, just like any other beggar boy. But the squire himself and all his household were in the kitchen watching the roast. Just as they were doing this, the youth let one hare go, and it set off and ran round and round the yard in front of the house.

"Oh, just look at that hare!" said the folk in the kitchen, and were all for running out to catch it.

Yes, the squire saw it running too. "Oh, let it run," said he. "There's no use in trying to catch a hare on the spring."

A little while after the youth let the second hare go, and they saw it in the kitchen, and thought it was the same they had seen before, and still wanted to run out and catch it; but the squire said again it was no use. It was not long before the youth let the third hare go, and it set off and ran round and round the yard as the others before it. Now they saw it from the kitchen, and still thought it was the same hare that kept on running about, and were all eager to be out after it.

"Well, it is a fine hare," said the squire. "Come, let's see if we can't lay our hands on it."

So out he ran, and the rest with him—away they all went, the hare before, and they after; so that it was rare fun to see. But meantime the youth took the roast and ran off with it; and where the squire got a roast for his dinner that day I don't know; but one thing I know, and that is that he had no roast hare, though he ran after it till he was both warm and weary.

Now it chanced that the priest came to dinner that day, and when the squire told him what a trick the master thief had played him, he made such game of him that there was no end of it.

"For my part," said the priest, "I can't think how it could ever happen to me to be made such a fool of by a fellow like that."

"Very well—only keep a sharp lookout," said the squire; "maybe he'll come to see you before you know a word of it." But the priest stuck to his text, that he did, and made game of the squire because he had been so taken in.

Later in the afternoon came the master thief and wanted to have the squire's daughter, as he had given his word. But the squire began to talk him over and said, "Oh, you must first prove your skill a little more; for what you did today was no great thing after all. Couldn't you now play off a good trick on the priest, who is sitting in there and making game of me for letting such a fellow as you twist me round his thumb?"

"Well, as for that, it wouldn't be hard," said the master thief. So he dressed himself up like a bird, threw a great white sheet over his body, took the wings of a goose, and tied them to his back, and so climbed up into a great maple which stood in the priest's garden. And when the priest came home in the evening, the youth began to bawl out, "Father Laurence! Father Laurence!" for that was the priest's name.

"Who is that calling me?" said the priest.

"I am an angel," said the master thief, "sent from God to let you know that you shall be taken up alive into heaven for your piety's sake. Next Monday night you must hold yourself ready for the journey, for I shall come then to fetch you in a sack; and all your gold and your silver, and all that you have of this world's goods, you must lay together in a heap in your dining-room."

Well, Father Laurence fell on his knees before the angel and thanked him; and the very next day he preached a farewell sermon, and gave it out how there had come down an angel unto the big maple in his garden, who had told him that he was to be taken up alive into heaven for his piety's sake; and he preached and made such a touching discourse that all who were at church wept, both young and old.

So the next Monday night came the master thief like an angel again, and the priest fell on his knees and thanked him before he was put into the sack; but when he had got him well in, the master thief drew and dragged him over stocks and stones.

"*Ow! Ow!*" groaned the priest inside the sack, "wherever are we going?"

"This is the narrow way which leadeth unto the kingdom of heaven," said the master thief, and went on dragging him along till he had nearly broken every bone in his body. At last he tumbled him into a goose-house that belonged to the squire, and the geese began pecking and pinching him with their bills, so that he was more dead than alive.

"Now you are in the flames of purgatory, to be cleansed and purified for life everlasting," said the master thief; and with that he went his way and took all the gold which the priest had laid together in his dining-room. The next morning, when the goose-girl came to let the geese out, she heard how the priest lay in the sack and bemoaned himself in the goose-house.

"In heaven's name, who's there, and what ails you?" she cried.

"Oh," said the priest, "if you are an angel from heaven, do let me out, and let me return again to earth, for it is worse here than in hell. The little fiends keep on pinching me with tongs."

"Heaven help us, I am no angel at all," said the girl as she helped the priest out of the sack. "I only look after the squire's geese, and like enough they are the little fiends which have pinched your reverence."

"Oh," groaned the priest, "this is all that master thief's doing. Ah, my gold and my silver and my fine clothes!" And he beat his breast

and hobbled home at such a rate that the girl thought he had lost his wits all at once.

Now when the squire came to hear how it had gone with the priest, and how he had been along the narrow way, and into purgatory, he laughed till he well-nigh split his sides. But when the master thief came and asked for his daughter as he had promised, the squire put him off again and said, "You must do one masterpiece better still, that I may see plainly what you are fit for. Now I have twelve horses in my stable, and on them I will put twelve grooms, one on each. If you are so good a thief as to steal the horses from under them, I'll see what I can do for you."

"Very well, I daresay I can do it," said the master thief. "But shall I really have your daughter if I can?"

"Yes, if you can, I'll do my best for you," said the squire.

So the master thief set off to a shop and bought brandy enough to fill two pocket flasks, and into one of them he put a sleepy drink, but into the other only brandy. After that he hired eleven men to lie in wait at night behind the squire's stableyard; and last of all, for fair words and a good bit of money, he borrowed a ragged gown and cloak from an old woman; and so, with a staff in his hand and a bundle at his back, he limped off, as evening drew on, toward the squire's stable. Just as he got there they were watering the horses for the night, and had their hands full of work.

"What the devil do you want?" said one of the grooms to the old woman.

"Oh, oh! Hutetu! It is so bitter cold," said she, and shivered and shook and made wry faces. "Hutetu! It is so cold, a poor wretch may easily freeze to death"; and with that she fell to shivering and shaking again. "Oh, for the love of heaven, can I get leave to stay here awhile and sit inside the stable door?"

"To the devil with your leave," said one. "Pack yourself off this minute, for if the squire sets his eye on you, he'll lead us a pretty dance."

"Oh, the poor old bag of bones," said another, whose heart took pity on her. "The old hag may sit inside and welcome; such a one as she can do no harm."

And some of the rest said she should stay and some she shouldn't; but while they were quarreling she crept farther and farther into the stable, till at last she sat herself down behind the door; and when she had got so far, no one gave any more heed to her.

As the night wore on the men found it cold work to sit so still and quiet on horseback.

"Hutetu! It is so devilish cold," said one and beat his arms crosswise.

"That it is," said another. "I freeze so that my teeth chatter."

"If one only had a quid to chew," said a third.

Well, there was one who had an ounce or two; so they shared it among them, though it wasn't much, after all, that each got; and so they chewed and spat, and spat and chewed. This helped them somewhat; but in a little while they were just as bad as ever.

"Hutetu!" said one, and shivered and shook.

"Hutetu!" said the old woman, and shivered so that every tooth in her head chattered. Then she pulled out the flask with brandy in it, and her hand shook so that the spirits splashed about in the flask, and then she took such a gulp that it went bop in her throat.

"What's that you've got in your flask, old girl?" said one of the grooms.

"Oh, it's only a drop of brandy, old man," said she.

"Brandy! Well, I never! Do let me have a drop," screamed the whole twelve, one after another.

"Oh, but it is such a little drop," mumbled the old woman, "it will not even wet your mouths round." But they must and would have it; there was no help for it; and so she pulled out the flask with the sleepy drink in it and put it to the first man's lips; then she shook no more, but guided the flask so that each of them got what he wanted, and the twelfth had not done drinking before the first sat and snored. Then the master thief threw off his beggar's rags, and took one groom after the other softly off their horses, and set them astride on the beams between the stalls; and so he called his eleven men and rode off with the squire's twelve horses.

When the squire got up in the morning and went to look after his grooms, they had just begun to come to; and some of them fell to spurring the beams with their spurs till the splinters flew again. and some fell off, and some still hung on and sat there looking like fools.

"Ho, ho!" said the squire. "I see very well who has been here; but as for you, a pretty set of blockheads you must be to sit here and let the master thief steal the horses from between your legs." So they all got a good leathering because they had not kept a sharper lookout.

Further on in the day came the master thief again, and told how he had managed the matter, and asked for the squire's daughter, as he had promised; but the squire gave him one hundred dollars down and said he must do something better still.

"Do you think now," said he, "you can steal the horse from under me while I am out riding on his back?"

"Oh, yes! I daresay I could," said the master thief, "if I were really sure of getting your daughter."

Well, well, the squire would see what he could do; and he told the master thief a day when he would be taking a ride on a great common where they drilled the troops. So the master thief soon got hold of an old worn-out jade of a mare, and set to work, and made traces and collar of withies and broom twigs, and bought an old beggarly cart and a great cask. After that he told an old beggar woman he would give her ten dollars if she would get inside the cask and keep her mouth agape over the taphole, into which he was going to stick his finger. No harm should happen to her; she should only be driven about a little; and if he took his finger out more than once, she was to have ten dollars more. Then he threw a few rags and tatters over himself, and stuffed himself out, and put on a wig and a great beard of goat's hair, so that no one could know him again, and set off for the common, where the squire had already been riding about a good bit. When he reached the place he went along so softly and slowly that he scarce made an inch of way. "Gee up! Gee up!" and so he went on a little; then he stood stock still, and so on a little again; and altogether the pace was so poor it never once came into the squire's head that this could be the master thief.

At last the squire rode right up to him and asked if he had seen anyone lurking about in the wood thereabouts.

"No," said the man, "I haven't seen a soul."

"Hark ye, now," said the squire, "if you have a mind to ride into the wood, and hunt about and see if you can fall upon anyone lurking about there, you shall have the loan of my horse, and a shilling into the bargain, to drink my health for your pains."

"I don't see how I can go," said the man, "for I am going to a wedding with this cask of mead, which I have been to town to fetch, and here the tap has fallen out by the way, and so I must go along holding my finger in the taphole."

"Ride off," said the squire. "I'll look after your horse and cask."

Well, on these terms the man was willing to go; but he begged the squire to be quick in putting his finger into the taphole when he took his own out, and to mind and keep it there till he came back. At last the squire grew weary of standing there with his finger in the taphole, so he took it out.

"Now I shall have ten dollars more!" screamed the old woman inside the cask; and then the squire saw at once how the land lay and took himself off home; but he had not gone far before they met him with a fresh horse, for the master thief had already been to his house and told them to send one.

The day after, he came to the squire and would have his daughter, as he had given his word; but the squire put him off again with fine words, and gave him two hundred dollars, and said he must do one more masterpiece. If he could do that, he should have her. Well,

well, the master thief thought he could do it, if he only knew what it was to be.

"Do you think now," said the squire, "you can steal the sheet off our bed, and the shift off my wife's back. Do you think you could do that?"

"It shall be done," said the master thief. "I only wish I was as sure of getting your daughter."

So when night began to fall the master thief went out, and cut down a thief who hung on the gallows, and threw him across his shoulders, and carried him off. Then he got a long ladder and set it up against the squire's bedroom window, and so climbed up, and kept bobbing the dead man up and down, just for all the world like one that was peeping in at the window.

"That's the master thief, old lass!" said the squire and gave his wife a nudge on the side. "Now see if I don't shoot him, that's all." So saying, he took up a rifle which he had laid at his bedside.

"No, no! Pray don't shoot him after telling him he might come and try," said his wife.

"Don't talk to me, for shoot him I will," said he. And so he lay there and aimed and aimed; but as soon as the head came up before the window, and he saw a little of it, so soon was it down again. At last he thought he had a good aim. Bang! went the gun, down fell the dead body to the ground with a heavy thump, and down went the master thief too, as fast as he could.

"Well," said the squire, "it is quite true that I am the chief magistrate in these parts; but people are fond of talking, and it would be a bore if they came to see this dead man's body. I think the best thing to be done is that I should go down and bury him."

"You must do as you think best, dear," said his wife. So the squire got out of bed and went downstairs, and he had scarce put his foot out of the door before the master thief stole in and went straight upstairs to his wife.

"Why, dear, back already!" said she, for she thought it was her husband.

"Oh, yes, I only just put him into a hole and threw a little earth over him. It is enough that he is out of sight, for it is such a bad night out of doors; by and by I'll do it better. But just let me have the sheet to wipe myself with–he was so bloody–and I have made myself such a mess with him."

So he got the sheet.

After a while he said, "Do you know I am afraid you must let me have your night-shift too, for the sheet won't do by itself—that I can see."

So she gave him the shift also. But just then it came across his mind that he had forgotten to lock the house door, so he must step down and look to that before he came back to bed, and away he went with both shift and sheet.

A little while after came the true squire.

"Why, what a time you've taken to lock the door, dear!" said his wife. "And what have you done with the sheet and shift?"

"What do you say?" said the squire.

"Why, I am asking what you have done with the sheet and shift that you had to wipe off the blood," said she.

"What, in the devil's name!" said the squire. "Has he taken me in this time too?"

Next day came the master thief and asked for the squire's daughter as he had been promised; and then the squire dared not do anything else than give her to him, and a good lump of money into the bargain; for, to tell the truth, he was afraid lest the master thief should steal the eyes out of his head, and that the people would begin to say spiteful things of him if he broke his word. So the master thief lived well and happily from that time forward. I don't know whether he stole any more; but if he did, I am quite sure it was only for the sake of a bit of fun.

From *Popular Tales from the Norse*, a translation by Sir George Webbe Dasent of tales collected by Peter Asbjörnsen and Jörgen Moe.

BJARNI SVEINSSEN AND HIS SISTER SALVÖR

THERE was a man named Sveinn who was a farmer in Skagafjördr. He was well off and had two children, a son by the name of Bjarni, and a daughter called Salvör. These were twins, about twenty years old, and loved each other deeply.

One summer, about midsummer night, it happened that many of the Skagafjördr people went into the woods on the mountainside to gather Icelandic moss. Farmer Sveinn intended to let his son go with the others, but when Salvör heard of it, she wanted to go too. To this the parents at first objected, but they at last gave way to the girl's entreaties.

The night before the young people went away, farmer Sveinn had a dream that he had two white birds and loved both of them dearly; and he dreamed that he lost the she-bird and missed it sorely. When he awoke Sveinn interpreted his dream to mean that he would lose his daughter, and this gave him not a little anxiety. So he wanted to prevent Salvör from going to the moss-gathering, but she did not give up entreating him until she had coaxed him to let her go.

So the two loving young folk went into the woods. On the first day they gathered moss along with the others, and were always together and very happy. But the next night Salvör fell suddenly ill, so ill that on the morrow she could not go with the others. Bjarni took care of his sister in their tent, and thus three days passed. Salvör grew worse and worse. On the fourth day Bjarni got some of the other folk to stay with his sister and went out by himself into the woods. When he had filled his bag with moss he sat down under a great stone and leaned his cheek against his hand, thinking of his sister's illness, deeply grieved and full of fear for her life. After he had sat a little while he heard a clatter in the distance, and, looking up, saw two men riding up toward him at a great speed, one dressed in red and riding a chestnut horse, the other dressed in black and riding a black horse. They dismounted at the rock and saluted Bjarni by name.

The one dressed in red asked Bjarni what grieved him.

Bjarni would not tell him until the man assured him it would be none the worse for him to tell the truth. Then Bjarni told the man of his sister's illness. "And now our companions are going away," added Bjarni, "and I shall be left alone with my sister and I fear she may die."

"You are indeed in trouble, Bjarni," said the man in red, "and I am deeply sorry for you and grieve with you. But will you not give me your sister?"

"No," answered Bjarni, "that I surely cannot do, since I know nothing about you, not even where you live. Where are you from?"

"That is no business of yours," said the other, and took from his pocket a snuff box of gilded silver with a jewel in the lid, and said, "Will you sell your sister for this snuff box?"

"No," answered Bjarni, "I will not give her to you for any price."

"Very well," quoth the man, "but take this box as a present from me and as a token of the stranger you met in the mountains."

Bjarni took the box and thanked the man for his gift. The stranger then took his leave, and Bjarni went home to the tent.

Next morning Bjarni's companions started homeward, leaving him alone with his sister. The youth did not dare to sleep, fearing that the stranger might steal Salvör from him. So all that day Bjarni watched over her, but the ensuing night his desire for sleep grew so strong that he could keep awake no longer, and, lying down by his sister, he clasped her in his arms, hoping thus to prevent her from being taken away from him without his knowledge. Then he fell fast asleep.

But when he awoke, lo! his sister was gone. He was seized with unspeakable grief and searched all that day, weeping and crying over the loss of his sister. But it was all in vain. So that night he got on his horse and rode home to his parents and told them the grievous news.

"This was my foreboding," said Sveinn. "It is fate."

Now men gathered from all quarters to search for Salvör, but although they searched high and wide, they found no trace of her. Everyone shared the family's grief, for the girl had been the most promising of maidens and a favorite in the neighborhood.

The years passed until Bjarni was thirty years old, had married, and had begun farming for himself. One autumn day his herdsman missed his flock of sheep. For three days he searched but found nothing. Bjarni then bade his wife prepare a week's provender for him and a pair of good shoes, for he had decided to go in search of the sheep. His parents, who were still alive, begged him not to go. But he bade them fear not and not to look for him till after at least a week had passed.

So off he went and walked continually for three days and three nights. At last he came to a cave, and there lay down to sleep. When he awoke a heavy mist lay on all the land around him. He did not, however, stop in his search but continued on, and after a while he lost his way and knew neither where he was nor whither he went.

After trudging a long and wearisome time, he found himself in a large valley, and when the mist had lifted he saw before him a farm of goodly size, with large buildings. He turned his steps toward it, and soon came upon men and women making hay in the meadows. Approaching a group of three women, he asked one of them, a woman of stately bearing, whether he could stay for the night at the farm.

She answered yes, and another one of the three, a well-favored young woman, escorted him to the farmhouse.

It seemed to Bjarni that this woman bore a likeness to his sister, the Salvör who had long since disappeared in the mountains. At once the memory of that whole unhappy affair was recalled to him and awakened many a pang of sorrow in his breast, but he hid all sign of his grief from the young woman.

When they came to the farmhouse the girl led Bjarni in and showed him into a large, beautifully furnished room, and bade him sit down. After that she went out, but returned in a moment with meat and wine, which she put on the table before him. When he had partaken of the meal, the girl led him to a bedroom in which a fine bed waited for him. Bjarni went to bed, and the girl, taking his muddied clothes from him, bade him good night.

Now Bjarni began wondering where he was and why this lovely maiden should so sharply recall to him the memory of his old sorrow; but in the midst of all his sad thoughts he dropped off to sleep.

It seemed not long after that he awoke to the sound of singing somewhere in the house. In a moment he realized that on the floor above the family had gathered for prayer, as is the custom in Iceland. There were many voices, both of men and women, but one excelled all the others. And this one again stirred up in him the most painful memories, for it seemed to him to be the voice of Salvör. For a while he thought sadly of his lost sister, then slept again soundly, till the maiden who had waited on him the evening before aroused him in the broad daylight of a sunny, beautiful morning. She brought him fresh clothes and persuaded him to stay there for the day, which was a Sunday. Then she went out.

While Bjarni was dressing a good-looking boy in a blue cloth coat entered the room, greeted Bjarni pleasantly, and asked why he was traveling and what he sought.

"I am searching for my sheep," said Bjarni.

"I do not think they are in this valley," the boy answered. "But you will stay with us today and tarry a while, for my father is going to perform the service in the church."

After a while the girl opened the door and cried, "Sveinn, you will tire the man with your chatter!"

She then brought food to the table for Bjarni, and when he had eaten a good breakfast he went out. Then Bjarni saw many people streaming toward the church, and the lad, taking him by the hand, led him to the church and showed him to a seat. When Bjarni looked around he saw at his side the red-clothed man whom he had met on the mountain. Also he saw that the priest was the man who had been dressed in black. There were many people in the church, some dressed in sheep-brown knitted garments and most of them rascally looking and of giant size.

Bjarni took out his precious box and offered his neighbor a pinch of snuff, which the man accepted. And then, as he gazed around him, Bjarni saw in a near-by seat a young woman of fine bearing and dress. They stared at one another intently, and then the girl began to smile and weep by turns. Then Bjarni realized that this was, beyond all doubt, his sister.

The service over, the lad took Bjarni by the hand and led him to his room. After a while the man clothed in red and the one in black came in, greeted Bjarni friendlily, and asked him if he knew them. He answered that he did, and at that moment the woman whom he had seen in the church and thought was his sister entered the room and flung herself into his arms, crying out, "We were born into the world from the same womb. Then in a moment of woe I was torn from thee, my brother. It is with a heart overflowing with joy that I embrace thee again."

Having greeted each other thus touchingly, Bjarni began telling her all that had passed in Skagafjördr during the years since her disappearance. Then the red-clad man said, "It was I who carried off your beloved sister, Bjarni, and married her to this man clad in black. He is my son, and is the priest of our people, the dale-dwellers. I am their magistrate. I took your sheep and by means of spells led you astray hither in order that you might have a chance to see your sister again and that you might be able to tell one another what has happened to you since your parting. Tomorrow I shall give you back your sheep and lead you away again, but tonight you may stay with us and talk with your sister to your heart's content."

Next morning Bjarni took a tearful farewell of his sister. He drove the sheep before him and, guided almost all the way by the man dressed in red and the one in black, made his way down to the peopled land below. When the two men left him, the man in black said to Bjarni, "I will send for you next spring to come to settle in our valley and live with us."

Then Bjarni returned home and told his parents and wife all about his journey and begged them by all means to keep it secret.

Spring arrived, and one night three men, along with many horses, came to the house where Bjarni lived, and the next night he moved with all his possesions, his parents and his wife and children to the valley in the mountains. There a joyous meeting took place between the kinsmen and Salvör.

Bjarni lived there a long, long time, but finally he returned to Skagafjördr when he was an old man, and there told all this tale.

Based on a story in *Icelandic Legends,* collected by Jón Arnason and translated by C. E. J. Powell and Eirikr Magnusson.

NOW I SHOULD LAUGH IF I WERE NOT DEAD

ONCE two married women had a dispute about which of their husbands was the greater fool. At last they agreed to make trial of the two men to see if they were as foolish as they seemed to be. One of the women then played the following trick on her husband. When he came home from his work she took a spinning wheel and carders, and began to card and spin, but without using any wool. Her husband, observing this, asked her if she had gone mad to scrape teazles together and spin a wheel without using any wool, and prayed her to tell him the meaning of her behavior. She replied firmly that it was scarcely to be expected that he should be able to see what she was doing, for the linen she was using was of a kind too fine to be seen with such eyes as his. She was going to make him clothes of it, she said. He seemed much impressed by this explanation, was struck with the thought of how clever his wife was, and began to look forward to having such marvelous clothes.

When his wife had spun, as she claimed, enough for the clothes, she set up a loom and began weaving. Occasionally her husband watched her, and he came to wonder more and more at the skill of his good lady. The wife played her game to the end. She took the invisible cloth from the loom when it was finished, went through the motions of washing it, and finally of cutting it and sewing clothes out of it. When she had finished all this, she bade her husband come and try the garments, and insisted on helping him put them on. So she pretended to dress him in the clothes, and, although the poor man was in reality naked, yet he firmly believed that it was all his own blindness and that actually his clever wife had made him the most wonderful clothes in the world. And so glad was he at this that he could hadly keep from jumping for joy.

As for the other wife, when her husband came home from work she asked him why in the world he was up and going about upon his feet. The poor man was startled by the question. "Why on earth do you ask that?" he said. Whereupon the woman proceeded to persuade him that he was very ill and that he had better go to bed. She was so convincing that the husband began to feel that he must be ill and soon took to his bed. In a short time the wife announced that she would have to hold final services for him. He pleaded with her to tell him why. At that she cried out impatiently, "You are behaving like a fool! Don't you know you died this morning? I must go at once and have your coffin made." The poor man, convinced that it was all true, resigned himself to being put into his coffin.

His wife appointed a day for the burial, hired six pallbearers, and

asked the other couple to follow her dear husband to his grave. She also had a window made in one side of the coffin so that her husband might see all that went on around him.

When the hour came for removing the coffin, the other couple came as they had promised, the man stark naked, thinking that everybody would admire his extraordinarily fine-spun, wonderfully weightless clothes. Although the coffin-bearers were naturally in a sad mood, everyone could hardly help laughing when he saw the naked fool. And when the man in the coffin caught sight of him, he cried out as loud as he could, "Now I should laugh, if I were not dead!"

There was of course a great to-do, the burial was put off, the man was let out of the coffin, and when the story of how the women had tricked their husbands came out, they got a public whipping at a parish court.

Based on a story in *Icelandic Legends.*

THE PRINCESS ON THE PEA

THERE was once a prince who wanted to marry a princess; but she was to be a *real* princess. So he traveled about, all through the world, to find a real one, but everywhere there was something in the way. There were princesses enough, but whether they were *real* princesses he could not make out; there was always something that did not seem quite right. So he came home again, and was quite sad, for he wished very much to have a real princess.

One evening a terrible storm came on. It lightened and thundered, and rain streamed down; it was fearful! Then there was a knocking at the town gate, and the old king went out to open it.

It was a princess who stood outside the gate. But how she looked, from the rain and the rough weather! The water ran down from her hair and her clothes; it ran in at the points of her shoes and out at her heels; and yet she declared that she was a real princess.

"Yes, we will soon find that out," thought the old queen. But she said nothing, only went into the bedchamber, took all the bedding off, and put a pea on the flooring of the bedstead; then she took twenty mattresses and laid them upon the pea, and then twenty eiderdown beds upon the mattresses. On this the princess had to lie all night. In the morning she was asked how she had slept.

"Oh, miserably!" said the princess. "I scarcely closed my eyes all night long. Goodness knows what was in my bed. I lay upon something hard, so that I am black and blue all over. It is dreadful!"

Now they saw that she was a real princess, for through the twenty mattresses and the twenty eiderdown beds she had felt the pea. No one but a real princess could be so delicate.

So the prince took her for his wife, for now he knew that he had a true princess; and the pea was put in the museum, and it is there now, unless somebody has carried it off.

Look you, this is a true story.

From *Stories and Tales* (Boston: Houghton Mifflin Company, n.d.), a translation of tales by Hans Christian Andersen.

THE TINDERBOX

THERE came a soldier marching along the highroad—*one, two! one two!* He had his knapsack on his back and a saber by his side, for he had been in the wars, and now he wanted to go home. And on the way he met an old witch: she was very hideous, and her underlip hung down upon her breast. She said, "Good evening, soldier. What a fine sword you have, and what a big knapsack! You're a proper soldier! Now you shall have as much money as you like."

"I thank you, old witch!" said the soldier.

"Do you see that great tree?" said the witch, and she pointed to a tree which stood beside them. "It's quite hollow inside. You must climb to the top, and then you'll see a hole through which you can let yourself down and get deep into the tree. I'll tie a rope round your body, so that I can pull you up again when you call me."

"What am I to do down in the tree?" asked the soldier.

"Get money," replied the witch. "Listen to me. When you come down to the earth under the tree, you will find yourself in a great hall; it is quite light, for more than three hundred lamps are burning there. Then you will see three doors; these you can open, for the keys are hanging there. If you go into the first chamber, you'll see a great chest in the middle of the floor; on this chest sits a dog, and he's got a pair of eyes as big as two teacups. But you need not care about that. I'll give you my blue checked apron, and you can spread it out upon the floor; then go up quickly and take the dog and set him on my apron; then open the chest and take as many shillings as you like. They are of copper; if you prefer silver, you must go into the second chamber. But there sits a dog with a pair of eyes as big as millwheels. But do not care about that. Set him upon my apron and take some of the money. And if you want gold, you can have that too—in fact, as much as you can carry—if you go into the third chamber. But the dog that sits on the money chest there has two eyes as big as round towers. He is a fierce dog, you may be sure. But you needn't be afraid, for all that. Only set him on my apron, and he won't hurt you; and take out of the chest as much gold as you like."

"That's not so bad," said the soldier. "But what am I to give you, you old witch? For you will not do it for nothing, I fancy."

"No," replied the witch, "not a single shilling will I have. You need only bring me an old tinderbox which my grandmother forgot when she was down there last."

"Then tie the rope round my body," cried the soldier.

"Here it is," said the witch, "and here's my blue checked apron."

Then the soldier climbed up into the tree, let himself slip down into the hole, and stood, as the witch had said, in the great hall where the three hundred lamps were burning.

Now he opened the first door. Ugh! there sat the dog with eyes as big as teacups, staring at him. "You're a nice fellow!" exclaimed the soldier; and he set him on the witch's apron, and took as many copper shillings as his pockets would hold, and then locked the chest, set the dog on it again, and went into the second chamber. Aha! there sat the dog with eyes as big as millwheels.

"You should not stare so hard at me," said the soldier, "you might strain your eyes." And he set the dog upon the witch's apron. And when he saw the silver money in the chest, he threw away all the copper money he had and filled his pockts and his knapsack with silver only. Then he went into the third chamber. Oh, but that was horrid! The dog there had eyes as big as Copenhagen's Round Tower, and they turned round and round in his head like wheels.

"Good evening!" said the soldier, and he touched his cap, for he had never seen such a dog as that before. When he had looked at him a little more closely, he thought, "That will do," and lifted him down to the floor and opened the chest. Mercy! what a quantity of gold was there! He could buy the whole town with it, and all the sugar cake woman's sucking pigs, and all the tin soldiers, whips, and rocking-horses in the whole world. Yes, that was a quantity of money! Now the soldier threw away all the silver coin with which he had filled his pockets and his knapsack and took gold instead; yes, all his pockets, his knapsack, his boots, and his cap were filled, so that he could scarcely walk. Now, indeed, he had plenty of money. He put the dog on the chest, shut the door, and then called up through the tree, "Now pull me up, you old witch."

"Have you the tinderbox?" asked the witch.

"Plague on it!" exclaimed the soldier. "I have clean forgotten that." And he went and brought it.

The witch drew him up, and he stood on the highroad again, with pockets, boots, knapsack, and cap full of gold.

"What are you going to do with the tinderbox?" asked the soldier.

"That's nothing to you," retorted the witch. "You've had your money. Just give me the tinderbox."

"Nonsense!" said the soldier. "Tell me directly what you're going to do with it or I'll draw my sword and cut off your head."

"No!" cried the witch.

So the soldier cut off her head. There she lay! But he tied up all his money in her apron, took it on his back like a bundle, put the tinderbox in his pocket, and went straight off toward the town.

That was a splendid town! And he put up at the very best inn, and asked for the finest rooms, and ordered his favorite dishes, for now he was rich, since he had so much money. The servant who had to clean his boots certainly thought them a remarkably old pair for such a rich gentleman; but he had not bought any new ones yet. The next day he procured good boots and handsome clothes. Now our soldier had become a fine gentleman; and the people told him of all the splendid doings in their city, and about the king, and what a pretty princess the king's daughter was.

"Where can one get to see her?" asked the soldier.

"She is not to be seen at all," said they all together. "She lives in a great copper castle, with a great many walls and towers round about it. No one but the king may go in and out there, for it has been prophesied that she shall marry a common soldier, and the king can't bear that."

"I should like to see her," thought the soldier, but he could not get leave to do so. Now he lived merrily, went to the theater, drove in the king's garden, and gave much money to the poor; and this was very kind of him: he knew from his old life how hard it is when one has not a shilling. Now he was rich, had fine clothes, and gained many friends, who all said he was a fine and noble fellow; and that pleased the soldier well. But as he spent money every day and never earned any, he had at last only two shillings left; and he was obliged to get out of the fine rooms in which he had dwelt, and had to live in a little garret under the roof, and clean his boots for himself, and mend them with a darning needle. None of his friends came to see him, for there were too many stairs to climb.

It was quite dark one evening, and he could not even buy himself a candle, when it occurred to him that there was a candle end in the tinderbox which he had taken out of the hollow tree into which the witch had helped him. He brought out the tinderbox and the candle end; but as soon as he struck fire and the sparks rose up from the flint, the door flew open, and the dog who had eyes as big as a couple of teacups, and whom he had seen in the tree, stood before him and said, "What are my lord's commands?"

"What is this?" said the soldier. "That's an excellent tinderbox if I can get everything with it that I want! Bring me some money," said he to the dog; and *whisk!* the dog was gone, and *whisk!* he was back again, with a great bag full of shillings in his mouth.

Now the soldier knew what a capital tinderbox this was. If he struck it once, it brought the dog who guarded the copper money; if twice, it summoned the dog who guarded the silver; and if he struck it three times, then appeared the dog who had the gold. Now the soldier moved back into the fine rooms and appeared again in handsome clothes; and all his friends knew him again and cared very much for him indeed.

One day he thought to himself, "It is a strange thing that one cannot get to see the princess. They all say she is very beautiful; but what's the use of that, if she always must sit in that great copper castle with the many towers? Can I not get to see her at all? Where is my tinderbox?" And so he struck a light, and *whisk!* came the dog with eyes as big as teacups.

"It is midnight, I know," said the soldier, "but I should very much like to see the princess, even if only for a moment."

The dog was outside the door at once, and, before the soldier could imagine it, was back with the princess. She sat upon the dog's back and slept; and everyone could see she was a real princess, for she was so lovely. The soldier could not refrain from kissing her, for he was a bold fellow. Then the dog ran back again with the princess. But when morning came, and the king and queen were drinking tea, the princess said she had had a strange dream the night before, about a dog and a soldier—that she had ridden upon the dog, and the soldier had kissed her.

"That's a fine story!" said the queen.

So one of the old court ladies had to watch the next night by the princess's bed, to see if this was really a dream or what it might be.

The soldier had a great longing to see the lovely princess again; so the dog came in the night, took her away, and ran as fast as he could. But the old lady put on storm boots and ran just as fast after him. When she saw that they both entered a great house, she thought, "Now I know where it is"; and with a bit of chalk she drew a great cross on the door. Then she went home and lay down. Afterwards, as the dog was leaving the soldier's house with the princess he saw the cross on the door. So he took a piece of chalk and drew crosses on all the doors in the town. And that was cleverly done, for now the lady could not find the right door, because all the doors had crosses upon them.

Early in the morning the king and the queen, the old court lady and all the courtiers come to see where the princess had been. "Here it is!" said the king, when he saw the first door with a cross upon it. "No, my dear husband, it is there!" said the queen, coming upon another door which also showed a cross. "But here is one, and there is another!" they all cried, for wherever they looked there were crosses on the doors. So they saw that it would avail them nothing if they relied on that mark.

But the queen was an exceedingly clever woman, who could do more than ride in a coach. She took her great gold scissors, cut a piece of silk into pieces, and made a neat little bag; this bag she filled with fine wheat flour and tied it around the princess's neck; then she cut a little hole in the bag, so that the flour would be scattered along all the way which the princess would take.

In the night the dog came again, took the princess on his back, and ran with her to the soldier, who loved her very much, and would gladly have been a prince so that he might have her for his wife. The dog did not notice at all how the flour ran out in a stream from the castle to the windows of the soldier's house, where he ran up the wall with the princess. In the morning the king and queen saw well enough where their daughter had been, and they took the soldier and put him in prison.

There he sat. Oh, but it was dark and disagreeable there! And they said to him, "Tomorrow you shall be hanged." That was not pleasant to hear, and he had left his tinderbox at the inn. In the morning he could see, through the iron grating of the little window, how the people were hurrying out of the town to see him hanged. He heard the drums beat and saw the soldiers marching. All the people were running out, and among them was a shoemaker's boy with leather apron and slippers, and he galloped so fast that one of his slippers flew off and fell right against the wall where the soldier sat looking through the iron grating.

"Hello, you shoemaker's boy! you needn't be in such a hurry," cried the soldier to him. "It will not begin till I come. But if you will run to where I lived, and bring me my tinderbox, you shall have four shillings; but you must put your best foot foremost."

The shoemaker's boy wanted to get the four shillings, so he went and brought the tinderbox, and—well, we shall hear now what happened.

Outside the town a great gallows had been built, and round it stood the soldiers and many hundred thousand people. The king and queen sat on a splendid throne, opposite the judges and the whole council. The soldier was already mounting the ladder; but as they were about to put the rope round his neck, he said that before a poor criminal suffered his punishment, an innocent request was always granted to him. He wanted very much to smoke a pipe of tobacco, and it would be the last pipe he should smoke in the world. The king would not say no to this; so the soldier took his tinderbox and struck it once—twice—thrice! and there suddenly stood all the dogs—the one with eyes as big as teacups, the one with eyes as large as millwheels, and the one with eyes as big as the Round Tower.

"Help me now, so that I may not be hanged," said the soldier.

And the dogs fell upon the judges and all the council, seized one by the leg and another by the nose, and tossed them all so high into the air that they fell and were all killed at once.

"Stop it!" cried the king, but the biggest dog took him and the queen and threw them after the others. Then the soldiers were afraid,

and the people cried, "Soldier, you shall be our king, and marry the beautiful princess!"

So they put the soldier into the king's coach, and all the three dogs darted on in front and cried "Hurrah!" and the boys whistled through their fingers, and the soldiers presented arms. The princess came out of the copper castle, and became queen, and she liked that well enough. The wedding lasted a week, and the three dogs sat at the table too, and opened their eyes wider than ever at all they saw.

Adapted from *Wonder Stories,* by Hans Christian Andersen (Boston: Houghton Mifflin Company, n.d.).

Spanish

I Ate the Loaf

ONE OF the paths followed by folk tales, as well as by the great body of learning coming from the East in the Middle Ages, was translation from Arabic into Latin and then into a European vernacular. In Spain this was facilitated by the contact between Moor and Spaniard; and one of the most popular works that resulted was a small collection of stories called *Disciplina Clericalis*. The author, Petrus Alfonsus, was a native of Aragon, but like so many of the scholars who linked the Moslem East and the Christian West, he was born a Jew, and drew almost as much on the Hebrew Talmud as on Arabic sources. "I Ate the Loaf," the infinitely popular jest of the three travelers who match dreams—or lies—for a loaf of bread is generally considered a "Joe Miller" anecdote no more than two or three centuries old, but the *Disciplina* version, though it is surely not the earliest, was written down more than eight hundred years ago.

Another popular collection, *El Conde Lucanor*, was put together early in the fourteenth century by Don Juan Manuel, a cultured nobleman. In typical medieval fashion, its stories, taken from every conceivable source, are set in a framework of moral instruction. Readers will recognize in "What Happened to a Man on His Wedding Day" and in "The Invisible Cloth" very early versions respectively of Shakespeare's "Taming of the Shrew" and Andersen's "The Emperor's New Clothes."

Although Spanish in flavor, the tales from modern Spain are traditionally European in theme, with the possible qualification that religious faith, God, and the devil play important roles in an extraordinary number of them. How deep-rooted this tendency is is evident in the way it makes itself felt in the folklore of Latin America, the Philippines, and wherever Spanish culture has flourished. Another deep-seated Spanish story tradition is represented by "Pedro el Malas," one of a cycle of tales dealing with a young knave and his escapades. It offers a folk parallel to those sixteenth- and seventeenth-century

Spanish novels (of which *Lazarillo de Tormes* and *Gil Blas* are the best known) called picaresque, which also deal with the life and adventures of a rogue. As Pedro de Urdemalas, or just Pedro, the young trickster is a familiar character throughout Central and South America.

I ATE THE LOAF

Two citizens and a rustic, going to Mecca, shared provisions till they reached that place, and then their food failed, so that nothing remained save so much flour as would make a single loaf, and that a small one. The citizens, seeing this, said to each other, "We have too little bread, and our companion eats a great deal. Wherefore we ought to have a plan to take away from him part of the loaf and eat it by ourselves alone."

Accordingly they proposed the following plan to him: to make and bake the loaf, and while it was being baked to sleep, and whoever of them saw the most wonderful things in a dream should eat the loaf alone. These words they spake artfully, as they thought the rustic too simple for inventions of the kind. They made the loaf and baked it, and at length lay down to sleep. But the rustic, more crafty than they thought, whilst his companions were asleep, took the half-baked loaf, ate it up, and again lay down. One of the citizens, as if terrified out of his sleep, awoke and called his companion, who inquired, "What is the matter?" He said, "I have seen a wondrous vision, for it seemed to me that two angels opened the gates of paradise and let me within." Then his companion said to him, "This is a wondrous vision you have seen. But I dreamed that two angels took me and, cleaving the earth, led me to the lower regions." The rustic heard all this and pretended to be asleep; but the citizens, being deceived, and wishing to deceive, called on him to awake. Whereupon the rustic cunningly cried out, as though terrified, "Who are they that call me?" Then they said, "We are your companions." "Have you returned already?" he exclaimed. To this they rejoined, "Where did we go, that we should return?" Then the rustic said, "Now it seemed to me that two angels took one of you, opened the gates of heaven and led him within; then two others took the other, opened the earth, and took him to hell. Seeing this, I thought neither of you would return any more; so I rose and ate the loaf."

From the *Disciplina Clericalis* of Petrus Alfonsus, translated by W. A. Clouston in *Popular Tales and Fictions* (Edinburgh: W. Blackwood and Sons, 1887).

THE INVISIBLE CLOTH

COUNT LUCANOR, conversing at another time with Patronio, his adviser, said, "Patronio, a man came to me and told me something, giving me to understand it would be of great advantage to me if I followed his suggestions; but he said no man must be informed of the secret, that I must trust in him, and, more than this, affirmed that if I should confide it to any man in the world I should place not only my property but my life in danger. And as I know no man able to detect a fraud so quickly as yourself, I pray you give me your opinion in this case."

"My lord," said Patronio, "in order that you may know how to act under these circumstances, it would please me to be permitted to inform you what happened to a king and three impostors."

The count requested to know what that was.

"My lord," said Patronio, "three impostors came to a king, and told him they were cloth weavers, and could fabricate a cloth of so peculiar a nature that a legitimate son of his father could see the cloth; but if he were illegitimate, though believed to be legitimate, he could not see it.

"Now the king was much pleased at this, thinking that by this means he would be able to distinguish the men in his kingdom who were legitimate sons of their supposed fathers from those who were not, and so be enabled to increase his treasures, for among the Moors only legitimate children inherit their father's property; and for this end he ordered a palace to be appropriated to the manufacture of this cloth. And these men, in order to convince him that they had no intention of deceiving him, agreed to be shut up in this palace until the cloth was manufactured, which satisfied the king.

"When they were supplied with a large quantity of gold, silver, silk, and many other things, they entered the palace, and, putting their looms in order, gave it to be understood that they were working all day at the cloth.

"After some days one of them came to the king and told him the cloth was commenced, that it was the most curious thing in the world, describing the design and construction; he then prayed the king to favor them with a visit, but begged he would come alone. The king was much pleased, but wishing to have the opinion of someone first, sent the lord chamberlain to see it, in order to know if they were deceiving him. When the lord chamberlain saw the workmen, and heard all they had to say, he dared not admit he could not see the cloth, and when he returned to the king he stated that he had seen it; the king sent yet another, who gave the same report. When they whom he had sent declared that they had seen the cloth he determined to go himself.

"When he entered the palace, the men at work began to describe the design and color of the cloth, in which they all seemed to agree. When the King saw how they appeared to work, heard the cloth minutely described, and yet could not see it, although those he had sent had seen it, he began to feel very uneasy, fearing he might not be the son of the king, who was supposed to be his father, and that if he acknowledged he could not see the cloth he might lose his kingdom; under this impression he commenced praising the fabric, describing its peculiarities after the manner of the workmen.

"On the return to his palace he related to his people how good and marvelous was the cloth, yet at the same time suspected something wrong.

"At the end of two or three days the king requested his alguacil [officer of justice] to go and see the cloth. When the alguacil entered and saw the workmen, who, as before, described the figures and pattern of the cloth, knowing that the king had been to see it, and yet could not see it himself, he thought he certainly could not be the legitimate son of his father, and therefore could not see it. He, however, feared if he was to declare that he could not see it he would lose his honorable position; to avoid this mischance he commenced praising the cloth even more vehemently than the others.

"When the alguacil returned to the king and told him that he had seen the cloth, and that it was the most extraordinary production in the world, the king was much disconcerted; for he thought that if the alguacil had seen the cloth, which he was unable to see, there could no longer be a doubt that he was not the legitimate son of the king, as was generally supposed; he therefore did not hesitate to praise the excellency of the cloth and the skill of the workmen who were able to make it.

"On another day he sent one of his councilors, and it happened to him as to the king and the others of whom I have spoken; and in this manner, and for this reason, they deceived the king and many others, for no one dared to say he could not see the cloth.

"Things went on thus until there came a great feast, when all requested the king to be dressed in some of the cloth; so the work-

men, being ordered, brought some rolled up in a very fine linen and inquired of the king how much of it he wished them to cut off; so the king gave orders how much and how to make it up.

"Now when the clothes were made and the feast day had arrived, the weavers brought them to the king, informing his Majesty that his dress was made of the cloth as he had directed, the king all this time not daring to say he could not see it.

"When the king had professed to dress himself in this suit he mounted on horseback and rode into the city; but fortunately for him it was summertime. The people seeing his majesty come in this manner were much surprised; but, knowing that those who could not see this cloth would be considered illegitimate sons of their fathers, kept their surprise to themselves, fearing the dishonor consequent upon such a declaration. Not so, however, with a slave, who happened to notice the king thus equipped; for he, having nothing to lose, came to him and said, 'Sire, to me it matters not whose son I am, therefore I tell you that you are riding without any clothes.' On this the king commenced beating him, saying that he was not the legitimate son of his supposed father, and therefore it was that he could not see the cloth. But no sooner had the slave said this than others were convinced of its truth and said the same; until, at last, the king and all with him lost their fear of declaring the truth and saw through the trick of which these impostors had made them the victims. When the weavers were sought for they were found to have fled, taking with them all they had received from the king by their imposition.

"Now you, Count Lucanor, since that man of whom you speak forbids your trusting to anyone, and demands your entire confidence, be careful you are not deceived; for, you ought to know very well that he can have no reason for seeking your advantage more than his own; nor has he more reason to serve you than have those who are indebted to you and are already in your service."

Count Lucanor found this to be good advice, so adopted it.

And Don Juan, also seeing that it was a good example, wrote it in this book and made these lines:

> Who counsels thee to secrecy with friends
> Seeks to entrap thee for his own base ends.

From *Count Lucanor*, by Prince Don Juan Manuel, translated by James York (London, 1868).

WHAT HAPPENED TO A YOUNG MAN ON HIS WEDDING DAY

ONE DAY Count Lucanor was talking to Patronio his counselor and said to him, "Patronio, one of my dependents tells me he can make a very advantageous marriage with a woman much richer and more honorable than himself; but there is one difficulty in the way, which is this: he tells me he has been informed that she is of a very violent and impetuous temper. Now I beg you to counsel me whether I should allow him to marry this woman, knowing such to be her disposition, or whether I should forbid it."

"Count Lucanor," replied Patronio, "if the man is like the son of a certain good Moor, advise the marriage by all means; but if such be not the case, forbid it."

The count begged of him to relate the narrative.

"There lived in a city," said Patronio, "a Moor who was much respected, and who had a son, the most promising youth in the world; but, not being rich enough to accomplish the great deeds which he felt in his heart equal to, he was greatly troubled, having the will and not the power.

"Now in the same town there lived another Moor, who held a higher position, and was very much richer than his father, and who had an only daughter, the very reverse in character and appearance of the young man, she being of so very violent a temper that no one could be found willing to marry such a virago.

"One day the young man came to his father and said, 'You know that your means will not allow you to put me in a position to live honorably,' adding that, as he desired to live an easy and quiet life, he thought it better to seek to enrich himself by an advantageous marriage, or to leave that part of the country.

"The father told him that he would be very happy if he could succeed in such a union. On this, the son proposed, if it were agreeable to his father, to seek the daughter of their neighbor in marriage. Hearing this, the father was much astonished and asked how he could think of such a thing when he knew that no man, however poor, could be induced to marry her.

"Nevertheless the son insisted; and, although the father thought it a strange whim, in the end he gave his consent. The good man then visited his neighbor, telling him the wish of his son.

"When the good man heard what his friend said, he answered, 'By heaven, my friend, were I to do such a thing I should prove myself a very false friend, for you have a worthy son, and it would be base in me to consent to his injury or death; and I know for certain that, were he to live with my daughter, he would soon die, or death, at least, would be preferable to life. Do not think I say this from any objection to your alliance, for I should only be too grateful to any man who would take her out of my house.'

"The young man's father was much pleased at this, as his son was so intent on the marriage. All being ultimately arranged, they were in the end married, and the bride taken home, according to the Moorish fashion, to the house of her husband, and left to supper; the friends and relations returning to their respective homes, waiting anxiously for the following day, when they feared to find the bridegroom either dead or seriously injured.

"Now, being left alone, the young couple sat down to supper, when the bridegroom, looking behind him, saw his mastiff and said to him, 'Bring me water wherewith to wash my hands.' The dog naturally taking no notice of this command, the young man became irritated and ordered the animal more angrily to bring him water for his hands, which the latter not heeding, the young man arose in

a great rage and, drawing his sword, commenced a savage attack on the dog, who, to avoid him, ran away; but, finding no retreat, jumped on the table, then to the fireplace, his master still pursuing him, who, having caught him, first cut off his head, then his paws, hewing him to pieces, covering everything with blood. Thus furious and bloodstained, he returned to the table and, looking round, saw a cat. 'Bring me water for my hands,' said he to it. The animal not noticing the command, the master cried out, 'How, false traitor, did you not see how I treated the mastiff for disobeying me? If you do not do as I tell you this instant, you shall share his fate.' The poor little harmless cat continuing motionless, the master seized him by the paws and dashed him to pieces against the wall. His fury increasing, he again placed himself at the table, looking about on all sides as if for something to attack next. His wife, seeing this, and supposing he had lost his senses, held her peace. At length he espied his horse, the only one he had, and called to him fiercely to bring him water to wash his hands. The animal not obeying, he cried out in a rage, 'How is this? Think you that because you are the only horse I have that you dare thus to disobey my orders? Know then that your fate shall be the same as the others, and that anyone living who dares to disobey me shall not escape my vengeance.' Saying this, he seized the horse, cut off his head, and hacked him to pieces.

"And when the wife saw this, and knowing he had no other horse, felt that he was really in earnest, she became dreadfully alarmed.

"He again sat down to table, raging and all bloody as he was, swearing he would kill a thousand horses, or even men or women, if they dared to disobey him. Holding at the same time his bloody sword in his hand, he looked around with glaring eyes until, fixing them on his wife, he ordered her to bring him water to wash his hands. The wife, expecting no other fate than to be cut to pieces if she demurred, immediately arose and brought him the water.

" 'Ha! thank God you have done so,' said he. 'Otherwise, I am so irritated by these senseless brutes that I should have done by you as by them.' He afterward commanded her to help him to meat. She complied; but he told her, in a fearful tone of voice, to beware as he felt as if he were going mad.

"Thus passed the night; she not daring to speak, but strictly obeying all his orders. After letting her sleep for a short time, he said to her, 'Get up, I have been so annoyed that I cannot sleep; take care that nothing disturbs me, and in the meanwhile prepare me a good and substantial meal.'

"While it was yet early the following morning, the fathers, mothers, and other relatives came stealthily to the door of the young people, and, hearing no movement, feared the bridegroom was either dead or wounded; and, seeing the bride approach the door alone, were still more alarmed.

"She, seeing them, went cautiously and trembling toward them and exclaimed, 'Traitors, what are you doing? How dare you approach this gate? Speak not—be silent, or all of us, you as well as I, are dead.'

"When they heard this they were much astonished, and, on learning what had taken place the night previous, they esteemed the young man very much who had made so good a commencement in the management of his household; and from that day forward his wife became tractable and complaisant, so that they led a very happy life.

"A few days later his father-in-law, wishing to follow the example of his son, likewise killed a horse in order to intimidate his wife, but she said to him, 'My friend, it is too late to begin now; it would not avail you to kill a hundred horses: we know each other too well.'

"And you, Count Lucanor, if your dependent wishes to marry such a woman, if he be like this young man, advise him that he may do it with safety, for he will know how to rule his house: but if he be not likely to act with resolute determination at the beginning, and to sustain his position in his household, advise him to have nothing to do with her. As also I would counsel you in all cases where you have dealings with men to act with that decision which will leave them no room to think that you can be imposed upon."

The count thought this a very good example, and Don Juan had it written in this book, and made these lines, saying:

> Who would not for life be a henpeck'd fool
> Must show, from the first, that he means to rule.

From *Count Lucanor.*

DON DEMONIO'S MOTHER-IN-LAW

ONCE upon a time there lived in the little village of La Zubia a widow woman who was known for her long tongue and her short temper. She was thin and brown, her face and body as dried up as a piece of esparto grass. Her voice was as shrill as a cricket's chirp, and her tongue as sharp as a butcher's knife on market day. From the hour when God hung out the daylight till the hour when He drew it in again she was never still.

Now Tía Pía, as she was known to her neighbors, had one daughter who was pretty to look at but so lazy that even an earthquake would not move her. Her name was Pánfila, and what she liked to do best was to put on her dress of red and white muslin and sit, with folded hands, in the window, waiting for a lover to come and marry her. Every handsome youth who passed that way was a possible husband to Pánfila. And more than one of them looked back over his shoulder at her demure face and dark, carefully dressed hair. But when old Tía Pía poked her head around the doorway, each one made off as fast as he could go. Pánfila was not worth the risk of having such a one for a mother-in-law!

Day after day Pánfila sat and looked out the window, and day after day Tía Pía scolded her roundly for her idleness. Wielding her broom vigorously and raising a cloud of dust with every stroke, she would say, "In my day girls did their share of the work of the house." Swish, swish, went the broom! "They did not sit idle with

folded hands." Swish, swish! "They did not waste the good daylight waiting for fortune to come to them." Swish, swish! "They thought of something besides a possible sweetheart." Swish, swish! "The sweetheart who comes to such as you will be a good-for-nothing." Swish, swish!

One day Tía Pía called to Pánfila to help her lift from the fire a pot of hot lye. Now it may have been that Tía Pía was too quick in her movements, or it may have been that Pánfila's mind was on a handsome youth who had passed the door that morning and had been frightened away by her mother's voice. Whatever the reason, the pot of lye slipped, and a bit of the hot liquid splashed on Tía Pía's foot. You could have heard her screeching half a mile away!

"It is all your fault," she stormed. "Lazy, worthless creature! You are not worth your salt. You think of nothing but sweethearts! May you marry the Devil himself and be done with it!"

Now not long after this a young stranger appeared in the village of La Zubia. He was tall and dark, courtly in manner, and obviously well off in this world's goods. Over his shoulders he wore a long cape of scarlet silk, and on his head a curious draped cap that no one ever saw him without. He said that he was a traveler from a far country, and he lost no time in making himself popular among the men of the village. The young men were willing enough to be friends with him. He evidently knew a thing or two, and no one need give his own centimos for a glass of *valdepañas* when the stranger was in the village inn! But the old men were less easily won. They muttered among themselves and shook their heads.

"There is something queer about him," said old Tío Blas. "His manners are too good and his hands are too white, and I don't like the look in his eyes."

"He doesn't know a lamb from a kid," muttered old Tío Gil. "He has never been near the church since he came. I saw him hide himself in a doorway the other night when the *cura* went by."

But in spite of this gossip the stranger, who called himself Don Demonio, became a familiar figure in the village. And in no time at all Pánfila, from her window, had fallen in love with him. At first it was only a glance and a smile and a slight gesture of the hand. But Don Demonio, unlike the others, soon showed that he had no fear of old Tía Pía. Her shrill voice seemed only to amuse him, her ugly, wrinkled face to draw his eyes. His manner to her was as courtly as always, and he showered compliments upon her as extravagant as those that he paid Pánfila. By Corpus Christi Day the affair was settled and the marriage arranged.

Now old Tía Pía was as shrewd as she was ugly. She had not forgotten the wish that she had made for Pánfila when the hot lye fell on her toes. Neither was she at all sure that the draped scarlet silk of Don Demonio's cap did not conceal horns! When the wedding day arrived she called Pánfila to her and said, "There is one thing that you must surely do. When you are alone with your husband, see that every door and window is securely locked. See that every crack and cranny in the walls is covered. Cover the chimney even; leave free only the keyhole of the door. Then take an olive branch that has been blessed by the *cura* and switch your husband with it. That is what all brides must do to show that they rule in the home."

Pánfila, who was a meek creature, promised. And the wedding was celebrated with much feasting and rejoicing.

Now the house that Don Demonio had prepared for Pánfila was just outside the village on the road to Granada. When the bride and groom had entered it, no one noticed old Tía Pía stealing along the side of the road with a small, empty glass bottle in her hand.

Inside the house Pánfila had carefully done all that her mother had told her to do. And, having shut the house up as tight as a drum and taken the key from the keyhole, she turned to her husband with the blessed olive branch in her hand. The instant he saw it he went, to her amazement, into a panic of fear and tried to get out of the house. Cringing and whining and begging, his courtly manners completely forgotten, he desperately sought some way of escape, while Pánfila, no longer wondering but now suspicious, followed him about with the olive branch. But there was no way out for Don Demonio except through the keyhole. And he was finally forced to take that way. Driven to it, he at last assumed his own form with the tail and the horns that were rightly his, but he was no higher than a man's little finger! Through the keyhole he slipped before Pánfila's astonished eyes—only to find himself inclosed in a glass bottle!

Old Tía Pía chuckled to herself as she firmly forced in the cork. "This is one of the times," she said, "when the Devil himself was no match for a woman."

The very next morning old Tía Pía, leaving Pánfila alternately weeping and gazing out the window for another suitor, put the bottle in her pocket, mounted on her donkey, and set out for the Sierra Nevada. It is a long ride to Monte Mulhacén, which is the highest mountain in Spain and is covered with snow the whole year round. But Tía Pía took it, every foot of the way. And there on the top of the mountain she buried the bottle deep in the snow—an element which must have been quite new to his satanic majesty. Then she went back to La Zubia.

Ten years went by—ten years of peace and prosperity for the world. Wives were patient and long-suffering toward their husbands, husbands tender and indulgent toward their wives, children so good that they might have been angels already. Only the lawyers were unhappy, because no man sued his neighbor and time hung heavy on their hands.

Now there passed through the village of La Zubia a gallant soldier of fortune whose name was Ricardo. He chanced to ask his way of old Tía Pía, who still wielded her broom and her tongue as briskly as ever, although Pánfila had long ago married and gone to live in Córdoba. Sharp as her tongue still was, Tía Pía found that she had met her match in Ricardo, who, when she told him that his road lay over the mountains, answered cheerfully, "If the mountains are in my way, old woman, I will ride over them even though I crack my head against heaven's arch."

Now this was an answer that met with Tía Pía's approval, and after a dialogue that left them both breathless, they parted good friends.

Ricardo made his way up the steep, winding *cañada* that led to the top of the mountain. At the top he unsaddled his horse so that it could rest and crop the short grass, and threw himself down under a stunted tree. As he lay there idly, he saw something gleam at his feet. Stooping, he picked up a small glass bottle. Moreover, something inside the bottle moved!

"Now," said Ricardo aloud, "what strange, black insect is this?"

To his surprise a voice–a rather thin and weak voice it is true, but unquestionably a voice–answered from the bottle, "It is no insect," said this voice, "but an honorable and worthy devil, who, owing to the unnatural cunning of his mother-in-law has been shut up in this bottle and buried in this most hateful of elements for ten years. Free me, good soldier, and I will grant you your heart's desire."

"My heart's desire," Ricardo repeated slowly. "As it happens, good sir, I am in love. My heart's desire is the king's youngest daughter, the lovely Princess Blanca."

The Devil flicked his tail. "Nothing could be simpler than to get her for you," he answered contemptuously.

"And how," Ricardo asked, "do you propose to manage it?"

The Devil beat his tiny fists impatiently against the glass. "Let me out of this bottle," he snarled, "and I will manage it with no trouble at all."

But Ricardo was not a soldier of fortune for nothing.

"There is no hurry," he said mildly. "Tell me first just exactly how you propose to get the Princess Blanca for me."

The Devil, seeing what kind of a man he had to deal with, settled himself more comfortably in his bottle and unfolded his plan. He proposed to bewitch the princess with a strange illness in such a way that every doctor in the country would be called to cure her.

"But no doctor will cure her but you," he said, chuckling. "I will see that the king, in desperation, offers her hand in marriage to whoever rids her of the trouble. And then you can step in and, at your command, I will go back to the place that I came from."

Ricardo did not entirely approve of this plan. He did not like to be the cause of suffering to the lovely princess. But the Devil assured him that her pain would be brief, and he finally consented.

"And now," said the Devil, "let me out of this bottle!"

"Not so fast," Ricardo answered coolly. "There is no need for haste. Time enough when we get to the palace." And he slipped the bottle, Devil and all, into the pocket of his coat. "And you might tell me," he went on, "how you got into this fix in the first place."

So as they went down the mountain the Devil told Ricardo the story of Don Demonio and his mother-in-law, and Ricardo laughed until the sides of the mountain rang again.

It soon became known throughout the kingdom that the Princess Blanca suffered from a strange illness, and that the man who cured her would be given her hand in marriage. From far and from near came the doctors, native and foreign, old and young, grave and gay. But no one of them succeeded in ridding the princess of her trouble. Finally Ricardo presented himself at the palace. And a fine figure he made, in his black suit and black cape with a black velvet cap set on his curly hair.

In an upper room of the palace the Princess Blanca lay on her bed with closed eyes and a face as white as a jasmine flower.

"I have come to the end of my patience," the stern old king told Ricardo. "If you cure her before sunset today, she is yours. If you fail to cure her, you will be hanged from the scaffold that is even now being built in the courtyard."

Now this was rather more than Ricardo had bargained for. But he had faith in his compact with the Devil. So he answered calmly, "Leave me alone with the princess, and I will cure her in an hour."

The king and the attendants withdrew. Going over to the bed, Ricardo called upon the Devil to lift the spell and to go back to the place that he came from.

But there was no answer!

For three long hours Ricardo begged and pleaded, blustered and threatened. Once he heard a thin, mocking laugh and a tiny voice that said, "Not so fast! No need for hurry!"

And the Princess Blanca lay scarcely breathing, her eyes closed, her face as white as a jasmine flower. The sun was sinking in the west, and the old king rapping impatiently on the door, before, like a flash, an idea came to Ricardo. He went to the door and opened it, just a little.

"The princess is almost cured," he whispered to the anxious group waiting outside. "Tell them quickly to ring all the bells of every church in the city to celebrate. It will please her."

The king gave the order, and in a short time the air was filled with the clamor of church bells, ringing joyously, a sound that no devil approves. Out from behind Blanca's pillow popped a small, black head with horns, and a harsh, impatient voice demanded, "What is all that noise about?"

And then Ricardo made his master stroke. "That noise," he answered deliberately, "is the sound of the church bells ringing to celebrate the arrival in Granada of old Tía Pía, your mother-in-law."

With a bellow of mingled rage and fear the Devil leaped to the window and was gone, leaving behind him a strong smell of brimstone. While on the bed the color returned to the face of the Princess Blanca, and her gray eyes opened to look, first with wonder and then with shy approval, at Ricardo.

And did old Tía Pía ever know that it was she and none other who had brought happiness to Ricardo and the Princess Blanca?

Probably not. But to the end of her days she chuckled with satisfaction whenever she thought of the part she had played as Don Demonio's mother-in-law.

From *Three Golden Oranges and Other Spanish Folk Tales*, by Ralph Steele Boggs and Mary Gould Davis (New York: Longmans, Green & Co., 1936).

PEDRO THE TRICKSTER

THIS one I am telling you about was a father who had two sons, Pedro and Juan. Pedro was known as Pedro el de Malas—Pedro of the Bad Tricks. And they were very badly off, very poor, and in view of their poverty the older son, Juan, told his father that he was going away to seek his fortune. The father consented, and before his son went away he gave him this advice, "Do not trust a jagged stone, a lap dog, or a blond man."

Juan left, and on the way he came to a brook and to cross it there was a jagged rock that served as a steppingstone. Forgetting his father's advice, he stepped on the stone in order to cross the brook and fell and hurt himself. And farther on he met a lap dog and went up to it and it bit him.

Then Juan came to the house of a blond man. Forgetting what his father had said, he asked the man if he needed a servant in the house. The man said he did, and so Juan stayed to be his servant, making a bargain with him that the first one who became angry was to have three strips of flesh taken from him, from the back of his neck down to his rump. And the lad was to be paid when the cuckoo sang.

First the master sent Juan to bring a cartload of wood, telling him that he was not to come in either by the main gate or the rear one. And Juan went and came back with the cart. But since there were only two gates he was unable to enter, and he began to shout, "But, master, how am I to come in?" The master came out and said to him, "Why, man, are you angry?" And he answered, "Naturally I am angry. Who would not be when there is no way to enter?" And the master then said to him, "Very well, then I will take the three strips." And he took the three strips of flesh from the back of lad's neck down to his rump, and poor Juan died.

Seeing that Juan did not return, Pedro said to his father, "Father, my brother Juan has not come back, and I wish to go and look for him." The father said very well and gave him the same advice he had given the older son, and Pedro took to the road.

And Pedro came to the same brook with the jagged stone, and when he saw it he remembered his father's advice and said, "There is nothing for me to do here but take off my sandals." And he took off his sandals and crossed without touching the stone. And after he had crossed he met a lap dog, and took up a club and killed it. Then he too came to the house of the blond man. And he asked the man if he needed a servant, and the man said yes, and Pedro became his servant, making the same bargain as his brother. But when he saw that the man was blond, he said, "I am going to have to be careful with this man, for my father told me not to trust a blond man."

And, as with Juan, the master sent Pedro for a cartload of wood and told him he was not to come in either by the main gate or the rear one, and Pedro went for the cartload of wood and returned. And when he saw there were only two gates he went and got a pickax and came back to the wall and opened a gate in it and in that way brought the cart through. When the master saw what the servant had done to the wall he began grumbling. So Pedro said, "Are you angry, master?" And the master replied, "I am not angry, but I don't like it."

The next day the master sent Pedro for a cartload of brushwood. Pedro went with his cart to get the brushwood, and since it took him quite a while to dig up a root, he fell asleep. At noon his master came to bring him something to eat and found him alseep. And his master said to him, "But, Pedro, why are you not working? What are you doing?" And Pedro answered him, "Why, master, how do you expect an empty bag to stand up? Are you angry, master?" And his master replied, "I am not angry, but I don't like it." And the master went away and left Pedro in the field to work.

In the afternoon when he came back he again found Pedro lying on the ground, and he said to him, "But, man, why are you not working?" And Pedro said, "Why, master, how do you expect a full bag to stand up and work? If I work I will burst." The master began muttering, and Pedro said to him, "Are you angry, master?" And the master replied, "I am not angry, but I don't like it."

With this they went off to the house, and the master came and had a talk with his wife and said to her, "This fellow is going to have the three strips of flesh from me. So what we will do now is let him go a couple of days without food to see if he will leave and we can get rid of him." And for a day and a half they gave him nothing to eat. Then at night time Pedro came and stretched out on the stone seat in the kitchen to see what they were doing. He pretended to be asleep, and he saw the wife take out some dough to bake a loaf. And when it was baked, Pedro got up and took the tongs and began hacking at it until he had slashed it to pieces. And the master and his wife cried out, "What are you doing there, man?" And Pedro answered, "It's very cold, and since I was freezing I got up to stir the fire." Then the master said they should all have something to eat, and after that they went to bed.

The next day his master said to Pedro, "Today you are going to sell a drove of mares at the fair." And Pedro went away with the drove of mares to the fair, and each mare had a bell on it. He sold all the mares except one, which was a white one. But the bells he did not sell. He took the bells and came home with them on the white mare. Along the road a huge cloud came up, and he took his knife and killed the mare in order to get inside its skin so he would not get wet. Then some vultures swooped down to eat the mare. Pedro caught them and put a bell one each of them. And finally he caught a white one and went to where his master was and ran in, saying, "Master, a miracle from heaven! The mares have turned into vultures! Just look at them flying there with the bells on them. And see, this is the white mare on which I have come from the fair." And the master saw the vultures flying with the bells and as usual he suspected that Pedro was setting some trap for him and he began to grumble. And Pedro said to him, "Are you angry, master?" But the master did not want him to get the three strips of flesh, and so he answered, "I am not angry, but I don't like it."

Then the master sent him with a drove of pigs to a forest in which there was a giant who did not allow anyone to enter. And Pedro went and sold all the pigs except one sow. He cut off all their tails and then went and stuck all the tails and the sow that he had not sold into the mud. And Pedro said to his master, "Pull on them and see if we can get them out." The master pulled and pulled and all he brought out was the tails, and Pedro said, "You see, master, they can't get out." Then Pedro began to pull on the tail of the sow that he had not sold and called to his master and said, "Come here, master, for I believe we are going to get this sow out." The two of them took hold and pulled and pulled until they had her out. But since in the other cases all they got was the tails, the master said, "Ah, Pedro, you have ruined me! I have lost all my pigs." And Pedro said to him, "Are you angry, master?" And the master replied, "No, I am not angry, but I don't like it!"

The next day the master again sent Pedro to where the giant lived, so that the giant might kill him. And this time he sent him with a flock of sheep. And since this time Pedro found no one to sell them to, he kept on with the sheep until he came to where the giant was. And the giant came out and cried, "I smell human flesh! Give me some or I will eat you!" And Pedro said to him, "Don't eat me, for I have many sheep here and you may eat as many as you like."

Then the giant said, "I am going to give you three chances to see if you can win from me, and if you lose you die. We will see who it is that dies." "Very well," said Pedro. "First of all," said the giant, "we are going to see who can eat more. Go and kill that bull and bring me the flesh." And Pedro went to where the bulls were and came back with them. And the giant said to him, "What are you doing?" And Pedro answered, "I am going to kill all of them so that we can start eating." "One will be enough," the giant told him. And Pedro replied, "If it's only one you want, kill it yourself. That is not even a beginning for me."

Then the giant went and killed the bull and flayed it and said to Pedro, "Take the skin and bring it back to me full of water." And since Pedro saw that he could not carry it when it was empty, much less when it was full of water, he went to the spring and began driving in some stakes. And the giant came up to him and said, "What are you doing, man?" And Pedro answered, "Nothing; I am just

driving in a few stakes so that I can bring up all the water from the spring, for a skinful would not be even a beginning for me when I start to drink." And the giant said to him, "No, man, this water flask will be enough." And Pedro then said, "Seeing it's only a flask of water that you want, get it yourself."

Then the giant said, "Now you are going to the forest for wood." And Pedro went and gave four slashes with his ax and not a bough fell. Then he went and took a ball of yarn and began binding the entire forest. And the giant came and said to him, "Why, what are you doing?" And Pedro answered, "I am going to bring the entire forest." "One holly tree would be enough," said the giant. And Pedro said, "If it's only one tree you want, bring it yourself."

"Now we are going to see who can take a stone and throw it farther."

With that Pedro went and caught a turtledove and carried it in his hand. And the giant picked up a stone and threw it, and when the giant threw the stone Pedro let his dove go. The giant's stone fell, but the dove kept on flying, and Pedro said, "There goes my stone!" And the giant said, "That is twice you have won from me. Now we are going to see who can crush a stone." And the giant picked up a stone and squeezed it and crushed it to bits in his hand. Pedro had already picked up a piece of cheese and he put it in his mouth and ate it. And the giant said to him, "That is three times you have won from me. Now you are my friend."

But Pedro said, "I am going to fix this old giant." And he took out two packets of gunpowder and gave them to the giant and said, "Look, if you put these in your eyes you will be able to see everything in the world that is most heavenly." And the giant put them in his eyes and Pedro went and struck a light and the giant's eyes popped out. And the giant said to Pedro, "Now that you have done this to me you are not going to pass through the entrance to my cave." And in order that the sheep might pass he touched them one by one and said, "Pass, little white sheep; pass, little white sheep." And then Pedro went and killed a sheep and dressed himself in its skin and he too passed. And the giant, thinking it was a sheep, touched him and said, "Pass little white sheep." And Pedro said, "No, it is Pedro of the Bad Tricks." And seeing that he was already outside the cave, he took a dagger and killed the giant.

Pedro then went to his master's house and said to him, "Too bad, master, but some wild animals have eaten the sheep." And the master said, "Why, what have you done with my sheep, man? You will be the ruination of me." "Are you angry, master?" said Pedro. "I am not angry, but I don't like it," said the master.

And master and mistress talked it over to see how they could get rid of Pedro. "This fellow is going to ruin us," said the master to his wife. "There is nothing for it now but for you to stand at the window tomorrow and sing like the cuckoo so that the time to pay his wages will come and he will go away." And so early next morning the wife stood at the window and sang, "Cuckoo, cuckoo, cuckoo, cuckoo!" And Pedro got up and said, "I am going to see whether it is a he-cuckoo or a she-cuckoo." And he took his shotgun and shot at the woman and killed her. And the master came out very angry and cried, "Why, man, what have you done? You have killed my wife." And Pedro said to him, "Are you angry, master?" "Of course I am angry," replied his master. "Haven't I a right to be angry when you have killed my wife?" And then Pedro came up and took the three strips of flesh, from the back of the neck down to the rump. And the poor man died, and Pedro then sent for his father and they stayed on as the masters of the house.

From *Cuentos populares españoles,* collected by Aurelio M. Espinosa (Stanford University, Calif.: Stanford University Press, 1923–1927). This story was translated especially for this volume by Samuel Putnam, with the kind permission of Aurelio M. Espinosa. An objectionable episode has been omitted.

BIBLIOGRAPHICAL NOTE

THE MOST important periodicals in English devoted to folk tales are the *Journal of American Folklore*, quarterly publication of the American Folklore Society, and *Folk-Lore*, the quarterly of the British Folk-Lore Society.

A good recent handbook of folk tales is Stith Thompson's *The Folktale*. Helpful to those especially interested in tracing the motifs of folk tales is the five-volume *Motif-Index of Folk-Literature*, also by Stith Thompson. Among the collections of folk tales whose notes and comment are noteworthy are N. M. Penzer's edition of the *Katha Sarit Sagara* and his edition of Basile's *Pentamerone*, and the *Anmerkungen zu den Kinder- und Hausmärchen der Brüder Grimm* by Johannes Bolte and Georg Polivka.

Notable among the other critiques available in English are those by W. A. Clouston, Joseph Jacobs, Andrew Lang, Richard Burton, George Webbe Dasent, Archer Taylor, A. H. Krappe, and Max Müller. For studies in other languages, particularly in German, French, Finnish, and Swedish, the reader should refer to the bibliographies in Thompson's *The Folktale*.

Two rich collections of American folklore are *A Treasury of American Folklore* by B. A. Botkin and *The American Imagination at Work* by Ben C. Clough.

INDEX OF SOURCES, EDITORS, AND TRANSLATORS

1763